STATISTICAL PHYSICS

STATISTICAL
PHYSICS

Edward A. Desloge *Florida State University*

HOLT, RINEHART AND WINSTON, INC.
New York • Chicago • San Francisco • Toronto • London

To My Parents
Angela Burdeau Desloge and Louis F. Desloge

And My Wife
Moira Dunne Desloge

AD MAJOREM DEI GLORIAM ·

PREFACE

Statistical mechanics and kinetic theory, usually referred to collectively as statistical physics, provide the bridge between the microscopic and macroscopic in physics, and as such are essential in the development and application of a large portion of physical theory.

This book is designed as an introduction to the concepts and techniques of statistical physics, and is intended to be used primarily as a one- or two-semester text for an advanced undergraduate or a beginning graduate-level course.

An attempt has been made to develop the material gradually, beginning with relatively simple mathematical and physical ideas and proceeding to a reasonably sophisticated level. In the early chapters of the book it is assumed that the student has a thorough grasp of calculus and has had intermediate-level courses in mechanics and modern physics. In the later chapters a greater maturity in the latter two areas of physics is expected.

The subject matter has been arranged pedagogically rather than logically or historically. In Part I an attempt has been made to arrive quickly and yet convincingly at useful results in order to familiarize the student with some of the big ideas and techniques of statistical physics, and to aid him in developing some physical insight. In Parts II and III, the same general problems are attacked with a great deal more rigor, sophistication, detail, and depth. If the book is used in an undergraduate course, a great deal of emphasis should be placed on Part I. If the book is used in a graduate course, all that is necessary in Part I are Chapters 1, 2, and 3. The presence of the remaining material in Part I can serve in a graduate course as a useful self-study aid for the student whose background is weak.

Emphasis has been placed on the careful development of theoretical techniques and a clear exposition of the fundamental assumptions rather than on an elaborate discussion of experimental results or a complete survey of all possible areas of statistical physics. The applications which are made have been chosen on the basis of their ability to illustrate the theory and not on the basis of their current importance.

Although it is customary in the development of statistical mechanics to introduce thermodynamics at an early stage, it has been my experience that for many students thermodynamics is a hindrance rather than a help in their attempt to understand the basic ideas of statistical mechanics. I have therefore taken up the subject of thermodynamics only after thoroughly developing the principles of statistical mechanics. With this order I feel the student not only has a better chance of grasping statistical mechanics, but will also develop a greater appreciation and understanding of thermodynamics.

In a further attempt to strip powerful but pedagogically confusing techniques from the fundamental framework of statistical mechanics, I have initially developed all of equilibrium statistical mechanics in Part II, using only the canonical ensemble. The other ensembles are discussed after the student has had a chance to develop one approach thoroughly.

In most texts in statistical physics greater emphasis is placed on statistical mechanics than on kinetic theory. In its initial stages of growth, the present book started as a kinetic theory text and developed into a text on statistical physics. As a result, there is strong emphasis on kinetic theory.

The various parts of the book have been made sufficiently independent so that it is possible to use it as a text in a variety of courses. Chapters 1 to 9 together with some of the early chapters in Parts II and III will provide more than enough material for a one- or two-semester undergraduate course in statistical physics. Chapters 1, 2, and 3, all of Part II, and some of the early chapters in Part III would provide a standard one-semester graduate course in statistical mechanics. Chapters 1, 2, 3, 10, 11, and all of Part III could be used for a graduate course in kinetic theory.

It is hoped that this book will make it easier for students to use the techniques of statistical physics, and to read and understand the numerous more advanced treatises in statistical physics which are available.

EDWARD A. DESLOGE

Tallahassee, Florida
March 1966

CONTENTS

PART
I

ELEMENTARY STATISTICAL PHYSICS

Chapter 1

A MOLECULAR MODEL OF MATTER

INTRODUCTION

If we set out to examine the physical properties of a simple gas, our result will depend to a large degree on our scale of measurements, or the sensitivity of our observations.

If the sensitivity of our instruments restricts us to relatively large-scale or macroscopic observations, then the gas will appear to be a continuous substance requiring a small number of parameters to describe its behavior.

Starting from such a view, it is possible to arrive at simple relations among these parameters which successfully catalogue a vast portion of the phenomena associated with the gas. The whole field of thermodynamics is, for example, an unfolding of the logical implications of a few laws which establish a relatively simple relationship between a small number of parameters. All the equilibrium properties of a simple gas can, as a matter of fact, be contained in a simple function of three variables—the energy, volume, and mass—and the rules for the extrication of this information can be contained in a few simple statements.

To restrict oneself to such a view, however, is inadequate because a closer look reveals new features which are inconsistent with the idea of a gas as a homogeneous substance. Small foreign objects drifting in the gas are found to move erratically, revealing the existence of unexpected local pressure fluctuations. Numerous other phenomena reveal the same lack of homogeneity.

Nor is a strictly macroscopic view entirely satisfying, for it leaves us with a collection of loosely related theories ruling over the different realms of our experience. A more fundamental, more unifying approach is needed, a view which takes into account the discrete, nonhomogeneous, or molecular aspects of a gas.

The kinetic theory and statistical mechanics of gases represent attempts to explain the macroscopic behavior of a gas, and to account for the fluctuations in the macroscopic parameters from a molecular point of view.

Kinetic theory and statistical mechanics differ in the amount of information with which they start. In general, kinetic theory starts with the assumption that a gas is composed of molecules, together with some detailed knowledge of the mechanism by which these molecules collide or interact, while statistical mechanics begins with the fact that there are molecules and they do interact. Since it is physically more fundamental, kinetic theory can handle problems which are beyond the scope of statistical mechanics. On the other hand, since statistical mechanics is mathematically simpler than kinetic theory, it can be used to handle problems which would be mathematically too tedious and complex for kinetic theory. Each has its role to play in our quest for a molecular understanding of matter.

THE MOLECULAR HYPOTHESIS

In order to explain the properties of a simple gas, we shall assume that the gas is composed of a large number of identical molecules which are moving around rapidly and randomly. The macroscopic properties of such a collection of molecules will depend on the structure of the molecules and their interaction with one another, with the walls of the container, and with external fields. In the interest of simplicity we will initially make the following additional assumptions:

1. Each molecule is surrounded by a field of force. The effect of this force on another molecule can be neglected beyond a certain short range. Each molecule may therefore be imagined to be surrounded by a small volume defining its range of influence. When the range of influence of one molecule falls within the range of influence of a second molecule, the two will interact. The resultant interaction is called a collision.

2. The duration of a collision is so short and the range of influence of each molecule is so small that the probability of more than two molecules interacting simultaneously with one another is negligible. A collision or interaction in which only two molecules participate is called a binary collision.

3. In a short period of time a given molecule will undergo a large number of collisions with the other molecules in the gas.

4. The average distance traveled between collisions is small compared

to the dimensions of the container, so that any effect of the walls of the container can be ignored.

5. The duration of a collision is so short, and the range of influence of a particular molecule is so small, that we can neglect any effect which the external forces might have on the collisional process.

6. In a collision between two molecules the total translational kinetic energy of the two molecules taken together is conserved.

7. The distribution of molecules in the neighborhood of a particular molecule is exactly the same as it would be if the molecule were not present.

8. Due to their rotation and random orientation, the molecules appear on the average to be spherically symmetric. The geometrical configuration of the molecules can thus be ignored.

9. The volume occupied by the molecules is small compared to the volume of the container so that any effects due to the finite size of the molecules can be neglected.

The assumptions (1) through (9) have been introduced to facilitate the initial study of our model. Some of these restrictions will eventually be removed. The removal of others would lead us into areas of research beyond the immediate scope of this book.

In Chapter 4 we will begin our investigation by using the above model to derive the equilibrium properties of an ideal gas. But first it will be necessary in Chapters 2 and 3 to acquaint ourselves with a few useful mathematical tools.

PROBLEMS

1. Distinguish between an elastic and an inelastic collision of two molecules.
2. One of the basic assumptions which we have made is that in a short period of time a given molecule will undergo a large number of collisions with the other molecules in the gas. What is meant by a short period of time?
3. A continuous stream of pellets, each of mass m, strikes one pan of a balance at an angle of θ with the normal. When a mass M is put in the other pan, the balance is balanced. Assuming that the pellets bounce off elastically, what is the number of pellets per second striking the pan?
4. A vertical cylinder as shown in Figure 1.1 is fitted with a frictionless piston of mass M. The cylinder contains a sphere of mass m and radius r moving vertically up and down. The collision of the sphere with the piston and the bottom of the cylinder is perfectly elastic. The cylinder is evacuated.
    (a) Ignoring the dimensions of the sphere and assuming that the speed of the sphere remains practically constant, show that in equilibrium

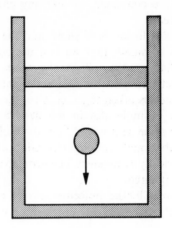

Fig. 1.1

$pV = 2E$ where p is the average pressure exerted by the piston, V the average volume enclosed in the cylinder by the piston, and E the kinetic energy of the sphere.

(b) Show that if the dimensions of the sphere are taken into account, the resulting expression becomes $p(V - 2rA) = 2E$ where A is the cross-sectional area of the cylinder.

5. A gas is contained within a cylinder by a piston. The piston is moved out slowly with a velocity V which is small compared with the average speed of the molecules. Show that a molecule of speed v rebounding from the piston loses $2mvV\cos\theta$ in kinetic energy, where θ is the angle of incidence. Show that the kinetic energy lost by all of the molecules rebounding from the piston is equal to the work done by the expanding gas.

2

TRANSFORMATION OF COORDINATES

NOTATION

Throughout this text we will have to carry out integrations over a large number of variables, at times as many as twelve. For convenience we therefore introduce the following notational abbreviations.

Suppose x is a position vector having components x_1, x_2, x_3. Let $f(x_1, x_2, x_3)$ be some function of the variables x_1, x_2, x_3. For convenience we will then write

$$f(x_1, x_2, x_3) \equiv f(\mathbf{x}) \tag{2.1}$$

Similarly, we will designate the volume element $dx_1\, dx_2\, dx_3$ by writing

$$dx_1\, dx_2\, dx_3 \equiv d\mathbf{x} \tag{2.2}$$

and the triple integral over $d\mathbf{x}$ as

$$\iiint f(x_1, x_2, x_3) dx_1\, dx_2\, dx_3 \equiv \int f(\mathbf{x}) d\mathbf{x} \tag{2.3}$$

There is of course the possibility of confusing $d\mathbf{x}$ with the vector representing an infinitesimal displacement of $\mathbf{x}$, but since we will seldom have occasion to use this quantity, the danger is negligible. The difficulty could be avoided, if desired, by writing the volume element as $d(\mathbf{x})$ or the infinitesimal displacement as $d\mathbf{x}$. It should be noted that $f(\mathbf{x})$ and $d\mathbf{x}$ are not themselves vectors but are scalars. A vector function of the vector $\mathbf{x}$ such as $\mathbf{A} \times \mathbf{x}$ would be designated $\mathbf{f}(\mathbf{x})$.

Using the above notation, the function $f(\mathbf{x} + \mathbf{y})$ would be interpreted as $f(x_1 + y_1, x_2 + y_2, x_3 + y_3)$ and $f(\mathbf{x} \cdot \mathbf{y})$ as $f(x_1y_1 + x_2y_2 + x_3y_3)$.

TRANSFORMATION OF COORDINATES

Let us consider the following double integral

$$A = \iint_R f(x, y)dxdy \qquad (2.4)$$

where R indicates the region of integration. We wish to convert (2.4) from an integration in x–y space to an integration in another space u–v. We assume for simplicity that there is a one-to-one relationship between the points (x, y) and the points (u, v) given by the transformation

$$x = x(u, v) \qquad (2.5)$$

$$y = y(u, v) \qquad (2.6)$$

From (2.5) and (2.6) it follows that

$$dx = (\partial x/\partial u)du + (\partial x/\partial v)dv \qquad (2.7)$$

$$dy = (\partial y/\partial u)du + (\partial y/\partial v)dv \qquad (2.8)$$

As a first step in the desired transformation we rewrite Eq. (2.4)

$$A = \int \left\{ \int f dx \right\} dy \qquad (2.9)$$

where the range of integration R and the arguments of f have been dropped for notational simplicity. In order to carry out the integration in the braces we hold y constant. But if y is constant, then $dy = 0$ and Eqs. (2.7) and (2.8) become

$$dx = (\partial x/\partial u)du + (\partial x/\partial v)dv \qquad (2.10)$$

$$0 = (\partial y/\partial u)du + (\partial y/\partial v)dv \qquad (2.11)$$

Solving for dx, we find

$$dx = \frac{\begin{vmatrix} \partial x/\partial u & \partial x/\partial v \\ \partial y/\partial u & \partial y/\partial v \end{vmatrix}}{\partial y/\partial v} du \qquad (2.12)$$

Defining

$$J\left(\frac{x, y}{u, v}\right) = \begin{vmatrix} \partial x/\partial u & \partial x/\partial v \\ \partial y/\partial u & \partial y/\partial v \end{vmatrix} \qquad (2.13)$$

and substituting (2.12) and (2.13) in (2.9) we have

$$A = \iint f J\left(\frac{x, y}{u, v}\right)(\partial y/\partial v)^{-1}dudy \qquad (2.14)$$

Assuming our functions are such that the order of integration can be reversed, we have

$$A = \int \left\{ \int f J\left(\frac{x, y}{u, v}\right)(\partial y/\partial v)^{-1}dy \right\} du \qquad (2.15)$$

In order to carry out the integration in braces, we hold u constant. But if u is constant, then from (2.8)

$$dy = (\partial y / \partial v)dv \qquad (2.16)$$

Substituting (2.16) in (2.15) and again reversing the order of integration, we have

$$A = \iint fJ\left(\frac{x, y}{u, v}\right)dudv \qquad (2.17)$$

If we always choose our limits of integration in such a way that $\iint_R dudv > 0$ and $\iint_R dxdy > 0$, then we can write (2.17) as

$$A = \iint_R f \left| J\left(\frac{x, y}{u, v}\right) \right| dudv \qquad (2.18)$$

and thus with this convention for integration over R we eliminate many difficulties which would otherwise arise in transforming the limits of integration. Gathering our results, we have

$$\iint_R f(x, y)dxdy = \iint_R f[x(u, v), y(u, v)] \left| J\left(\frac{x, y}{u, v}\right) \right| dudv \qquad (2.19)$$

In a similar fashion we can show that

$$\iiint_R f \, dxdydz = \iiint_R f \left| J\left(\frac{x, y, z}{u, v, w}\right) \right| dudvdw \qquad (2.20)$$

where

$$J\left(\frac{x, y, z}{u, v, w}\right) = \begin{vmatrix} \partial x/\partial u & \partial x/\partial v & \partial x/\partial w \\ \partial y/\partial u & \partial y/\partial v & \partial y/\partial w \\ \partial z/\partial u & \partial z/\partial v & \partial z/\partial w \end{vmatrix} \qquad (2.21)$$

The functions $J\left(\dfrac{x, y}{u, v}\right)$ and $J\left(\dfrac{x, y, z}{u, v, w}\right)$ are called Jacobians.

In terms of the notation introduced in the previous section, if $\mathbf{x}$ is a vector with components (x_1, x_2, x_3) and $\mathbf{y}$ is a vector with components $[y_1(x_1, x_2, x_3),$ $y_2(x_1, x_2, x_3), y_3(x_1, x_2, x_3)]$ then

$$\int f(\mathbf{x})d\mathbf{x} = \int f[\mathbf{x}(\mathbf{y})] \left| J\left(\frac{\mathbf{x}}{\mathbf{y}}\right) \right| d\mathbf{y} \qquad (2.22)$$

The following properties of Jacobians can be easily proved,

$$J\left(\frac{x, y}{u, v}\right) = -J\left(\frac{y, x}{u, v}\right) = -J\left(\frac{-x, y}{u, v}\right) = -J\left(\frac{x, -y}{u, v}\right) \qquad (2.23)$$

$$J\left(\frac{ax, y}{u, v}\right) = aJ\left(\frac{x, y}{u, v}\right) \qquad (2.24)$$

$$J\left(\frac{x^m, y}{u, v}\right) = (mx^{m-1})J\left(\frac{x, y}{u, v}\right) \qquad (2.25)$$

$$J\left(\frac{x, y}{u, v}\right) = \left[J\left(\frac{u, v}{x, y}\right)\right]^{-1} \tag{2.26}$$

$$J\left(\frac{x + z, y}{u, v}\right) = J\left(\frac{x, y}{u, v}\right) + J\left(\frac{z, y}{u, v}\right) \tag{2.27}$$

$$J\left(\frac{xz, y}{u, v}\right) = xJ\left(\frac{z, y}{u, v}\right) + zJ\left(\frac{x, y}{u, v}\right) \tag{2.28}$$

$$J\left(\frac{x, y}{u, v}\right)J\left(\frac{u, v}{r, s}\right) = J\left(\frac{x, y}{r, s}\right) \tag{2.29}$$

PROBLEMS

1. (a) Prove that $J\left(\dfrac{ax, y}{u, v}\right) = aJ\left(\dfrac{x, y}{u, v}\right)$

    (b) Prove that $J\left(\dfrac{a\mathbf{x}, \mathbf{y}}{\mathbf{u}, \mathbf{v}}\right) = a^3 J\left(\dfrac{\mathbf{x}, \mathbf{y}}{\mathbf{u}, \mathbf{v}}\right)$

2. (a) Prove that $J\left(\dfrac{x + z, y}{u, v}\right) = J\left(\dfrac{x, y}{u, v}\right) + J\left(\dfrac{z, y}{u, v}\right)$

    (b) Derive the analogous expression for $J\left(\dfrac{\mathbf{x} + \mathbf{z}, \mathbf{y}}{\mathbf{u}, \mathbf{v}}\right)$

3. Given: find:

$$\begin{aligned} x &= r \sin \theta \cos \phi \\ y &= r \sin \theta \sin \phi \\ z &= r \cos \theta \end{aligned} \qquad J\left(\frac{r, \theta, \phi}{x, y, z}\right)$$

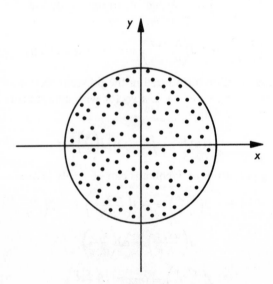

Fig. 2.1

4. (a) *N* points are distributed uniformly over a circular area of radius *R* as shown in Figure 2.1. Write down an expression for the density of points.

   (b) Each point in Figure 2.1 is specified by a particular set of values of the coordinates x, y. Each point could also be specified by a set of values of the polar coordinates r, θ where $x = r\cos\theta$ and $y = r\sin\theta$. Suppose we transform each point in Figure 2.1 to its corresponding point in the space represented in Figure 2.2, restrict-

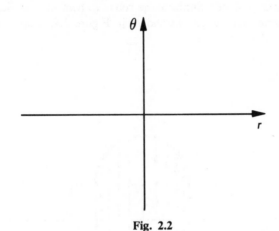

Fig. 2.2

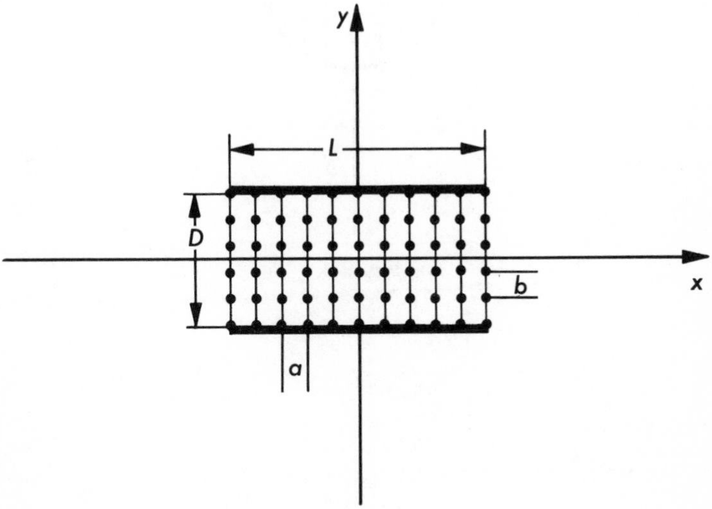

Fig. 2.3

ing ourselves to values of θ between 0 and 2π. What is the density of points in this space, which we shall refer to as r, θ space?

5. Two straight rods of length L separated by a distance D are placed in the x–y plane as shown in Figure 2.3. A series of rubber bands are stretched between the rods as shown. The rubber bands are separated by a distance $a \ll L$. Particles of negligible mass are placed along each rubber band. The distance between the particles on a rubber band is $b \ll D$. Assuming that the distribution of particles in the x–y plane can be treated as a continuous distribution, what is the density of particles in the x–y plane? Suppose the rods are bent into semicircles without increasing their length, as shown in Figure 2.4, what is the density of points in the x–y plane?

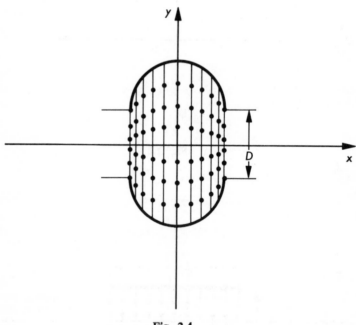

Fig. 2.4

Chapter 3

DISTRIBUTION
FUNCTIONS

In the present chapter we wish to find out what a distribution function is and also some of the properties of distribution functions. The subject is most easily introduced by discussing a particular distribution function which is encountered quite often in physics, the number density of particles in a gas.

DENSITY

Before considering the distribution of molecules in space, let us consider the analogous one-dimensional problem of a distribution of points along a line, as shown in Figure 3.1. A complete description of the distribution

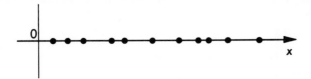

Fig. 3.1

would require the specification of the position of each point. Suppose, however, that we could not measure the location of a particular point exactly but could only locate it within a range Δx, or suppose that we simply were not interested in knowing the location more exactly. Our x axis could then be divided into a set of cells each of length Δx, and labeled from 1 to ∞, as shown in Figure 3.2. A complete description now would require that we

Fig. 3.2

know the number of points in each cell. If we designate N_i as the number of points in cell i, then a complete description would require a knowledge of the whole set of N_i which we can designate $\{N_i\}$.

The distribution could be further represented graphically by replacing each point by a rectangle of base Δx and height $(1/\Delta x)$ i.e., a rectangle of unit area which just fits into a cell. The distribution represented in Figure 3.2 would then appear as in Figure 3.3. The number of points in a particular

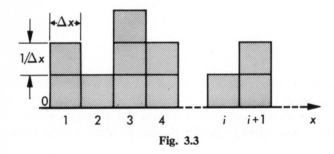

Fig. 3.3

cell would then be determined by measuring the shaded area within that cell.

If the variation in the number of points from cell to adjoining cell is small compared to the number of points in the cells, then the boundary of the shaded region will become more regular in appearance, and can often be approximated by a continuous function and the exact boundaries of the cells ignored, as in Figure 3.4. The function that is shown in Figure 3.4 is

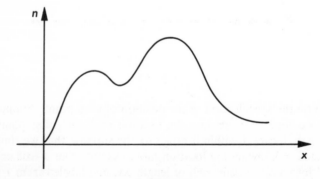

Fig. 3.4

defined as the linear density of points on the line, and is designated as $n(x)$.

If we wish to know the number of points N between two points $x = a$ and $x = b$, we simply integrate $n(x)$ from a to b, obtaining

$$N(a < x < b) = \int_a^b n(x)dx \qquad (3.1)$$

It follows that $n(x)dx$ can be considered to represent the number of points between x and $x + dx$, and this is often the manner in which $n(x)$ is defined, i.e., $n(x)$ is the function having the property that $n(x)dx$ represents the number of points between x and $x + dx$.

It is a simple matter to extend our analysis to three dimensions. Thus the three-dimensional density $n(\mathbf{x})$ is defined as the function having the property that $n(\mathbf{x})d\mathbf{x}$ represents the number of points having their x_1 coordinate between x_1 and $x_1 + dx_1$. their x_2 coordinate between x_2 and $x_2 + dx_2$, and their x_3 coordinate between x_3 and $x_3 + dx_3$, or simply the number of points within the volume element $d\mathbf{x}$ centered at $\mathbf{x}$, as shown in Figure 3.5.

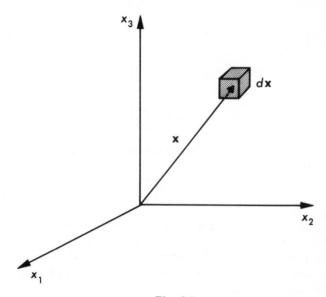

Fig. 3.5

TRANSFORMATION OF THE DENSITY

Suppose we have a distribution of N points along a line $0x$. Let $0y$ be a second line along which N points are also distributed. Suppose there is a one-to-one correspondence given by $y = y(x)$ between the points on line $0y$ and the points on $0x$. That is, if point i is located at $x(i)$ on $0x$, then it will be located at $y[x(i)]$ on $0y$. Although there is a one-to-one correspondence between the points on $0x$ and the points on $0y$, the density of points along line $0x$ may be quite different from the density of points along $0y$. To distinguish between the two densities we will let n_x be the density on the line $0x$ and n_y the density on the line $0y$. To determine the relation between n_x and n_y we note that in terms of n_x the number of points between $x = a$ and $x = b$ is

$$N(a < x < b) = \int_a^b n_x dx \qquad (3.2)$$

while in terms of n_y the same number is

$$N(a < x < b) = \int_{y(a)}^{y(b)} n_y dy \qquad (3.3)$$

Equating (3.2) and (3.3) and changing the variable of integration in (3.3), we obtain

$$\int_a^b n_x dx = \int_a^b n_y \left| J\left(\frac{y}{x}\right) \right| dx \qquad (3.4)$$

Since the range of integration is arbitrary, the integrands must be equal and we have

$$n_x = n_y \left| J\left(\frac{y}{x}\right) \right| \qquad (3.5)$$

or

$$n_y = n_x \left| J\left(\frac{x}{y}\right) \right| \qquad (3.6)$$

In a similar fashion, if $n_\mathbf{x}$ is the density of points in $\mathbf{x}$ space and $n_\mathbf{y}$ the density in $\mathbf{y}$ space, then

$$n_\mathbf{y} = n_\mathbf{x} \left| J\left(\frac{\mathbf{x}}{\mathbf{y}}\right) \right| \qquad (3.7)$$

It is important when giving a density function to specify in what space it is a density. To avoid ambiguity we shall, unless it is obvious from the context, interpret n to mean the density in ordinary Cartesian space, and designate a density in some other space, e.g., r, θ, ϕ space, by appending the appropriate subscripts, e.g., $n_{r\theta\phi}$.

Suppose we are given the density $n(\mathbf{x})$ and wish to find n_{x_1} where $n_{x_1} dx_1$ is the number of particles between x_1 and $x_1 + dx_1$. Since x_2 and x_3 are arbitrary, we obtain n_{x_1} by integrating $n(\mathbf{x})$ over x_2 and x_3:

$$n_{x_1} = \int\int n(\mathbf{x}) dx_2 dx_3 \qquad (3.8)$$

Thus if we are given $n(\mathbf{x})$ and wish to find the radial density n_r, we have

$$n_r = \int_0^{2\pi} \int_0^{\pi} n_{r\theta\phi} d\theta d\phi$$

$$= \int_0^{2\pi} \int_0^{\pi} n(\mathbf{x}) \left| J\left(\frac{x_1, x_2, x_3}{r, \theta, \phi}\right) \right| d\theta d\phi$$

$$= \int_0^{2\pi} \int_0^{\pi} n(\mathbf{x}) r^2 \sin\theta d\theta d\phi \qquad (3.9)$$

THE PROBABILITY DENSITY

Frequently we need to know the probability that a particular particle will fall in a certain range dx rather than the number of particles in dx. If we designate $n'(\mathbf{x})dx$ as the probability that the particle will fall in dx, we can obtain $n'(\mathbf{x})$ by simply dividing $n(\mathbf{x})$ by the total number of particles in the volume;

$$n'(\mathbf{x}) = \frac{n(\mathbf{x})}{N} = \frac{n(\mathbf{x})}{\int n(\mathbf{x})dx} \qquad (3.10)$$

There are a number of other useful probabilities that one can derive from $n(\mathbf{x})$. Suppose, for instance, we wish to know the probability that a particular particle has its x_1 component between x_1 and $x_1 + dx_1$. If we designate this probability $n_1' \, dx_1$, then we have

$$n_1' = \frac{n_{x_1}}{N} = \frac{\iint n dx_2 dx_3}{\iiint n dx_1 dx_2 dx_3} \qquad (3.11)$$

AVERAGE VALUES

Suppose we wish to determine the average distance from the origin of a set of points distributed along a line. Let $x(i)$ be distance of the ith point from the origin; $<x>$, the average distance from the origin; and N, the total number of points. Then

$$<x> = \frac{\sum_{i=1}^{N} x(i)}{N} \qquad (3.12)$$

If the line is divided into cells, and the distribution is given in terms of the number of points in each cell then,

$$<x> = \frac{\sum_i N_i x(i)}{N} \qquad (3.13)$$

where N_i is the number of points in the ith cell, and $x(i)$ is the location of the ith cell.

If our distribution is given in the form of a continuous function $n(x)$, we have

$$<x> = \frac{\int_{-\infty}^{\infty} xn(x)dx}{N} \tag{3.14}$$

or noting that $\int_{-\infty}^{\infty} n(x)dx = N$ we have

$$<x> = \frac{\int_{-\infty}^{\infty} xn(x)dx}{\int_{-\infty}^{\infty} n(x)dx} \tag{3.15}$$

The same analysis could be applied to any property of the points which is a function of the distance from the origin. For example, we might wish the average value of the distance from the origin squared, $<x^2>$, or the points might be moving with a velocity v which is a function of the distance and we might want to know the average velocity, $<v(x)>$. In general if $g(x)$ is any arbitrary property of the points which depends on their distance from the origin, we have

$$<g(x)> = \frac{\int_{-\infty}^{\infty} g(x)n(x)dx}{\int_{-\infty}^{\infty} n(x)dx} \tag{3.16}$$

The generalization to three dimensions is straightforward and we obtain

$$<g(\mathbf{x})> = \frac{\int g(\mathbf{x})n(\mathbf{x})d\mathbf{x}}{\int n(\mathbf{x})d\mathbf{x}} \tag{3.17}$$

From expression (3.16) or (3.17) it is easy to show that the average value of the sum of two functions is the sum of their average values,

$$<g(x) + h(x)> = <g(x)> + <h(x)> \tag{3.18}$$

THE DIRAC DELTA FUNCTION

Suppose our distribution of points along the line $0x$ consists of a single point which we know without error is located at the point $x = a$. The density function corresponding to this distribution is represented by the notation $\delta(x - a)$. Since integration over the range from $-\infty$ to ∞ should give us the total number of points, which in this case is one, we have

$$\int_{-\infty}^{\infty} \delta(x - a)dx = 1 \tag{3.19}$$

Furthermore, the average value of some function $g(x)$ is simply $g(a)$ since there is only one point and thus

$$\int_{-\infty}^{\infty} g(x)\delta(x - a)dx = g(a) \tag{3.20}$$

The quantity $\delta(x - a)$ is called the Dirac delta function. It is very useful in many other problems in physics besides the representation of the density of a point particle. It has meaning, however, only as part of the process of integration. The properties of the delta function can be reproduced by a number of "functions." For example,

$$\int f(x)\delta(x)dx = \lim_{\epsilon \to 0} \int f(x)[(1/\epsilon\sqrt{\pi}) \exp(-x^2/\epsilon^2)]dx \tag{3.21}$$

$$\int f(x)\delta(x)dx = \lim_{m \to \infty} \int f(x)[\sin mx/\pi x]dx \tag{3.22}$$

$$\int f(x)\delta(x)dx = \lim_{a \to 0} \int f(x)g(x)dx \tag{3.23}$$

where
$$\begin{aligned} g(x) &= 1/a & -(a/2) < x < (a/2) \\ &= 0 & |x| > (a/2) \end{aligned} \tag{3.24}$$

If the order of the limiting process and the integration could be reversed in (3.21) we could simply write

$$\delta(x) = \lim_{\epsilon \to 0} (1/\epsilon\sqrt{\pi}) \exp(-x^2/\epsilon^2)$$

Similar results would hold for (3.22) and (3.23). This is not strictly correct, however, since the order of the limit and the integration cannot be reversed in these cases.

DISTRIBUTION IN POSITION AND VELOCITY

Suppose the points on the line discussed in the previous section are each moving with a different velocity v along the line. A single point can no longer be characterized by its position alone, but requires in addition that its velocity be given. If we introduce a two-dimensional space whose coordinates are x, the position, and v, the velocity, then the state of each point at some instant can be represented by a point in this space, and the state of the entire collection of points is represented by a set of points as shown in Figure 3.6.

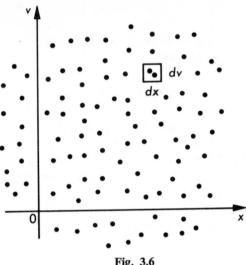

Fig. 3.6

The distribution of points in x–v space can be represented by a density function $f(x, v, t)$ in this space, having the property that $f(x, v, t)dxdv$ represents the number of points in the infinitesimal element $dxdv$ at time t. The density $f(x, v, t)$ is usually referred to as the distribution function to distinguish it from the ordinary density $n(x, t)$. The ordinary density n can be obtained from the distribution function $f(x, v, t)$ by integrating $f(x, v, t)$ over all values of velocity:

$$n(x, t) = \int f(x, v, t)dv \qquad (3.25)$$

Let us now consider the state at some time t of a gas consisting of N molecules in a volume V. Each molecule is at a different point in the gas, and since there are an infinite number of possible velocities, is very probably moving with a velocity different from the velocity of any other molecules. The state of an individual molecule is determined by its position and velocity. The state of the gas is determined by the positions and velocities of all of the N molecules.

If we introduce a six-dimensional space whose coordinates are the position coordinates x_1, x_2, x_3 and the velocity coordinates v_1, v_2, v_3, then the state of an individual molecule can be represented by a single point in this space, and the state of the gas by a set of N points, each point representing the state of a particular molecule.

It is impossible to graphically construct a six-dimensional space. We shall, however, for purposes of illustration only, represent the x–v space and the state of the gas as shown in Figure 3.7.

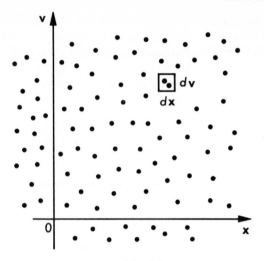

Fig. 3.7

The distribution of points in x–v space can be represented by a density function $f(\mathbf{x}, \mathbf{v}, t)$ in this space having the property that $f(\mathbf{x}, \mathbf{v}, t)d\mathbf{x}d\mathbf{v}$ represents the number of points in the six-dimensional element $d\mathbf{x}d\mathbf{v}$ at time t.

As in the one-dimensional case, the ordinary density $n(\mathbf{x}, t)$ is given by

$$n(\mathbf{x}, t) = \int f(\mathbf{x}, \mathbf{v}, t)d\mathbf{v} \tag{3.26}$$

and the average value of any function of the position and velocity [e.g., $g(\mathbf{x}, \mathbf{v})$] is given by

$$<g(\mathbf{x}, \mathbf{v})> = \frac{\int_V \int_{-\infty}^{\infty} g(\mathbf{x}, \mathbf{v})f(\mathbf{x}, \mathbf{v}, t)d\mathbf{v}d\mathbf{x}}{\int_V \int_{-\infty}^{\infty} f(\mathbf{x}, \mathbf{v}, t)d\mathbf{v}d\mathbf{x}} \tag{3.27}$$

where the integration $d\mathbf{x}$ is over the volume V, and the integration $d\mathbf{v}$ is over all velocities.

If we wanted to find the average value of $g(\mathbf{v})$ for the molecules contained within some subvolume ΔV of V, then we would integrate $\mathbf{x}$ over ΔV instead of V. In particular, if $\Delta V \equiv d\mathbf{x}$, then we obtain for the average value of the function $g(\mathbf{v})$ in the region around the point $\mathbf{x}$

$$\overline{g(\mathbf{v})} = \frac{\int_{-\infty}^{\infty} g(\mathbf{v})f(\mathbf{x}, \mathbf{v}, t)d\mathbf{v}}{\int_{-\infty}^{\infty} f(\mathbf{x}, \mathbf{v}, t)d\mathbf{v}} \tag{3.28}$$

$$= (1/n)\int_{-\infty}^{\infty} g(\mathbf{v})f(\mathbf{x}, \mathbf{v}, t)d\mathbf{v}$$

where we have indicated the average with a bar over the function to distinguish it from the average obtained by integrating over x and v.

For convenience we often introduce a function $f'(\mathbf{x}, \mathbf{v}, t)$ which is defined in such a way that $f'(\mathbf{x}, \mathbf{v}, t)d\mathbf{v}$ is the probability that a particle which is located at x at time t has its velocity in $d\mathbf{v}$. Our earlier analysis of the probability density can easily be extended to handle this problem and we obtain

$$f'(\mathbf{x}, \mathbf{v}, t) = \frac{f(\mathbf{x}, \mathbf{v}, t)}{\int f(\mathbf{x}, \mathbf{v}, t)d\mathbf{v}} = \frac{f(\mathbf{x}, \mathbf{v}, t)}{n(\mathbf{x}, t)} \tag{3.29}$$

In terms of f' the average value $\overline{g(\mathbf{v})}$ can then be written

$$\overline{g(\mathbf{v})} = \int g(\mathbf{v})f'(\mathbf{x}, \mathbf{v}, t)d\mathbf{v} \tag{3.30}$$

PROBLEMS

1. Given a set of molecules with the following speeds: two are moving with speeds of 7 m/sec, three are moving with speeds of 8 m/sec, one is moving with a speed of 15 m/sec, and four are moving with speeds of 20 m/sec,
   (a) What is the average or mean speed?
   (b) What is the root-mean-square speed, i.e., the square root of the mean value of the square of the speed?
   (c) What is the most probable value of the speed?
2. The density of a set of points is given by

$$n(\mathbf{x}) = C \qquad r = |\mathbf{x}| \leq R$$
$$= 0 \qquad r = |\mathbf{x}| > R$$

where C is a constant and $n(\mathbf{x})d\mathbf{x}$ is the number of points in the range x to $\mathbf{x} + d\mathbf{x}$.
   (a) What is the number of points in the range r to $r + dr$?
   (b) What is the number of points in the solid angle $\sin\theta d\theta d\phi$?
   (c) What is the number of points with θ between θ and $\theta + d\theta$ and ϕ between ϕ and $\phi + d\phi$ where $x_1 = r \sin\theta \cos\phi$; $x_2 = r \sin\theta \sin\phi$; $x_3 = r \cos\theta$?
   (d) What is the average distance of a point from the origin?
3. The speed distribution function for a group of N particles contained in a volume V is

$$f(v) = kv^2 \qquad 0 < v < a$$
$$f(v) = 0 \qquad v > a$$

(*a*) Determine k in terms of N and a.

(*b*) Compute the average energy, and the most probable energy of the particles.

4. The density of points along a line is given by

$$n(x) = a/\pi(a^2 + x^2)$$

(*a*) What is the average distance of a point from the origin?

(*b*) What is the root-mean-square distance of a point from the origin?

5. A set of molecules has the following distribution in **x**–**v** space:

$$f(\mathbf{x}, \mathbf{v}) = n(\lambda/\pi)^{3/2} \exp(-\lambda v^2)$$

where λ and n are constants.

(*a*) What is the density of molecules in **x** space?

(*b*) What is the average velocity of the molecules?

(*c*) What is the average speed of the molecules?

(*d*) What is the root-mean-square speed?

(*e*) What is the most probable speed?

(*f*) What is the average kinetic energy of a molecule?

6. It is found that following a certain crushing process, rock diameters, d, are approximately normally distributed

$$f(d) = (1/\sigma\sqrt{2\pi}) \exp\left[-\frac{1}{2}\left(\frac{d - \mu}{\sigma}\right)^2 \right]$$

with mean diameter 1.5 inches ($<d> = 1.5$ inches) and standard deviation 0.3 inches ($[<(d - <d>)^2>]^{1/2} = 0.3$ inches).

(*a*) Approximately what percentage of the rocks have diameters exceeding 2 inches?

(*b*) Assuming the weight of a rock to be kd^3, what is the approximate average weight?

(*c*) Why is the normal distribution necessarily only approximately valid?

7. Planck's radiation formula is given by

$$f(\nu) = \frac{a\nu^3}{\exp(b\nu) - 1}$$

where $f(\nu)d\nu$ is the probability of a photon being emitted with frequency between ν and $\nu + d\nu$. Find the probability of a photon being emitted with a wavelength between λ and $\lambda + d\lambda$.

8. A great number, N, of bullets are fired at the bull's-eye of a target. Assume (1) that the chance of a horizontal error h in aim and the chance of a vertical error v in aim are totally independent, (2) that the hits will be distributed isotropically about the bull's-eye, and (3) the average distance from the center of the bull's-eye which the bullets hit is d cm.

(a) Find the chance of a shot having a horizontal error between h and $h + dh$.

(b) Write down an expression for the density of holes on the target.

(c) Suppose the target is inclined to the vertical at an angle α. Find the chance of a shot lying between h and $h + dh$ and v and $v + dv$ on this target.

9. The distribution function in $\mathbf{x}$–$\mathbf{v}$ space for a certain gas is given by

$$f(\mathbf{x}, \mathbf{v}) = n(\lambda/\pi)^{3/2}[1 + (av_3/v)] \exp(-\lambda v^2)$$

(a) What is the average velocity of the molecules?

(b) What is the average speed of the molecules?

(c) How many molecules per second are crossing, in the positive x_3 direction, a unit area of the x_1–x_2 plane?

(d) How many molecules per second are crossing in the negative x_3 direction?

10. Ten thousand telephone conversations of a certain teenager were monitored and it was found that the number of calls of less than x minutes duration could be expressed by the function $A(1 - e^{-x})$.

(a) How many phone calls lasted between x and $x + dx$ minutes?

(b) What was the average length of a phone call?

11. A set of N molecules has a distribution in speeds given by $f(v)$. Using this distribution, it is found that the average speed is 100 m/sec, and the root-mean-square speed is also 100 m/sec. Evaluate $f(v)$ as completely as possible. Justify your answer.

Chapter 4

THE CLASSICAL EQUILIBRIUM DISTRIBUTION

We are now in a position to actually determine the classical equilibrium distribution function $f(\mathbf{x}, \mathbf{v}, t)$ for a gas of N point molecules contained in a volume V. In the present chapter we will derive this distribution in an elementary nonrigorous fashion. In a later chapter a more complete and rigorous derivation will be given.

THE MAXWELLIAN DISTRIBUTION

In the absence of any external forces, a gas will come to equilibrium. In equilibrium we expect the distribution to be homogeneous, isotropic, and time independent. A gas is homogeneous if to an observer in the gas it looks the same at different places; it is isotropic if it looks the same in different directions; it is time independent if it looks the same at different times.

Since the gas is homogeneous, we expect f to be independent of the position $\mathbf{x}$. Since the gas is time independent, we expect f to be independent of time. We can therefore write

$$f = f(\mathbf{v}) \equiv f(v_1, v_2, v_3) \qquad (4.1)$$

If we introduce the variables v, θ, and ϕ where

$$v_1 = v \sin\theta \cos\phi \qquad (4.2)$$

$$v_2 = v \sin\theta \sin\phi \qquad (4.3)$$

$$v_3 = v \cos\theta \qquad (4.4)$$

we can write

$$f = f(v, \theta, \phi) \tag{4.5}$$

Since f is isotropic, it will be independent of θ and ϕ and therefore f is a function of v alone or what is equivalent, a function of $v_1{}^2 + v_2{}^2 + v_3{}^2$. Thus

$$f = f(v_1{}^2 + v_2{}^2 + v_3{}^2) \tag{4.6}$$

We still do not have enough information to determine f. We therefore introduce one additional and not so obvious assumption, namely, that the probability of a molecule having one component of its velocity in a certain range is independent of the value of its other components—a molecule having $v_1 = 1000$ units and $v_2 = 10$ units is just as likely to have v_3 in the neighborhood of 100 units as a molecule having $v_1 = 10{,}000$ units and $v_2 = 100{,}000$ units. If $f_1{}'dv_1$ is the probability that a certain molecule has v_1 between v_1 and $v_1 + dv_1$; $f_2{}'dv_2$ is the probability that the molecule has v_2 between v_2 and $v_2 + dv_2$; $f_3{}'dv_3$ is the probability that the molecule has v_3 between v_3 and $v_3 + dv_3$; and $f'dv_1dv_2dv_3$ the probability that the molecule is in the range $dv_1dv_2dv_3$, then the above statement is equivalent to saying that

$$f'dv_1dv_2dv_3 = (f_1{}'dv_1)(f_2{}'dv_2)(f_3{}'dv_3) \tag{4.7}$$

or simply

$$f' = f_1{}'f_2{}'f_3{}' \tag{4.8}$$

This result follows from the fact that if the probabilities of two events are completely independent then the probability of both events is simply the product of the separate probabilities. Thus if the probability of heads coming up on one coin is $1/2$ and the probability of heads coming up on a second coin is $1/2$, then the probability of the joint event of heads coming up on the first coin and heads coming up on the second coin is simply $(1/2)(1/2) = 1/4$.

In terms of the distribution function f we have

$$f_1{}' = \frac{\iint f(v_1{}^2 + v_2{}^2 + v_3{}^2)dv_2dv_3}{\iiint f(v_1{}^2 + v_2{}^2 + v_3{}^2)dv_1dv_2dv_3}$$

$$= (1/n) \iint f(v_1{}^2 + v_2{}^2 + v_3{}^2)dv_2dv_3 = g(v_1{}^2) \tag{4.9}$$

$$f_2{}' = (1/n) \iint f(v_1{}^2 + v_2{}^2 + v_3{}^2)dv_1dv_3 = g(v_2{}^2) \tag{4.10}$$

$$f_3{}' = (1/n) \iint f(v_1{}^2 + v_2{}^2 + v_3{}^2)dv_1dv_2 = g(v_3{}^2) \tag{4.11}$$

$$f' = (1/n)f(v_1{}^2 + v_2{}^2 + v_3{}^2) \tag{4.12}$$

Gathering results, we have

$$f'(v_1^2 + v_2^2 + v_3^2) = g(v_1^2)g(v_2^2)g(v_3^2) \tag{4.13}$$

The only function g which will satisfy this functional relationship is, as we shall show, a function of the form

$$g(v_1^2) = A \exp(-\lambda v_1^2) \tag{4.14}$$

where A and λ are arbitrary constants.

To demonstrate (4.14) let us consider the equivalent two-dimensional problem, namely, solving the following functional equation

$$F(x + y) = G(x)G(y) \tag{4.15}$$

If we take the derivative of both sides of (4.15) with respect to x we obtain

$$\frac{dF(x + y)}{d(x + y)} \frac{\partial(x + y)}{\partial x} = \frac{dG(x)}{dx}G(y) \tag{4.16}$$

Noting that $[\partial(x + y)/\partial x] = 1$ and dividing (4.16) by (4.15) we have

$$\frac{\dfrac{dF(x + y)}{d(x + y)}}{F(x + y)} = \frac{\dfrac{dG(x)}{dx}}{G(x)} \tag{4.17}$$

Similarly, if we take the derivative of both sides of (4.15) with respect to y we obtain

$$\frac{\dfrac{dF(x + y)}{d(x + y)}}{F(x + y)} = \frac{\dfrac{dG(y)}{dy}}{G(y)} \tag{4.18}$$

Equating (4.17) and (4.18) we obtain

$$\frac{dG(x)/dx}{G(x)} = \frac{dG(y)/dy}{G(y)} \tag{4.19}$$

Equation (4.19) must be true for all values of x and y. Since the left-hand side is a function of x only and the right-hand side a function of y only, the only way this can be true is if both sides are equal to the same constant, which we designate $-\lambda$. Thus

$$\frac{dG(x)/dx}{G(x)} = \frac{dG(y)/dy}{G(y)} = -\lambda \tag{4.20}$$

From (4.20) we obtain the following differential equation for $G(x)$:

$$dG(x)/dx = -\lambda G(x) \tag{4.21}$$

the solution of which is

$$G(x) = A \exp(-\lambda x) \tag{4.22}$$

This result can readily be extended to the equivalent three-dimensional problem, and thus the solution to (4.13) is given by (4.14).

Substituting (4.14) in (4.13) and remembering that $f = nf'$ we obtain

$$f = nA^3 \exp[-\lambda(v_1{}^2 + v_2{}^2 + v_3{}^2)] = nA^3 \exp(-\lambda v^2) \qquad (4.23)$$

If we use the relation

$$n = \int f \, d\mathbf{v} \qquad (4.24)$$

to solve for A, we find

$$A = (\lambda/\pi)^{1/2} \qquad (4.25)$$

Gathering results, we have for the density in $\mathbf{x}$–$\mathbf{v}$ space

$$f = n(\lambda/\pi)^{3/2} \exp(-\lambda v^2) \qquad (4.26)$$

This distribution is called the Maxwellian distribution.

Using the distribution (4.26), the average value of v^n is

$$\overline{v^n} = \frac{\Gamma\left(\dfrac{n+3}{2}\right)}{\lambda^{n/2}\Gamma\left(\dfrac{3}{2}\right)} \qquad n \geq -1 \qquad (4.27)$$

where

$$\Gamma(n) = \int_0^\infty e^{-x}x^{n-1}dx = (n-1)\Gamma(n-1) \qquad (4.28)$$

$$\Gamma(1) = 1 \qquad (4.29)$$

$$\Gamma(1/2) = \sqrt{\pi} \qquad (4.30)$$

The physical interpretation of λ is not evident from what we have done so far. In a later section it will be shown that $\lambda = m/2kT$ where m is the mass of a molecule, k is Boltzmann's constant, and T the temperature.

FLUX DENSITY

In deriving the properties of a gas having a distribution $f(\mathbf{x}, \mathbf{v})$ it will frequently be convenient to consider only those particles whose velocities lie in a certain range $d\mathbf{v}$. The collection of particles having velocities in $d\mathbf{v}$ constitute a beam of particles all moving with an approximate velocity $\mathbf{v}$ and having a density $f d\mathbf{v}$. Actually, the particles will be moving with slightly different speeds, in slightly different directions, but as long as $d\mathbf{v}$ is small the dispersion of the beam will be negligible. The beam is not constituted of a unique set of particles, but is constantly being depleted and replenished by collisions.

Let us consider the properties of a beam constituted of particles moving with velocity **v** and having a constant density n. We define the flux density of such a beam as **J** where

$$\mathbf{J} = n\mathbf{v} \tag{4.31}$$

Suppose the beam of flux density **J** encounters a plane surface S. The surface S can be represented by a vector $S\mathbf{k}$ where **k** is a unit vector normal to the surface, as shown in Figure 4.1.

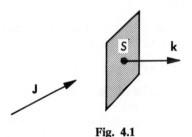

Fig. 4.1

We wish to find the number of particles which pass through S per unit time. The positive direction of passage through S is the direction indicated by **k**. Let us construct a parallelepiped by translating the area **k**S a distance $-\mathbf{v}$, as shown in Figure 4.2.

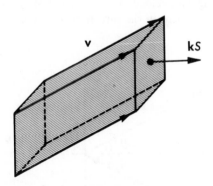

Fig. 4.2

In one second all of the particles in the parallelepiped will pass through S. The number of particles in the parallelepiped thus represents the desired rate of flow through S. The height of the parallelepiped is $\mathbf{k} \cdot \mathbf{v}$. The area of the base is S. Its volume is thus $(\mathbf{k} \cdot \mathbf{v})S$. The density of particles is n, and thus the number of particles in the parallelepiped is $(\mathbf{k} \cdot \mathbf{v})Sn$. Remembering that $\mathbf{J} = n\mathbf{v}$, the number per second passing through S is given by $\mathbf{J} \cdot \mathbf{k}S$.

If our surface is an infinitesimal surface $\mathbf{k}dS$, then the number per second passing through dS is $\mathbf{J} \cdot \mathbf{k}dS$. This relation is often used as a definition of $\mathbf{J}$, i.e., $\mathbf{J}$ at a given point P is defined as the vector whose direction is determined by finding the orientation of the surface element dS located at P such that the maximum number of particles pass through in a unit time, and whose magnitude is this number divided by the area dS. This definition allows $\mathbf{J}$ to be a function of position and time.

THE PERFECT GAS LAW

From experiments it is found that the pressure, volume, and temperature of a dilute gas are related by the equation

$$pV = \nu RT = NkT \tag{4.32}$$

where ν is the number of moles of the gas, and N is the number of molecules. The gas constant R and Boltzmann's constant k are universal constants.

Since knowledge of the density f is sufficient to enable us to calculate the macroscopic properties of a gas, we should be able to obtain (4.32), starting with the distribution obtained in the first section of this chapter.

To calculate the pressure exerted by a gas having a distribution $f(\mathbf{v})$, we first consider only those particles whose velocities lie in $d\mathbf{v}$. These particles constitute a beam of density $fd\mathbf{v}$ moving with velocity $\mathbf{v}$, and thus having a flux density given by $(fd\mathbf{v})\mathbf{v}$.

If a particle moving with velocity $\mathbf{v}$ encounters a smooth wall whose normal is given by $\mathbf{k}$, its component in the direction of $\mathbf{k}$ will be reversed, as shown in Figure 4.3.

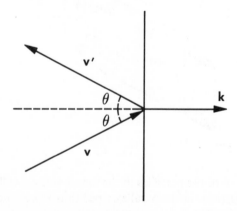

Fig. 4.3

Its change in momentum is given by $-(2m\mathbf{v} \cdot \mathbf{k})\mathbf{k}$. This change in momentum was provided by an impulse exerted by the wall on the particle.

The particle exerts an equal and opposite impulse of $(2m\mathbf{v} \cdot \mathbf{k})\mathbf{k}$ on the wall.

The number of particles in the beam $(f d\mathbf{v})\mathbf{v}$ hitting a unit area of the wall per second is given by

$$[(f d\mathbf{v})\mathbf{v}] \cdot \mathbf{k} \tag{4.33}$$

The average force exerted by the particles on a unit area of the wall is then found by multiplying the number of particles hitting per second by the impulse per particle. Thus

$$\mathbf{F} = \{[(f d\mathbf{v})\mathbf{v}] \cdot \mathbf{k}\}\{(2m\mathbf{v} \cdot \mathbf{k})\mathbf{k}\}$$
$$= [2m(\mathbf{v} \cdot \mathbf{k})^2 f d\mathbf{v}]\mathbf{k} \tag{4.34}$$

The magnitude of this quantity is the contribution to the pressure by the particles whose velocity is in $d\mathbf{v}$. We designate this quantity dp. Thus

$$dp = 2m(\mathbf{v} \cdot \mathbf{k})^2 f d\mathbf{v} \tag{4.35}$$

For convenience we choose $\mathbf{k}$ to be a unit vector in the x_3 direction, and thus $\mathbf{v} \cdot \mathbf{k} = v_3$. To obtain the total pressure we integrate over all velocities for which $v_3 > 0$, since those particles for which $v_3 < 0$ will be moving away from the wall and will not hit it. We thus have for the total pressure

$$p = \int_0^\infty \int_{-\infty}^\infty \int_{-\infty}^\infty 2m v_3^2 f \, dv_1 dv_2 dv_3$$
$$= m \int_{-\infty}^\infty \int_{-\infty}^\infty \int_{-\infty}^\infty v_3^2 f \, dv_1 dv_2 dv_3 = mn \overline{v_3^2} \tag{4.36}$$

The distribution of velocities is assumed to be isotropic, and therefore

$$\overline{v_1^2} = \overline{v_2^2} = \overline{v_3^2} = \tfrac{1}{3}(\overline{v_1^2} + \overline{v_2^2} + \overline{v_3^2}) \tag{4.37}$$

And since the sum of the average value of two quantities is equal to the average value of the sum, we have

$$\overline{v_3^2} = \tfrac{1}{3}(\overline{v_1^2 + v_2^2 + v_3^2}) = \tfrac{1}{3}\overline{v^2} \tag{4.38}$$

Substituting this in our previous result (4.36) we have

$$p = (nm/3)\overline{v^2} \tag{4.39}$$

But from Eq. (4.27) we have

$$\overline{v^2} = 3/2\lambda \tag{4.40}$$

And therefore

$$p = nm/2\lambda \tag{4.41}$$

There are a number of ways this same result could have been obtained somewhat more simply. However, part of the purpose of the preceding derivation was to develop a point of view which will be extremely useful in later, more complicated calculations.

As an example of a simple derivation, consider a single particle moving with velocity $\mathbf{v}$ in a box of unit volume, as shown in Figure 4.4.

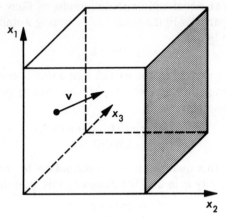

Fig. 4.4

The particle will collide with the shaded wall $|v_2|/2$ times a second, imparting an impulse $2m|v_2|$ with each collision. The pressure due to this particle is then mv_2^2. If there are n particles moving with random velocities, the pressure will be $nm\overline{v_2^2}$. We then proceed exactly as in our previous derivation.

Actually, a particular particle will not move freely from wall to wall but will undergo an immense number of collisions in a very short distance. However, it will be later shown that when a gas is in equilibrium the collisions have no effect on the macroscopic properties and for the purpose of analysis can be ignored.

Equation (4.41) is the microscopic equivalent of Eq. (4.32). By comparing (4.32) and (4.41) we can connect the microscopic parameter λ with the macroscopic parameter T. We obtain

$$nm/2\lambda = NkT/V \tag{4.42}$$

and since $n = N/V$, this gives us

$$\lambda = m/2kT \tag{4.43}$$

We thus have for the Maxwellian distribution

$$f = n(m/2\pi kT)^{3/2} \exp(-mv^2/2kT) \tag{4.44}$$

As discussed earlier, $f\,dv\,dx$ represents the number of molecules in the six-dimensional element $dv\,dx$. We are often interested, however, in the number of molecules per unit volume with speed in dv, or the number per unit volume whose 1 component of velocity lies in dv_1. We designate the former quantity as $f_v\,dv$, and the latter quantity as $f_{v_1}\,dv_1$. The functions f_v and f_{v_1}

represent densities in v-space and in v_1 space and can easily be obtained if we know f. To obtain f_v we integrate f over all directions. Thus

$$f_v = \int_0^{2\pi} \int_0^\pi f \left| J\left(\frac{v_1, v_2, v_3}{v, \theta, \phi} \right) \right| d\theta d\phi = \int_0^{2\pi} \int_0^\pi f v^2 \sin\theta \, d\theta d\phi = 4\pi v^2 f \quad (4.45)$$

To obtain f_{v_1} we integrate over v_2 and v_3. Thus

$$f_{v_1} = \int_{-\infty}^\infty \int_{-\infty}^\infty f dv_2 dv_3 \quad (4.46)$$

which for a Maxwellian distribution becomes simply

$$f_{v_1} = n(\lambda/\pi)^{1/2} \exp(-\lambda v_1^2) \quad (4.47)$$

The distributions f_v and f_{v_1} are shown in Figures 4.5 and 4.6.

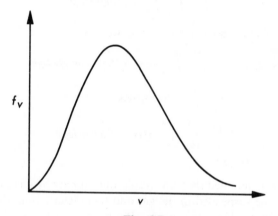

Fig. 4.5

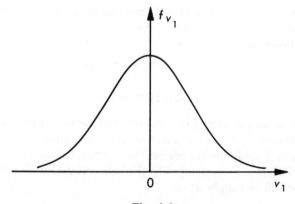

Fig. 4.6

Many authors when referring to the Maxwellian distribution mean f_v rather than f. In reading the literature, great care should be taken to ascertain what distribution is meant.

EFFUSION

As discussed in the preceding section, the number of molecules whose velocities lie in $d\mathbf{v}$ which strike a unit area of wall in unit time is given by $(\mathbf{k} \cdot \mathbf{v})f d\mathbf{v}$ where $\mathbf{k}$ is a unit vector normal to the area. If the area is normal to the x_3 axis, this becomes $v_3 f d\mathbf{v}$. To find the total number striking the unit area per unit of time which we designate C, we integrate over all values of $\mathbf{v}$ for which $v_3 > 0$, and obtain

$$C = \int_0^\infty \int_{-\infty}^\infty \int_{-\infty}^\infty v_3 f(v) dv_1 dv_2 dv_3 \tag{4.48}$$

Switching to spherical coordinates v, θ, ϕ we have

$$
\begin{aligned}
C &= \int_0^{\pi/2} \int_0^{2\pi} \int_0^\infty v \cos\theta\, f(v) v^2 \sin\theta\, dv d\phi d\theta \\
&= \tfrac{1}{2} \int_0^{2\pi} \int_0^\infty v f(v) v^2 dv d\phi \\
&= \tfrac{1}{4} \int_0^\pi \int_0^{2\pi} \int_0^\infty v f(v) v^2 \sin\theta\, dv d\phi d\theta \\
&= \tfrac{1}{4} n\bar{v} \tag{4.49}
\end{aligned}
$$

We could have obtained the same result more simply by imagining a sphere of radius R to be suspended in the gas and then determining the number of molecules which would hit the sphere. If a beam J strikes a sphere of radius R, there are $J\pi R^2$ particles striking the sphere per second. Thus if the beam $(f d\mathbf{v})\mathbf{v}$ strikes the sphere, the number of particles per second striking the sphere will be $\pi R^2 v f d\mathbf{v}$. Integrating over $\mathbf{v}$ and dividing by the total area of the sphere we obtain immediately $C = n\bar{v}/4$.

For the Maxwellian distribution

$$\bar{v} = 2/\pi^{1/2}\lambda^{1/2} = (8kT/\pi m)^{1/2} \tag{4.50}$$

and therefore

$$C = n(kT/2\pi m)^{1/2} \tag{4.51}$$

Now suppose we put a small hole of area A in the side of the gas container. If the dimensions of A are the same order of magnitude or less than the distance which a molecule travels on the average between collisions, then the distribution f will be unchanged by the hole and the number of molecules which escape will be simply AC or

$$An(kT/2\pi m)^{1/2} \tag{4.52}$$

The inverse dependence of the rate of effusion on the square root of the mass can be exploited to separate two gases of different masses.

Consider a mixture of two gases, with molecular masses and densities given by m_1 and m_2, and n_1 and n_2 respectively. If F_1 and F_2 are the rates of effusion per unit area of the two gases, we have

$$F_1 = n_1(kT/2\pi m_1)^{1/2} \tag{4.53}$$

$$F_2 = n_2(kT/2\pi m_2)^{1/2} \tag{4.54}$$

The ratio of the densities in the container is n_1/n_2. The ratio of the densities in the gas effusing from the container is $(F_1/F_2) = (n_1/n_2)(m_2/m_1)^{1/2}$. If $m_2 > m_1$, then $(F_1/F_2) > (n_1/n_2)$. That is, there is a greater concentration of the lighter gas in the gas which has escaped. The ratio $(F_1/F_2)/(n_1/n_2) = (m_2/m_1)^{1/2}$ is called the separation factor f. As the gas in a container effuses, the efficiency of the separation decreases, since the gas in the container is progressively becoming poorer in the lighter species. Ultimately a point will be reached at which the ratio F_1/F_2 is less than the original value of n_1/n_2 at the start of the process.

This technique is used to separate U^{235} from U^{238}. The uranium is combined with fluorine to form the gas uranium hexafluoride, UF_6. The separation factor $f = 1.0043$, and $(n_1/n_2) = 0.0073$. The separation is accomplished in successive stages and over 4000 stages are needed.

DISTRIBUTION OF MOLECULES IN A MOVING CONTAINER

Suppose we wish to find the equilibrium distribution of a gas which is contained within a box moving with some arbitrary velocity $\bar{\mathbf{v}}$. (The reason for the use of this symbol will soon become apparent.) In the reference frame moving with the box, the laws of mechanics assume the same form as in the reference system which is at rest. Therefore we expect the distribution which we designate f^* to take the same form in this reference system as we previously obtained when the box was at rest. Thus

$$f^*(\mathbf{v}^*) = n(\lambda/\pi)^{3/2} \exp(-\lambda v^{*2}) \tag{4.55}$$

where $\mathbf{v}^*$ is the velocity in the moving frame. But if $\mathbf{v}$ is the velocity in the rest frame, then

$$\mathbf{v}^* = \mathbf{v} - \bar{\mathbf{v}} \tag{4.56}$$

and consequently the distribution in the rest system is given by

$$f(\mathbf{v}) = f^*(\mathbf{v} - \bar{\mathbf{v}}) \left| J\left(\frac{\mathbf{v} - \bar{\mathbf{v}}}{\mathbf{v}}\right) \right| = f^*(\mathbf{v} - \bar{\mathbf{v}}) \tag{4.57}$$

The distribution in the rest system is thus

$$f(\mathbf{v}) = n(\lambda/\pi)^{3/2} \exp[-\lambda(\mathbf{v} - \bar{\mathbf{v}})^2] \tag{4.58}$$

$$\lambda = m/2kT \tag{4.59}$$

The distribution (4.58) is the most general form of the Maxwellian distribution.

The velocity $\bar{\mathbf{v}}$ is the velocity of the container. It is also the average velocity of the molecules in the rest frame, as can be verified by evaluating the average value of $\mathbf{v}$ using the above distribution f.

THE MAXWELL-BOLTZMANN DISTRIBUTION

We have seen that the equilibrium distribution of a collection of molecules in a container at rest is described by the distribution function

$$f = n(\lambda/\pi)^{3/2} \exp(-\lambda v^2) \tag{4.60}$$

where

$$\lambda = m/2kT \tag{4.61}$$

In deriving this distribution, we assumed that there were no external forces acting on the molecules. We would now like to consider a gas in a force field. We will restrict ourselves to conservative force fields. For conservative fields there exists a potential function $U(\mathbf{x})$ from which the components of the force can be derived through the relation $F_i = -\partial U/\partial x_i$. If $\mathbf{F}$ is the force on a molecule, then $U(\mathbf{x})$ is the potential energy of a molecule at the point $\mathbf{x}$.

In the present section we wish to give an elementary derivation of the distribution function for a gas in a potential field $U(\mathbf{x})$. In a later chapter the same result will be derived in a completely rigorous fashion.

In equilibrium we expect the gas to assume a distribution which locally appears to be Maxwellian, and such that there is no net flow of energy, momentum, or molecules. This can be accomplished if we assume

$$f = n(\mathbf{x})(\lambda/\pi)^{3/2} \exp(-\lambda v^2) \tag{4.62}$$

provided the dependence of n on $\mathbf{x}$ is appropriately chosen. To determine this dependence, let us for simplicity assume that the potential $U(\mathbf{x})$ is a function of x_1 only, and then let us examine a small element of the gas of thickness dx_1 and unit cross section as shown in Figure 4.7.

In equilibrium, the net flow of particles into and out of this volume is zero. If the element were surrounded by a massless, perfectly reflecting wall, the properties of the gas inside and out would remain unchanged.

The sum of the forces acting on this little element will in equilibrium be zero. There are $n(x_1)dx_1$ molecules within the element, each experiencing a force $-\partial U/\partial x_1$. There is a force on the lower face due to the pressure of the neighboring gas, directed in the positive x_1 direction and of magnitude

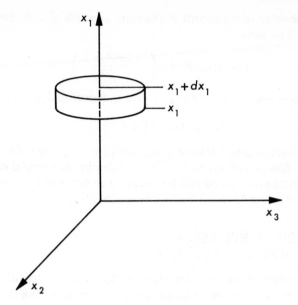

Fig. 4.7

$p(x_1) = n(x_1)kT$.   There is a similar force on the upper face given by $-p(x_1 + dx_1) = -n(x_1 + dx_1)kT$. Summing these forces and setting them equal to zero, we have

$$n(x_1)dx_1\left(-\frac{\partial U}{\partial x_1}\right) + n(x_1)kT - n(x_1 + dx_1)kT = 0 \qquad (4.63)$$

Dividing by dx_1 and letting $dx_1 \to 0$, we have

$$-n(x_1)\left(\frac{\partial U}{\partial x_1}\right) - \left(\frac{\partial n}{\partial x_1}\right)kT = 0 \qquad (4.64)$$

This can be rewritten as

$$\frac{\partial U}{\partial x_1} = -\frac{kT}{n}\frac{\partial n}{\partial x_1} = -kT\frac{\partial}{\partial x_1}(\ln n) \qquad (4.65)$$

Integrating, we obtain

$$U = -kT\ln n + \text{const} \qquad (4.66)$$

or
$$n = C\exp(-U/kT) \qquad (4.67)$$

If $U = 0$ when $x_1 = x_{10}$, then $C = n(x_{10}) \equiv n_0$ and we obtain

$$n = n_0\exp(-U/kT) \qquad (4.68)$$

where n_0 is the value of the density at the point at which $U = 0$. Substituting (4.68) in (4.62) we have

$$f = n_0(\lambda/\pi)^{3/2} \exp\left(-\frac{\frac{1}{2}mv^2 + U}{kT}\right) \tag{4.69}$$

But $\frac{1}{2}mv^2 + U$ is just the total energy ϵ of a molecule and we can therefore write

$$f = n_0(\lambda/\pi)^{3/2} \exp(-\epsilon/kT) \tag{4.70}$$

Although we have assumed U to be a function of x_1 only, our result is equally valid if U is a function of x_2 and x_3. This distribution is a special case of the Boltzmann distribution which will be discussed in detail in Chapter 12. We shall refer to it as the Maxwell-Boltzmann distribution.

DISTRIBUTION OF MOLECULES IN AN ISOTHERMAL ATMOSPHERE

As an illustration of the use of the Maxwell-Boltzmann distribution, we will determine the distribution of molecules in the atmosphere. We shall assume the atmosphere to have a constant temperature T. The potential energy of a molecule of mass m in a gravitational field is given by

$$U = mgx_1 + \text{const} \tag{4.71}$$

Setting the constant equal to zero, and substituting this potential into the Maxwell-Boltzmann distribution, we obtain

$$f = n(0) \exp(-mgx_1/kT)(\lambda/\pi)^{3/2} \exp(-\lambda v^2) \tag{4.72}$$

The density of the molecules is thus given by

$$n = n(0) \exp(-mgx_1/kT) \tag{4.73}$$

From (4.73) we see that the density of molecules in a gravitational field decreases exponentially with height.

PROBLEMS

1. Given a gas of particles with a Maxwellian distribution:
   (a) What is the most probable velocity?
   (b) What is the average velocity?
   (c) What is the root-mean-square speed?
   (d) What is the most probable speed?
   (e) What is the average speed?
   (f) What is the average energy of a particle?
   (g) What is the average value of the reciprocal speed?

2. What fraction of the molecules in a Maxwellian gas have speeds greater than the average speed?

3. Write down an expression for the number of molecules in a Maxwellian gas which have their translational energy between ϵ and $\epsilon + d\epsilon$.

4. What fraction of the molecules of a gas have their x component of velocity between $-a$ and $+a$? Express your answer in terms of the error function of x, defined by

$$\phi(x) = (2/\sqrt{\pi}) \int_0^x \exp(-z^2)dz$$

5. What is the probability that two molecules picked at random from a Maxwellian gas will have a total energy between E and $E + dE$?

6. Determine the number of molecules per cubic meter in a Maxwellian gas at a temperature $T = 300°K$ and a pressure $p = 10^5\,N/m^2$.

7. Find the root-mean-square speed of:
   (a) Oxygen molecules at 300°K.
   (b) Hydrogen molecules at 300°K.

8. Consider a two-dimensional gas consisting of N point particles of mass m contained within a two-dimensional "box" of dimensions $L \times L$ as shown in Figure 4.8. Imagine the box to be a frictionless plate on which the particles are free to slide.

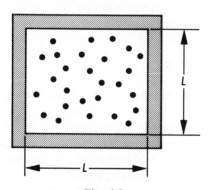

Fig. 4.8

   (a) If the total kinetic energy of the particles is E, what is the temperature of the gas in terms of E?
   (b) What is the specific heat per particle at constant area?
   (c) Show that $pA = E$ where p is the force per unit length, A is the area of the box, and E the total energy of the particles.
   (d) Show that the number of particles striking a unit length of the boundary per unit time is $n < v > /\pi$ where n is the number of particles per unit area.

9. A dilute gas of weakly interacting molecules is contained in a volume V. There are no external forces. The gas is in equilibrium. At what value of the speed does the density of representative points in x–v space have half its maximum value?

10. Dalton's law states: If several gases not reacting chemically with one another are contained in the same volume, the pressure of the resulting mixture is equal to the sum of the pressures which would be observed if each gas were separately enclosed in the volume. This law is only approximately valid for real gases, but rigorously true for ideal gases. Prove Dalton's law for a mixture of ideal gases.

11. If an atom radiates light of wavelength λ_0 and the atom is moving away from the observer at a rate C cm/sec, the wavelength as measured by the observer is

$$\lambda = \lambda_0\left(1 + \frac{C}{c}\right)$$

where c is the velocity of light. This is known as the Doppler effect. Consider a gas at temperature T composed of atoms of mass M which are radiating light at a wavelength λ_0. An observer looking at the gas from some distance away, instead of observing a single wavelength λ_0 will observe a spread of wavelengths of differing intensities. Let $I(\lambda)d\lambda$ be the intensity of light the observer sees with wavelength between λ and $\lambda + d\lambda$. Let I_0 be the total intensity.
(a) Show that $I(\lambda)$ has the form

$$I(\lambda) = A \exp[-B(\lambda - \lambda_0)^2]$$

and determine the value of the constants A and B in terms of T, m, c, and I_0.

12. A gas at low pressure and a temperature T is contained in a vessel. The gas is leaking out through a small hole whose diameter is much less than the mean-free path of the molecules. Show that the average kinetic energy of the escaping molecules is $2kT$.

13. A clean tungsten filament is introduced into a vessel containing oxygen at a pressure of 10^{-4} mm of Hg and a temperature of $300°$K. Assume (1) every oxygen molecule which hits the filament remains attached (2) the molecules can be considered to be spheres of diameter 3 Å and (3) the molecules arrange themselves in a close-packed pattern. How long does it take for a monomolecular layer to be formed?

14. How large is a pinhole through the thin wall of a high-vacuum system at $27°$C if the observed rate of pressure increase due to the air leak is approximately 0.01 mm/hr? Assume that every air molecule which reaches the pinhole passes into the vacuum system.

15. A dilute gas is enclosed within a volume V. Find the number of molecules colliding with the wall per unit area per unit time with normal component of velocity greater than some arbitrary value v_0.

16. A vessel contains mercury vapor which is maintained at a pressure of $35 \text{ N}/m^2$. The vapor is effusing out through a small circular hole 0.2 mm in diameter. An evacuated hemisphere with center coincident with the hole is fixed to the outside of the vessel as shown in Figure 4.9. Assume the mercury atoms adhere to the surface of the hemisphere when they hit, and that there are no collisions between the effusing molecules after they escape through the hole. Construct a coordinate system with origin at the hole and z axis normal to the surface of the vessel. Let $B \sin\theta d\theta d\phi$ represent the rate of deposition of mercury atoms on the surface lying in the solid angle $\sin\theta d\theta d\phi$. Determine the value of B in kilograms per second per steradian.

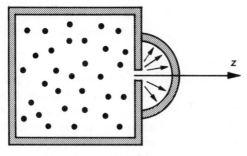

Fig. 4.9

17. A gas mixture contained in a region A at a temperature T as shown in Figure 4.10 is effusing out through a series of small holes of total area S into an evacuated region B. The gas is pumped from B into a region C. Let n_1 and n_2 be the total number of molecules respectively of the two species in region A, and N_1 and N_2 the total number of molecules of each of the two species in region C. Let m_1 and m_2 be the respective

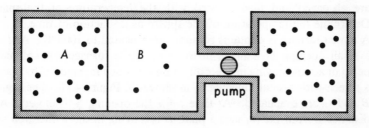

Fig. 4.10

molecular masses of the two species. At time $t = 0$ $n_1 = n_1(0)$, $n_2 = n_2(0)$ and $N_1 = N_2 = 0$. Find $n_1(t)$, $n_2(t)$, $N_1(t)$, and $N_2(t)$ in terms of t, m_1, m_2, S, T, $n_1(0)$, and $n_2(0)$.

18. A container of gas is separated into two regions by a thin wall with a very small hole in it. If the two parts are kept at different pressures p_1 and p_2 and different temperatures T_1 and T_2, show that there will be no net flow of molecules through the hole when

$$(p_1/\sqrt{T_1}) = (p_2/\sqrt{T_2})$$

19. A spherical bulb 10 cm in radius is maintained at a temperature of $300°K$ except for 1 cm^2 of its surface which is maintained at a very low temperature. The bulb contains water vapor initially at a pressure 10^3 N/m^2. Assuming that every molecule which strikes the cold area sticks to the surface, how long a time is required for the pressure to decrease to 10^{-2} N/m^2?

20. Compare the formula for the rate of efflux of gas through a small hole with Torricelli's formula for the flow of fluid through a hole, using the same pressure and density for both cases. Explain why the formulae differ.

21. A disk of radius a spins at an angular velocity ω in a vessel containing gas at so low a pressure that the free path is much greater than a. If molecules striking the disk are momentarily attached, and evaporated later in a random direction, show that the torque exerted by the gas on the disk is $\pi n m < v > \omega a^4/4$ where n is the number density of molecules, m the mass of a molecule, and $<v>$ the average speed of a molecule.

22. A molecule AB dissociates if it hits the surface of a solid catalyst with a translational kinetic energy greater than 10^{-19} J. Show that the rate of the reaction $AB \rightarrow A + B$ is about doubled by raising the temperature from $300°K$ to $310°K$.

23. A small sphere of radius r, mass density ρ, and specific heat per unit mass c is immersed in an ideal gas having n molecules of mass m per unit volume at a temperature T_0. Initially, the temperature of the sphere is T_1. Assume (1) the radius of the sphere is much smaller than the average distance traveled between collisions, (2) incident molecules are absorbed and then emitted with the temperature of the sphere. Determine the temperature of the sphere as a function of time.

24. A closed furnace A contains sodium vapor heated to $1000°K$. At $t = 0$ a small opening S_1 is made in the wall of the furnace. A collimated beam of atoms moving in the x direction is formed in region C by placing a screen with a small opening S_2 as shown in Figure 4.11. The regions B and C are evacuated. At time $t = \tau$ the opening S_1 is closed. At a distance L from the furnace a plate D is moving in the y direction with

velocity V. The sodium atoms hit the plate and stick. Obtain a formula for the density of deposition of sodium as a function of distance along the plate in the y direction.

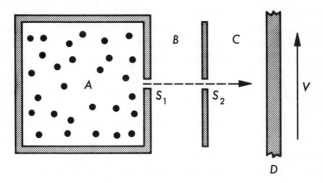

Fig. 4.11

25. Assume (1) the atmosphere has a uniform temperature $T = 220\,°K$, (2) the pressure at sea level is $p_0 = 10^5\,N/m^2$ (3) the composition by volume of the atmosphere at sea level is; 78 percent N_2, 21 percent O_2, and 1 percent H_2.
    (a) Find the pressure of the atmosphere at 10 km, 50 km, and 500 km.
    (b) Find the number of molecules per unit volume of N_2, O_2, and H_2 at sea level, 10 km, 60 km, and 500 km.
26. Find the mean gravitational potential energy of a molecule in an isothermal atmosphere.
27. Compute the average specific heat per mole of an infinite column of a monatomic gas in a gravitational potential $V = mgh$ $(0 \leq h \leq \infty)$.
28. Assume the atmosphere to be composed of a single species of molecule of molecular weight 29 and to have a uniform temperature of $0\,°C$. Below what height will be found just half the gas molecules in the earth's gravitational field?
29. Find the variation of pressure with elevation in an adiabatic atmosphere, i.e., one in which $(pV)^{c_p/c_V}$ rather than pV is constant. The quantity c_p is the specific heat at constant pressure, and c_V is the specific heat at constant volume. Assume the atmosphere to be composed of a single species of molecule of mass m, and also that c_p/c_V is a constant.
30. When a gas of particles of mass m is whirled in a centrifuge with angular velocity ω, its molecules can be considered to be acted upon by a radially outward centrifugal force of magnitude $m\omega^2 r$ where r is the distance of the molecule from the axis of rotation. Find an expression for the density of the gas as a function of r.

31. Find the average potential energy of a gas in a force field given by

$$F = -a - bz$$

where a and b are constant and z is the distance above the plane $z = 0$. The particles are all restricted to the region $z > 0$.

32. A heated wire which is thermionically emitting electrons is placed along the axis of a hollow cylinder and charged positively with respect to the cylinder so that the field (in rationalized mks units) between the wire and the cylinder is

$$E = q/2\pi\epsilon_0 r$$

where r is the distance from the axis, and q is the charge per unit length. Neglecting the effect of space charge, find the dependence of the density of electrons on the distance r.

33. Use the Maxwell-Boltzmann distribution to calculate
   (a) The variation of the density of colloid particles with height in a colloidal suspension.
   (b) The variation of the density of colloid particles with the distance from the axis of rotation in an ultracentrifuge.

34. Assume: (1) a metal may be considered as a box of free electrons of charge e and mass m, (2) the electrons are distributed according to a Maxwellian distribution, (3) any electron for which the energy associated with the component of velocity normal to the surface of the metal exceeds a value ϵ_0 will escape, (4) all electrons escaping from the surface are collected by an electrode which is maintained at a strong positive potential with respect to the metal, (5) electrons are supplied to the metal so that the density of electrons, n, remains constant (e.g., the metal is grounded). Find the current density of the emitted electrons, i.e., how many electrons per second are emitted from a unit area of the metal surface.

Chapter 5

ELEMENTARY
QUANTUM
STATISTICS

INTRODUCTION

The Maxwell-Boltzmann distribution which was derived in Chapter 4 is quite successful in explaining many properties of matter from a molecular point of view. However, it is found experimentally that there are a large number of problems for which this distribution is simply inadequate. The interested reader can find a detailed discussion of some of these failures in Chapter 14.

One difficulty, as we shall see, lies with the fact that the laws of classical mechanics as applied to large visible objects on the macroscopic level begin to fail when we get to the molecular level. As it turns out, the laws of classical mechanics are only limiting cases of a more general set of laws which form the basis of the quantum theory of matter.

In the present chapter, we will derive the correct quantum mechanical distribution, or rather distributions, for a collection of weakly interacting particles. In order to arrive as quickly as possible at the results, we will take the shortest and most unsophisticated route. In later chapters the groundwork will be laid with considerably more care.

THE WILSON-SOMMERFELD QUANTIZATION CONDITION

In attempting to explain the spectroscopic properties of atoms in terms of the motion of electrons around a central nucleus, Bohr assumed that the electrons could only move in certain orbits. The theory which was subsequently developed to determine the allowed orbits can be applied to a large number of mechanical systems.

Let us assume we have a mechanical system whose configuration can be uniquely specified by a set of s coordinates q_i which can be varied independently without violating any of the constraints acting on the system. If the forces acting on the system are conservative, then we can define a set of generalized momenta by the relation

$$p_i = \partial K(\mathbf{q}, \dot{\mathbf{q}})/\partial q_i \tag{5.1}$$

where K is the kinetic energy of the system.

We further assume that the motion of the system is such that each of the q_i and the corresponding p_i are periodic functions with period T_i, and each of the p_i is a function only of q_i. Wilson and Sommerfeld assumed that for such a system the only orbits allowed were those which satisfied the quantization condition:

$$\oint p_i dq_i = n_i h \tag{5.2}$$

where n_i is an integer, h, Planck's constant, and the integration is carried out over a complete cycle of motion.

We will not worry about the application of Eq. (5.2) to the motion of electrons in atoms, but will consider a number of simpler cases.

Consider a particle in a cubic box of side L with perfectly reflecting walls. If we locate the origin of a set of Cartesian coordinates at the center of the box and let x_1, x_2, and x_3 be the position coordinates of the particle and p_1, p_2, and p_3 the components of momentum, then the quantization conditions become

$$\oint p_i dx_i = n_i h \tag{5.3}$$

Let us consider the motion of the particle in a particular direction, say the x_1 direction. For convenience, we will drop the subscript and simply write

$$\oint p dx = nh \tag{5.4}$$

where it is to be understood that $p \equiv p_1$, $x \equiv x_1$, and $n \equiv n_1$.

The trajectory of the particle in a space whose coordinates are x and p is shown in Figure 5.1. The condition (5.4) is equivalent to assuming that the shaded area shown in Figure 5.1 must be an integer multiple of h. Only certain values of p, which we designate p_n, satisfy this condition.

Equating the area under the curve to nh, we have

$$2p_n L = nh \tag{5.5}$$

Thus, p can assume only the values $p_n = nh/2L$.

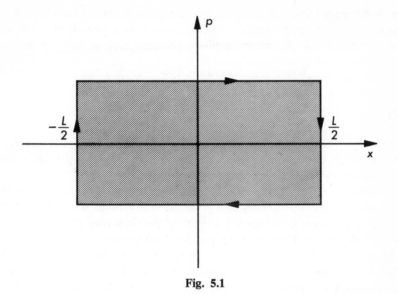

Fig. 5.1

The same analysis applies to the 2 and 3 components of momentum, and we obtain in general

$$p_{n_i} = n_i h/2L \qquad (5.6)$$

Since the momentum is quantized, the energy is also quantized and can assume only the values

$$\epsilon_{n_1 n_2 n_3} = \frac{(n_1^2 + n_2^2 + n_3^2)h^2}{8mL^2} \qquad (5.7)$$

where n_1, n_2, and n_3 are positive integers.

As a second example of the Wilson-Sommerfeld quantization conditions, let us consider a mass m on a spring of spring constant κ. Let x be the displacement of the mass from its equilibrium position and $\nu = (\kappa/4\pi^2 m)^{1/2}$ the frequency of oscillation. The energy of the system is

$$\epsilon = (p^2/2m) + 2\pi^2 m \nu^2 x^2 \qquad (5.8)$$

If we plot p as a function of x, we obtain an ellipse whose semiaxes are $(2m\epsilon)^{1/2}$ and $(\epsilon/2\pi^2 m\nu^2)^{1/2}$. The area of the ellipse is $\pi(2m\epsilon)^{1/2}(\epsilon/2\pi^2 m\nu^2)^{1/2}$. The Wilson-Sommerfeld quantization condition is equivalent to setting this area equal to nh. We obtain

$$\epsilon_n = nh\nu \qquad (5.9)$$

The Wilson-Sommerfeld quantization condition can be shown to be an approximation in the present form of quantum mechanics (cf. Chapter 15, the *WKB* approximation). However, the more rigorous theory leads to exactly the same energy quantization conditions for a particle in a box, and gives for the simple harmonic oscillator the only slightly different result

$$\epsilon_n = (n + \tfrac{1}{2})h\nu \tag{5.10}$$

SPIN

Although the quantization conditions (5.2) were able to account for a great deal of the spectroscopic data associated with the simpler atomic structures, they failed to account for certain details.

In order to explain these details, Uhlenbeck and Goudsmit assumed that we could not treat an electron as a point particle without structure, but that in addition to their translational degrees of freedom they possessed a spin, i.e., an intrinsic angular momentum of fixed magnitude.

In general it is found that when dealing with a collection of particles, whether electrons, atoms, ions, or molecules, we cannot treat them as structureless point particles. The simplest type of particle we can work with is a point particle with spin. It is further found that the total intrinsic angular momentum of such a particle can have only the values $[s(s + 1)\hbar^2]^{1/2}$ where $s = 0, \tfrac{1}{2}, 1, 3/2, \ldots$ and $\hbar = h/2\pi$. For simplicity we usually simply give the value of s when we are designating the spin.

Electrons, protons, and neutrons have a fixed value of spin $s = 1/2$. Photons have a spin $s = 1$. The spin is an intrinsic property of these particles, just as their charge and mass are intrinsic properties.

Atoms, ions, nuclei, and molecules made up of an odd number of electrons, neutrons, and protons will have spins of $1/2$, $3/2$, $5/2$, etc. Atoms, ions, nuclei, or molecules made up of an even number of electrons, neutrons, and protons have spins of 0, 1, 2, 3, etc.

A point particle which is free to move in three dimensions requires three quantization rules to specify its orbit. There are therefore three quantum numbers associated with each orbit. If in addition the particle has an intrinsic spin, there will be a fourth quantum number which we designate m_s. It can be shown that except for the photon, m_s can assume only $(2s + 1)$ different values. An electron, for instance, which has a spin of $1/2$ has two possible spin states. The different spin states are associated with the different possible orientations of the spin angular momentum. A photon, however, which has a spin one has only two and not three possible spin states.

If we are dealing with complex systems such as polyatomic molecules, the determination of the energy states can become quite complicated. We shall therefore restrict ourselves to the simplest type of systems, those which can be treated as point particles with spin.

THE PAULI EXCLUSION PRINCIPLE

The state of a particle in a box can be characterized by four numbers: the three positive integers n_1, n_2, n_3 which determine the components of linear momentum, and the spin quantum number m_s. In a similar fashion, there are four quantum numbers which determine the state of an electron in an atom. They are usually written n, l, m_l, and m_s.

In building up the periodic table of the elements, it was found necessary to assume that no two electrons in the same atom could have the same four quantum numbers.

More generally, it is found that no two particles with half odd integer values of spin s can be in the same volume and in the same state. This law is known as Pauli's exclusion principle.

If we apply Pauli's exclusion principle to a collection of noninteracting particles in a box, having half odd integer value of s, then we conclude that we can at the most have $2s + 1$ such particles with the same values of n_1, n_2, and n_3, since such particles have $2s + 1$ possible spin states.

INDISTINGUISHABILITY

We need one more experimental fact before we can derive the correct quantum statistics for a collection of noninteracting particles in the same box.

Up to this point we have been implicitly assuming that we could follow the motion of a single particle as it moved around inside our box. It is found, however, that if we have two particles in the same box, then in order to get agreement with experiment we must assume that it is impossible to distinguish between the two particles. We can at most say that we have one particle in one state and another in a second state. We cannot say that *this* particle is in the one state, and *that* particle in the other state. The two particles must be thought of as a single system having some properties similar to those we would expect if we had two distinct particles, but with some properties different.

MICROSTATES AND MACROSTATES

The state of a gas of identical noninteracting particles in the absence of any external fields is specified completely if we designate how many particles are in each of the single particle states characterized by the set of quantum numbers n_1, n_2, n_3, and m_s. For convenience we will label these states from 1 to ∞. If we let n_i (not to be confused with the quantum numbers n_1, n_2, n_3) be the number of particles in the state i and ϵ_i the corresponding energy, then the state of the gas as a whole is specified by giving the set of occupation numbers $\{n_i\}$. A particular arrangement of the particles among the states, i.e., a particular set of n_i, is called a microstate. A typical microstate is schematically represented by (5.11).

$$\underline{|\bullet\bullet|\bullet\bullet\bullet|\ \bullet\ |\bullet\bullet|\ \bullet\ |}\cdots\underline{|\bullet\bullet\bullet|}\ \cdots \qquad (5.11)$$

$$\begin{array}{cccccccc} 1 & 2 & 3 & 4 & 5 & 6 & i & i+1 \end{array}$$

In this microstate there are two particles in state 1, three in state 2, and so on.

The separation between adjacent single-particle energy levels in a box of unit volume is given by

$$\frac{d}{dn}\,(n^2h^2/8m) = nh^2/4m$$

For the extreme case in which we let m be the mass of the electron and n be equal to 10^{30}, we obtain $nh^2/4m = 1.2 \times 10^{-7}$J.

We are usually not interested in the properties of the gas to this degree of accuracy. We therefore arrange the states of roughly the same energy into convenient groups in such a way that there are a large number of single particle states in each group, and in general a large number of particles. We label the groups from 1 to ∞, and let M_r be the number of states in the rth group, N_r the number of particles, and E_r the average energy of the group of states.

It is now possible to designate the state of the gas by giving the set of occupation numbers $\{N_i\}$ instead of the set of occupation numbers $\{n_i\}$. A particular set of N_i constitutes what we shall refer to as a macrostate.

Each microstate corresponds to a particular macrostate, but with each macrostate there are many possible microstates.

THERMODYNAMIC PROBABILITY

We shall assume that each microstate is a priori equally probable. By this we mean that in the absence of any other information, we have no reason to assume that one microstate is more probable than another, so we assume they are all equally probable. The validity of this assumption is verified by the correctness of the results which it predicts.

In order to determine the a priori probability of a macrostate, we must determine how many distinct microstates there are associated with the macrostate. We shall designate this number $W(N_i)$ and refer to it as the thermodynamic probability.

The thermodynamic probability is a measure of the probability of a particular macrostate in the absence of any other information. In practice, however, we do have some additional information about the gas. If the gas is contained in an impermeable and well-insulated box, then the number of particles N and the total energy E are constant, so that only those macrostates for which

$$\Sigma N_i = N \tag{5.12}$$

and

$$\Sigma N_i E_i = E \tag{5.13}$$

are acceptable. We are interested only in those macrostates which satisfy these constraints.

FERMI-DIRAC STATISTICS

Let us consider a gas of particles with half odd integer spin contained in a box of volume V. Such a gas is called a Fermi gas. By Pauli's exclusion principle, no more than one particle can be in the same single particle state, so the occupation numbers n_i (not to be confused with the quantum numbers n_1, n_2, and n_3) can assume only the values 0 or 1.

In Appendix 4 we have calculated the number of distinct ways we can arrange indistinguishable particles among cells, with no more than one particle to a cell, in such a way that there are a specific number of particles in each group of states. This is just the thermodynamic probability which thus assumes the value

$$W(N_i) = \prod_i \frac{M_i!}{(M_i - N_i)!\, N_i!} \tag{5.14}$$

where N_i is the number of particles in the ith group and M_i the number of states.

We now assume that the macroscopic properties of the gas will be the same as those associated with the most probable macrostate (see Appendix 5), where, of course, we consider only those macrostates which satisfy the constraints (5.12) and (5.13). We wish therefore to maximize W subject to the constraints (5.12) and (5.13). Instead of maximizing W, we will find it more convenient to maximize $\ln W$.

By the method of Lagrange multipliers (Appendix 6), the maximization of $\ln W(N_i)$ subject to the constraints (5.12) and (5.13) is equivalent to maximizing the function

$$F(N_i, \alpha, \ \beta) = \ln W(N_i) + \alpha(\Sigma N_i - N) - \ \beta(\Sigma N_i E_i - E) \tag{5.15}$$

Using Stirling's approximation (Appendix 7), we obtain

$$\ln W(N_i) = \sum_i \ln M_i! - \sum_i \ln(M_i - N_i)! - \sum_i \ln N_i!$$

$$\approx \sum_i \left[(N_i - M_i)\ln\left(\frac{M_i}{N_i} - 1\right) + M_i \ln\left(\frac{M_i}{N_i}\right) \right] \tag{5.16}$$

Substituting (5.15) into (5.16), taking the partial derivative of $F(N_i, \alpha, \beta)$ with respect to N_i, and setting the result equal to zero, we have

$$\ln\left(\frac{M_i}{N_i} - 1\right) + \alpha - \beta E_i = 0 \tag{5.17}$$

Solving (5.17) we obtain

$$\frac{N_i}{M_i} = \frac{1}{\exp(\beta E_i - \alpha) + 1} \tag{5.18}$$

The energy E_i is approximately equal to any of the energies which belong to the ith group. Furthermore, if there are N_i particles distributed among M_i single particle states in the ith group, then the average occupation number of one of the single particle states is approximately N_i/M_i. We can therefore rewrite (5.18) to a good approximation.

$$n_i = \frac{1}{\exp(\beta \epsilon_i - \alpha) + 1} \tag{5.19}$$

The constants α and β can be determined from the constraint conditions, which in terms of n_i and ϵ_i are

$$\Sigma n_i \epsilon_i = E \tag{5.20}$$

$$\Sigma n_i = N \tag{5.21}$$

Equation (5.19) is called the Fermi-Dirac distribution. Since the energy levels are very close together we can replace (5.19) by a continuous distribution. To carry this out, let us first rewrite (5.19) as

$$n_{n_1 n_2 n_3 m_s} = \frac{1}{\exp(\beta \epsilon_{n_1 n_2 n_3 m_s} - \alpha) + 1} \tag{5.22}$$

where $n_{n_1 n_2 n_3 m_s}$ is the occupation number of the state $n_1 n_2 n_3 m_s$. If the energy does not depend on the spin then with each set of values of n_1, n_2, n_3 there are $2s + 1$ spin states with the same energy which we write $\epsilon_{n_1 n_2 n_3}$, and Eq. (5.22) can be written

$$n_{n_1 n_2 n_3} = \frac{2s + 1}{\exp(\beta \epsilon_{n_1 n_2 n_3} - \alpha) + 1} \tag{5.23}$$

In the absence of any external fields $\epsilon_{n_1 n_2 n_3}$ is given by Eq. (5.7). Substituting (5.7) in (5.23) and going over to a continuous distribution, we have

$$f_n d\mathbf{n} = \frac{(1/L^3)(2s + 1) d\mathbf{n}}{\exp\left(\dfrac{\beta n^2 h^2}{8 m L^2} - \alpha\right) + 1} \tag{5.24}$$

where $f_n d\mathbf{n}$ is the number of particles per unit volume with n_1 between n_1 and $n_1 + dn_1$ with n_2 between n_2 and $n_2 + dn_2$ and with n_3 between n_3 and $n_3 + dn_3$.

The factor $(1/L^3)$ is introduced, so that f_n represents the number per unit volume and not the number in a volume L^3.

Converting to spherical coordinates n, θ, ϕ we obtain

$$f_n dn = \left\{ \int_0^{\pi/2} \int_0^{\pi/2} f_n\, n^2 \sin\theta d\theta d\phi \right\} dn \tag{5.25}$$

Since n_1, n_2, and n_3 are positive integers, the integration is over one octant only.

Carrying out the integration, we obtain

$$f_n = \frac{(\pi n^2/2L^3)(2s+1)}{\exp\left(\dfrac{\beta n^2 h^2}{8\,m\,L^2} - \alpha\right) + 1} \tag{5.26}$$

The distribution in energy f_ϵ is given by

$$f_\epsilon = f_n \left| \frac{dn}{d\epsilon} \right| = f_n \left| \frac{d}{d\epsilon}\left(\frac{8mL^2\epsilon}{h}\right)^{1/2} \right| = \frac{C\epsilon^{1/2}}{\exp(\beta\epsilon - \alpha) + 1} \tag{5.27}$$

where $$C = (2s+1)2\pi(2m/h^2)^{3/2}$$

The distribution in **x–v** space is given by

$$f(\mathbf{x}, \mathbf{v}) = f_v/4\pi v^2 = (1/4\pi v^2)f_\epsilon \left| \frac{d\epsilon}{dv} \right| = \frac{(2s+1)(m/h)^3}{\exp(\beta\epsilon - \alpha) + 1} \tag{5.28}$$

where $$\epsilon = \tfrac{1}{2}mv^2$$

In a later section we will show

$$\beta = 1/kT \tag{5.29}$$

THE CLASSICAL LIMIT

If the temperature of a Fermi gas is increased, we expect the particles to distribute themselves over a wider range of energy levels, and ultimately we will reach a temperature at which $N_i \ll M_i$. If the volume is increased, the number of levels in a given energy range will increase, and we will ultimately arrive at a volume for which $N_i \ll M_i$. In the first case, we decrease N_i holding M_i fixed, and in the second case we increase M_i holding N_i fixed.

Let us assume we have reached a volume or temperature at which

$$N_i \ll M_i \tag{5.30}$$

then

$$W(N_i) = \prod_i \frac{M_i!}{(M_i - N_i)!\, N_i!}$$

$$= \prod_i \frac{M_i(M_i - 1)\dots(M_i - N_i + 1)}{N_i!} \approx \prod_i \frac{(M_i)^{N_i}}{N_i!} \tag{5.31}$$

Using Stirling's approximation, we obtain

$$\ln W(N_i) \approx \sum_i N_i \left[\ln \left(\frac{M_i}{N_i} \right) + 1 \right] \tag{5.32}$$

If we maximize $\ln W(N_i)$ subject to the constraints $\Sigma N_i = N$ and $\Sigma N_i E_i = E$, we obtain

$$(N_i/M_i) = \exp(\alpha - \beta E_i) \tag{5.33}$$

or in terms of the occupation numbers n_i, we have

$$n_i = \exp(\alpha - \beta \epsilon_i) \tag{5.34}$$

and in terms of a continuous distribution in x–v space

$$f(\mathbf{x}, \mathbf{v}) = (2s + 1)(m/h)^3 \exp(\alpha - \beta \epsilon) \tag{5.35}$$

This distribution is formally identical with the Maxwellian distribution. Thus in the limit in which $N_i \ll M_i$, the classical Maxwellian distribution is valid.

Comparing (5.35) with the Maxwellian distribution, we see that in the limit as $N_i \ll M_i$

$$\beta = \frac{1}{kT} \tag{5.36}$$

$$(2s + 1)(m/h)^3 \exp \alpha = n(\lambda/\pi)^{3/2} \tag{5.37}$$

It should be noted that we have not shown that these relations are true when $N_i \sim M_i$. We will show in the following section that when $N_i \sim M_i$, β is still $1/kT$ but (5.37) is no longer valid.

IDENTIFICATION OF THE TEMPERATURE

Suppose we have an isolated composite system consisting of two Fermi gases in separate containers, but in thermal contact as shown in Figure 5.2.

The state of gas A' is determined by the set of occupation numbers $\{N_i'\}$; the state of gas A'' is determined by the set of occupation numbers $\{N_i''\}$; and the state of the composite system is determined by the set of occupation numbers $\{N_i', N_i''\}$.

We shall assume that the gas A' is so dense that $N_i' \sim M_i'$, while gas A'' is so dilute that $N_i'' \ll M_i''$.

Since the two gases are independent except for the possibility of an energy exchange, the thermodynamic probability for the composite system $W(N_i', N_i'')$ will simply be equal to the product of the thermodynamic probabilities of gas A' and gas A'' separately, i.e.,

$$W(N_i', N_i'') = W(N_i')W(N_i'') \tag{5.38}$$

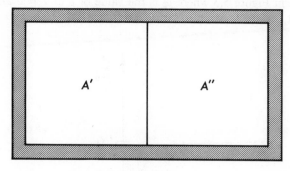

Fig. 5.2

To find the most probable macrostate for the composite system, we maximize $\ln W(N_i', N_i'')$ subject to the constraints

$$\Sigma N_i' = N' \tag{5.39}$$

$$\Sigma N_i'' = N'' \tag{5.40}$$

$$\Sigma N_i' E_i' + \Sigma N_i'' E_i'' = E = E' + E'' \tag{5.41}$$

Carrying this out, we find

$$N_i' = \frac{1}{\exp(\beta E_i' - \alpha') + 1} \tag{5.42}$$

$$N_i'' = \exp(\alpha'' - \beta E_i'') \tag{5.43}$$

The quantity β is the same for the two systems, while α' and α'' are different. But for gas A'', $\beta = 1/kT$. Therefore for gas A' we also have $\beta = 1/kT$.

THE FERMI ENERGY

If we define a new quantity μ, called the Fermi energy, by the relation $\mu = \alpha kT$, then the Fermi distribution takes the form

$$f_\epsilon = \frac{C\epsilon^{1/2}}{\exp[(\epsilon - \mu)/kT] + 1} \tag{5.44}$$

$$C = (2s + 1)2\pi(2m/h^2)^{3/2} \tag{5.45}$$

We will later show that the quantity μ is the chemical potential of the gas, but for our present purposes it is sufficient to consider μ to be a parameter which can be determined by the relation

$$\frac{N}{V} = \int_0^\infty f_\epsilon d\epsilon \tag{5.46}$$

If we substitute (5.46) in (5.44) and solve numerically for μ we obtain the result shown in Figure 5.3 where μ_0 is the value of μ at $T = 0$ and T_0 is the value of T at $\mu = 0$. It can also be shown that $kT_0 = 3.37\mu_0$.

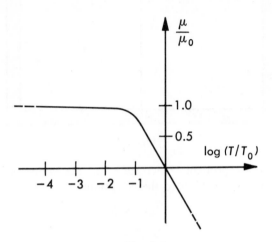

Fig. 5.3

If $T = 0$ and $\epsilon < \mu_0$, then $\exp[(\epsilon - \mu)/kT] = 0$. If $T = 0$ and $\epsilon > \mu_0$, then $\exp[(\epsilon - \mu)/kT] = \infty$. Therefore at $T = 0$

$$f_\epsilon = C\epsilon^{1/2} \qquad\qquad \epsilon < \mu_0 \qquad (5.47)$$

$$f_\epsilon = 0 \qquad\qquad \epsilon > \mu_0 \qquad (5.48)$$

Substituting these results in (5.46) we have

$$\frac{N}{V} = \int_0^{\mu_0} C\epsilon^{1/2}d\epsilon = 2C\mu_0^{3/2}/3 \qquad (5.49)$$

or

$$\mu_0 = \left(\frac{3N}{2CV}\right)^{2/3} = \left[\frac{3N}{4\pi V(2s + 1)}\right]^{2/3} \frac{h^2}{2m} \qquad (5.50)$$

For ordinary gases T_0 is of the order of $0.1\,°K$ or less. At these temperatures most materials would be liquid or solid, and our theory would be invalid. For most gases therefore, T will be much larger than T_0 and μ will be large and negative. In these cases

$$\exp[(\epsilon - \mu)/kT] \gg 1 \qquad (5.51)$$

and

$$f_\epsilon \approx C\epsilon^{1/2} \exp[(\mu - \epsilon)/kT] \qquad (5.52)$$

which is just the Maxwellian distribution.

We will consider in the next section a rather unique situation in which $T \ll T_0$.

ELECTRONS IN A METAL

If we consider the electrons in a metal to constitute an ideal Fermi gas, then $T_0 \sim 10^5$°K. It follows that at ordinary temperatures we must use the Fermi distribution and since we are usually dealing with metals at temperatures well below 10^5°K, the Fermi energy μ will be approximately μ_0.

The Fermi distribution at $T = 0$°K and $T = 300$°K are shown in Figure 5.4. Increasing the temperature of the metal will cause the distribution to alter its shape only slightly. The average energy of an electron will not change a great amount, and as a consequence we do not expect the specific heat of the electron gas in a metal to be appreciable at ordinary temperatures. This is borne out by experiment. A quantitative investigation of the specific heat will be carried out in a later chapter.

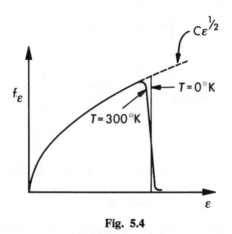

Fig. 5.4

As a quantitative illustration of the use of Fermi-Dirac distribution, we will in the following section discuss the phenomena of thermionic emission from a metal.

THERMIONIC EMISSION

We can imagine the electrons within a metal to be contained within a three-dimensional well. If a particular electron acquires enough energy, it is possible to escape from the well. If an electrode at a sufficiently large positive potential with respect to the metal is placed near the surface of the metal, all of the escaping electrons can be drawn to the electrode. If the emitting surface and the collecting electrode are part of a circuit and the potential difference is maintained constant, a continuous flow of electrons can be established. The rate of flow is considerably enhanced if we heat the metal, since the electrons will have a greater energy. This effect is called thermionic emission. In the present section we will derive some quantitative results for the rate of thermionic emission.

The problem is graphically illustrated in Figure 5.5. The energy W is the depth of the well, μ_0 is the Fermi energy at $T = 0$, and ϕ is called the work function. The values of W, μ_0, and ϕ differ for different metals. In tungsten $\mu_0 = 9.0$ eV and $\phi = 4.5$ eV.

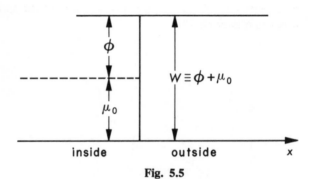

Fig. 5.5

If the surface of the metal is normal to the x_1 axis then any electron for which

$$\tfrac{1}{2}mv_1^2 > W \tag{5.53}$$

should escape. Actually, some of the electrons which satisfy this condition are reflected at the surface. We let the fraction reflected be r.

The flux density of electrons with velocity in the element $d\mathbf{v}$ is given by $(f d\mathbf{v})\,\mathbf{v}$. The number per second that hit a unit area normal to the x_1 axis is then $(f d\mathbf{v})\,v_1$, and therefore the thermionic emission current density is

$$J = (1 - r)e \int_{-\infty}^{\infty} \int_{-\infty}^{\infty} \int_{(2W/m)^{1/2}}^{\infty} v_1 f dv_1 dv_2 dv_3 \tag{5.54}$$

where e is the charge on an electron. Using the Fermi distribution in (5.54) and letting $\mu \approx \mu_0$ we have

$$J = e(1 - r)2\left(\frac{m}{h}\right)^3 \int_{-\infty}^{\infty} \int_{-\infty}^{\infty} \int_{(2W/m)^{1/2}}^{\infty} \frac{v_1 dv_1 dv_2 dv_3}{\exp[(\epsilon - \mu_0)/kT] + 1} \tag{5.55}$$

where

$$\epsilon = \tfrac{1}{2}m(v_1^2 + v_2^2 + v_3^2) \tag{5.56}$$

When $v_1 > (2W/m)^{1/2}$ then $\epsilon \gg \mu_0$ and $\exp[(\epsilon - \mu)/kT] \gg 1$. We can therefore rewrite (5.55)

$$J \approx 2e(1 - r)\left(\frac{m}{h}\right)^3 \exp(\mu_0/kT)\int_{-\infty}^{\infty}\int_{-\infty}^{\infty}\int_{(2W/m)^{1/2}}^{\infty} v_1 \exp(-\epsilon/kT)dv_1 dv_2 dv_3$$

$$= 2e(1 - r)\left(\frac{m}{h}\right)^3 \exp\left(\frac{\mu_0}{kT}\right)\left(\frac{2kT}{m}\right)^2$$

$$\int_{-\infty}^{\infty}\int_{-\infty}^{\infty}\int_{(W/kT)^{1/2}}^{\infty} x\exp[-(x^2 + y^2 + z^2)]dxdydz$$

$$= (4\pi em/h^3)(kT)^2(1 - r)\exp(-\phi/kT)$$

$$= 120(1 - r)T^2 \exp(-\phi/kT) \text{ amps/cm}^2 \tag{5.57}$$

This is the Richardson-Dushman equation for thermionic emission. The experimentally observed dependence of J on T agrees quite well with this expression. Because of the uncertainty in the factor r, it is difficult to determine the accuracy of the constant $(4\pi emk^2/h^3)$. It is possible, however, to use Eq. (5.57) to obtain an accurate value for the work function.

BOSE-EINSTEIN STATISTICS

Let us now consider a gas of particles with integer spin contained in a box of volume V. Such a gas is called a Bose-Einstein gas. For such a gas there is no restriction on the occupation numbers n_i.

In Appendix 3 we have calculated the number of distinct ways we can arrange indistinguishable particles among cells in such a way that there are N_1 particles in the first group of states, N_2 particles in the second group of states, etc. This is just the thermodynamic probability which thus has the value

$$W(N_i) = \prod_i \frac{(M_i + N_i - 1)!}{N_i!\,(M_i - 1)!} \tag{5.58}$$

Using Stirling's approximation, we obtain

$$\ln W(N_i) = \sum\left[(N_i + M_i)\ln\left(\frac{M_i}{N_i} + 1\right) - M_i\ln\left(\frac{M_i}{N_i}\right)\right] \tag{5.59}$$

Maximizing $\ln W(N_i)$ subject to the constraints

$$\Sigma N_i = N \tag{5.60}$$

$$\Sigma N_i E_i = E \tag{5.61}$$

we obtain

$$\frac{N_i}{M_i} = \frac{1}{\exp(\beta E_i - \alpha) - 1} \qquad (5.62)$$

In terms of the single particle states we have

$$n_i = \frac{1}{\exp(\beta \epsilon_i - \alpha) - 1} \qquad (5.63)$$

We can identify β as $1/kT$ as in the Fermi-Dirac case, and let $\alpha = \mu/kT$ and we obtain

$$n_i = \frac{1}{\exp[(\epsilon_i - \mu)/kT] - 1} \qquad (5.64)$$

This distribution is called the Bose-Einstein distribution. In the limit of high temperatures or low densities it, like the Fermi distribution, will, in the absence of external fields, go over to the classical Maxwellian distribution.

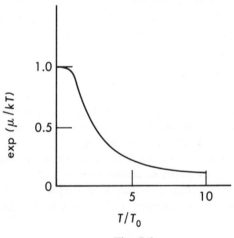

Fig. 5.6

If we solve for $\exp(\mu/kT)$ using the relation

$$\Sigma n_i = N \qquad (5.65)$$

we obtain the result displayed in Figure 5.6.

RADIATION IN A CAVITY

As an example of a practical application of Bose-Einstein statistics, let us consider the electromagnetic energy contained in a cubical metal box of unit volume, with perfectly conducting walls. Such a box is able to contain electromagnetic energy, since any electromagnetic radiation in the box will simply be reflected back and forth inside the box and will not escape. If a small object at temperature T is introduced into the box we expect the radiation to come into equilibrium with the object. We would like to know qualitatively and quantitatively what this means.

Since we will in later chapters consider the same problem from several different points of view and in considerably more detail, we will at this point simply state a few preliminary results which will allow us to illustrate the Bose-Einstein distribution without getting sidetracked into a long discussion on electromagnetic theory.

An electromagnetic wave of frequency ν and velocity c can be considered to consist of particles called photons of energy $h\nu$, momentum $h\nu/c$, and spin 1. There are two possible spin states associated with a photon, corresponding to the two possible directions of polarization. The intensity of the wave is determined by the number of photons.

If we have a particle in a cubical box of unit volume, the allowed values of the i component of momentum are from our earlier analysis $p_i = n_i h/2$. It follows that

$$p^2 = \sum_i p_i^2 = (n_1^2 + n_2^2 + n_3^2)h^2/4 \tag{5.66}$$

Substituting $p = h\nu/c$ in (5.66) we find that the allowed values of the energy and frequency for the photons in a box of unit volume are

$$\epsilon_{n_1 n_2 n_3} = h\nu_{n_1 n_2 n_3} = (n_1^2 + n_2^2 + n_3^2)^{1/2} hc/2 \tag{5.67}$$

Since photons have integer spin they obey Bose statistics. However, photons unlike the particles with which we have been dealing, can be easily created and destroyed so that their number is not restricted. If in deriving the Bose statistics we had neglected the constraint $\Sigma N_i = N$, we would not have had to introduce the parameter α and would have obtained simply

$$n_i = \frac{1}{\exp(\epsilon_i/kT) - 1} \tag{5.68}$$

The number of photons in the state characterized by the quantum numbers n_1, n_2 and n_3 is thus

$$n_{n_1 n_2 n_3} = \frac{2}{\exp(h\nu_{n_1 n_2 n_3}/kT) - 1} \tag{5.69}$$

The factor two occurs because with each set of values for $n_1 n_2 n_3$ there are two possible spin states.

If we go over to a continuous approximation and let $f_n d\mathbf{n}$ be the number of photons with $\mathbf{n}$ in $d\mathbf{n}$, $f_n d\mathbf{n}$ be the number of photons per unit volume with

$n = (n_1{}^2 + n_2{}^2 + n_3{}^2)^{1/2}$ in dn, and $f_\nu d\nu$ be the number of photons per unit volume with ν in $d\nu$, then we have

$$f_\nu = f_n \left| J\left(\frac{n}{\nu}\right) \right| = \int_0^{\pi/2} \int_0^{\pi/2} f_n n^2 \sin\theta d\theta d\phi \left| J\left(\frac{n}{\nu}\right) \right|$$

$$= \left(\frac{\pi n^2}{2}\right) \left| J\left(\frac{n}{\nu}\right) \right| \left\{ \frac{2}{\exp(h\nu/kT) - 1} \right\} \tag{5.70}$$

From (5.67) $n = 2\nu/c$ and therefore

$$f_\nu = \frac{(8\pi\nu^2/c^3)}{\exp(h\nu/kT) - 1} \tag{5.71}$$

The total energy per unit volume is

$$\frac{E}{V} = \int_0^\infty h\nu f_\nu d\nu$$

$$= (8\pi h/c^3)(kT/h)^4 \int_0^\infty \frac{x^3}{\exp(x) - 1} dx$$

$$= (8\pi h/c^3)(kT/h)^4(\pi^4/15) \tag{5.72}$$

In an isotropic distribution of particles of density n the number of particles striking a unit area of surface is, from Chapter 4, simply $n < v > /4$. Since the photons in our container are all moving with velocity c, it follows that the number of photons in the cavity with frequency between ν and $\nu + d\nu$ which strike a unit area of surface is $(c/4)f_\nu d\nu$. A black body is an object which absorbs all radiation which falls on it. If a small black body of unit surface area is placed in the cavity discussed above, and comes to equilibrium with the radiation at a temperature T, then it is absorbing energy at the rate $\int(c/4)h\nu f_\nu d\nu$. It must therefore be emitting radiation at the same rate, i.e.,

$$J = \sigma T^4 \tag{5.73}$$

where

$$\sigma = \frac{cE}{4} = \frac{2\pi^5 k^4}{15c^2 h^3} \tag{5.74}$$

This is the well-known Stefan-Boltzmann law for the radiation from a black body. The constant σ is known as Stefan's constant.

DISTINGUISHABLE PARTICLES

In the derivation of the Fermi and Bose statistics, the assumption of indistinguishability of particles was an essential factor in the determination of the distribution function. There are situations, however, where we have a collection of weakly interacting systems which are not contained in the same box. As an example, it is possible to describe many of the properties of a solid of volume V by imagining each atom to be contained within a little cell of volume V/N, and bound to the lattice site by springs. This model is called the Einstein model. The atoms in this model are not moving in the same volume, and as a result are distinguishable or localizable.

A microstate for such a collection of atoms is no longer specified by telling how many particles are in each single particle state ϵ_i. We must in addition, know which ones are in which states. If we label the atoms 1 to N, we can characterize a microstate schematically as follows

$$\underline{\left| \begin{array}{c} 1,2 \end{array} \right| \begin{array}{c} 3,4,5 \end{array} \left| \begin{array}{c} 6,7 \end{array} \right|} \quad \bullet\bullet\bullet \quad \underline{\left| \begin{array}{c} 15,16 \end{array} \right|} \quad \bullet\bullet\bullet \tag{5.75}$$

$$1234ii+1$$

In this microstate atoms 1 and 2 are in state 1; atoms 3, 4, and 5 are in state 2, and so on.

As previously, we divide the various states into groups and designate the state of the collection of atoms by giving the set of occupation numbers $\{N_i\}$.

To determine the thermodynamic probability $W(N_i)$, we have to find out how many distinct ways N distinguishable objects can be arranged among the cells in such a way that the group occupation numbers are given by the set $\{N_i\}$. In Appendix 2 we show that this number is

$$W(N_i) = N! \prod_i \frac{(M_i)^{N_i}}{N_i!} \tag{5.76}$$

If we maximize (5.76) subject to the constraints $\Sigma N_i = N$ and $\Sigma N_i E_i = E$, we obtain

$$\left(\frac{N_i}{M_i}\right) = \exp(\alpha - \beta E_i) \tag{5.77}$$

Going over to the single particle states, identifying β as $1/kT$, and applying the condition $\Sigma N_i = N$ to determine α, we obtain

$$n_i = \frac{N \exp(-\epsilon_i/kT)}{\sum_i \exp(-\epsilon_i/kT)} \tag{5.78}$$

We call this distribution the (quantum mechanical) Boltzmann distribution.

THE SPECIFIC HEAT OF A SOLID

As an example of an application of Eq. (5.78) let us calculate the specific heat of a solid using the model introduced in the preceding section.

From the Sommerfeld quantization conditions, the energy levels for a three-dimensional isotropic simple harmonic oscillator are:

$$\epsilon_{n_1 n_2 n_3} = (n_1 + n_2 + n_3)h\nu \tag{5.79}$$

where n_1, n_2, and n_3 are integers ranging from 0 to ∞. The distribution of atoms among the various states is thus

$$n_{n_1 n_2 n_3} = \frac{N \exp\left(-\dfrac{\epsilon_{n_1 n_2 n_3}}{kT}\right)}{\displaystyle\sum_{n_1}\sum_{n_2}\sum_{n_3} \exp\left(-\dfrac{\epsilon_{n_1 n_2 n_3}}{kT}\right)} \tag{5.80}$$

The average energy of an atom can be written

$$<\epsilon> = kT^2 \frac{\partial}{\partial T}(\ln q) \tag{5.81}$$

where

$$q = \sum_{n_1}\sum_{n_2}\sum_{n_3} \exp\left(-\frac{\epsilon_{n_1 n_2 n_3}}{kT}\right)$$

$$= \left\{\sum_n \exp(-nh\nu/kT)\right\}^3$$

$$= \{1 - \exp(-h\nu/kT)\}^3 \tag{5.82}$$

The specific heat per atom is

$$c_V = \frac{\partial}{\partial T}[<\epsilon>] = 3k\left\{\frac{(h\nu/kT)^2 \exp(h\nu/kT)}{[\exp(h\nu/kT) - 1]^2}\right\} \tag{5.83}$$

This is the Einstein equation for the specific heat of a solid. If $kT \gg h\nu$ then

$$\exp(h\nu/kT) \approx 1 + (h\nu/kT) \approx 1$$

and therefore

$$c_V \approx 3k \tag{5.84}$$

If $kT \ll h\nu$ then $\exp(h\nu/kT) - 1 \approx \exp(h\nu/kT)$ and therefore

$$c_V \approx 3k(h\nu/kT)^2 \exp(-h\nu/kT) \tag{5.85}$$

The specific heat per atom is therefore $3k$ at high temperatures and drops off to zero at low temperatures. Classically, the theoretical value of the specific heat is $3k$ at all temperatures. Experimentally, the specific heat falls off to zero as the temperature approaches zero, but not quite, according to (5.85). The disagreement is due to our model, not to any error in the theory.

SUMMARY

Quantum mechanics introduces three features which are quite different from classical mechanics: (a) Only certain discrete states are allowed (b) identical particles contained in the same volume are indistinguishable and (c) we cannot have two identical particles with half odd integer spin in the same volume and in the same state.

If we have a collection of independent and distinguishable particles, then we have to take into account condition a but not conditions b or c and we obtain the Boltzmann distribution

$$n_i = \frac{N \exp\left(-\frac{\epsilon_i}{kT}\right)}{\sum_i \exp\left(-\frac{\epsilon_i}{kT}\right)} \tag{5.86}$$

If we have a collection of independent indistinguishable particles with integer spin then we have to take into account conditions a and b but not c and we obtain the Bose-Einstein distribution

$$n_i = \frac{1}{\exp[(\epsilon_i - \mu)/kT] - 1} \tag{5.87}$$

where μ is determined from the condition $\Sigma n_i = N$.

If we have a collection of independent indistinguishable particles with half odd integer spin then we have to take into account conditions a, b, and c and we obtain the Fermi-Dirac distribution.

$$n_i = \frac{1}{\exp[(\epsilon_i - \mu)/kT] + 1} \tag{5.88}$$

where μ is determined from the condition $\Sigma n_i = N$.

In the limiting case in which $n_i \ll 1$ all three distributions reduce to (5.86).

PROBLEMS

1. Determine the energy levels of a particle bouncing in a gravitational field of acceleration g, off a level and perfectly elastic floor.
2. Consider a body rotating about an axis. Apply the Wilson-Sommerfeld quantization rule, and show that the possible values of its total energy are predicted to be

   $$E = n^2\hbar^2/2I \qquad n = 0, 1, 2, 3, \ldots$$

   where I is the moment of inertia of the body about the axis of rotation.
3. A certain system consists of four particles distributed among two levels E_1 and E_2 for which $M_1 = 5$ and $M_2 = 3$. Calculate the thermodynamic probabilities associated with the macrostates $(N_1 = 2; N_2 = 2)$ and $(N_1 = 4; N_2 = 0)$ for each of the following cases:
   (a) the particles are distinguishable and there is no restriction on the number of particles to a state.
   (b) the particles are indistinguishable and there is no restriction on the number of particles to a state.

(c) the particles are indistinguishable and no more than one particle to a state is allowed.

4. Plot the Fermi-Dirac speed distribution for the free electrons in tungsten (a) at $0°K$ and (b) at $3000°K$. Let $\mu_0 = 9.0$ eV.

5. Calculate the mean speed, the rms speed, and the mean reciprocal speed in terms of the maximum speed for an electron gas at $0°K$.

6. Determine the number of collisions with a wall for an electron gas at absolute zero.

7. Find the number of electrons per unit time and per unit area crossing a surface within a metal at $0°K$ in either direction. (b) What is the corresponding current density in amp/cm²?

8. Find the pressure for a Fermi gas of free electrons at $0°K$.

9. Show that the kinetic energy per particle of a Fermi gas at absolute zero is $3\mu_0/5$.

10. Evaluate μ_0 for tungsten, assuming two free electrons per tungsten atom.

11. Calculate the fraction of the electrons in tungsten ($\mu_0 = 9.0$ eV; $\phi = 4.5$ eV) at $3000°K$ having a total kinetic energy greater than 13.5 eV. Calculate the fraction of the electrons for which the energy associated with the x component of velocity exceeds 13.5 eV.

12. Give numerical estimates for the Fermi energy at $T = 0$ for
    (a) electrons in a typical metal
    (b) nucleons in a heavy nucleus
    (c) He³ atoms in liquid He³ (atomic volume = 46.2 Å³/atom).
    Treat all the above particles as free particles.

13. Show that the average energy of the thermionic electrons associated with the normal component of velocity is kT.

14. A typical number density of electrons in a vacuum tube may be about 10^{17}/cubic meter. Should one use the Fermi-Dirac results to discuss this case, or will the Boltzmann limit be adequate?

15. Over which frequency interval is the number of photons greater than the number of states available, so there must be multiple occupancy of states? Over which states is the converse true? Prove that for these latter frequencies, Boltzmann statistics would be correct.

16. Derive the Planck radiation law for a two-dimensional space. Using this result, derive the Stefan-Boltzmann law for a two-dimensional space.

17. Find the energy density in kcal/m³ and pressure of radiation in atmospheres of black body radiation at temperatures of $500°K$ and $5000°K$.

18. Determine the number of photons in a square cavity 10 cm on a side at a temperature of (a) $300°K$ (b) $3000°K$.

19. It has been reported that the atomic bomb produced a temperature of a million degrees. Assuming this to be true over a sphere 10 cm in diameter,
    (a) What was the radiant energy density in the sphere?
    (b) What was the rate of radiation from the surface?

(c) What was the radiant flux density 1 km away?

(d) What was the wavelength of maximum energy per unit frequency interval?

20. Find the frequency at which the radiation per unit frequency interval of a black body is a maximum. How does this compare with the frequency at which the radiation per unit wavelength interval is maximum? The maximum radiation per unit frequency interval occurs at a wavelength of 5000 Å in the solar spectrum. What is the surface temperature of the sun?

21. Calculate the wavelength at which the energy density per unit frequency interval in black body radiation is a maximum. Calculate the temperatures for which λ_{max} falls in the red and in the blue portions of the radiation spectrum.

22. A device absorbs a fraction $a(\nu)$ of photons of frequency ν falling on it. It is illuminated by black radiation of temperature T. Find an expression for the energy E absorbed per unit area per unit time. Show that if $a(\nu) = A\nu^n$ then $E = BT^{n+4}$ where A, B, and n are constants.

23. Assume: (1) the radiation in a cavity can be described in terms of an infinite number of distinguishable simple harmonic oscillators; (2) the number of oscillators with frequency between ν and $\nu + d\nu$ is $(8\pi\nu^2/c^3)d\nu$. Find the energy density of the radiation.

24. Find the characteristic temperature $\theta = h\nu/k$ for copper such that the Einstein equation for c_V agrees with experiment at a temperature of 100°K. (b) Using this value of θ, calculate c_V at 20°K and at 1200°K and compare your results with the experimental values.

25. According to Einstein, due to quantum effects the specific heat falls at low temperatures from the value $3k$ per molecule expected if the equipartition of energy holds, and is only $3k/2$ at a temperature T at which $h\nu \approx 3kT$ where ν is the frequency of oscillation of an atom in the solid. According to Lindemann, a solid melts when the amplitude of the atomic vibrations reaches a certain fraction of the interatomic spacing. Use these ideas and the following data for copper and lead, which both have face-centered cubic structures, to estimate the melting point of lead.
Copper: $c_V = 3k/2$ at 81°K; atomic weight = 63.5; density = 9.0 g/cm;
melting point = 1356°K.

Lead: $c_V = 3k/2$ at 22°K; atomic weight = 207; density = 11.3 g/cm³.

26. Consider a gas of identical particles in equilibrium. Let the single-particle energy states ϵ_i be arranged in groups of approximately the same energy. Let M_r be the number of states in the rth group and E_r the energy of the rth group of states. Consider a collision between two particles such that before the collision their energies are E_k and E_l, and after the collision E_m and E_n.

(a) Assume that the number of transitions $k, l \to m, n$ per second is given by $AN_kN_lM_mM_n$ and that the number of transitions $m, n \rightarrow k, l$ is given by $AN_mN_nM_kM_l$ where A is a constant. Show that the equilibrium condition and the law of conservation of energy lead to the distribution function

$$N_k = CM_k \exp(-\beta E_k)$$

for all k.

(b) Suppose the number of transitions $k, l \rightarrow m, n$ per second is given by $AN_kN_l(M_m - N_m)(M_n - N_n)$. Show that this leads to the Fermi-Dirac distribution function.

(c) Assuming the number of transitions $k, l \rightarrow m, n$ is proportional to $N_kN_l(M_m + N_m)(M_n + N_n)$ show that the same reasoning leads to the Bose-Einstein distribution.

(d) Comment on the physical meaning of the assumed expressions for the number of transitions $k, l \rightarrow m, n$ for the three types of statistics.

Chapter 6

THE MEAN FREE PATH

INTRODUCTION

If we could observe a single molecule traveling through a gas, its path would look something like that shown in Figure 6.1.

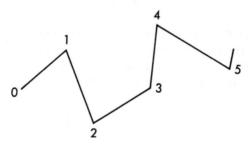

Fig. 6.1

The numbered vertices correspond to points at which the molecule undergoes a collision. Between collisions the molecule is moving freely with a constant velocity. The distance between two successive collisions e.g., l_{23}, is called a free path. The average length of these free paths is called the mean free path l.

In the present chapter we will discuss some of the properties of the mean free path. Before doing this it will be necessary to take up the concept of collision frequency.

THE COLLISION FREQUENCY IN A GAS OF HARD SPHERES

Consider a sphere of diameter d and velocity $\mathbf{v}$ moving through a gas of spheres of density n, diameter d and velocity $\mathbf{V}$ as shown in Figure 6.2.

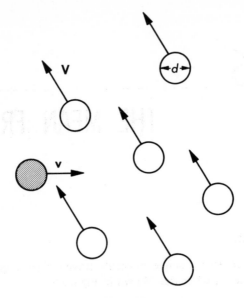

Fig. 6.2

If the center of the sphere of velocity **v** comes within a distance d of the center of one of the other spheres, a collision will take place. An equivalent situation is generated if we replace the sphere of velocity **v** by a sphere of diameter $2d$, and the other spheres by points as shown in Figure 6.3.

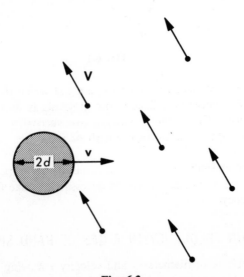

Fig. 6.3

We can further simplify our analysis by viewing the system from a reference frame which is moving with velocity **V**. From such a vantage point, our system takes on the appearance shown in Figure 6.4. The points are at rest and the sphere is moving with velocity **v–V**, which is just the relative velocity.

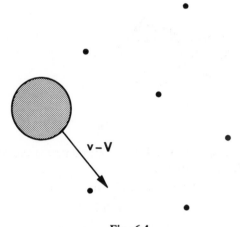

Fig. 6.4

We now consider the same situation one unit of time later. The sphere has now moved a distance $|\mathbf{v}-\mathbf{V}|$ as shown in Figure 6.5. What is the probability that in a unit of time the sphere has collided with one of the points? Since there are n points per unit volume, one would expect that there is on the average one point in a volume $1/n$. The volume swept out by the sphere in one unit of time is simply $\pi d^2|\mathbf{v}-\mathbf{V}|$. It follows that the probability that a collision takes place in a unit time is simply $\pi d^2|\mathbf{v}-\mathbf{V}|/(1/n)$. We designate this quantity $\nu(\mathbf{v},\mathbf{V})$. Thus

$$\nu(\mathbf{v},\mathbf{V}) = n\pi d^2|\mathbf{v}-\mathbf{V}| \qquad (6.1)$$

The quantity $\nu(\mathbf{v},\mathbf{V})$ can be interpreted as either the probability that in a unit time a collision will take place between a sphere of diameter d moving with velocity $\mathbf{v}$, through a gas of spheres of diameter d and velocity $\mathbf{V}$, or as the collision frequency, i.e., the number of collisions per second. If the latter interpretation is used, one must imagine the collisions taking place with no change in the velocities of the colliding particles. Generally if $\nu(\mathbf{v},\mathbf{V})$ is less than one, the first interpretation is preferred, while if $\nu(\mathbf{v},\mathbf{V})$ is greater than one, the second interpretation is preferred. However, both interpretations can be used interchangeably.

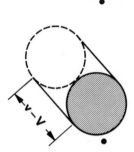

Fig. 6.5

Suppose now the sphere of velocity $\mathbf{v}$ encounters a collection of spheres having a Maxwellian distribution

$$f(\mathbf{V}) = n(\lambda/\pi)^{3/2} \exp(-\lambda V^2) \tag{6.2}$$

$$\lambda = m/2kT \tag{6.3}$$

then the collision frequency which we designate $\nu(\mathbf{v})$ is obtained by averaging $\nu(\mathbf{v}, \mathbf{V})$ over all velocities $\mathbf{V}$, i.e.,

$$\nu(\mathbf{v}) = \frac{\int \nu(\mathbf{v}, \mathbf{V}) f(\mathbf{V}) d\mathbf{V}}{\int f(\mathbf{V}) d\mathbf{V}} \tag{6.4}$$

Finally, suppose we have a collection of spheres whose distribution is f, and we wish to know the average collision frequency of an arbitrary one of the spheres. We designate this collision frequency ν. It can be obtained by averaging $\nu(\mathbf{v})$ over $\mathbf{v}$. Thus

$$\nu = \frac{\int \nu(\mathbf{v}) f(\mathbf{v}) d\mathbf{v}}{\int f(\mathbf{v}) d\mathbf{v}} = \frac{\iint \nu(\mathbf{v}, \mathbf{V}) f(\mathbf{v}) f(\mathbf{V}) d\mathbf{v} d\mathbf{V}}{\iint f(\mathbf{v}) f(\mathbf{V}) d\mathbf{v} d\mathbf{V}}$$

$$= \frac{n\pi d^2 \iint |\mathbf{v} - \mathbf{V}| \exp[-\lambda(v^2 + V^2)] d\mathbf{v} d\mathbf{V}}{\iint \exp[-\lambda(v^2 + V^2)] d\mathbf{v} d\mathbf{V}} \tag{6.5}$$

We now introduce a new set of variables

$$\mathbf{u} = \frac{\mathbf{v} - \mathbf{V}}{\sqrt{2}} \tag{6.6}$$

$$\mathbf{w} = \frac{\mathbf{v} + \mathbf{V}}{\sqrt{2}} \tag{6.7}$$

The Jacobian of the transformation $J\left(\dfrac{\mathbf{v}, \mathbf{V}}{\mathbf{u}, \mathbf{w}}\right)$ is a constant since the transformations between $\mathbf{u}$, $\mathbf{w}$ and $\mathbf{v}$, $\mathbf{V}$ are linear, and therefore all the partial derivatives and products of the partial derivatives are constant. We will designate the Jacobian as simply J.

Making the transformation, we then have

$$\nu = \frac{(\pi d^2 \sqrt{2} n) \iint u \exp[-\lambda(u^2 + w^2)]\,|J|\,dudw}{\iint \exp[-\lambda(u^2 + w^2)]\,|J|\,dudw} \tag{6.8}$$

The integration over w gives the same result in numerator and denominator, and thus

$$\nu = \frac{(\pi d^2 \sqrt{2} n) \int u \exp(-\lambda u^2)du}{\int \exp(-\lambda u^2)du} \tag{6.9}$$

the ratio of the integrals is simply the average speed $\bar{v}$. We therefore have

$$\nu = \sqrt{2} \pi d^2 n \bar{v} \tag{6.10}$$

THE MEAN FREE PATH

We are now in a position to calculate the mean free path. If a molecule is moving through a gas with speed v then in time dt it travels a distance vdt, and if it undergoes on the average $\nu(v)$ collisions per second then it will have undergone $\nu(v)dt$ collisions in time dt. The average distance traveled between collisions while moving with the speed v is therefore

$$l(v) = \frac{vdt}{\nu(v)dt} = \frac{v}{\nu(v)} \tag{6.11}$$

In a long time T a given molecule will spend a time

$$dt = \left[\frac{f(\mathbf{v})d\mathbf{v}}{\int f(\mathbf{v})d\mathbf{v}}\right]T \tag{6.12}$$

in the range $d\mathbf{v}$. During this time it will undergo $\nu(v)dt$ collisions, the average distance between collisions being $v/\nu(v)$. It follows that the average distance between collisions over the time T, i.e., the mean free path is

$$l = \frac{\displaystyle\int_0^T [v/\nu(v)]\nu(v)dt}{\displaystyle\int_0^T \nu(v)dt}$$

$$= \frac{\int vf(\mathbf{v})d\mathbf{v}}{\int v(v)f(\mathbf{v})d\mathbf{v}} = \frac{\bar{v}}{v} \tag{6.13}$$

For a Maxwellian gas of hard spheres $v = \sqrt{2}\pi d^2 n \bar{v}$ and therefore

$$l = 1/\sqrt{2}\pi d^2 n \tag{6.14}$$

DISTRIBUTION OF FREE PATHS

The mean free path is a very useful quantity in discussing the transport properties of a gas. In applying the notion of a mean free path to these problems, we will make frequent use of the fact (which we will now prove) that if a set of N molecules originating at $x = 0$ move off at random speeds in the positive x direction then the fraction of molecules which arrive a distance x from the origin without a collision will be given by $F(x)$ where

$$F(x) \approx \exp(-x/l) \tag{6.15}$$

To prove this, let us imagine a set of N molecules all starting at $x = 0$ and moving in the positive x direction with the same speed v as shown in Figure 6.6.

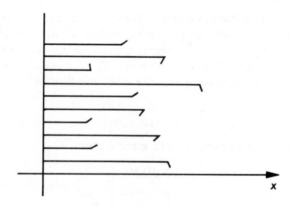

Fig. 6.6

Each molecule will travel a certain distance and then collide with one of the molecules of the gas. Let $N(x, v)$ be the number of molecules which reach x without a collision. The quantity $N(x, v)$ will decrease with increasing x, and the rate of decrease will be proportional to $N(x, v)$, i.e.,

$$\frac{\partial N(x, v)}{\partial x} = -\alpha(v)N(x, v) \tag{6.16}$$

where α is a proportionality constant which is different for different speeds v. If the beam, instead of being composed of molecules of the same speed had been composed of molecules of random speed, $dN(x)/dx$ would not be equal to $-\alpha N(x)$. This follows from the fact that the average distance traveled between collisions is different for molecules moving with different speeds and therefore the composition of the beam would be changing with x, since molecules moving with different speeds would be disappearing from the beam at different rates. Thus collisions not only change the number of molecules in the beam but also the distribution in speeds.

If we solve Eq. (6.16) we obtain

$$N(x, v) = N(0, v) \exp[-\alpha(v)x] \tag{6.17}$$

Letting $n(x, v)dx$ be the number of free paths which end between x and $x + dx$ we have

$$n(x, v)dx = N(x, v) - N(x + dx, v) \tag{6.18}$$

and therefore

$$n(x, v) = \frac{N(x, v) - N(x + dx, v)}{dx} = -\frac{\partial N(x, v)}{\partial x}$$

$$= \alpha(v)N(0, v) \exp[-\alpha(v)x] \tag{6.19}$$

Knowing $n(x, v)$ we can calculate the average free path for molecules moving with speed v, which we designate $l(v)$. Thus

$$l(v) = \frac{\displaystyle\int_0^\infty xn(x, v)dx}{\displaystyle\int_0^\infty n(x, v)dx} = \frac{\displaystyle\int_0^\infty xe^{-\alpha(v)x}dx}{\displaystyle\int_0^\infty e^{-\alpha(v)x}dx} = \frac{1}{\alpha(v)} \tag{6.20}$$

But the average free path for molecules moving with speed v can also be expressed in terms of the collision frequency, i.e.,

$$l(v) = v/\nu(v) \tag{6.21}$$

Substituting (6.21) and (6.20) in (6.17) we have

$$N(x, v) = N(0, v) \exp[-\nu(v)x/v] \tag{6.22}$$

The fraction which reaches x without a collision is given by

$$F(x, v) = \frac{N(x, v)}{N(0, v)} = \exp[-\nu(v)x/v] \tag{6.23}$$

If the beam had been composed of molecules moving with random speeds, then the fraction $F(x)$ which would reach x is obtained by averaging $F(x, v)$ over all speeds. Thus

$$F(x) = \frac{\int \exp[-\nu(v)x/v]f(\mathbf{v})d\mathbf{v}}{\int f(\mathbf{v})d\mathbf{v}} \tag{6.24}$$

This integral cannot be reduced to a simple expression; however, it can be approximated to within a few percent by simply replacing $\nu(v)$ by ν and v by $\bar{v}$, in which case we obtain

$$F(x) \approx \exp[-\nu x/\bar{v}] = \exp(-x/l) \tag{6.25}$$

The justification of this approximation is tedious, and since the mean free path concept will only be used to obtain approximate results which will later be replaced by more rigorous expressions, it would not profit us to dwell on this approximation excessively.

PROBLEMS

1. Find the root-mean-square free path and the most probable free path in terms of the mean free path.
2. Show that the gas molecules crossing an imaginary plane in a gas originate from a collision an average distance of $2l/3$ from the plane, where l is the mean free path of the molecule in the gas.
3. An ideal gas consisting of N hard sphere molecules of radius r is contained in a spherical container of radius R. Assuming a Maxwellian distribution, what is the probability that a molecule at the center of the sphere will hit the side of the container before hitting one of the other molecules?
4. Given a gas of nitrogen molecules at a temperature of 300°K and a pressure of 10^5 N/m^2, assume the radius of a nitrogen molecule to be 1.88×10^{-10}m.
    (a) What is the collision frequency for a nitrogen molecule in the above gas?
    (b) What is the total number of collisions per second per unit volume?
    (c) What is the average speed of the molecules?
    (d) What is the mean free path of the molecules?
    (e) If the total volume of the gas were considered as divided up into equal-sized cubes, one for each molecule, what would be the length of a side of the cubes?
    (f) If the above gas is contained in a 1-m cube what is the mean distance between an arbitrary pair of molecules?
5. The mean free path of the molecules in a certain gas at a temperature of 300°K is 2.5×10^{-5}m. The diameter of a molecule is 5×10^{-10}m.

(a) What is the average number of collisions made by a molecule per meter of path?

(b) What fraction of the free paths will be longer than 2.5×10^{-5}m?

(c) What fraction of the free paths are between 2×10^{-5} and 3×10^{-5}m in length?

6. The free time is defined as the time taken to execute a free path. Show that starting at time $t = 0$ (not an instant of collision) the probability that the molecule has not yet had its next collision at time t is $\exp(-t/T)$ where T is the mean free time. Indicate clearly any approximation made.

7. A group of oxygen molecules start their free paths at the same instant. The pressure is such that the mean free path is 2 cm. After how long a time will half of the group still remain, i.e., half the group will not as yet have made a collision? Assume all particles to have a speed equal to the average speed. The temperature is 300°K.

8. Consider an arbitrary particle in a gas at some arbitrary instant of time. The expected distance to the next collision is l.

(a) Show that the probability that its last collision was a distance L away is $\exp(-L/l)$.

(b) What is the average distance of this previous collision?

(c) Why does it not follow that the average distance between collisions is $2l$?

9. A beam of electrons is projected from an electron gun into a gas at pressure p, and the number remaining in the beam at a distance x from the gun is determined by allowing the beam to strike a collecting place and measuring the current to the plate. The electron current emitted by the gun is 100 μA and the current to the collector when $x = 10$ cm and $p = 1$ mm of mercury is 37 μA.

(a) What is the electron mean free path?

(b) What current would be collected if the pressure were reduced to 0.5 mm of mercury?

10. Aluminum is evaporated in a small furnace under a bell jar. Its atoms immediately pass through a small aperture and then travel to a clean glass plate which is to be aluminized. The distance between the aperture and the glass plate is 40 cm. What should the pressure under the bell jar be in order that 90 percent of the aluminum atoms which leave the aperture reach the plate?

11. Satellites travel in a region where the mean free path is much greater than the characteristic size of the body. Calculate the drag on a spherical satellite due to this rarefied gas. Assume that the molecules collide elastically with the surface. (Hint: Since the satellite velocity is much greater than the speed of sound, assume the satellite is moving through a stationary cloud of particles.) Obtain the answer in terms of the number density of particles n, the molecular mass m, the speed v of the satellite, and the radius r of the satellite.

Chapter 7

ELEMENTARY TRANSPORT THEORY OF A SIMPLE GAS

LOCAL EQUILIBRIUM

In Chapter 4 we saw that the most general form of the distribution function for an ordinary gas in the absence of any external fields is given by

$$f = n(\lambda/\pi)^{3/2} \exp[-\lambda(\mathbf{v} - \bar{\mathbf{v}})^2] \qquad (7.1)$$

where $\lambda = m/2kT$. The quantities n, λ, and $\bar{\mathbf{v}}$ are constants.

Suppose, however, the gas is subjected to conditions which destroy the equilibrium. Consider, for instance, a gas contained between two infinite plates parallel to the $x_1 - x_2$ plane and intersecting the x_3 axis at $x_3 = a$ and $x_3 = b$ as shown in Figure 7.1.

If conditions on the two boundaries represented by the two planes are identical, then the gas will arrive at the equilibrium given by Eq. (7.1). Suppose, however, that the planes are maintained at different temperatures, or are moving with different velocities in the x_2 direction, or radioactive molecules are being introduced at one plane and absorbed at the other; then we no longer have an equilibrium situation, and the distribution is no longer given by Eq. (7.1). However, if the boundary conditions are constant in time we expect a steady state situation to set in.

If we can divide our gas into regions whose dimensions are large compared to a mean free path and yet small enough that the variation of the properties of the gas within each of these regions is small, we might expect the distribution within each region to approximate the equilibrium distribution, i.e., the Maxwellian distribution. The value of the n, λ, and $\bar{\mathbf{v}}$, however, would

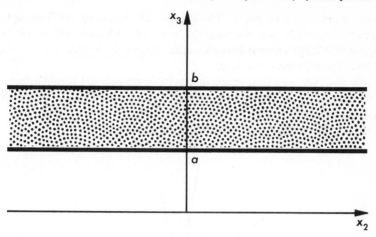

Fig. 7.1

vary from region to region. This is equivalent to assuming that our steady state distribution can be approximated by the distribution

$$f(\mathbf{x}, \mathbf{v}) \approx n(\mathbf{x}) \left[\frac{m}{2\pi k T(\mathbf{x})} \right]^{3/2} \exp\left\{ -\frac{m[\mathbf{v} - \bar{\mathbf{v}}(\mathbf{x})]^2}{2kT(\mathbf{x})} \right\} \qquad (7.2)$$

If the above approximation is valid, we say the gas is in local equilibrium. The above distribution is not the exact distribution. In fact, if the above distribution were exact it would not, among other things, account for the flow of heat when a difference in temperature of the two plates was maintained.

THE MEAN FREE PATH AND TRANSPORT PHENOMENA

Consider a gas in local equilibrium. Each point in the gas is characterized by a certain value of T, $\bar{\mathbf{v}}$, and n. Let us now imagine that the quantities T and $\bar{\mathbf{v}}$ are properties of the space within which the molecules move, and assume that if a molecule undergoes a collision at a point $\mathbf{x}$, it immediately assumes the properties characteristic of that point, i.e., the characteristics of the molecules in a Maxwellian gas having temperature $T(\mathbf{x})$ and average velocity $\bar{\mathbf{v}}(\mathbf{x})$. This is equivalent to assuming that in each collision the memory of a molecule is completely destroyed. It can trace its history back only to its last collision. Beyond that it has no idea from whence it came. It is as if the molecule were reborn in the collision.

To illustrate the effect of this assumption, let us imagine that we have a collection of small, hard, invisible particles with a Maxwellian distribution within a large volume V, and suppose there is a small region ΔV within V having the property that all particles undergoing a collision within ΔV immediately become visible, and remain visible until they undergo a collision in some other region of space. The volume ΔV should be small enough that in general a particle will not undergo multiple collisions within ΔV before escaping, but large enough that in a unit of time an appreciable number of collisions are occurring within ΔV.

To an observer who cannot see the invisible particles, it would appear that the volume ΔV is a source of particles which suddenly appear, move out radially from ΔV, and then disappear at varying distances from ΔV. This situation is schematically represented in Figure 7.2.

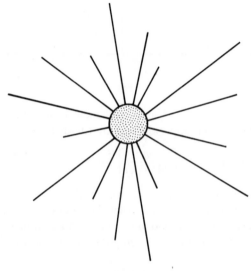

Fig. 7.2

Knowing the mechanism behind this phenomenon, we can predict the intensity of the source of particles, and also the flux of particles at any distance from the source. If there are n particles per unit volume then there will be $n\Delta V$ particles within ΔV, and if ν is the probability per unit time that a particle will undergo a collision, then there will be $\nu n\Delta V$ particles appearing per unit time. Note that each collision produces two particles, but the total number of collisions is $\nu n\Delta V/2$ if we avoid double counting of a collision. To prove this, suppose there are two particles in a box of unit volume. The probability of a collision is simply $\pi d^2\sqrt{2}\bar{v}$. If there are n particles in the box this probability must be multiplied by the number of possible pairs of the n particles, which can be shown to be $n!/(n-2)!2! = n(n-1)/2 \approx n^2/2$. Thus the number of collisions per second is $n\pi d^2\sqrt{2}\bar{v}/2$ which is just $n\nu/2$. If we are considering a volume ΔV this should be multiplied by ΔV.

Since there are $\nu n\Delta V$ particles emanating from ΔV per second, in the absence of any further collisions, there would be $\nu n\Delta V$ particles per second crossing any sphere which is centered on ΔV. The surface area of a sphere of radius r is $4\pi r^2$. The number of particles per second crossing a unit area of such a sphere would then be $\nu n\Delta V/4\pi r^2$. The particles would be directed radially outward. Thus if there were no collisions outside of ΔV, the flux density $\mathbf{J}$ would be simply

$$\frac{\nu n\Delta V}{4\pi r^2}\ \frac{\mathbf{r}}{r} \tag{7.3}$$

However, we know from the previous chapter that if a particle starts off at $r = 0$, the probability that it will reach r is given by $\exp(-r/l)$ where l is the mean free path. Thus

$$\mathbf{J} = (\nu n\Delta V/4\pi r^2)\ \exp(-r/l)(\mathbf{r}/r) \tag{7.4}$$

In a similar fashion, we can imagine a gas in local equilibrium to be broken up into small volume elements. Each volume element appears as a source of particles radiating out in all directions with flux density given by (7.4). The particles radiating out from a particular volume element possess, on the average, the properties associated with the volume element from which they are radiating, and can act as carriers of these properties, as we shall see in the following sections.

SELF-DIFFUSION

Consider a gas contained between the plates described in the first section. Suppose the plates at $x_3 = a$ and $x_3 = b$ are permeable. Let the region $x_3 < a$ be filled with a gas of the same species, and at the same temperature and pressure as the gas between the plates, but the molecules of which are radioactive. Let the region $x_3 > b$ be filled with a nonradioactive gas of the same species, and at the same temperature and pressure as the gas between the plates. Let the regions $x_3 < a$ and $x_3 > b$ be equipped with fans which keep the gases in these regions slowly circulating.

The radioactive molecules will seep through the permeable plate at $x_3 = a$ and diffuse through the gas in the region $a < x_3 < b$ until they arrive at $x_3 = b$. They will then seep through the plate at $x_3 = b$ and be dissipated in the region $x_3 > b$. A steady state situation will be eventually established in which there is a concentration gradient of radioactive molecules in the region $a < x_3 < b$. We wish to find out the rate of diffusion of radioactive molecules through this region.

Let n be the combined density of radioactive and nonradioactive molecules and n^* the density of radioactive molecules. In steady state n will be constant but n^* will be a function of x_3.

We wish to find the number of radioactive molecules which pass through an area ΔS, normal to the x_3 axis in 1 second. Let us put our origin of coordinates at ΔS as shown in Figure 7.3.

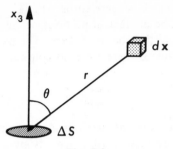

Fig. 7.3

As in the previous section, we can imagine each element of volume dx in the gas to be a source of radioactive molecules. A particular radioactive molecule will appear to emanate from the volume element in which its last collision took place.

Let us find the number of radioactive molecules which undergo a collision in dx and then pass through ΔS. The number of radioactive particles in dx is simply $n^*(x_3)dx$ and the number which undergo a collision in dx is $n^*(x_3)\nu dx$. The flux of particles originating in dx is given by

$$dJ = [n^*(x_3)\nu dx/4\pi r^2] \exp(-r/l)(-\mathbf{r}/r) \qquad (7.5)$$

The number passing through ΔS in the positive x_3 direction is

$$dJ \cdot (e_3 \Delta S) = -[n^*(x_3)\nu dx/4\pi r^2] \exp(-r/l)\Delta S \cos\theta \qquad (7.6)$$

where e_3 is a unit vector in the x_3 direction.

Integrating over all values of x and dividing by ΔS, we obtain

$$J_3 = -(1/4\pi) \int [n^*(x_3)\nu \cos\theta/r^2] \exp(-r/l)dx \qquad (7.7)$$

Actually, the integration is over the region $a < x_3 < b$, but since the major contribution to the integral comes from the region within a few mean free paths of ΔS, we can integrate over all space without introducing any appreable error. Switching to spherical coordinates, we can rewrite (7.7)

$$J_3 = -(\nu/4\pi) \iiint n^*(x_3) \sin\theta \cos\theta \exp(-r/l)drd\theta d\phi \qquad (7.8)$$

If $n^*(x_3)$ does not vary much over a mean free path, then we can approximate $n^*(x_3)$ by the first few terms in a Taylor series about $x_3 = 0$ since, as was mentioned previously, the main contribution to the integral comes from the region within a few mean free paths of ΔS. Thus

$$n^*(x_3) = n^*(0) + (dn^*/dx_3)_{x_3=0}x_3 + (d^2n^*/dx_3{}^2)_{x_3=0}(x_3{}^2/2) + \ldots$$

$$= n^*(0) + (dn^*/dx_3)_{x_3=0}r\cos\theta + (d^2n^*/dx_3{}^2)_{x_3=0}(r^2\cos^2\theta/2) + \ldots \qquad (7.9)$$

If we substitute (7.9) into (7.8), the first and third terms will vanish. Dropping all terms higher than the third order, we then have

$$J_3(0) = -(\nu/4\pi)(dn^*/dx_3)_{x_3=0} \int_0^\infty r\exp(-r/l)dr \int_0^{2\pi} d\phi \int_0^\pi \sin\theta\cos^2\theta d\theta$$
$$= -(\nu l^2/3)(dn^*/dx_3)_{x_3=0} \tag{7.10}$$

Noting that $(dn^*/dx_3)_{x_3=0}$ simply represents the derivative at the location of ΔS, we drop the subscript. We can also replace ν by $\bar{v}/l$ and (7.10) becomes

$$J_3 = -(l\bar{v}/3)(dn^*/dx_3) \tag{7.11}$$

The flux of radioactive particles is seen to be directly proportional to the density gradient, the mean free path, and the average speed.

The proportionality factor between J_3 and (dn^*/dx_3) is called the coefficient of self-diffusion and is written D. Thus

$$J_3 = -D(dn^*/dx_3) \tag{7.12}$$

$$D = l\bar{v}/3 \tag{7.13}$$

For a Maxwellian gas of hard spheres $l = 1/\sqrt{2}n\pi d^2$ and $\bar{v} = (8kT/\pi m)^{1/2}$ and therefore

$$D = \left(\frac{2}{3n\pi d^2}\right)\left(\frac{kT}{\pi m}\right)^{1/2} \tag{7.14}$$

VISCOSITY

Consider again a gas between the plates $x_3 = a$ and $x_3 = b$. Now suppose however, that the plates are impermeable, but the plate at $x_3 = b$ is moving with speed $\bar{v}_2(b)$ in the x_2 direction while the plate at $x_3 = a$ is at rest. The various layers of the gas will exert forces on the neighboring layers until eventually a steady state will be established in which

$$\bar{\mathbf{v}} = \mathbf{e}_2\,\bar{v}_2(x_3) \tag{7.15}$$

where $\mathbf{e}_2$ is a unit vector in the 2 direction. Even when steady state has been established, a force is required on the upper plate to maintain the steady state, since the various layers of the gas are rubbing against one another. We wish to find the tangential force per unit area exerted by one layer of the gas on a neighboring layer in the steady state. This also can be explained as the result of a transport process, a transport of momentum from layer to layer, as we shall now show.

Consider two trains moving along parallel tracks in the same direction but with different speeds, as shown in Figure 7.4. As they pass one another, a mass m is thrown from train 1 to train 2 and an equal mass m is thrown from train 2 to train 1. The initial velocity of the mass thrown from 1 to 2 was v_1 and its final velocity is v_2. In order for the velocity to increase, train 2 must impart an impulse $p = mv_2 - mv_1$ to the mass. The mass imparts an equal and opposite impulse to train 2, in a direction tending to slow it down. Similarly, the slower train 1 receives an equal impulse tending to speed it up.

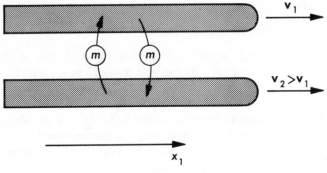

Fig. 7.4

If n pairs of masses m are exchanged per unit time between train 1 and train 2 there will be an average force $-n(mv_2 - mv_1)$ tending to slow down train 2 and an average force $n(mv_2 - mv_1)$ tending to speed up train 1. The quantity $n(mv_2 - mv_1)$ is simply the net momentum transfer from train 2 to train 1.

Similarly, in a gas in which $\bar{v}$ is given by Eq. (7.15), there will be a transport of momentum from layer to layer. Let p_{23} represent the transport of momentum e_2mv_2 across a unit area normal to the 3 direction. Then p_{23} represents the shear force per unit area between layers on opposite sides of the unit area.

To evaluate p_{23} we proceed exactly as previously. Consider an element of area ΔS normal to the 3 axis as shown in Figure 7.3. The number of particles whose last collision was in dx which pass per unit time through ΔS is given by

$$-(nv dx/4\pi r^2) \exp(-r/l) \Delta S \cos \theta \tag{7.16}$$

In this case n is constant. The momentum transported across ΔS by particles whose last collision was in dx is then given by

$$-(nv dx/4\pi r^2) \exp(-r/l) \Delta S \cos \theta \, m\bar{v}_2(x_3) \tag{7.17}$$

We now integrate over dx and expand $\bar{v}_2(x_3)$ in a Taylor series exactly as in the diffusion case, and finally obtain

$$p_{23} = -(mn\bar{v}l/3)(d\bar{v}_2/dx_3) \tag{7.18}$$

The ratio $-p_{23}/(dv_2/dx_3)$ is called the coefficient of viscosity μ. Thus

$$p_{23} = -\mu(d\bar{v}_2/dx_3) \tag{7.19}$$

where

$$\mu = mn\bar{v}l/3 \tag{7.20}$$

For a Maxwellian gas of hard spheres

$$\mu = \left(\frac{2}{3\pi d^2}\right)\left(\frac{mkT}{\pi}\right)^{1/2} \tag{7.21}$$

It is surprising to note that the viscosity does not depend on the density.

THERMAL CONDUCTIVITY

Let us now assume we have a gas between the plates in Figure 7.1, and that the plates are maintained at different temperatures T_a and T_b. When the gas has arrived at steady state the temperature in the gas will be a function of x_3, and energy will be flowing through the gas from the hot plate to the cold plate.

The average energy of a molecule in a gas at temperature T is given by

$$\tfrac{1}{2}m\overline{v^2} = 3kT/2 \tag{7.22}$$

Let us define q_3 as the flux of energy across a unit area normal to the 3 direction. To evaluate q_3, we proceed exactly as we did in calculating p_{23}, only now the energy $3kT(x_3)/2$ is being transported instead of the momentum $mv_2(x_3)$.

Our final result is

$$q_3 = -(n\bar{v}lk/2)(dT/dx_3) \tag{7.23}$$

The proportionality factor between q_3 and dT/dx_3 is called the coefficient of thermal conductivity and is designated by κ. Thus

$$q_3 = -\kappa(dT/dx_3) \tag{7.24}$$

where

$$\kappa = n\bar{v}lk/2 \tag{7.25}$$

The validity of this result is restricted to monatomic gases, since as we shall see in a later chapter, the internal motions of polyatomic molecules are able to store energy which is also being transported as a molecule moves from collision to collision, and which thus increases the value of κ.

For a Maxwellian gas of hard spheres

$$\kappa = \left(\frac{k}{\pi d^2}\right)\left(\frac{kT}{\pi m}\right)^{1/2} \tag{7.26}$$

It is again surprising to note that the coefficient of thermal conductivity does not depend on the density.

ACCURACY OF THE MEAN PATH RESULTS

In order to obtain some idea of the accuracy of the results which we have obtained using mean free path techniques, it will be helpful to compare our results with both the results of the more advanced theory, and with some experimental values.

Using mean free path techniques, we have obtained the following values for D, μ, and κ, for a Maxwellian gas of hard spheres

$$D = \frac{2}{3}\left(\frac{1}{n\pi d^2}\right)\left(\frac{kT}{\pi m}\right)^{1/2} \tag{7.27}$$

$$\mu = \frac{2}{3\pi d^2}\left(\frac{mkT}{\pi}\right)^{1/2} \tag{7.28}$$

$$\kappa = \frac{k}{\pi d^2}\left(\frac{kT}{\pi m}\right)^{1/2} \tag{7.29}$$

The more advanced theory, which we shall develop in a later chapter, gives for these same coefficients

$$D = \frac{3\pi}{8}\left(\frac{1}{n\pi d^2}\right)\left(\frac{kT}{\pi m}\right)^{1/2} \tag{7.30}$$

$$\mu = \frac{5\pi}{16}\left(\frac{1}{\pi d^2}\right)\left(\frac{mkT}{\pi}\right)^{1/2} \tag{7.31}$$

$$\kappa = \frac{75\pi}{64}\left(\frac{k}{\pi d^2}\right)\left(\frac{kT}{\pi m}\right)^{1/2} \tag{7.32}$$

These results are larger than the mean free path results by factors of 1.77, 1.47, and 3.69 respectively. The dependence on T, n, m, and d, however, agree exactly.

In order to compare these theoretical results with the experimental results, it is necessary to have values for the molecular diameters. Since molecules are not hard spheres, they do not have an exact diameter. Their boundaries are fuzzy. The exact meaning of a molecular diameter depends on the particular experiment, and on the interpretation of the experiment. Molecular diameters are, as a matter of fact, often obtained by measuring D, μ, and κ and using the expressions (7.30), (7.31), and (7.32) to determine d. The agreement or disagreement between the different approaches is, however, a measure of the validity of the general theoretical structure in this area.

With this in mind, let us evaluate the expected molecular diameter for argon using the experimental values for D, μ, and κ, and the expressions (7.30), (7.31), and (7.32).

The coefficient of self-diffusion of argon at 0°C is given by 0.158×10^{-4} m²/sec, the coefficient of viscosity is 209.6×10^{-7} kg/m-sec, and the coefficient of thermal conductivity is 1.62×10^{-2} J/m-sec-deg.

Using the above experimental value for μ and equation (7.31) we obtain for the diameter of an argon atom $d_\mu = 3.64 \times 10^{-10}$ m. Using the value of D given and Eq. (7.30), we obtain $d_D = 0.945\ d_\mu$. Using the value of κ given and equation (7.32) we obtain $d_\kappa = 1.005\ d_\mu$.

The disagreement between these three values is due to the fact that the interaction between the molecules in a gas cannot be considered with complete accuracy to be the same as the interaction between two hard spheres. The more general theory, which we will develop in a later chapter, takes this fact into account. The expressions (7.30), (7.31), and (7.32) represent the specialization of the more general theory, which is valid for any type of inter-action, to the case of hard sphere collisions.

We can conclude from the fact that the disagreement between d_μ, d_D, and d_κ is not too great, that the use of the hard sphere approximation, though not absolutely correct, is not a bad approximation.

In order to discover the source of error between the mean free path results (7.27), (7.28), and (7.29) and the correct hard sphere results (7.30), (7.31), and (7.32), we have to go back and re-examine the assumptions which we made.

Our first source of error was in using the same value of the mean free path for all molecules independent of their speed. Actually, the average distance traveled between collisions is different for particles moving with different speeds. This error was implicitly introduced in Chapter 6 when we averaged the collision frequency over all velocities to obtain ν rather than working with $\nu(\mathbf{v})$ and treating the molecules in each velocity range separately and then averaging at the end of our calculations. Mathematically we have made the error of replacing the average value of a product by the product of the average values. The two are not equal.

Our second source of error was in assuming that the memory of a molecule is completely destroyed in a single collision. If a beam of point masses m are scattered off a very small rigid elastic sphere, it can be shown, and will be shown in a later chapter, that the scattered particles will emanate uniformly in all directions away from the scattering sphere which we assume to be practically a point. In this case the memory of the scattered particles is destroyed since it is impossible by studying the scattered particles to recon-struct the original beam direction. If, however, the scattering sphere has a mass M, and is assumed to be at rest before each collision, the scattered particles, due to the recoil of the sphere, will not emanate uniformly in all directions. In this case by studying the distribution in direction of the scattered masses we can determine the direction of the incident beam, and thus the memory of the particles has not been completely destroyed. In general, it takes more than one collision to randomize the direction of the scattered particles. In the case of a charged particle, for example, being scattered by another charged particle, a very large number of collisions are needed. The extension of the memory of a particle beyond its last collision is known as the persistence of velocities and must be taken into account if we wish to improve our mean free path calculations.

PROBLEMS

1. A tube 2 m long and $10^{-4}m^2$ in cross section contains CO_2 at atmospheric pressure and at a temperature of 273°K. The coefficient of diffusion is about $10^{-5}m^2/sec$. The carbon atoms in one half of the CO_2 molecules

are radioactive isotope C^{14}. At time $t = 0$, all of the molecules at the extreme left end of the tube contain radioactive carbon, and the number of such molecules per unit volume decreases uniformly to zero at the other end of the tube. Determine (a) the initial concentration gradient of radioactive molecules, (b) the initial rate of transport of radioactive molecules through the midpoint of the tube from left to right, (c) the initial rate of transport of radioactive molecules through the midpoint of the tube from right to left, (d) the initial net rate of diffusion of radioactive molecules through the midpoint.

2. Show that the root-mean-square displacement of a diffusing molecule is approximately the geometric mean of its mean free path and the total distance it traverses.

3. Show that if the density of radioactive molecules in a gas is given by $n^*(x_1, x_2, x_3)$ the ith component of the flux of radioactive molecules is given by

$$J_i = - D(\partial n^* / \partial x_i)$$

4. Show that the viscosity of a gas which is constrained to move in two dimensions is given by $nml\bar{v}/2$.

5. The coefficient of viscosity and density for xenon at 0°C are 21.01×10^{-6} N-sec/m² and 5.851 kg/m³. Compute values for the average speed, mean free path, collision diameter, and collision frequency of the xenon atoms. Do this also for water vapor at 100°C where the coefficient of viscosity equals 12.55×10^{-6} N-sec/m² and the density equals 0.598 kg/m³.

6. At 0°C and a pressure of 10^6 dyn cm⁻² the viscosity of nitrogen (molecular weight 28) is 1.67×10^{-4} g cm⁻¹ sec ⁻¹ and the density is 1.25×10^{-3} g cm⁻³. The density of liquid nitrogen is 0.78 g cm⁻³. Use this information to estimate the diameter of the nitrogen molecule and Avogadro's number.

7. The thermal conductivity of helium at STP is 1.4×10^{-3} J, cm⁻¹ sec⁻¹ deg⁻¹. At what pressure at 0°C is the mean free path 1 cm long?

8. A molecule of methane (molecular weight 16) can be considered as a sphere having about five times the volume of an argon atom (atomic weight 40). What should be the ratio of the viscosities and of the thermal conductivities of methane and argon at normal temperature and pressure?

9. The effect of temperature on the viscosity of water vapor between 100°C and 600°C is represented rather well by the Sutherland semiempirical equation

$$\mu = AT^{1/2}/(1 + B/T)$$

in which $A = 1.501 \times 10^{-5}$ P-deg⁻⁽¹ᐟ²⁾ and $B = 446.8$°K. What is the ratio of the effective collision cross sections for viscosity at 100°C and 600°C? If the Sutherland equation were to apply outside this range of temperatures, at what temperatures would the effective cross section be one half that at 100°C and twice that at 100°C?

10. In an experiment on transport phenomena, a gas of variable pressure p is contained between two large parallel plates separated by a distance of 2 cm. The plates are maintained at constant temperatures of $T_1 = 295\,°K$ and $T_2 = 305\,°K$ respectively. The transport of heat is studied as a function of pressure, and is found to be independent of p for $p \gg 1$ mm of Hg and to be proportional to p for $p \ll 10^{-2}$ mm of Hg.

    (a) Obtain an order of magnitude estimate of the diameter of a molecule.
    (b) Explain the low-pressure behavior.
    (c) Explain the high-pressure behavior.

11. Determine the total scattering cross section for a collision between two carbon dioxide molecules using the experimental data at 0°C for
    (a) the coefficient of self-diffusion
    (b) the coefficient of thermal conductivity
    (c) the coefficient of viscosity.

Chapter 8

THE DIFFUSION EQUATION

INTRODUCTION

In Chapter 7 we assumed that a steady state existed and that the properties of the gas did not change appreciably over a distance of the order of a mean free path. The results we obtained are also applicable even if the gas is not in a steady state, provided the rate at which the macroscopic properties are changing is not too rapid. Since local equilibrium is established by collisions between the molecules, and since we have assumed that one collision is sufficient to destroy the memory of a molecule, we can define "not too rapid" as meaning slow compared to the time between collisions, i.e., $1/\nu$.

The quantity $1/\nu$ is a measure of the time required for a local equilibrium to be established. It does not, however, represent the time required for absolute equilibrium to be established. If, for example, the boundary conditions which are producing the steady state distributions discussed in Chapter 7 are suddenly removed and equilibrium boundary conditions are applied instead, it will take an appreciable length of time before the gas passes from a state of local equilibrium to a state of absolute equilibrium.

In the following sections we will attempt to acquire some idea of the order of magnitude of this time.

THE CONTINUITY EQUATION

In the absence of sources and sinks, or external force fields, the total number of molecules, the total momentum, and the total energy contained within a region can only be changed by transport across the boundaries of the region.

Suppose $n(x, t)$ represents a one-dimensional density of particles distributed along a line, and $J(x, t)$ the flux density, i.e., the net rate at which the particles cross the point x at the time t in the positive direction. Consider the region R given by the condition $a \leq x \leq b$. The total number of particles in R is simply $\int_a^b n dx$. The time rate of change of the number of particles in R is

$$\frac{d}{dt}\int_a^b n dx \qquad (8.1)$$

The change in the number of particles in R is due to the flux of particles across the boundaries. The net increase per unit time in the number of particles in R is thus

$$J(a, t) - J(b, t) \qquad (8.2)$$

Equating (8.1) and (8.2) we obtain

$$\frac{d}{dt}\int_a^b n dx = J(a, t) - J(b, t) \qquad (8.3)$$

Interchanging the integration and the differentiation on the left-hand side of (8.3) and making use of Eq. (8.1) in Appendix 8 on the right-hand side of (8.3), we can rewrite (8.3) as

$$\int_a^b (\partial n/\partial t) dx = -\int_a^b (\partial J/\partial x) dx \qquad (8.4)$$

Since the region R is arbitrary, the only way (8.4) can be true is if the integrands are equal. We thus obtain

$$\frac{\partial n}{\partial t} + \frac{\partial J}{\partial x} = 0 \qquad (8.5)$$

This is the continuity equation in one dimension.

Let us consider the analogous three-dimensional situation. Let $n(\mathbf{x}, t)$ and $\mathbf{J}(\mathbf{x}, t)$ be the density and flux density respectively of a set of particles. Consider an arbitrary volume V surrounded by a surface S. The number of particles in V is given by $\int_V n dV$ and the rate of change of the number is

$$\frac{d}{dt}\int_V n dV \equiv \int_V (\partial n/\partial t) dV \qquad (8.6)$$

The net flux of particles into V through S is

$$-\oint_S \mathbf{J} \cdot \mathbf{n} dS \equiv -\Sigma_i \oint_S J_i n_i dS \qquad (8.7)$$

From Eq. (8.6) in Appendix 8, letting $P \equiv J_i$ we obtain

$$-\Sigma_i \oint_S J_i n_i dS = -\Sigma_i \int_V (\partial J_i/\partial x_i) dV \qquad (8.8)$$

Equating (8.8) and (8.6) we obtain

$$\int_V \left(\frac{\partial n}{\partial t}\right) dV = -\sum_i \int_V \left(\frac{\partial J_i}{\partial x_i}\right) dV \tag{8.9}$$

Since V is arbitrary we can equate the integrands in (8.9) and we obtain

$$\frac{\partial n}{\partial t} + \sum_i \frac{\partial J_i}{\partial x_i} = 0 \tag{8.10}$$

This is the continuity equation in three dimensions.

Our result can easily be extended to s dimensions. In s dimensions we have

$$\frac{\partial n}{\partial t} + \sum_{i=1}^s \frac{\partial J_i}{\partial x_i} = 0 \tag{8.11}$$

The analysis leading to Eq. (8.10) would have been exactly the same if instead of particles being transported into or out of the region we had considered energy, or some component of the momentum. If we let ρ represent the density of some conserved quantity and $\mathbf{R}$ the corresponding flux density, then in the absence of any sources or sinks, or external fields

$$\frac{\partial \rho}{\partial t} + \sum_i \frac{\partial R_i}{\partial x_i} = 0 \tag{8.12}$$

THE DIFFUSION EQUATION

In discussing the diffusion of radioactive molecules through a gas, we assumed that a steady state existed in which n^* was a function of x_3 only. We would now like to allow n^* to be a function of x_3 and also of time, and to find the equation from which we can determine the functional dependence of n^* on x_3 and t for a particular set of boundary conditions.

Letting $\mathbf{R} = e_3 J_3(x_3, t)$ and $\rho = n^*$ in Eq. (8.12) we have

$$\frac{\partial J_3}{\partial x_3} + \frac{\partial n^*}{\partial t} = 0 \tag{8.13}$$

But we have seen earlier that

$$J_3 = -D\left(\frac{\partial n^*}{\partial x_3}\right) \tag{8.14}$$

Substituting (8.14) in (8.13) we have

$$\frac{\partial}{\partial x_3}\left(D\frac{\partial n^*}{\partial x_3}\right) = \frac{\partial n^*}{\partial t} \tag{8.15}$$

For constant D

$$D\frac{\partial^2 n^*}{\partial x_3^2} = \frac{\partial n^*}{\partial t} \tag{8.16}$$

Equation (8.16), or more correctly, Eq. (8.15), is the one-dimensional diffusion equation. By solving (8.16) for a particular set of boundary conditions, it is possible to determine the dependence of n^* on both x_3 and t.

Before looking at this equation in greater detail let us consider the parallel situations in which there is a velocity gradient or temperature gradient in the x_3 direction.

Consider first the case of a gas contained between two plates normal to the x_3 axis and maintained at different temperatures. If the boundary conditions are changed, the temperature of the gas will change. We would like to get some idea of the rate at which this change takes place. In Chapter 32 we will consider the equations which are necessary to solve this problem in detail. In the present chapter we simply wish to get an order of magnitude estimate of the times involved.

When the boundary conditions are changed, not only the temperature but the density will change and as a result there will be a transport of energy between various regions in the gas due both to heat conduction and to particle transport. In order to get an estimate of the contribution to the change due to heat conduction, let us assume that the density of the gas remains constant. The energy flux and the energy density will then be given by

$$\mathbf{R} = \mathbf{e}_3 \, q_3(x_3, t) = -\mathbf{e}_3 \, \kappa(\partial T/\partial x_3) \tag{8.17}$$

$$\rho = 3nkT/2 \tag{8.18}$$

Substituting these values in (8.12) we obtain

$$\frac{\partial}{\partial x_3}\left(\alpha \frac{\partial T}{\partial x_3}\right) = \frac{\partial T}{\partial t} \tag{8.19}$$

where $\alpha = 2\kappa/3nk$, and is referred to as the coefficient of thermal diffusivity.

Our expression for α is only valid for monatomic gases, since, as we discussed earlier, polyatomic molecules possess rotational and vibrational energy in addition to their translational energy.

If the thermal diffusivity is constant, then Eq. (8.19) becomes

$$\alpha \frac{\partial^2 T}{\partial x_3^2} = \frac{\partial T}{\partial t} \tag{8.20}$$

Eq. (8.20), or more generally Eq. (8.19), is the one-dimensional heat diffusion equation.

Consider finally the case of a gas maintained between two plates normal to the x_3 axis and moving with different velocities in the x_2 direction. If the velocities of the plates are changed, the gas will pass from one steady state to another. To obtain an estimate of the rate at which the viscosity is able to cause the change, let us assume that there is no instantaneous flow of particles at any time in the x_3 direction, i.e., $\bar{v}_3 = 0$.

The momentum transported in the x_3 direction is then due to viscosity only. The density of the x_2 component of momentum is $nm\bar{v}_2$. The flux of this component of momentum in the x_3 direction is given by $p_{23} = -\mu(\partial\bar{v}_2/\partial x_3)$. Therefore

$$\frac{\partial}{\partial x_3}\left[-\mu\left(\frac{\partial\bar{v}_2}{\partial x_3}\right)\right] = -nm\frac{\partial\bar{v}_2}{\partial t} \tag{8.21}$$

and if μ is constant

$$\frac{\mu}{nm}\frac{\partial^2\bar{v}_2}{\partial x_3{}^2} = \frac{\partial\bar{v}_2}{\partial t} \tag{8.22}$$

The three diffusion equations (8.16), (8.20), and (8.22) are all formally identical. We will restrict further discussion to the diffusion equation (8.16). The results which we obtain in this case can easily be taken over in discussing either of the other two diffusion equations.

In solving (8.16) we shall use the technique of separation of variables. We first assume the solution $n^*(x_3, t)$ can be written in the form

$$n^*(x_3, t) = g(x_3)h(t) \tag{8.23}$$

Substituting (8.23) in (8.16), and dividing the result by $Dg(x_3)h(t)$ we obtain

$$\frac{g''(x_3)}{g(x_3)} = \frac{h'(t)}{Dh(t)} \tag{8.24}$$

Equation (8.24) is valid for all values of x_3 and t. The only way this could be is if both sides are equal to the same constant, which for convenience we write $-a^2$. Thus

$$\frac{g''(x_3)}{g(x_3)} = -a^2 \tag{8.25}$$

$$\frac{h'(t)}{h(t)} = -a^2 D \tag{8.26}$$

Solving (8.25) and (8.26) we have

$$g(x_3) = C_1 \cos ax_3 + C_2 \sin ax_3 \qquad a \neq 0 \tag{8.27}$$

$$g(x_3) = C_3 x_3 + C_4 \qquad a = 0 \tag{8.28}$$

$$h(t) = C_5 \exp(-a^2 Dt) \tag{8.29}$$

where C_1, C_2, C_3, C_4, C_5 and a are arbitrary constants. The solutions (8.27), (8.28), and (8.29) actually represent an infinite number of solutions. By appropriately combining solutions, we can find *the* solution which satisfies a particular set of initial conditions and boundary conditions.

Elaborate discussions of these solutions can be found in any good book on partial differential equations. For our purposes, it will suffice to look at some particular solution, for example

$$n^* = A \cos(2\pi x_3/L) \exp(-4\pi^2 Dt/L^2) + B \tag{8.30}$$

This solution is shown for time $t = 0$ and a later time $t = \tau$ in Figure 8.1. As time progresses, the original density (n^*) inhomogeneity is slowly disappearing. In order to give some measure of the rate at which the density (n^*) inhomogeneity is disappearing, we determine at what time τ the amplitude of the cosine function will have dropped from A to $(1/e)A$. Solving, we find

$$\tau = L^2/4\pi^2 D \qquad (8.31)$$

The time τ is known as the relaxation time and is different for each problem. However, some general conclusions can be drawn from the example given above. From (8.31) it can, for example, be seen that the relaxation time will depend on the geometry of the inhomogeneities as indicated by the presence of L^2 and will also depend inversely on the diffusion coefficient D.

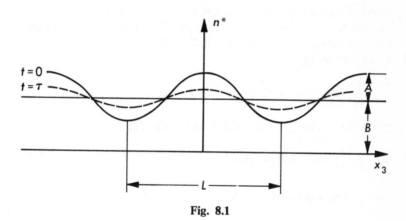

Fig. 8.1

The analysis for the cases in which the original steady state situation is a velocity gradient in the x_3 direction or a temperature gradient in the x_3 direction proceeds along the same lines, with D replaced by (μ/mn) or α, as the case may be.

PROBLEMS

1. The density of radioactive molecules in a gas is given by

   $$n^*(x, t) = [N/2(\pi Dt)^{1/2}] \exp(-x^2/4Dt)$$

   where D is the coefficient of diffusion
   (a) Show that this distribution satisfies the appropriate one-dimensional diffusion equation.
   (b) What initial conditions would produce such a distribution of radioactive molecules?

2. A compressible fluid obeys the continuity equation

$$\frac{\partial \rho}{\partial t} + \sum_i \frac{\partial}{\partial x_i} (\rho v_i) = 0$$

Show that an incompressible fluid obeys the equation

$$\sum_i \frac{\partial v_i}{\partial x_i} = 0$$

3. Prove in three dimensions

$$\int_V (\partial P/\partial x_i) dV = \oint_S P n_i dS$$

where $P(\mathbf{x})$ and $\partial P/\partial x_i$ are single-valued and continuous functions in the volume V, dV is a volume element, dS is a surface element and $\mathbf{n}$ is the unit outward normal to the surface dS.

4. Using the result

$$\int_V (\partial P/dx_i) dV = \oint_S P n_i dS$$

prove for arbitrary vector field $\mathbf{A}$ and scalar field ϕ

(a) $\int \nabla \cdot \mathbf{A} \, dV = \oint \mathbf{n} \cdot \mathbf{A} \, dS$

(b) $\int \nabla \times \mathbf{A} \, dV = \oint \mathbf{n} \times \mathbf{A} \, dS$

(c) $\int \nabla \phi \, dV = \oint \mathbf{n} \phi \, dS$

5. A test tube contains a little ether that evaporates and diffuses through the air about it. Assume that air currents above the test tube keep the concentration of ether at the top of the tube effectively at zero without disturbing diffusion in the tube. Let x = height above the liquid surface, h = height from the liquid surface to the top of the tube, n = total molecular density of air-ether mixture, $n_1(x)$ = molecular density of ether, and $n_1(0)$ the saturation density of ether at the liquid surface. Show that

$$n_1(x) = n\{1 - [1 - (n_1(0)/n)]^{1-(x/h)}\}$$

Chapter 9

THE ELEMENTARY THEORY
OF THE TRANSPORT PROPERTIES
OF A GAS MIXTURE

INTRODUCTION

In Chapter 7 we derived the transport properties of a simple gas using mean free path techniques. In this chapter we wish to derive a few of the transport properties of a gas mixture. We will consider two problems: (1) mutual diffusion in a mixture of two ordinary gases, and (2) the electrical conductivity of an ionized gas.

The usefulness of mean free path arguments lies in their ability to give quick qualitative insights into the behavior of gases, thus enabling one to get a feel for the behavior of gases without becoming excessively entwined in mathematical complexities. The application of the mean free path techniques to a simple gas is relatively straightforward. However, the application of these techniques to a gas mixture demands considerably more caution, and as a consequence, their utility in the study of gas mixtures is not as great as in the study of a simple gas. We will therefore employ techniques which though approximate are a little more rigorous than the mean free path techniques. Since we will consider these same problems in complete mathematical detail in later chapters, we will not, in this chapter, pursue these techniques beyond their application to a few simple problems.

COLLISIONS BETWEEN HARD SPHERES

Let us suppose we have a mixture of two types of hard spheres. Let m, M, d, D, n, N be their respective masses, diameters, and densities. Let us assume that the distribution function for the spheres of mass m is given by

$$f(\mathbf{v}) = n(\lambda/\pi)^{3/2} \exp(-\lambda v^2) \tag{9.1}$$

$$\lambda = m/2kT \tag{9.2}$$

and the distribution function for the spheres of mass M is given by

$$F(\mathbf{V}) = N(\Lambda/\pi)^{3/2} \exp(-\Lambda V^2) \tag{9.3}$$

$$\Lambda = M/2kT \tag{9.4}$$

Let $\nu_{12}(\mathbf{v}, \mathbf{V})$ be the probability per unit time that a sphere of mass m and velocity $\mathbf{v}$ will collide with one of a gas of spheres of velocity $\mathbf{V}$ and density N. Generalizing the arguments of Chapter 6, we obtain

$$\nu_{12}(\mathbf{v}, \mathbf{V}) = N\pi[(d + D)/2]^2 \, |\mathbf{v} - \mathbf{V}| \tag{9.5}$$

Averaging over $\mathbf{v}$ and $\mathbf{V}$ as in Chapter 6, we obtain for the average collision frequency ν_{12} of a sphere of mass m with the spheres of mass M

$$\nu_{12} = \frac{\iint \nu_{12}(\mathbf{v}, \mathbf{V}) f(\mathbf{v}) F(\mathbf{V}) d\mathbf{v} d\mathbf{V}}{\iint f(\mathbf{v}) F(\mathbf{V}) d\mathbf{v} d\mathbf{V}} \tag{9.6}$$

We now introduce the variables

$$\mathbf{u} = \mathbf{v} - \mathbf{V} \tag{9.7}$$

$$\mathbf{w} = \frac{m\mathbf{v} + M\mathbf{V}}{m + M} \tag{9.8}$$

Substituting (9.5) in (9.6) and making the transformation (9.7), (9.8), we obtain

$$\nu_{12} = \frac{N\pi[(d + D)/2]^2 \int \psi^*(\mathbf{u}) \Psi^*(\mathbf{w}) u \, d\mathbf{u} d\mathbf{w}}{\int \psi^*(\mathbf{u}) \Psi^*(\mathbf{w}) d\mathbf{u} d\mathbf{w}} \tag{9.9}$$

where

$$\psi^*(\mathbf{u}) = n(\lambda^*/\pi)^{3/2} \exp(-\lambda^* u^2) \tag{9.10}$$

$$\Psi^*(\mathbf{w}) = N(\Lambda^*/\pi)^{3/2} \exp(-\Lambda^* w^2) \tag{9.11}$$

$$\lambda^* = \lambda\Lambda/(\lambda + \Lambda) = mM/(m + M)2kT \equiv m^*/2kT \tag{9.12}$$

$$\Lambda^* = \lambda + \Lambda = (m + M)/2kT \tag{9.13}$$

Integrating over **u** and **w**, using Eq. (4.27), we obtain

$$\nu_{12} = N\pi[(d + D)/2]^2 \, [\Gamma(2)/(\lambda^*)^{1/2} \, \Gamma(3/2)]$$

$$= N\pi[(d + D)/2]^2 \, (8kT/\pi m^*)^{1/2} \qquad (9.14)$$

THE COEFFICIENT OF MUTUAL DIFFUSION

Suppose we have a mixture of two gases with densities n and N respectively, which are functions of x_1, i.e.,

$$n = n(x_1) \qquad (9.15)$$

$$N = N(x_1) \qquad (9.16)$$

Due to the inhomogeneity of the gas there will be an interdiffusion of the particles of mass M and the particles of mass m. If $\bar{v}_1$ is the average value of the 1 component of velocity of the gas whose density is n, and $\bar{V}_1$ is the average value of the 1 component of velocity of the gas whose density is N, then $\bar{v}_1 \neq 0$ and $\bar{V}_1 \neq 0$.

The partial pressure due to the gas of density n is given by

$$p = nkT \qquad (9.17)$$

The partial pressure due to the gas of density N is given by

$$P = NkT \qquad (9.18)$$

In the steady state we expect the total pressure $P + p$ and the temperature T to be constant. It follows that $n + N$ is constant and therefore

$$\frac{dn}{dx_1} = -\frac{dN}{dx_1} \qquad (9.19)$$

Furthermore, since we are interested in diffusion and not a flow of particles due to any macroscopic motion of the gas as a whole, we will also assume that the net flux of particles is zero, i.e.,

$$n\bar{v}_1 + N\bar{V}_1 = 0 \qquad (9.20)$$

Let us consider just the particles of mass m which are contained in a slab of thickness dx_1 and unit cross section as shown in Figure 9.1.

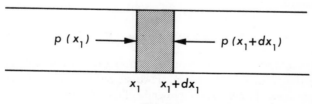

Fig. 9.1

There is a net force on this slab due to the pressure p given by $p(x_1) - p(x_1 + dx_1)$. However, there is also a force due to collisions of the particles of mass m with the particles of mass M. This force is equal to the rate at which momentum is being transferred from the gas of particles of mass M to the particles of mass m. If we define $(\Delta mv_1)_{12}$ as the average amount of the 1 component of momentum transferred from the particles of mass M to the particles of mass m per unit volume per unit time then the latter force is given by $(\Delta mv_1)_{12}dx_1$. In steady state the above two forces must be equal and opposite. Therefore

$$-(\Delta mv_1)_{12}dx_1 = p(x_1) - p(x_1 + dx_1) \qquad (9.21)$$

or

$$dp/dx_1 = (\Delta mv_1)_{12} \qquad (9.22)$$

As we shall see in Chapter 36, it is not too difficult to evaluate $(\Delta mv_1)_{12}$ accurately. We will, however, simply obtain a good estimate of its value in this chapter. Consider a collision between a particle of mass m and velocity $\mathbf{v}$, and a particle of mass M and velocity $\mathbf{V}$. Let $\mathbf{v}'$ and $\mathbf{V}'$ be their respective velocities after collision. Let $\mathbf{w}$ be the center of mass velocity, and $\mathbf{u}$ and $\mathbf{u}'$ be the relative velocities before and after collision:

$$\mathbf{w} = \frac{m\mathbf{v} + M\mathbf{V}}{m + M} = \frac{m\mathbf{v}' + M\mathbf{V}'}{m + M} \qquad (9.23)$$

$$\mathbf{u} = \mathbf{v} - \mathbf{V} \qquad (9.24)$$

$$\mathbf{u}' = \mathbf{v}' - \mathbf{V}' \qquad (9.25)$$

We can then write

$$\mathbf{v} = \mathbf{w} + (m^*/m)\mathbf{u} \qquad (9.26)$$

$$\mathbf{v}' = \mathbf{w} + (m^*/m)\mathbf{u}' \qquad (9.27)$$

Subtracting (9.26) from (9.27) and replacing $\mathbf{u}$ by $\mathbf{v} - \mathbf{V}$, we obtain

$$\mathbf{v}' - \mathbf{v} = (m^*/m)\mathbf{u}' - (m^*/m)(\mathbf{v} - \mathbf{V}) \qquad (9.28)$$

We now average (9.28) over all collisions, letting $< >_c$ indicate an average over collisions. Then

$$<\mathbf{v}' - \mathbf{v}>_c = (m^*/m)<\mathbf{u}'>_c - (m^*/m)<\mathbf{v} - \mathbf{V}>_c \qquad (9.29)$$

We now assume

$$<\mathbf{u}'>_c = 0 \qquad (9.30)$$

$$<\mathbf{v} - \mathbf{V}>_c = \bar{\mathbf{v}} - \bar{\mathbf{V}} \qquad (9.31)$$

The first assumption is equivalent to assuming that a collision destroys the memory of the relative motion, i.e., if we sit on a particle of mass M and watch the particles of mass m come in and collide with this mass, the scattered particles will be scattered uniformly in all directions.

The second assumption is equivalent to assuming that the average initial velocity of a particle taking part in a collision is equivalent to its ordinary average velocity. To illustrate the fact that this is an assumption, suppose the collision cross section was such that only particles with velocity v_0 would collide. Then the average initial velocity of a particle taking part in a collision would be v_0 which need not, in general, be the same as $\bar{v}$.

Finally, we assume that the net momentum transfer per unit volume per unit time is just the product of the number of collisions $n\nu_{12}$ and the average change in momentum in a collision, i.e.,

$$(\Delta m v)_{12} = n\nu_{12} < mv' - mv >_c \qquad (9.32)$$

Combining (9.29), (9.30), (9.31) and (9.32), we have

$$(\Delta m v)_{12} = -n\nu_{12}m^*(\bar{v} - \bar{V}) \qquad (9.33)$$

Substituting (9.17) and (9.33) in (9.22), we obtain

$$kT(dn/dx_1) = -n\nu_{12}m^*(\bar{v}_1 - \bar{V}_1) \qquad (9.34)$$

Solving (9.20) for $\bar{v}_1$ and substituting the result in (9.34), we obtain

$$n\bar{v}_1 = -[NkT/(n+N)m^*\nu_{12}](dn/dx_1) \qquad (9.35)$$

Substituting (9.14) in (9.35), we get

$$n\bar{v}_1 = -D_{12}(dn/dx_1) \qquad (9.36)$$

$$D_{12} = (\pi kT/8m^*)^{1/2}/(n+N)\pi[(d+D)/2]^2 \qquad (9.37)$$

The factor D_{12} is called the coefficient of mutual diffusion. The result which would be obtained for hard sphere collisions if we had used a more rigorous value of $(\Delta m v_1)_{12}$ is

$$D_{12} = (3/4)(\pi kT/8m^*)^{1/2}/(n+N)\pi[(d+D)/2]^2 \qquad (9.38)$$

It is interesting to note that the coefficient of mutual diffusion depends on the total density $n+N$ and not on the relative composition. A higher order approximation will reveal a slight dependence on the composition.

THE CONDUCTIVITY OF A SLIGHTLY IONIZED GAS

An ionized gas may be considered as a gas mixture composed of electrons, ions, and neutral molecules. Because of the greater mobility of the electrons, the electrical properties are primarily due to the electrons.

Let us consider a slightly ionized gas in a homogeneous electric field

$$e_1 E \cos \omega t$$

where e_1 is a unit vector in the 1 direction.

An electron will experience two forces, the force due to the electric field, and the force due to collisions. If the gas is only slightly ionized, then the electrons will undergo many more collisions with neutral molecules than with either ions or other electrons. We shall therefore assume that we can neglect all collisions except those between electrons and neutral molecules. Let us designate by F_c the force on the electrons due to collisions with the neutral molecules. Setting the forces on the electron equal to its time rate of change of momentum, we get

$$\frac{d}{dt}(m\mathbf{v}) = e_1 eE \cos \omega t + \mathbf{F}_c \tag{9.39}$$

where e is the charge on an electron.

We now average this equation. We then have

$$\frac{d}{dt}(m\bar{\mathbf{v}}) = e_1 eE \cos \omega t + (1/n)(\Delta m\mathbf{v})_{12} \tag{9.40}$$

where $(\Delta m\mathbf{v})_{12}$ is the average amount of momentum transferred from the molecules to the electrons per unit volume per unit time. As in the preceding section, we assume

$$(\Delta m\mathbf{v})_{12} \approx -n\nu_{12}m^*(\bar{\mathbf{v}} - \bar{\mathbf{V}}) \tag{9.41}$$

Since the mass M of the molecules is very much greater than the mass m of the electrons, $m^* \approx m$. Furthermore, we can assume that the molecular distribution is relatively unaffected by the collisions of electrons with molecules, so that $\bar{\mathbf{V}} \approx 0$. Finally, since we are dealing with only one collision frequency, we can let $\nu_{12} \equiv \nu$ without confusion. With the above observations, Eq. (9.41) becomes

$$(\Delta m\mathbf{v})_{12} \approx -n\nu m\bar{\mathbf{v}} \tag{9.42}$$

Substituting (9.42) into (9.40) and considering only the 1 component, we have

$$\frac{d}{dt}(m\bar{v}_1) = eE \cos \omega t - \nu m\bar{v}_1 \tag{9.43}$$

The current density J in the 1 direction is given by

$$J = ne\bar{v}_1 \tag{9.44}$$

Substituting (9.44) in (9.43), we obtain

$$\frac{dJ}{dt} + \nu J = \left(\frac{ne^2 E}{m}\right)\cos \omega t \tag{9.45}$$

Solving for J, we obtain

$$J = \frac{ne^2 E}{m}\left(\frac{\nu \cos \omega t + \omega \sin \omega t}{\omega^2 + \nu^2}\right) \tag{9.46}$$

This form for the conductivity can be made to fit the experimental data moderately well, and is the most frequently encountered expression. We cannot, however, use the collision frequency ν which one would get for hard sphere collisions. Since several chapters will be devoted to a thorough discussion of the electrical conductivity of an ionized gas, we will not dwell on this subject at present in any further detail.

PROBLEMS

1. If one gas diffuses through a second gas that is stationary, that is, there is no net transport of the second gas, the process is sometimes referred to as "single diffusion." If D_1 is the coefficient of single diffusion, then $- D_1 dn_1/dz$ represents the net transport rate per square centimeter per second of gas 1. Show that $D_1 = (n/n_2)D_{12}$ where $n = n_1 + n_2$ is the total density and D_{12} is the mutual-diffusion coefficient.

2. A beam of electrons is projected from an electron gun into a gas at a pressure p, and the number remaining in the beam at a distance x from the gun is determined by allowing the beam to strike a collecting plate and measuring the current to the plate. The electron current emitted by the gun is 100μA, and the current to the collector when $x = 10$ cm and $p = 100 \ n/m^2$ (about 1 mm of mercury) is 37μA.
   (a) What is the electron mean free path?
   (b) What current would be collected if the pressure were reduced to $50 \ n/m^2$?

3. Find the mean free path of an electron within a binary gas mixture of uniform density. The two types of gas molecules have densities n_A and n_B, respectively, and cross sections for electron interactions σ_A and σ_B, respectively. Show that

$$\frac{1}{l} = \frac{1}{l_A} + \frac{1}{l_B}$$

   where $l_A = 1/n_A\sigma_A$ and $l_B = 1/n_B\sigma_B$

4. Given a gas consisting of hard spheres of diameters d and D respectively, obtain an expression for the fraction of the collisions between a molecule of diameter d and a molecule of diameter D in which the relative energy is greater than a specified energy ϵ_0.

5. An electron with an energy of 100 eV is produced in an atmosphere of helium at a pressure of 1 mm of mercury and a temperature of 300°K.
   (a) Prove that in a head-on elastic collision between a body of mass m and a second body of mass M, initially at rest, the fractional decrease in energy of the first body is approximately $4m/M$, where $m \ll M$.
   (b) If on the average the electron loses this fraction of its kinetic energy in each collision with a helium atom, after how many collisions does its energy decrease to within 10 percent of the average thermal energy of the helium atoms? (That is, after how many collisions

is its energy 110 percent of the average thermal energy of the helium atoms?)

(c) What is the original collision frequency of the electron when its kinetic energy is 100 eV?

(d) Assuming that the collision frequency is constant, find the time required for the process described in part (b).

6. Determine the pressure in a cathode ray tube such that 90 percent of the electrons leaving the cathode will reach the anode 10 cm away without making a collision. Assume (1) the electrons are emitted with an average speed appropriate to a Maxwellian gas at temperature of 2000°K (2) the electrons are accelerated through a potential difference of 2000 volts (3) the diameter of the gas molecules in the tube is 3.6 × 10⁻¹⁰m (4) the electrons may be treated as point particles (5) the speed of the molecules is negligible compared to the speed of the electrons.

7. Determine an expression for the electric field strength that will result in an average electron drift velocity which is 10 percent of the average thermal velocity. What is the value of the electric field strength in air at standard pressure and temperature?

8. A singly charged oxygen ion starts a free path in a direction at right angles to an electric field of intensity 10^4 v/m. The pressure is 1 atm and the temperature 300°K.

(a) Compute the distance moved in the direction of the field in a time equal to that required to traverse one mean free path.

(b) What is the ratio of the mean free path to this distance?

(c) What is the average velocity in the direction of the field?

(d) What is the ratio of the thermal velocity to this velocity?

(e) What is the ratio of the energy of thermal agitation to the energy gained from the field in one mean free path?

PART
II

STATISTICAL MECHANICS

In Part I, we investigated the properties of a collection of independent point masses. We were able, using arguments which were at times admittedly weak, to derive some exact equilibrium properties, and some approximate nonequilibrium or transport properties for such a collection.

In Part II we will reconsider the equilibrium properties of matter and will develop concepts and techniques which will not only enable us to improve the theoretical foundations of our earlier results but will also make it possible, at least in principle, to tackle collections of complex and strongly interacting mechanical systems.

The only material from Part I necessary to follow the development in Part II is that contained in Chapters 1, 2, and 3. Those students who are encountering statistical mechanics for the first time will find it helpful to also read Chapters 4 and 5.

Chapter 10

CLASSICAL MECHANICS

INTRODUCTION

Before tackling statistical mechanics, it will be helpful to review some results from classical mechanics. Although no prior knowledge of the material contained in this section is necessary to follow the arguments, it is assumed that the majority of readers have some previous experience with the topics to be covered.

GENERALIZED COORDINATES

Let us consider a system consisting of r particles, for example, a molecule. Let $\mathbf{x}(i)$ be the vector representing the position of the ith particle. The configuration of the system at some instant of time is specified by giving the set of vectors $\mathbf{x}(i)$ at that time. It is possible, however, to represent the configuration of the system by a single point in a $3r$ dimensional space, whose coordinates are the position coordinates of the r particles. Just as a point in ordinary three-dimensional space can be represented by a vector, so also can the configuration point in $3r$ dimensional space be represented by a vector. We designate this vector $\mathbf{x}$. Previously $\mathbf{x}$ represented a three-dimensional vector. Now $\mathbf{x}$ represents a $3r$ dimensional vector. Our previous notation can be readily extended to $3r$ dimensions. Thus

$$\int F(\mathbf{x})d\mathbf{x} \equiv \int \ldots \int F[\mathbf{x}(1), \mathbf{x}(2), \ldots, \mathbf{x}(r)]d\mathbf{x}(1)d\mathbf{x}(2)\ldots d\mathbf{x}(r) \quad (10.1)$$

There are many other sets of coordinates besides the $\mathbf{x}$ coordinates which could be used to specify the configuration of the system, and thus many other spaces within which a single point can be used to specify the configuration of the system. We shall designate a point in such a space as $\mathbf{q}$. The transformation by which a point in $\mathbf{q}$ space is transformed to a point in $\mathbf{x}$ space is given by

$$\mathbf{x} = \mathbf{x}(\mathbf{q}, t) \tag{10.2}$$

The explicit presence of the time is necessary, since it is possible to choose coordinate frames which are moving with respect to one another. For example, the $\mathbf{q}$ could be the rectangular Cartesian coordinates of a point as measured from a frame of reference moving with respect to the frame from which the $\mathbf{x}$ are measured.

If the motion of the system of particles is in some way constrained, as for example, would be the case if some of the particles were connected together by rigid rods, then it is not necessary to employ $3r$ coordinates to specify the configuration.

Let us suppose that the minimum number of coordinates required to specify the configuration of the system is s. We then define any set of s coordinates which uniquely determine the configuration of the system as a set of generalized coordinates. The number s is referred to as the number of degrees of freedom. The configuration can now be represented by a point in the corresponding s dimensional space. We will again designate this point $\mathbf{q}$. There is still a transformation from $\mathbf{q}$ space to $\mathbf{x}$ space represented by the transformation (10.2). However, the dimensionality of the $\mathbf{q}$ space may be less than the dimensionality of the $\mathbf{x}$ space.

Although the s generalized coordinates may be the minimum number of coordinates required to specify the configuration of a system, they may not all be independent. Consider a disk which is constrained to roll on a rough plane while always remaining vertical. If the x, y coordinates of the point of contact, the orientation of the plane of the disk, and the angular position of the disk about an axis normal to the disk and through its center are given, the disk is uniquely fixed. Thus four coordinates are adequate. This is, moreover, the minimum number of coordinates possible. These four coordinates are not, however, entirely independent. If the disk rotates about the axis through its center, it must also change its point of contact on the plane.

We will restrict ourselves to constraints such that the generalized coordinates *are* able to be independently varied.

The appearance of the time in the transformation Eq. (10.2) arises in the case of an unconstrained system from the possibility of moving coordinate frames. In the case of a constrained system, it is possible that the constraint itself will introduce an explicit dependence on time in the transformation. For example, a particle might be constrained to move on a plane which is moving.

In summary, for the systems which we will consider, it is possible to pick a set of generalized coordinates which can be independently varied without violating the constraints of the system, and from which the Cartesian coordinates of the individual particles can be obtained by a transformation of the form $\mathbf{x} = \mathbf{x}(\mathbf{q}, t)$.

LAGRANGE'S EQUATION

Let us, as in the previous section, consider a system of r particles. Let $m(i)$ be the mass of the ith particle, $\mathbf{x}(i)$ its position, and $\mathbf{F}(i)$ the force acting on this particle. If the masses $m(i)$ remain constant then the equations governing the motion of the particles are

$$F_j(i) = m(i)\ddot{x}_j(i) \qquad i = 1 \ldots r \qquad j = 1, 2, 3 \qquad (10.3)$$

where $\ddot{x}_j(i)$ is the second time derivative of the jth component of position of the ith particle, and $F_j(i)$ the jth component of the force acting on the ith particle.

Equation (10.3) can be notationally simplified if we define

$$F_1 = F_1(1), F_2 = F_2(1), F_3 = F_3(1), F_4 = F_1(2), \ldots \qquad (10.4)$$

$$x_1 = x_1(1), x_2 = x_2(1), x_3 = x_3(1), x_4 = x_1(2), \ldots \qquad (10.5)$$

$$m_1 = m_2 = m_3 = m(1), \qquad m_4 = m_5 = m_6 = m(2), \ldots \qquad (10.6)$$

with this notation, Eq. (10.3) becomes

$$F_i = m_i\ddot{x}_i \qquad\qquad i = 1 \ldots 3r \qquad (10.7)$$

We will make frequent use of the kinetic energy K of the system of particles. The kinetic energy is defined by the equation

$$K = \tfrac{1}{2} \sum_{i=1}^{r} \sum_{j=1}^{3} m(i)[\dot{x}_j(i)]^2 \equiv \tfrac{1}{2} \sum_{i=1}^{3r} m_i\dot{x}_i^2 \qquad (10.8)$$

In terms of the kinetic energy Eq. (10.7) can be written

$$F_i = \frac{d}{dt}\left(\frac{\partial K}{\partial \dot{x}_i}\right) \qquad (10.9)$$

For a system of even moderate complexity Eq. (10.7) is very difficult to apply. In the first place the Cartesian coordinates x_i may be a very awkward set of coordinates to use. In the second place it may be very difficult or impossible to handle the number of equations involved. For example, if our system consists of a rigid body subject to no rotational or translational constraints as a whole and made up of 10^{24} particles, then in order to solve for the motion of the system we would need in addition to the 10^{24} equations of motion, six numbers to describe the action of the external forces, and $(10^{24} - 6)$ equations of constraint to describe the rigidity of the system. As we shall see, the introduction of an appropriate set of generalized coordinates can greatly simplify the problem.

Let **q** be a set of s generalized coordinates satisfying the conditions discussed in the preceding section, and let the transformation equations be given by

$$x_i = x_i(\mathbf{q}, t) \qquad i = 1 \ldots 3r \tag{10.10}$$

Multiplying Eq. (10.9) by $\partial x_i/\partial q_j$ and summing over i we obtain

$$\sum_i \frac{d}{dt}\left(\frac{\partial K}{\partial \dot{x}_i}\right)\frac{\partial x_i}{\partial q_j} = \sum_i F_i \frac{\partial x_i}{\partial q_j} \tag{10.11}$$

Equation (10.11) can be rewritten

$$\sum_i \frac{d}{dt}\left(\frac{\partial K}{\partial \dot{x}_i}\frac{\partial x_i}{\partial q_j}\right) - \sum_i \frac{\partial K}{d\dot{x}_i}\frac{d}{dt}\left(\frac{\partial x_i}{\partial q_j}\right) = \sum_i F_i \frac{\partial x_i}{\partial q_j} \tag{10.12}$$

From (10.10) it follows that

$$\dot{x}_i = \sum_j \frac{\partial x_i}{\partial q_j}\dot{q}_j + \frac{\partial x_i}{\partial t} \tag{10.13}$$

and therefore

$$\frac{\partial \dot{x}_i}{\partial \dot{q}_j} = \frac{\partial x_i}{\partial q_j} \tag{10.14}$$

Furthermore

$$\frac{d}{dt}\left(\frac{\partial x_i}{\partial q_j}\right) = \frac{\partial}{\partial q_j}\left(\frac{dx_i}{dt}\right) = \frac{\partial \dot{x}_i}{\partial q_j} \tag{10.15}$$

Substituting (10.14) and (10.15) in (10.12) we obtain

$$\sum_i \frac{d}{dt}\left(\frac{\partial K}{\partial \dot{x}_i}\frac{\partial \dot{x}_i}{\partial \dot{q}_j}\right) - \sum_i \frac{\partial K}{\partial \dot{x}_i}\frac{\partial \dot{x}_i}{\partial q_j} = \sum_i F_i \frac{\partial x_i}{\partial q_j} \tag{10.16}$$

Equation (10.16) can be rewritten

$$\frac{d}{dt}\left(\frac{\partial K}{\partial \dot{q}_j}\right) - \frac{\partial K}{\partial q_j} = \sum_i F_i \frac{\partial x_i}{\partial q_j} \tag{10.17}$$

The force F_i can be broken down into the force due to the constraint, F_i'', and the force due to the external fields, F_i'. Thus

$$\frac{d}{dt}\left(\frac{\partial K}{\partial \dot{q}_j}\right) - \frac{\partial K}{\partial q_j} = \sum_i F_i' \frac{\partial x_i}{\partial q_j} + \sum_i F_i'' \frac{\partial x_i}{\partial q_j} \tag{10.18}$$

Let us now consider the system at some arbitrary but fixed time t. If the work done by the constraint forces in any displacement which does not violate the constraints is zero, then

$$\sum_i F_i'' \, dx_i = \sum_j \sum_i F_i'' \, (\partial x_i/\partial q_j)dq_j = 0 \tag{10.19}$$

and since the dq_j are independent, it follows that

$$\sum_i F_i'' \, (\partial x_i / \partial q_j) = 0 \tag{10.20}$$

All ordinary constraint forces encountered on a molecular level will be of this type. Equation (10.18) thus reduces to

$$\frac{d}{dt}\left(\frac{\partial K}{\partial \dot{q}_j}\right) - \frac{\partial K}{\partial q_j} = \sum_i F_i' \frac{\partial x_i}{\partial q_j} \tag{10.21}$$

The quantity $\sum_i F_i'(\partial x_i / \partial q_j)$ is defined as the generalized force Q_j. Thus

$$Q_j = \sum_i F_i' \, (\partial x_i / \partial q_j) \tag{10.22}$$

Substituting (10.22) in (10.21) we obtain

$$\frac{d}{dt}\left(\frac{\partial K}{\partial \dot{q}_j}\right) - \frac{\partial K}{\partial q_j} = Q_j \tag{10.23}$$

Thus if we can write down K in terms of the q_j and $\dot{q}_j$ and if we know the Q_j we can determine the motion of the system.

Instead of using Eq. (10.22) to determine Q_j it is often convenient to determine Q_j from the fact that $\sum Q_j dq_j$ represents the work done by the external forces in an arbitrary displacement of the coordinates q_j at a fixed time t.

If there exists a function $U(\mathbf{q}, \dot{\mathbf{q}}, t)$ such that

$$Q_j = \frac{d}{dt}\left(\frac{\partial U}{\partial \dot{q}_j}\right) - \frac{\partial U}{\partial q_j} \tag{10.24}$$

then (10.23) can be rewritten

$$\frac{d}{dt}\left(\frac{\partial L}{\partial \dot{q}_j}\right) - \frac{\partial L}{\partial q_j} = 0 \tag{10.25}$$

where $L = K - U$. The quantity L is called the Lagrangian and U the generalized potential. Equation (10.25) is usually called Lagrange's equation of motion, though occasionally this name is applied to Eq. (10.23).

For the majority of the problems we will encounter, the field will be conservative, i.e., there exists a function $U(\mathbf{x})$ such that

$$F_i' = -\partial U / \partial x_i \tag{10.26}$$

In this case

$$Q_j = \sum_i F_i' \frac{\partial x_i}{\partial q_j} = -\sum_i \frac{\partial U}{\partial x_i}\frac{\partial x_i}{\partial q_j} = -\frac{\partial U}{\partial q_j} \tag{10.27}$$

The potential U satisfies the condition (10.24) and therefore

$$L = K(\mathbf{q}, \dot{\mathbf{q}}) - U(\mathbf{q}) \tag{10.28}$$

Lagrange's equation (10.25) immensely simplifies our task of describing the motion of a system of r particles. If we know the Lagrangian L as a function of the generalized coordinates q_j, the generalized velocities $\dot{q}_j$ and the time t, and the dynamical state of the system is known at some instant of time t_0, then the equations of motion (10.25) enable us to predict the dynamical state of the system at any other time t. It should be noted that we must know the Lagrangian as a function of $\mathbf{q}$, $\dot{\mathbf{q}}$, and t for the above statement to be true. The Lagrangian thus represents a convenient and almost complete analytical description of the mechanical properties of a system, together with the forces acting on it. The only additional information that is needed to pin the problem down are the values of $\mathbf{q}$ and $\dot{\mathbf{q}}$ at some time t_0.

HAMILTON'S EQUATIONS

Instead of dealing with the generalized velocities $\dot{q}_j$, we will find it convenient to introduce a new set of quantities p_j called generalized momenta, defined by the relation

$$p_j = \partial L/\partial \dot{q}_j \tag{10.29}$$

In terms of the generalized momenta, Lagrange's equations become

$$\dot{p}_j = \partial L/\partial q_j \tag{10.30}$$

In this form the generalized equations of motion governing the behavior of our system are very analogous to the Cartesian equations of motion governing the behavior of a point particle in a potential U. In the latter case we have $p_i = -\partial U/\partial x_i$.

We have seen that if we know $L(\mathbf{q}, \dot{\mathbf{q}}, t)$ we have an almost complete description of the mechanical properties of the system and the forces acting on it. It does not follow that if we know $L(\mathbf{q}, \mathbf{p}, t)$ that we have as complete a description. In the present section we wish to find a function of $\mathbf{q}$, $\mathbf{p}$, and t which will provide us with exactly the same information as we have when we know L as a function of $\mathbf{q}$, $\dot{\mathbf{q}}$, and t.

To obtain such a function we can make a Legendre transformation of $L(\mathbf{q}, \dot{\mathbf{q}}, t)$. A discussion of Legendre transformations is given in Appendix 9. The appropriate Legendre transformation, and the resulting function $H(\mathbf{p}, \mathbf{q}, t)$, called the Hamiltonian, is given by

$$H(\mathbf{p}, \mathbf{q}, t) = \sum_j p_j \dot{q}_j - L \equiv \sum_j p_j \dot{q}_j(\mathbf{p}, \mathbf{q}) - L[\dot{\mathbf{q}}(\mathbf{q}, \mathbf{p}), \mathbf{q}, t] \tag{10.31}$$

If we know H as a function of $\mathbf{p}$, $\mathbf{q}$, and t then we can obtain L as a function of $\mathbf{q}$, $\dot{\mathbf{q}}$, and t. Similarly, if we know L as a function of $\mathbf{q}$, $\dot{\mathbf{q}}$, and t we can obtain H as a function of $\mathbf{p}$, $\mathbf{q}$, and t. Thus $H(\mathbf{p}, \mathbf{q}, t)$ provides as complete a description of the system, together with the forces acting on it as does $L(\mathbf{q}, \dot{\mathbf{q}}, t.)$

To obtain the appropriate equations of motion in terms of H we first take the derivative of (10.31) with respect to q_i, and obtain

$$\frac{\partial H}{\partial q_i} = \sum_j p_j \frac{\partial \dot{q}_j}{\partial q_i} - \sum_j \frac{\partial L}{\partial \dot{q}_j} \frac{\partial \dot{q}_j}{\partial q_i} - \sum_j \frac{\partial L}{\partial \dot{q}_j} \frac{\partial q_j}{\partial q_i} \qquad (10.32)$$

Substituting (10.29) and (10.30) in (10.32) we obtain

$$\partial H / \partial q_i = -\dot{p}_i \qquad (10.33)$$

Similarly

$$\partial H / \partial p_i = \dot{q}_i \qquad (10.34)$$

Equations (10.33) and (10.34) are known as Hamilton's equations of motion. If we know $H(\mathbf{q}, \mathbf{p}, t)$ and the dynamical state of the system at some instant of time, then the equations of motion (10.33) and (10.34) enable us to predict the dynamical state of the system at any other time.

Suppose the force is conservative and $\mathbf{x} = \mathbf{x}(\mathbf{q})$, then

$$L = K(\mathbf{q}, \dot{\mathbf{q}}) - U(\mathbf{q}) \qquad (10.35)$$

$$p_i = \frac{\partial L}{\partial \dot{q}_i} = \frac{\partial K}{\partial \dot{q}_i} \qquad (10.36)$$

$$K = \frac{1}{2} \sum_{i=1}^{3r} m_i \dot{x}_i^2 = \frac{1}{2} \sum_{i=1}^{3r} m_i \left(\sum_j \frac{\partial x_i}{\partial q_j} \dot{q}_j \right) \left(\sum_k \frac{\partial x_i}{\partial q_k} \dot{q}_k \right)$$

$$\equiv \sum_j \sum_k a_{jk}(\mathbf{q}) \dot{q}_j \dot{q}_k \qquad (10.37)$$

Since K is a homogeneous quadratic function of the $\dot{q}_j$ it follows from Euler's theorem (Appendix 10)

$$2K = \sum_i \frac{\partial K}{\partial \dot{q}_i} \dot{q}_i \qquad (10.38)$$

Combining (10.38) and (10.36) we have

$$2K = \sum_i p_i \dot{q}_i \qquad (10.39)$$

The Hamiltonian is then

$$H = \sum_i p_i \dot{q}_i - L = 2K - (K - U) = K + U = E \qquad (10.40)$$

where E is the total energy.

PROBLEMS

1. A bead of mass m is constrained to slide on a smooth wire which has the shape of a parabola in the xy plane and whose equation is $y = ax^2$. Gravity is acting downward in the y direction.
   (a) What are the equations of constraint?
   (b) How many degrees of freedom does the system have?
   (c) Write down the Lagrangian.
   (d) Determine the equations of motion.
   (e) Find the generalized momenta in terms of the generalized coordinates and generalized velocities.

2. The radius r of a spherical soap bubble in a gravitational field is increasing with time according to the equation

$$r = at + b$$

   where a and b are constants. A particle of mass m is constrained to remain on the surface.
   (a) What are the equations of constraint?
   (b) How many degrees of freedom does the particle have?
   (c) Write down the Lagrangian.
   (d) Determine the equations of motion.
   (e) Find the generalized momenta in terms of the generalized coordinates and generalized velocities.

3. A mass m_1 is free to slide on a horizontal wire. A mass m_2 is suspended by a weightless rod of length L from the mass m_1 as shown in Figure 10.1.
   (a) Write down the Lagrangian using x and θ as generalized coordinates.
   (b) Determine the equations of motion.
   (c) Determine the generalized momenta p_θ and p_x.

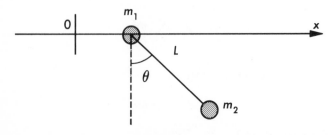

Fig. 10.1

4. Two particles of masses m_1 and m_2 respectively are connected together by a massless spring of spring constant K and unstretched length L.

Choose as generalized coordinates, the Cartesian coordinates of the center of mass X, Y, Z and the relative coordinates r, θ, ϕ which give the position of the mass m_2 with respect to m_1 in spherical coordinates.

(a) Write down the Lagrangian.

(b) Determine Lagrange's equations of motion.

(c) Find the generalized momenta in terms of the generalized velocities.

(d) Find the Hamiltonian.

(e) Determine Hamilton's equations of motion.

Chapter 11

PHASE SPACE

INTRODUCTION

In Part I we restricted ourselves to a gas of point particles. The dynamical state of a point particle at some instant of time is given by specifying its position $\mathbf{x}$ and velocity $\mathbf{v}$, and the dynamical state of a gas of such particles is described by giving the density of representative points in $\mathbf{x}$–$\mathbf{v}$ space. However, this is not the only way to describe such a gas. We can in general specify the dynamical state of a point particle by choosing any set of generalized coordinates $\mathbf{q}$ and the corresponding set of generalized velocities $\dot{\mathbf{q}}$ or generalized momenta $\mathbf{p}$. The dynamical state of the gas would then be described by a density function in $\mathbf{q}$–$\mathbf{p}$ space or $\mathbf{q}$–$\dot{\mathbf{q}}$ space.

In the same way the state of a system of r particles with s degrees of freedom, e.g., a molecule containing r atoms, and having $(3r–s)$ conditions of constraint, can be described by choosing an appropriate set of generalized coordinates $\mathbf{q}$ and the corresponding generalized velocities $\dot{\mathbf{q}}$ or momenta $\mathbf{p}$. The state of a collection of such systems which we will refer to as an assembly can then be described by giving the density of representative points in the $2s$ dimensional $\mathbf{q}$–$\dot{\mathbf{q}}$ space or the $2s$ dimensional $\mathbf{q}$–$\mathbf{p}$ space.

As we shall see, it is much more convenient to choose a set of generalized coordinates and momenta than a set of generalized coordinates and velocities. A $2s$ dimensional space whose coordinates are a complete set of s generalized coordinates and the corresponding s generalized momenta which describe the dynamical state of a system is called a phase space for the system or a system phase space. Where no ambiguity is likely to arise, we will simply call it a phase space.

In the following sections we will derive some very useful properties of phase space.

TRANSFORMATION BETWEEN PHASE SPACES

Let $\mathbf{q}$–$\mathbf{p}$ represent one phase space, and $\mathbf{Q}$–$\mathbf{P}$ a second phase space for the same system. The Jacobian for the transformation between the two spaces will be designated

$J\left(\dfrac{\mathbf{q},\mathbf{p}}{\mathbf{Q},\mathbf{P}}\right)$. We will now show that

$$J\left(\frac{\mathbf{q},\mathbf{p}}{\mathbf{Q},\mathbf{P}}\right) = 1 \tag{11.1}$$

Let us first rewrite the Jacobian in (11.1) as follows:

$$J\left(\frac{\mathbf{q},\mathbf{p}}{\mathbf{Q},\mathbf{P}}\right) = J\left(\frac{\mathbf{q},\mathbf{p}}{\mathbf{Q},\mathbf{p}}\right) J\left(\frac{\mathbf{Q},\mathbf{p}}{\mathbf{Q},\mathbf{P}}\right)$$

$$= \frac{J\left(\dfrac{\mathbf{Q},\mathbf{p}}{\mathbf{Q},\mathbf{P}}\right)}{J\left(\dfrac{\mathbf{Q},\mathbf{p}}{\mathbf{q},\mathbf{p}}\right)} = \frac{|\partial p_i/\partial P_j|}{|\partial Q_i/\partial q_j|} \tag{11.2}$$

We will now show that $\partial Q_i/\partial q_j = \partial p_j/\partial P_i$.

Consider the function

$$F(\mathbf{q},\mathbf{P}) \equiv \sum_i P_i Q_i(\mathbf{q}) \tag{11.3}$$

If we take the partial derivative of $F(\mathbf{q},\mathbf{P})$ with respect to q_j we obtain

$$\frac{\partial F}{\partial q_j} = \sum_i P_i \frac{\partial Q_i}{\partial q_j} \tag{11.4}$$

Since $\mathbf{Q} = \mathbf{Q}(\mathbf{q}, t)$ it follows that

$$\dot{Q}_i = \sum_j \frac{\partial Q_i}{\partial q_j}\dot{q}_j + \frac{\partial Q_i}{\partial t} \tag{11.5}$$

and therefore

$$\frac{\partial \dot{Q}_i}{\partial \dot{q}_j} = \frac{\partial Q_i}{\partial q_j} \tag{11.6}$$

Substituting (11.6) in (11.4) we obtain

$$\frac{\partial F}{\partial q_j} = \sum_i P_i \frac{\partial \dot{Q}_i}{\partial \dot{q}_j} \tag{11.7}$$

Remembering that $P_i = \partial L/\partial \dot{Q}_i$ we can rewrite (11.7) as

$$\frac{\partial F}{\partial q_j} = \sum_i \frac{\partial L}{\partial \dot{Q}_i}\frac{\partial \dot{Q}_i}{\partial \dot{q}_j} \tag{11.8}$$

and since $\partial Q_i/\partial q_j = 0$ we can rewrite this as

$$\frac{\partial F}{dq_j} = \sum_i \frac{\partial L}{\partial \dot{Q}_i}\frac{\partial \dot{Q}_i}{\partial q_j} + \sum_i \frac{\partial L}{\partial Q_i}\frac{\partial Q_i}{\partial q_j} = \frac{\partial L}{\partial q_j} \qquad (11.9)$$

Recalling that $\partial L/\partial \dot{q}_j = p_j$ we have

$$\partial F/\partial q_j = p_j \qquad (11.10)$$

If we take the partial derivative of $F(\mathbf{q}, \mathbf{P})$ with respect to P_i we obtain

$$\partial F/\partial P_i = Q_i \qquad (11.11)$$

Taking the derivative of (11.10) with respect to P_i and the derivative of (11.11) with respect to q_j, we obtain

$$\frac{\partial^2 F(\mathbf{q}, \mathbf{P})}{\partial P_i \partial q_j} = \frac{\partial p_j}{\partial P_i} \qquad (11.12)$$

$$\frac{\partial^2 F(\mathbf{q}, \mathbf{P})}{\partial q_j \partial P_i} = \frac{\partial Q_i}{\partial q_j} \qquad (11.13)$$

Equating (11.12) and (11.13) we have

$$\partial p_j/\partial P_i = \partial Q_i/\partial q_j \qquad (11.14)$$

Substituting (11.14) in (11.2) we obtain

$$J\left(\frac{\mathbf{q}, \mathbf{p}}{\mathbf{Q}, \mathbf{P}}\right) = \frac{|\partial Q_i/\partial q_j|}{|\partial Q_j/\partial q_i|} \qquad (11.15)$$

Since the rows and columns in a determinant can be interchanged without changing the value of the determinant, the numerator and denominator in (11.15) are equal and therefore

$$J\left(\frac{\mathbf{q}, \mathbf{p}}{\mathbf{Q}, \mathbf{P}}\right) = 1 \qquad (11.16)$$

which is the desired result.

The fact that the Jacobian for the transformation between two arbitrary phase spaces for the same system is one is very convenient. Suppose we have an assembly of systems for which the density of representative points in q–p space is given by $\phi(\mathbf{q}, \mathbf{p})$, and we wish to determine $\Phi(\mathbf{Q}, \mathbf{P})$, the density of representative points in Q–P space. Using the usual techniques for transforming a density function, we obtain

$$\Phi(\mathbf{Q}, \mathbf{P}) = \left|J\left(\frac{\mathbf{q}, \mathbf{p}}{\mathbf{Q}, \mathbf{P}}\right)\right| \phi[\mathbf{q}(\mathbf{Q}), \mathbf{p}(\mathbf{Q}, \mathbf{P})] = \phi[\mathbf{q}(\mathbf{Q}), \mathbf{p}(\mathbf{Q}, \mathbf{P})] \qquad (11.17)$$

Thus the density at a given point $(\mathbf{q}, \mathbf{p}) \equiv (\mathbf{Q}, \mathbf{P})$ is unchanged by the transformation. If we know the distribution function for one phase space for a system, we have it for all phase spaces for the system.

LIOUVILLE'S THEOREM

As we have seen, the dynamical state of a system at some instant of time can be represented by a point in the phase space $\mathbf{q}$–$\mathbf{p}$. This point will not be stationary but will move along a definite trajectory which is determined from the equations of motion $\dot{q}_i = \partial H/\partial p_i$ and $\dot{p}_i = -\partial H/\partial q_i$.

Each point in phase space lies on one and only one trajectory, since for a given set of initial conditions the dynamical history of the system is uniquely determined. It follows that no two trajectories can cross.

Let us now suppose that we have a large collection of identical, noninteracting systems. The state of each system can be represented by a point in phase space. The state of the collection of systems can be represented by a set of points in phase space, each point representing one system. We will now show that this collection of points move through phase space in the same manner as an incompressible fluid.

First consider an ordinary fluid flowing in three dimensions. Let $\rho(\mathbf{x}, t)$ be its density and $\mathbf{v}(\mathbf{x}, t)$ its velocity. Imagine an observer moving through the fluid along an arbitrary path

$$x_i = x_i(t) \tag{11.18}$$

The observer will note a change in density as he moves through the fluid, given by

$$\frac{d\rho}{dt} = \sum_{i=1}^{3} \frac{\partial \rho}{\partial x_i} \frac{dx_i}{dt} + \frac{\partial \rho}{\partial t} \tag{11.19}$$

Now suppose the observer stations himself on an element of the fluid and allows himself to be transported along with the element. Then his velocity corresponds with the velocity of the fluid, and thus

$$dx_i/dt = v_i \tag{11.20}$$

Substituting (11.20) into (11.19) we obtain

$$\frac{d\rho}{dt} = \sum_{i} \frac{\partial \rho}{\partial x_i} v_i + \frac{\partial \rho}{\partial t} \tag{11.21}$$

If the fluid is incompressible, then the observer moving with the fluid will always observe the same density in his immediate neighborhood, i.e.,

$$\frac{\partial \rho}{\partial t} + \sum \frac{\partial \rho}{\partial x_i} v_i = 0 \tag{11.22}$$

If Eq. (11.22) is always satisfied, the fluid is incompressible. It should be noted that an incompressible fluid is not necessarily a fluid of constant density. Imagine an incompressible and immiscible blob of oil, flowing along in a volume of water. The combined system of oil and water would constitute an incompressible fluid, and Eq. (11.22) would be satisfied. However, since the density of the oil and water are different, the density of the combined system would not be constant. It would vary with position, and with time.

We are now in a position to consider the collection of representative points in the phase space discussed above. Let $\phi(\mathbf{q}, \mathbf{p}, t)$ be the density of such points. Consider a point whose ith position coordinate is q_i and whose jth momentum coordinate is p_j. The velocity of this point in the q_i direction in phase space will be $\dot{q}_i$, and the component of the flux in the q_i direction will be $\phi\dot{q}_i$. The velocity of the point in the p_j direction in phase space will be $\dot{p}_j$ and the component of the flux in the p_j direction will be $\phi\dot{p}_j$. If we apply the equation of continuity to the points in phase space, we then have

$$\frac{\partial\phi}{\partial t} + \sum_i \frac{\partial}{\partial q_i}(\phi\dot{q}_i) + \sum_i \frac{\partial}{\partial p_i}(\phi\dot{p}_i) = 0 \tag{11.23}$$

Carrying out the differentiation we have

$$\frac{\partial\phi}{\partial t} + \sum_i \dot{p}_i \frac{\partial\phi}{\partial p_i} + \sum_i \dot{q}_i \frac{\partial\phi}{\partial q_i} + \sum_i \phi\left(\frac{\partial\dot{q}_i}{\partial q_i} + \frac{\partial\dot{p}_i}{\partial p_i}\right) = 0 \tag{11.24}$$

But from Hamilton's equation of motion $\dot{q}_i = \partial H/\partial p_i$ and $\dot{p}_i = -\partial H/\partial q_i$. If these values are substituted into the last term in (11.24), it will vanish and we are left with

$$\frac{\partial\phi}{\partial t} + \sum_i \dot{p}_i \frac{\partial\phi}{\partial p_i} + \sum_i \dot{q}_i \frac{\partial\phi}{\partial q_i} = 0 \tag{11.25}$$

This equation is known as Liouville's equation. It is the equation which governs the motion of the points in phase space representing the dynamical state of a collection of noninteracting systems. It is also the equation representing the flow of an incompressible fluid in the $2s$ dimensional phase space, as comparison with the three-dimensional case reveals.

CANONICAL TRANSFORMATIONS

One frequently finds statements that *seem* to say that Eq. (11.25) follows from Eq. (11.16). This is not the case. In the present section we will briefly point out the source of the apparent disagreement.

In the preceding sections we have restricted ourselves to coordinate systems q–p and Q–P for which

$$\mathbf{Q} = \mathbf{Q}(\mathbf{q}, t) \tag{11.26}$$

$$\mathbf{P} = \mathbf{P}(\mathbf{q}, \mathbf{p}, t) \tag{11.27}$$

The transformation (11.26)–(11.27) is called a point transformation or coordinate transformation.

There is a more general class of transformations of the form

$$Q = Q(q, p, t) \tag{11.28}$$

$$P = P(q, p, t) \tag{11.29}$$

for which Hamilton's equations and Lagrange's equations retain their usual form. Such transformations are called canonical transformations or contact transformations. The canonical transformations are a subset of the transformations (11.28) and (11.29). Similarly, the point transformations are a subset of the canonical transformations.

It can be shown that for canonical transformations

$$J\left(\frac{q, p}{Q, P}\right) = 1 \tag{11.30}$$

Thus this result which we obtained previously for point transformations is also valid for canonical transformations. It can also be shown that the change in q and p as the representative point moves along a trajectory in phase space can be regarded as a canonical transformation. Thus from (11.30) it is possible to show that the volume enclosed by a set of representative points remains unchanged as the points move through phase space. But this is equivalent to Liouville's theorem. It follows that Eq. (11.30), which is more general than Eq. (11.16) since it is valid for canonical transformations and not just point transformations, contains both of the results which were derived in the preceding two sections.

PROBLEMS

1. For a particle constrained to move in the x, y plane, either Cartesian coordinates (x, y) or polar coordinates (r, θ) are satisfactory generalized coordinates.
   Evaluate

   (a) $J\left(\dfrac{r, \theta}{x, y}\right)$

   (b) $J\left(\dfrac{r, \theta, \dot{r}, \dot{\theta}}{x, y, \dot{x}, \dot{y}}\right)$

   (c) $J\left(\dfrac{r, \theta, p_r, p_\theta}{x, y, p_x, p_y}\right)$

2. A particle moving vertically under the influence of gravity periodically strikes and rebounds elastically from a horizontal plane. Sketch its trajectory in phase space between bounces. If particle one is released

at $t = 0$ at a distance h above the plane, with no initial velocity, and if particle two is released under similar conditions at time Δt, how far apart in phase space are the two particles when particle two is released? How far apart are they when particle one just reaches the horizontal plane? Assume that Δt is small compared to the time between bounces of each particle. If the two particles are released simultaneously, one at height h and one at height $h + \Delta h$, how far apart in phase space are they when the first particle hits the plane?

3. Consider as a system a single particle of mass m in a gravitational field. Plot two surfaces of constant energy in the phase space p–q where q is the vertical distance above some arbitrary reference point, and p the corresponding momentum. Show that the group of representative points lying between $p = a$ and $p = b$ and the two surfaces at $t = 0$ will lie between $p = a'$ and $p = b'$ at time t such that $a' = a - mgt$ and $b' = b - mgt$. Prove also the invariance of the volume in which the points are lying.

4. Consider a simple linear harmonic oscillator:

   (a) Show that the orbit in phase space is an ellipse.

   (b) What area in phase space does the orbit enclose? Express your answer in terms of the energy ϵ and frequency ν.

   (c) If a simple harmonic oscillator could only move in orbits which enclose an area nh where n is an integer and h is Planck's constant, what energies would be allowed?

5. The generalized coordinate and momentum of a simple pendulum are given by the angular displacement θ and the corresponding momentum $p_\theta = ml^2\dot{\theta}$. It oscillates in a vertical plane.

   (a) Find its total energy.

   (b) Write down Hamilton's equations of motion.

   (c) What is the equation of its trajectory in phase space?

   (d) What is its trajectory when the oscillation becomes nonuniform rotation?

Chapter 12

CLASSICAL STATISTICAL MECHANICS

THE FUNDAMENTAL POSTULATE OF CLASSICAL STATISTICAL MECHANICS

In Chapter 11 we saw that the dynamical state of a gas can be represented by a set of points in a phase space q–p where q and p are a set of generalized coordinates and momenta appropriate to the description of the dynamical state of a single molecule.

In the absence of collisions, these representative points would move through phase space in the same fashion as an incompressible fluid. In some other space besides a phase space, this would not be true and an observer riding along with one of the representative points would find that the density of points surrounding him would vary as he passed from region to region. He would, as a consequence, be able to distinguish one region from another region by this change. In a phase space no such change would be observed, and all regions of phase space would appear the same to our mythical traveler.

To add to the anonymity of different regions in phase space, we can divide phase space into regions of equal size in such a way that the time spent by a representative point in traversing any one region is the same as that spent in traversing any other. To illustrate this point, let us consider the set of representative points which define the line A_0B_0 at time t_0, as shown in Figure 12.1. At the time $t_0 + \Delta t$, these points define the line A_1B_1 and at a time $t_0 + 2\Delta t$, they define the line A_2B_2, and at time $t_0 + n\Delta t$, they define the line A_nB_n. The points which at time t_1 are on the line A_0B_0 will at time t_2 be on the line A_1B_1. It follows that the points which at time t_1 define the region

$A_0 B_0 B_1 A_1$ will at time t_2 define the region $A_1 B_1 B_2 A_2$, and at time t_n will define the region $A_{n-1} B_{n-1} B_n A_n$. Since the points behave as an incompressible fluid, the regions $A_n B_n B_{n+1} A_{n+1}$ are therefore all equal in "volume."

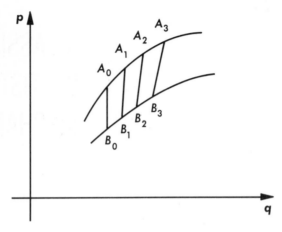

Fig. 12.1

Any representative point which at some instant of time is in one of these regions will be on the same trajectory as one of the points which were used to generate these regions, and will consequently be moving in such a way as to spend the same amount of time in each region since it always takes such a point a time Δt to go from boundary to boundary.

Proceeding in this fashion with other sections of phase space, we can break all of phase space into regions of the same size, and such that it takes a representative point a time Δt to traverse the region.

The above considerations suggest, but do not require, that we assign equal a priori probability to equal "volumes" in phase space. By this, we mean that in the absence of any other information, we have no reason to assume that a particular point is more likely to be found in one region of phase space than in another of equal "volume." It does not mean that the set of points which are used to represent a gas will distribute themselves uniformly throughout phase space, for there may be constraints on the gas which make some regions of phase space inaccessible. For instance, if the gas is contained within a box, only certain values of q are allowed. Or, if the total energy of the gas is fixed, then the points are restricted to lie on a surface of constant energy.

The above assumption of equal a priori probabilities for equal volumes in phase space is the fundamental postulate of classical statistical mechanics.

As we shall see, its use allows us to arrive at the equilibrium properties of a gas without any detailed discussion of collisions. The validity of this postulate is best justified by the success of the results which it predicts.

MICROSTATES AND MACROSTATES

In discussing the distribution of representative points in phase space we shall find it convenient to divide the phase space into cells of equal size, and to talk about the number of particles in a cell rather than the continuous density. As the reader will recall, this is the way the notion of a distribution function was originally introduced in Chapter 3.

In Figure 12.2 we have illustrated a typical distribution of points in the phase space **q–p**, which has been divided into cells of equal size. It should be remembered that since our phase space is in general a space of more than two dimensions, the diagram in Figure 12.2 is merely symbolic.

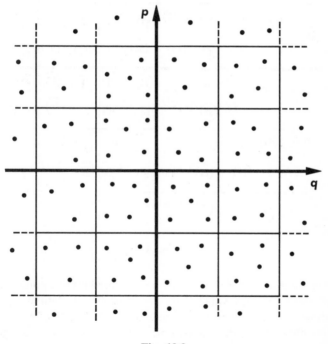

Fig. 12.2

If we label our cells from 1 to ∞ in some arbitrary fashion, or from 1 to M if the accessible phase space is limited to a finite amount, then the distribution can be described by giving the set of occupation numbers $\{N_i\}$, where N_i is the number of representative points in the cell i. Knowing the set of numbers

$\{N_i\}$, we know the macroscopic properties of the gas which is being represented by the set of points, at least within a degree of accuracy determined by our cell size. The set of numbers constitute what we shall call a macrostate.

Let us now imagine that we have some way of labeling the molecules in our gas from 1 to N, and an instrument capable of following the progress of a single molecule. We would then also be able to label the representative points in phase space from 1 to N. Such a situation is illustrated schematically in Figure 12.3.

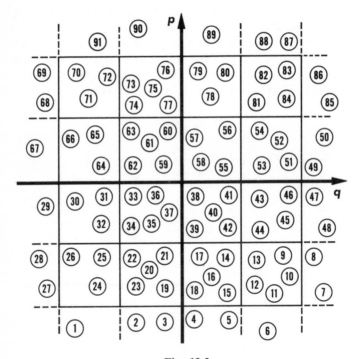

Fig. 12.3

Now, in addition to specifying how many representative points are in each cell, we can also specify which ones are in each cell. Although this added information tells us nothing about the macroscopic state of the gas, it does tell us something about the microscopic or molecular state of the gas. Let us designate a particular arrangement of the representative points among the M accessible cells as follows

$$
\underbrace{\boxed{\;5,6,7\;|\;1,2\;|\;3\;|\;\cdots\;|\;\;\;\;|\;\;\;\;}}_{1\qquad 2\qquad 3\qquad 4\qquad\qquad M\qquad M+1}
\tag{12.1}
$$

meaning that points 5, 6, and 7 are in cell 1, points 1 and 2 in cell 2, point 3 in cell 3, and so on. Such an arrangement is called a microstate.

THERMODYNAMIC PROBABILITY

According to the fundamental postulate of classical statistical mechanics, we must assign equal a priori probability to equal volumes in phase space. It follows that if the phase space is divided into M cells of equal size, then the a priori probability of each microstate is the same. This can readily be seen by imagining each representative point to be dropped at random into the phase space. Let us consider the chances of obtaining the microstate illustrated by the expression (12.1). The probability that point 1 will fall in cell 2 is simply $(1/M)$. The probability that point 2 will fall in cell 2 is $(1/M)$, and so on. Since there are N points altogether, the probability of the microstate is thus $(1/M)^N$. We would obtain the same result for any microstate.

For each microstate there is a particular macrostate. But for each macrostate there are many possible microstates, the number depending on the particular macrostate. The probability of different macrostates are therefore not the same. The probability of a particular macrostate is proportional to the number of possible microstates contained in it. We designate the number of microstates associated with the macrostate $\{N_i\}$ as its thermodynamic probability, which we write $W(N_i)$.

To determine the thermodynamic probability $W(N_i)$ for a particular macrostate $\{N_i\}$ we need to know the number of distinct ways we can arrange N particles among M cells in such a way that there are a certain fixed number of particles in each cell. In Appendix 2 (Eq. 12.2) we found this number to be $N!/\Pi N_i!$. Therefore

$$W(N_i) = N!/\Pi N_i! \tag{12.2}$$

THE BOLTZMANN DISTRIBUTION

Let us now consider a collection of identical molecules which are placed in a rigid, impermeable, and well insulated container. The dynamical state of each molecule is represented by a point in phase space. These points will move along a trajectory determined by the equations of motion. However, since the molecules in a box periodically collide with one another, the point representing a particular molecule will not follow a continuous trajectory but will jump from trajectory to trajectory with each collision.

The gas will furthermore pass rapidly from one microstate to another and from one macrostate to another. Not all macrostates or microstates are, however, possible. Since the molecules are contained within a rigid container, only those regions of phase space for which $\mathbf{q}$ lies within the box are accessible. Furthermore, since the container is also impermeable and insulated, the total number of molecules and the total energy remain fixed. If N is the number of molecules, E_i the energy associated with cell i, and E the total energy, then only those macrostates which are consistent with the following constraints are accessible.

$$\Sigma N_i = N \tag{12.3}$$

$$\Sigma N_i E_i = E \tag{12.4}$$

We now assume that as the molecules undergo successive collisions, and pass from microstate to microstate, that they will on the average spend the same amount of time in each microstate which is consistent with the above constraints. In order to obtain the macroscopic properties of the gas, we should then average over every accessible microstate. Since the macroscopic properties are, however, determined by the macrostate, we can, instead of averaging over the microstates, average over the accessible macrostates by simply weighting each accessible macrostate by the number of microstates associated with it. Thus if $g(N_i)$ is some property of the gas which is a function of the occupation numbers N_i, then the average value of g is given by

$$< g(N_i) > = \frac{\Sigma g(N_i)W(N_i)}{\Sigma W(N_i)} \tag{12.5}$$

where the summation is over all macrostates consistent with the constraints.

To carry out the summation in (12.5) is not an easy mathematical task. It turns out that due to the large numbers involved, the major contribution to the average comes from a limited number of macrostates, all very close to the most probable macrostate. We therefore assume that the macroscopic properties of the gas are identical with the properties associated with the most probable macrostate (see Appendix 5).

In order to find the most probable macrostate, we have to find the macrostate which is consistent with the constraints (12.3) and (12.4) and with which the most number of microstates are associated. Mathematically this is equivalent to maximizing $W(N_i)$ subject to the constraints (12.3) and (12.4). It will turn out that instead of maximizing $W(N_i)$, it is easier to consider the equivalent problem of maximizing $\ln W(N_i)$.

The maximization of $\ln W(N_i)$ subject to the constraints (12.3) and (12.4) can be handled by the method of Lagrange multipliers (Appendix 6) and by this technique is equivalent to maximizing the function

$$F(N_i, \alpha, \beta) = \ln W(N_i) + \alpha(\Sigma N_i - N) - \beta(\Sigma N_i E_i - E) \tag{12.6}$$

We have previously shown that $W(N_i) = N!/\Pi N_i!$ and therefore, if we make use of Stirling's approximation (Appendix 7)

$$\ln W(N_i) = \ln(N!/\Pi N_i!) = \ln N! - \Sigma \ln N_i!$$
$$\approx \ln N! - \Sigma N_i \ln N_i + \Sigma N_i \tag{12.7}$$

Substituting (12.7) in (12.6), we have

$$F(N_i, \alpha, \beta) = \ln N! - \Sigma N_i \ln N_i + \Sigma N_i + \alpha(\Sigma N_i - N) - \beta(\Sigma N_i E_i - E) \tag{12.8}$$

Taking the derivative of (12.8) with respect to N_i and setting the result equal to zero, we obtain

$$-\ln N_i + \alpha - \beta E_i = 0 \tag{12.9}$$

Solving for N_i, we obtain

$$N_i = \exp(\alpha - \beta E_i) \tag{12.10}$$

The number of points in a cell centered at the point $(\mathbf{p}, \mathbf{q})$ is thus given by

$$\exp[\alpha - \beta\epsilon(\mathbf{p}, \mathbf{q})] \tag{12.11}$$

If the volume of a cell is given by $\Delta\mathbf{p}\Delta\mathbf{q}$, then the average density of points in phase space at the point $(\mathbf{p}, \mathbf{q})$ is given by

$$\phi(\mathbf{p}, \mathbf{q}) = \frac{\exp[\alpha - \beta\epsilon(\mathbf{p}, \mathbf{q})]}{\Delta\mathbf{p}\Delta\mathbf{q}} \tag{12.12}$$

Since α and $\Delta\mathbf{p}\Delta\mathbf{q}$ are constant, we can rewrite (12.12) as simply

$$\phi(\mathbf{p}, \mathbf{q}) = C \exp[-\beta\epsilon(\mathbf{p}, \mathbf{q})] \tag{12.13}$$

The value of the constant C can be determined from the condition that the integration of ϕ over $\mathbf{p}$ and $\mathbf{q}$ must give us the total number of molecules. Thus

$$C = \frac{N}{\displaystyle\iint \exp(-\beta\epsilon)d\mathbf{p}d\mathbf{q}} \tag{12.14}$$

It should be noted that the integral over $\mathbf{q}$ is restricted to values lying within the container.

The distribution function (12.13) appears to be identical with the Maxwell-Boltzmann distribution which we have derived earlier. It is, however, more general since ϵ is not restricted to the energy of a monatomic molecule, but is equally applicable to complex polyatomic molecules for which s the number of degrees of freedom is greater than three.

For a monatomic ideal gas we can identify β as $1/kT$ (see Chapter 4). We shall now show that $\beta = 1/kT$ even if the gas is polyatomic.

Let us consider a composite system consisting of two gases separated by a diathermal wall and contained within a rigid, impermeable, and well-insulated container.

The two gases are completely independent of one another except for the fact that energy can be passed from one gas to the other. Let us let $\{N_i'\}$ represent a particular macrostate of one gas and $\{N_i''\}$ represent a particular macrostate of the second gas, and $W'(N_i')$ and $W''(N_i'')$ the respective thermodynamic probabilities. Since the two systems are independent, a macrostate for the composite system will be given by the product of W' and W''. Thus

$$W(N_i', N_i'') = W'(N_i')W''(N_i'') = \frac{N'!}{\Pi N_i'!} \; \frac{N''!}{\Pi N_i''!} \qquad (12.15)$$

where N' and N'' are the total number of molecules respectively of the gases. We now maximize $\ln W$ subject to the constraints

$$\Sigma N_i' = N' \qquad (12.16)$$

$$\Sigma N_i'' = N'' \qquad (12.17)$$

$$\Sigma N_i'E_i' + \Sigma N_i''E_i'' = E \qquad (12.18)$$

This is equivalent to maximizing the function

$$\begin{aligned} F(N_i', N_i'', \alpha', \alpha'', \beta) \\ = \ln W(N_i', N_i'') + \alpha'(\Sigma N_i' - N') + \alpha''(\Sigma N_i'' - N'') \\ - \beta(\Sigma N_i'E_i' - \Sigma N_i''E_i'' - E) \end{aligned} \qquad (12.19)$$

Taking the partial derivatives of F with respect to N_i' and N_i'' and setting them equal to zero, we obtain

$$N_i' = \exp(\alpha' - \beta E_i') \qquad (12.20)$$

$$N_i'' = \exp(\alpha'' - \beta E_i'') \qquad (12.21)$$

We see that all gases in thermal contact will have the same value of β which, since it is $1/kT$ for a monatomic gas, will therefore be $1/kT$.

Substituting the value of C and β into (12.13), we have for the density of points in phase space

$$\phi(\mathbf{p}, \mathbf{q}) = \frac{N \exp(-\epsilon/kT)}{\displaystyle\iint \exp(-\epsilon/kT)d\mathbf{p}d\mathbf{q}} \qquad (12.22)$$

We shall refer to this distribution as the Boltzmann distribution.

EQUIPARTITION OF ENERGY

Using the distribution which we have just derived, the average energy of molecule is given by

$$<\epsilon> = \frac{\iint \epsilon \exp(-\epsilon/kT)d\mathbf{p}d\mathbf{q}}{\iint \exp(-\epsilon/kT)d\mathbf{p}d\mathbf{q}} \tag{12.23}$$

In many cases the evaluation of this integral is greatly facilitated by making use of the so-called equipartition theorem, which states that if $\epsilon(\mathbf{p}, \mathbf{q})$ is a homogeneous quadratic function of any set of l of the generalized coordinates and momenta, then $<\epsilon> = lkT/2$, provided that, for each momentum in the set $\left[p_i \exp\left(\frac{-\epsilon}{kT}\right)\right]_{p_i'}^{p_i''} = 0$ and for each coordinate in the set $\left[q_i \exp\left(\frac{-\epsilon}{kT}\right)\right]_{q_i'}^{q_i''} = 0$ where p_i', p_i'', q_i' and q_i'' are the upper and lower limits respectively of the p_i and q_i.

A function $g(x_1, x_2, x_3 \ldots x_m)$ is homogeneous of degree n in the variables x_1 and x_2 if

$$g(\lambda x_1, \lambda x_2, x_3, \ldots, x_m) = \lambda^n g(x_1, x_2, x_3, \ldots, x_m) \tag{12.24}$$

The extension of this to more variables than x_1 and x_2 is straightforward.

To prove the equipartition theorem, let us assume that $\epsilon(\mathbf{p}, \mathbf{q})$ is a homogeneous quadratic function of the r generalized coordinates $q_1, q_2, \ldots, q_r$ and the $l - r$ generalized momenta $p_1, p_2, \ldots, p_{l-r}$. From Euler's theorem (Appendix 10) it follows that

$$2\epsilon = \sum_{i=1}^{r} q_i \frac{\partial \epsilon}{\partial q_i} + \sum_{i=1}^{l-r} p_i \frac{\partial \epsilon}{\partial p_i} \tag{12.25}$$

and therefore

$$<\epsilon> = \frac{1}{2}\sum_{i=1}^{r} < q_i \frac{\partial \epsilon}{\partial q_i} > + \frac{1}{2}\sum_{i=1}^{l-r} < p_i \frac{\partial \epsilon}{\partial p_i} > \tag{12.26}$$

Considering a typical term in the sum, we have

$$< p_i \frac{\partial \epsilon}{\partial p_i} > = \frac{\iint p_i(\partial\epsilon/\partial p_i) \exp(-\epsilon/kT)d\mathbf{p}d\mathbf{q}}{\iint \exp(-\epsilon/kT)d\mathbf{p}d\mathbf{q}} \tag{12.27}$$

Let us evaluate the integral over p_i in the numerator. Thus

$$I \equiv \int p_i(\partial\epsilon/\partial p_i) \exp(-\epsilon/kT)dp_i$$

$$= -kT \int p_i \frac{\partial}{\partial p_i} [\exp(-\epsilon/kT)]dp_i \tag{12.28}$$

Integrating by parts we have

$$I = -kT\Big[p_i \exp(-\epsilon/kT)\Big]_{p_i'}^{p_i''}$$

$$+kT \int exp(-\epsilon/kT)dp_i \qquad (12.29)$$

The first term will, in general, vanish. If it does, then we are left with

$$I \equiv \int p_i(\partial\epsilon/\partial p_i) \exp(-\epsilon/kT)dp_i$$

$$= kT \int \exp(-\epsilon/kT)dp_i \qquad (12.30)$$

substituting (12.30) in (12.27) we obtain

$$< p_i(\partial\epsilon/\partial p_i) > = kT \qquad (12.31)$$

In a similar fashion we can show

$$< q_i(\partial\epsilon/\partial q_i) > = kT \qquad (12.32)$$

Substituting (12.31) and (12.32) in (12.26) we obtain

$$<\epsilon> = lkT/2 \qquad (12.33)$$

As an example of the application of the equipartition theorem, let us consider the average kinetic energy of a typical molecule in a gas of diatomic molecules. Let us assume the diatomic molecule consists of one atom of mass m bound to a second atom of mass M by a force which can be approximated by considering the two atoms to be bound together by a massless spring of spring constant κ. The use of a spring to approximate the force is not entirely arbitrary. The restoring force of the spring is linearly proportional to the displacement from equilibrium and as such represents a first approximation to any restoring force. It is usually a good approximation, if the displacement from equilibrium is not too large.

Letting X, Y, Z be the coordinates of the center of mass and r, θ, ϕ the coordinates of atom 2 with respect to atom 1, then the energy of the system is given by

$$\epsilon = \tfrac{1}{2}M^*(\dot{X}^2 + \dot{Y}^2 + \dot{Z}^2) + \tfrac{1}{2}m^*(\dot{r}^2 + r^2\dot{\theta}^2 + r^2 \sin^2\theta\dot{\phi}^2) + \tfrac{1}{2}\kappa(r - r_0)^2 \qquad (12.34)$$

where $M^* = (m + M)$ and $m^* = mM/(m + M)$. The first two terms are the kinetic energy terms, and the last term the potential energy. The length r_0 is the equilibrium length of the spring.

If we introduce a new variable s defined by

$$s = r - r_0 \qquad (12.35)$$

then (12.34) can be rewritten

$$\epsilon = \tfrac{1}{2}M^*(\dot{X}^2 + \dot{Y}^2 + \dot{Z}^2)$$
$$+ \tfrac{1}{2}m^*[\dot{s}^2 + (r_0 + s)^2\dot{\theta}^2 + (r_0 + s)^2 \sin^2\theta\dot{\phi}^2] + \tfrac{1}{2}\kappa s^2 \qquad (12.36)$$

or in terms of the generalized coordinates X, Y, Z, θ, ϕ, s and the corresponding momenta, we have

$$\epsilon = \frac{p_X^2 + p_Y^2 + p_Z^2}{2M^*} + \frac{p_s^2}{2m^*} + \frac{p_\theta^2}{2m^*(r_0 + s)^2}$$
$$+ \frac{p_\phi^2}{2m^*(r_0 + s)^2 \sin^2\theta} + \tfrac{1}{2}\kappa s^2 \qquad (12.37)$$

The energy ϵ is not a homogeneous quadratic function in any set of the generalized coordinates and momenta. However, if the spring is very stiff, then $s \ll r_0$ and we can approximate ϵ by

$$\epsilon \approx \frac{p_X^2 + p_Y^2 + p_Z^2}{2M^*} + \frac{p_s^2}{2m^*} + \frac{p_\theta^2}{2m^*r_0^2} + \frac{p_\phi^2}{2m^*r_0^2 \sin^2\theta} + \tfrac{1}{2}\kappa s^2 \qquad (12.38)$$

This is a homogeneous quadratic function in the seven variables p_X, p_Y, p_Z, p_s, p_θ, p_ϕ, and s and therefore by the equipartition theorem

$$< \epsilon > \approx 7kT/2 \qquad (12.39)$$

We see that as long as the spring is stiff, or what is equivalent, as long as the rotation of the molecule is only weakly coupled with the vibration, then the energy can be broken down into the translational kinetic energy $(p_X^2 + p_Y^2 + p_Z^2)/2M^*$, the rotational kinetic energy $(p_\theta^2/2m^*r_0^2) + (p_\phi^2/2m^*r_0^2 \sin^2\theta)$ and the energy of vibration $(p_s^2/2m^*) + \tfrac{1}{2}\kappa s^2$. Each translational mode of motion contributes $kT/2$ to the energy, each rotational mode of motion contributes $kT/2$ to the energy, while each vibrational mode of motion contributes kT to the energy. This result is equally valid for a more complicated polyatomic molecule.

If the translational and rotational modes of motion of a polyatomic molecule are only weakly coupled, and if the forces acting between molecules can be approximated by springlike forces, then it is possible to quickly evaluate the expected average energy of the molecule, as was done for the diatomic molecule. Every molecule which is free to move in three dimensions has three translational modes of motion and thus the average translational kinetic energy is $3kT/2$. A nonlinear polyatomic molecule has three rotational modes of motion, since three coordinates are in general required to specify the orientation of a rigid body. The average rotational kinetic energy of a nonlinear polyatomic molecule is thus $3kT/2$. On the other hand, only two coordinates are required to specify the orientation of a linear polyatomic molecule. A linear polyatomic molecule has therefore two rotational modes of motion, and thus an average rotational kinetic energy of kT. In order to determine the number of vibrational modes of motion a molecule has, it is necessary to determine the number of independent ways in which the molecule can be set in vibration, such that each atom is vibrating with the same frequency. Although the frequencies are the same, the amplitudes of the vibrations of the atoms need not be the same and may even be zero. Such a mode of motion in which all the atoms are vibrating with the same frequency is called a normal mode. Each normal mode of motion is completely independent and all other vibrational motions can be composed of the normal mode motions. If there are N_a atoms in a molecule, and none are rigidly bound together, then there must be $3N_a$ degrees of freedom. There must then be enough normal modes of motion, such that these modes together with the rotational and translational modes of motion add up to $3N_a$. In a nonlinear polyatomic molecule there are therefore $3N_a - 6$ normal modes, while in a linear polyatomic molecule, there are $3N_a - 5$ normal modes. The average vibrational energy of a nonlinear polyatomic molecule is thus $(3N_a - 6)kT$ and for a linear polyatomic molecule is $(3N_a - 5)kT$.

In summary, for a monatomic molecule

$$< \epsilon > = 3kT/2 \tag{12.40}$$

for a linear polyatomic molecule

$$< \epsilon > = (3kT/2) + kT + (3N_a - 5)kT = (6N_a - 5)(kT/2) \tag{12.31}$$

and for a nonlinear polyatomic molecule

$$< \epsilon > = (3kT/2) + (3kT/2) + (3N_a - 6)kT = (6N_a - 6)(kT/2) \tag{12.42}$$

Knowing the average of the energy, the specific heat per molecule at constant volume can be readily obtained from the relation

$$c_V = \frac{1}{N}\left(\frac{\partial E}{\partial T}\right)_V = \frac{d}{dT}[< \epsilon >] \tag{12.43}$$

If the equipartition theorem is used to calculate the specific heat of a polyatomic gas, and the results compared with the experimental results, serious discrepancies will be found. We will consider this problem, along with some other failures of the Boltzmann distribution in Chapter 14.

PROBLEMS

1. The 52 cards of a deck are dealt into four hands by tossing the cards into a box containing four compartments. Any one card is equally likely to land in any one compartment.

   (a) How many microstates are there in the (13–13–13–13) macrostate? This is the number of possible deals at bridge.

   (b) What are the relative probabilities of the macrostates (12–13–14–13), (12–13–10–17), and (16–22–10–4) compared with the (13–13–13–13) macrostate?

2. Using the method of Lagrange multipliers, find which point of the sphere $x^2 + y^2 + z^2 = 1$ is at the greatest distance from the point $(1, 2, 3,)$.

3. Using the method of Lagrange multipliers, find the greatest and least distances of a point on the ellipse

$$\frac{x^2}{4} + \frac{y^2}{1} = 1$$

from the straight line $x + y - 4 = 0$.

4. Compute ln10! and ln20!
   (a) exactly
   (b) using Stirling's approximation in the form

   $$\ln N! = N\ln N - N$$

5. Consider a diatomic molecule which is constrained to rotate in the xy plane and which has a permanent dipole moment μ. Calculate the average polarization in the direction of a field E along the x axis.

6. A gas of rigid diatomic molecules each of which possesses a permanent electric dipole moment of magnitude μ is placed in a uniform electric field E. Let the spherical coordinates θ and ϕ determine the orientation of the molecule with respect to a polar axis in the direction of the field. The potential energy of molecule in the field is given by $V = -\mu E \cos\theta$.
   (a) What is the probability that a molecule will have its moment oriented between θ and $\theta + d\theta$?
   (b) Show that the average component of the dipole moment in the direction of the field is

   $$\mu[\coth(\mu E/kT) - (kT/\mu E)]$$

   (c) Show that if $\mu E \ll kT$ the average component of the dipole moment in the direction of the field is approximately $\mu^2 E/3kT$.
   (d) Show by the Boltzmann distribution that in a nonuniform field the concentration of molecules varies as

   $$\frac{\sinh(\mu E/kT)}{\mu E/kT}$$

7. A collection of simple pendula free to move in a vertical plane are in thermal equilibrium at temperature T.
   (a) Obtain an expression for the average energy of each pendulum.
   (b) Obtain an expression for the root-mean-square angular displacement.
   (c) What will the average energy be in the case of small oscillations?

8. Using the anharmonic potential $V(x) = cx^2 - gx^3 - fx^4$, show that the approximate heat capacity of the classical anharmonic oscillator is, to order T,

   $$c \approx k\left[1 + \left(\frac{3f}{2c^2} + \frac{15g^2}{8c^3}\right)kT\right]$$

9. Two masses m and M are supported by three identical springs as shown in Figure 12.4. The spring constant for each of the springs is κ and the length of each spring in the absence of any forces is a. Assume this system to be one of a collection of systems for which the Boltzmann distribution is applicable. Write down an expression for the probability that $0.2L < x < 0.3L$ and $0.7L < y < 0.8L$.

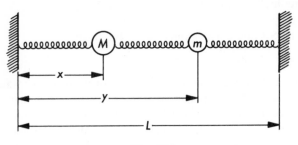

Fig. 12.4

10. Find the probability distribution for the angular velocity of a rotating molecule.

11. What specific heat per molecule would you expect under classical conditions for the following gases?
    (*a*) Ne
    (*b*) O_2
    (*c*) H_2O (nonlinear)
    (*d*) CO_2 (linear)
    (*e*) $CHCl_3$

12. Consider a two-dimensional "gas" consisting of N uniform disks of radius a and mass m. Assume (1) the disks are free to slide on a frictionless plate of dimensions $L \times L$. (2) the edges of the disk are perfectly rough so that the rotational energy of the disks can be changed in a collision, (3) the total kinetic energy, rotational and translational, of the disks is E, (4) collisions with the wall are perfectly elastic, (5) the area occupied by the disks is small compared to the area of the plate.
    (*a*) What is the average translational speed of the disks? Express your answer in terms of E, N, m, and a.
    (*b*) What is the average angular speed of the disks? Express your answer in terms of E, N, m, and a.

13. Consider a gas of identical diatomic molecules which are constrained to move in a plane. The number of molecules per unit area is n. Assume the masses of the atoms in a molecule can be considered to be point masses of mass m and M respectively, and that they are bound together by a spring of spring constant κ and equilibrium length l. Determine the exact specific heat per unit area, and compare this with the approximate value

which would be obtained using the equipartition theorem and assuming no coupling between the rotational and the vibrational motion.

14. The correct relativistic expression for the energy of a particle is

$$\epsilon = c(p_x^2 + p_y^2 + p_z^2 + m_0^2 c^2)^{1/2}$$

   (a) Show that

   $$< c^2 p_x^2/\epsilon > \; = \; < c^2 p_y^2/\epsilon > \; = \; < c^2 p_z^2/\epsilon > \; = kT$$

   (b) Show that in the extreme relativistic range, the specific heat of a perfect gas is $3kT$.

15. A very small mirror is suspended from a quartz strand whose elastic constant is D, and reflects a beam of light in such a way that the angular amplitudes caused by the impacts due to surrounding molecules (Brownian motion) can be read on a suitable scale. The position of equilibrium is at $\phi = 0$ (ϕ = angular amplitude). The probability of finding the mirror at an amplitude between ϕ and $\phi + d\phi$ is given by

$$W d\phi = a \, \exp(-u/kT) d\phi \qquad\qquad u = \tfrac{1}{2} D \phi^2$$

in accordance with the law of equipartition. From the observed value of $< \phi^2 >$ it is possible to determine the Boltzmann constant. Calculate the numerical value of Avogadro's number from the following data obtained at $T = 287°K$: $D = 9.43 \times 10^{-9}$ dyn cm; $< \phi^2 > \; = 4.18 \times 10^{-6}$; the value of the universal gas constant is known to be $R = 8.32 \times 10^7$ erg/deg mole.

16. The specific heat c_V of steam is roughly half "the specific heat" of water (i.e., respectively $1/2$ cal g^{-1} and 1 cal g^{-1}). What causes this large difference?

Chapter 13

THE CLASSICAL THEORY
OF REAL GASES

INTRODUCTION

If we use Eq. (12.13) and (12.14) to calculate the classical distribution in phase space for a gas of noninteracting point masses in the absence of any external fields, we obtain $\phi(\mathbf{x}, \mathbf{p}) = n(2\pi mkT)^{-3/2} \exp(-p^2/2mkT)$. Using this distribution to calculate the pressure we find

$$p = nkT \tag{13.1}$$

Experimentally Eq. (13.1) is only good for gases of moderate density. As the density of a gas is increased, the experimental values for the pressure are found to depart significantly from the values given by Eq. (13.1).

In this chapter we wish to consider what modifications in our theory must be made to describe the properties of gases in the density range where Eq. (13.1) begins to break down.

EMPIRICAL EQUATIONS OF STATE

As the density of a gas increases, the volume occupied by the molecules and the effect of the intermolecular forces becomes more and more significant. Both of these factors were ignored in our earlier analysis.

Before we attempt to include these features in a detailed fashion, it will be helpful to look at some of the empirical expressions which have been found useful in fitting the data.

One of the simplest and most frequently used expressions is van der Waal's equation

$$p = \frac{NkT}{V - bN} - a\left(\frac{N}{V}\right)^2 \tag{13.2}$$

The constants a and b are different for each gas, and are temperature dependent. By properly choosing a and b for a particular gas and a particular temperature, van der Waal's equation can be made to describe the behavior of the gas over a wide range of pressures.

The term bN is introduced to account for the fact that a particular molecule is not free to roam throughout the volume V, but due to the finite volume occupied by the other molecules, is restricted to some volume smaller than V. The effective volume occupied by the other molecules will be proportional to N and we therefore subtract a quantity bN from the original volume. The constant b will be of the same order of magnitude as the volume occupied by a single molecule.

The second term $-a(N/V)^2$ is introduced to account for the effect of the intermolecular forces on the pressure. If the intermolecular force is repulsive, the potential energy of the molecules increases as the density increases. A force would be required to bring the molecules together even if they were not moving. The gas therefore exerts in addition to the usual kinetic pressure, a static pressure due to the intermolecular forces. This static pressure will be positive if the intermolecular forces are repulsive and negative if they are attractive. The effect of the intermolecular forces is negligible at low densities and becomes more and more important as the density increases. Since the ordinary kinetic pressure nkT is linear in the density, the simplest way to introduce such an effect is to introduce a pressure term which is quadratic in the density. At low densities, it is small compared to the linear term nkT, but at high densities it becomes the dominant term.

Van der Waal's equation is most useful where a reasonable fit to the data is necessary over a limited range of densities and temperatures. Where greater accuracy is required, one usually resorts to some sort of expansion technique. The most common is the so-called virial expansion, in which we expand the pressure in powers of the density. Thus

$$p(n, T) = a_0(T) + a_1(T)n + a_2(T)n^2 + \dots \tag{13.3}$$

Since in the limit as $n \to 0$, $p \to nkT$, we must have $a_0 = 0$ and $a_1 = kT$. Our expansion can thus be written

$$p = nkT[1 + B(T)n + C(T)n^2 + \dots] \tag{13.4}$$

The functions $B(T)$ and $C(T)$ are called the second and third virial coefficients. By expanding van der Waal's equation, we can obtain a relationship between the second and third virial coefficients and the constants a and b in van der Waal's equation. We first write van der Waal's equation in the form

$$p = \frac{nkT}{1 - nb} - an^2 \tag{13.5}$$

Recalling that the Taylor expansion of $(1 + x)^{-1}$ is given by

$$(1 + x)^{-1} = 1 - x + x^2 - \ldots \tag{13.6}$$

we can rewrite (13.5) as

$$p = nkT[(1 + nb + n^2b^2 + \ldots)] - an^2 \tag{13.7}$$

and dropping all terms of order greater than n^2, we have

$$p \approx nkT\left(1 + nb - \frac{an}{kT} + n^2b^2\right) \tag{13.8}$$

Comparing (13.8) with (13.4), we find

$$B = b - \frac{a}{kT} \tag{13.9}$$

$$C = b^2 \tag{13.10}$$

Van der Waal's equation and the virial expansion are more usually found written in terms of the molar density, i.e., the number of moles per unit volume, which we will designate n_0. In terms of the molar density, van der Waal's equation becomes

$$p = \frac{n_0RT}{1 - b_0n_0} - a_0n_0^2 \tag{13.11}$$

where R is the gas constant per mole. The virial expansion becomes

$$p = n_0RT[1 + B_0(T)n_0 + C_0(T)n_0^2 + \ldots] \tag{13.12}$$

If L is Avogadro's number, then the constants have the relation

$$B_0 = BL \tag{13.13}$$

$$C_0 = CL^2 \tag{13.14}$$

$$a_0 = aL^2 \tag{13.15}$$

$$b_0 = bL \tag{13.16}$$

EVALUATION OF THE SECOND VIRIAL COEFFICIENT

In deriving the Boltzmann distribution, and in using it to evaluate the pressure in a gas, we assumed that the interactions between molecules have no other effect than to occasionally kick a molecule abruptly from one trajectory in phase space to another. Between collisions each molecule is assumed to follow the trajectory which it would if there were no other molecules present. The collisions therefore serve no other purpose than to keep the molecules randomly distributed among all possible trajectories, so that statistical techniques can be applied. We have also assumed that the volume occupied by the molecules is negligible compared to the volume of the container.

In visualizing the effect of these assumptions, it is helpful to imagine each molecule to be contained within a separate container of volume V and the containers to be separated by walls which by some mechanism allow the transmission of energy from one molecule to another when a molecule collides with the wall. This situation is schematically illustrated in Figure 13.1. If there is a force field, we assume that the force field is identically reproduced in each compartment.

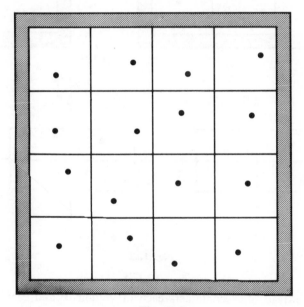

Fig. 13.1

Let us consider the system of N molecules as schematically represented in Figure 13.1, and let us assume that the total energy of the set of molecules is E. Let **q** represent a set of generalized coordinates for one of the molecules, and **p** the corresponding momenta. We shall assume that the **q** for each molecule is measured with respect to an origin located at the center of its container. If we assume the molecules obey classical mechanics and we plot the representative point of each molecule in the same **q–p** space, we will have a representation of the state of the N molecules. Since the total energy E is fixed and the molecules are constrained to move in a volume V, the representative points will be restricted to a limited region in the **q–p** space. This situation is schematically illustrated in Figure 13.2(a).

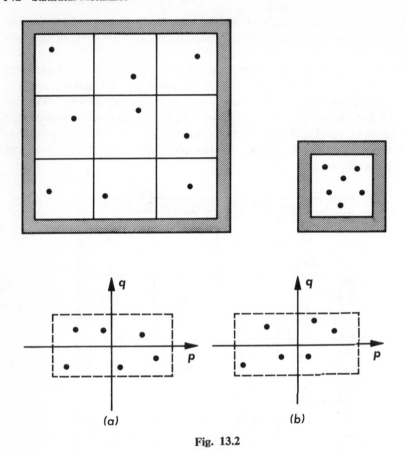

Fig. 13.2

Suppose instead of N containers each of volume V and each with one molecule in it, we had one container of volume V with N molecules in it. The total energy is again assumed to be E. We could, as before, specify the classical state of a molecule by a set of generalized coordinates and momenta $\mathbf{q}$–$\mathbf{p}$, and if we plot the representative point of each molecule in the same $\mathbf{q}$–$\mathbf{p}$ space we will have a collection of points moving around within the same limited region of phase space as previously. This situation is schematically illustrated in Figure 13.2(b).

The assumptions implicit in our derivation of the classical Boltzmann distribution are equivalent to assuming that the equilibrium distribution functions in phase space associated with the systems represented in Figures 13.2(a) and 13.2(b) will be the same.

This assumption is obviously in error if the interaction between the molecules in Figure 13.2(b) is important. To obtain the next order of approximation to the behavior of a real gas, let us assume that the gas is sufficiently dense that the range of influence of the molecules cannot be neglected in our calculations, but not so dense that the probability of more than two molecules interacting simultaneously is significant. Within this range any deviation from the ideal gas behavior will be due primarily to two-body interactions.

To see what effect this will have on our calculations, let us assume that we have a set of M containers each of volume V as previously described, but instead of one molecule per container let us put two molecules per container as shown in Figure 13.3. The number of containers M is large and is not

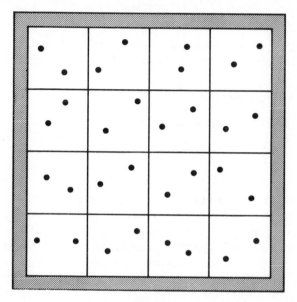

Fig. 13.3

necessarily equal to N. Energy can be exchanged between adjacent containers. Other than this there is no interaction between the molecules in one container and the molecules in any other container. We shall limit our discussion to monatomic molecules. Let us label the molecules in a particular container one and two. Let $x(1)$ be the position of molecule one with respect to the center of its container, and $x(2)$ the position of molecule two with respect to the center of its container. The corresponding momenta will be $p(1)$ and $p(2)$. We further assume that the interaction between molecule one and molecule two can be represented by a potential energy function u which is a function only of the distance between the two molecules which we designate r.

The dynamical state of the system consisting of molecule one and molecule two can be represented by a point in the twelve-dimensional phase space whose coordinates are $x(1)$, $x(2)$, $p(1)$ and $p(2)$. The state of the entire system of $2M$ molecules can be represented as a set of M points in the twelve-dimensional phase space $x(1)x(2)p(1)p(2)$. If we imagine each pair of molecules to constitute a single system, then our previous derivation of the Boltzmann distribution is perfectly applicable to this problem, and we obtain for the equilibrium density of points in the above twelve-dimensional phase space

$$\phi[p(1), p(2), x(1), x(2)] = C \exp(-\epsilon/kT) \tag{13.17}$$

where C is some constant, and

$$\epsilon = \frac{[p(1)]^2 + [p(2)]^2}{2m} + u(r) \tag{13.18}$$

The probability of simultaneously finding molecule one in $dx(1)$ with momentum in $dp(1)$, and molecule two in $dx(2)$ with momentum in $dp(2)$ is given by

$$\frac{\phi dx(1)dx(2)dp(1)dp(2)}{\iiiint \phi dx(1)dx(2)dp(1)dp(2)}$$

$$= \frac{\exp(-\epsilon/kT)dx(1)dx(2)dp(1)dp(2)}{\iiiint \exp(-\epsilon/kT)dx(1)dx(2)dp(1)dp(2)} \tag{13.19}$$

We now make the assumption that if we have a gas of N molecules in which two-body interactions only are important, then the probability of simultaneously having one particular molecule which we will call particle one in $dx(1)$ with momenta in $dp(1)$ and a second particular molecule which we will call particle two in $dx(2)$ with momentum in $dp(2)$ is also given by (13.19).

If we simply wish to know what the probability is of finding molecule one with momentum in $dp(1)$, we would integrate (13.19) over $x(1)$, $x(2)$, and $p(2)$ and we would find that this probability is proportional to $\exp[-p^2(1)/2mkT]$ which is exactly what we would obtain with the ordinary Maxwellian distribution. It follows that the contribution to the pressure due to the motion of the molecules, which we designate as the kinetic pressure p_k, is unchanged in our analysis and is given by

$$p_k = nkT \tag{13.20}$$

However, in addition to the kinetic pressure due to the motion of the molecules, there is also a static pressure p_s due to the attraction or repulsion between molecules. We will now use the above result to obtain p_s.

By integrating (13.9) over $p(1)$ and $p(2)$ we can obtain the probability that molecule one will be in $dx(1)$ and molecule two in $dx(2)$, which is simply

$$\frac{\exp(-u/kT)dx(1)dx(2)}{\iint \exp(-u/kT)dx(1)dx(2)} \tag{13.21}$$

Since there are $N(N - 1)$ possible combinations of different particles, the probability of simultaneously finding a particle in $dx(1)$ and another particle in $dx(2)$, which we will designate by $Pdx(1)dx(2)$ is given by

$$Pdx(1)dx(2) = \frac{N(N - 1) \exp(-u/kT)dx(1)dx(2)}{\iint \exp(-u/kT)dx(1)dx(2)} \qquad (13.22)$$

Since N is large

$$N(N - 1) \approx N^2 \qquad (13.23)$$

and since the interaction is weak

$$\iint \exp(-u/kT)dx(1)dx(2) \approx \iint dx(1)dx(2) = V^2 \qquad (13.24)$$

Substituting (13.23) and (13.24) in (13.22), we obtain

$$P = n^2 \exp(-u/kT) \qquad (13.25)$$

Let us now consider a gas of infinite dimensions, divided into two regions A and B by an infinite plane CC' as shown in Figure 13.4. We wish to calculate the static repulsive force per unit area exerted by the gas in region B on the gas in region A. Let $dx(1)$ be a volume element in region A and $dx(2)$ a volume element in B. If one molecule is in $dx(1)$ and a second in $dx(2)$ they will exert a repulsive force on one another of magnitude $-du/dr$. The component of this force normal to the plane CC' will be $-(du/dr)\cos \theta$.

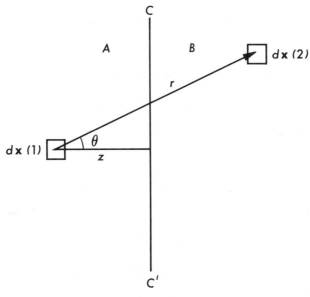

Fig. 13.4

If we wish to find the net repulsive force per unit area exerted by the molecules in B on the molecules in A we simply multiply $-du/dr$ by the probability that there is one molecule in $dx(1)$ and another in $dx(2)$; integrate $dx(1)$ over the region A and $dx(2)$ over the region B; and then divide by the area of the plane separating the regions. This force will be the static pressure p_s. Thus

$$p_s = -\frac{n^2 \int_B \int_A (du/dr) \cos\theta \exp(-u/kT)dx(1)dx(2)}{\text{AREA}} \qquad (13.26)$$

We now introduce the coordinates x, y, z, r, θ, and ϕ where x, y, z are Cartesian coordinates which give the position of $dx(1)$ with respect to a set of axes with x–y plane coincident with the plane CC', and r, θ, ϕ are the spherical coordinates which give the position of $dx(2)$ relative to $dx(1)$.

In terms of these new variables, Eq. (13.26) becomes

$$p_s =$$
$$-n^2 \frac{\int_0^\infty \int_{-\infty}^\infty \int_{-\infty}^\infty \int_z^\infty \int_0^{2\pi} \int_0^{\cos^{-1}(z/r)} (du/dr)r^2 \sin\theta \cos\theta \exp(-u/kT)d\theta d\phi dr dx dy dz}{\int_{-\infty}^\infty \int_{-\infty}^\infty dx dy}$$

$$(13.27)$$

Cancelling out the integration over x and y and integrating over θ and ϕ we obtain

$$p_s = -\pi n^2 \int_0^\infty \int_z^\infty (du/dr)(r^2 - z^2) \exp(-u/kT)dr dz \qquad (13.28)$$

The range of integration of z and r is indicated by the shaded region in Figure 13.5. From Figure 13.5, it can be seen that

$$\int_0^\infty \int_z^\infty \left\{ \quad \right\} dr dz = \int_0^\infty \int_0^r \left\{ \quad \right\} dz dr \qquad (13.29)$$

We can therefore write (13.28)

$$p_s = -\pi n^2 \int_0^\infty \int_0^r (du/dr)(r^2 - z^2) \exp(-u/kT)dz dr \qquad (13.30)$$

Integrating over z, we obtain

$$p_s = -(2\pi n^2/3) \int_0^\infty r^3(du/dr) \exp(-u/kT)dr$$

$$= -(2\pi n^2 kT/3) \int_0^\infty r^3 \frac{d}{dr}[1 - \exp(-u/kT)]dr \qquad (13.31)$$

Integrating by parts, we have

$$p_s = -(2\pi n^2 kT/3)\left\{\left[r^3[1 - \exp(-u/kT)]\right]_0^\infty - 3\int_0^\infty r^2[1 - \exp(-u/kT)]dr\right\}$$

$$(13.32)$$

Since $u(0) = \infty$ and $u(\infty) = 0$

$$\left[r^3[1 - \exp(-u/kT)]\right]_0^\infty = \lim_{r\to\infty}\{r^3[1 - \exp(-u/kT)]\}$$

$$= \lim_{r\to\infty}\{r^3[1 - 1 + (u/kT) + \ldots]\}$$

$$= \lim_{r\to\infty}\{r^3 u/kT\} \qquad (13.33)$$

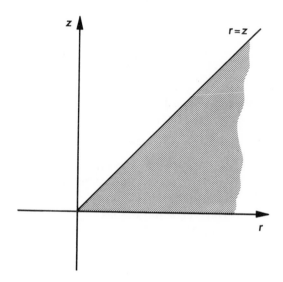

Fig. 13.5

As long as u vanishes faster than r^{-3}, this limit will be zero, in which case

$$p_s = 2\pi n^2 kT\int_0^\infty r^2[1 - \exp(-u/kT)]dr \qquad (13.34)$$

The equation of state for a real gas in which only two-body interactions are important can therefore be written

$$p = p_k + p_s = nkT\left\{1 + 2\pi n\int_0^\infty r^2[1 - \exp(-u/kT)]dr\right\} \qquad (13.35)$$

Comparing this result with the virial equation of state, we see that

$$B = 2\pi\int_0^\infty r^2[1 - \exp(-u/kT)]dr \qquad (13.36)$$

We have thus obtained an explicit expression for the second virial coefficient.

In the following sections we will use (13.36) to determine the equation of state for a number of common intermolecular potentials.

INTERMOLECULAR FORCES

No attempt will be made in this text to give an account of the nature and origin of intermolecular forces. It will, however, be helpful to write down a number of simple intermolecular potentials which are commonly used. For a more detailed discussion the reader is referred to the text by Hirschfelder, Curtiss, and Bird, p. 30ff (see bibliography).

The first characteristic of the intermolecular force which any potential should include is the existence of a strong repulsive effect at short ranges.

The simplest repulsive potential is the rigid sphere potential:

$$u(r) = \infty \qquad\qquad r < \sigma \qquad (13.37)$$

$$u(r) = 0 \qquad\qquad r > \sigma \qquad (13.38)$$

This potential is plotted in Figure 13.6(a).

Another simple repulsive potential is the inverse power potential.

$$u(r) = cr^{-n} \qquad\qquad (13.39)$$

A typical potential of this form is plotted in Figure 13.6(b).

In addition to the short-range repulsive force between molecules, there is generally a weaker, long-range attractive force.

The simplest way to combine a short-range repulsive force, and a long-range attractive force is to add a potential well to the rigid sphere potential as shown in Figure 13.6(c). Analytically we have

$$u = \infty \qquad\qquad r < \sigma \qquad (13.40)$$

$$u = -\epsilon \qquad\qquad \sigma < r < R\sigma \qquad (13.41)$$

$$u = 0 \qquad\qquad r > R\sigma \qquad (13.42)$$

This so-called square well potential is not realistic, but is useful in making quick calculations to determine the effect of the long-range attractive force.

The long-range attractive force may more realistically be added by introducing an inverse power attractive force to either the rigid sphere potential or the inverse power repulsive potential.

In the former case we obtain the Sutherland potential shown in Figure 13.6(d), which analytically is given by

$$u = \infty \qquad\qquad r < \sigma \qquad (13.43)$$

$$u = -cr^{-n} = -\epsilon(\sigma/r)^n \qquad\qquad r > \sigma \qquad (13.44)$$

The quantity σ is the distance between centers at the moment of collision.

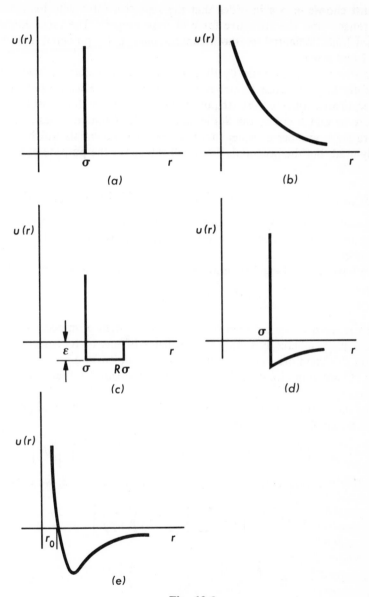

Fig. 13.6

By combining the inverse power attraction and the inverse power repulsion we obtain the Lennard-Jones potential shown in Figure 13.6(e).

$$u(r) = cr^{-m} - dr^{-n}$$
$$\equiv 4\epsilon[(r_0/r)^m - (r_0/r)^n] \qquad m > n \qquad (13.45)$$

We must choose $m > n$ in order that the repulsive force will dominate at short ranges, and the attractive force at long ranges. The most common Lennard-Jones potential is the Lennard-Jones 6–12 potential in which $m = 12$ and $n = 6$.

It can be shown theoretically that two neutral nonpolar molecules at a sufficiently large distance attract each other by a force whose potential is inversely proportional to the sixth power of the separation. It is most common therefore to find $n = 6$ in the Sutherland and the Lennard-Jones potential.

There are a number of other more complicated potentials which are frequently used, but the potentials listed will suffice for the purpose of illustration.

THE SECOND VIRIAL COEFFICIENT FOR VARIOUS POTENTIALS

The second virial coefficient can be obtained for a particular potential by making use of Eq. (13.36). We will evaluate the second virial coefficient using several of these models.

If we have a gas of rigid spheres, the second virial coefficient becomes

$$B \equiv \frac{B_0}{L} = 2\pi \int_0^\sigma r^2 dr = \frac{2\pi\sigma^3}{3} \tag{13.46}$$

where σ is the distance between centers at the moment of impact, which for identical hard spheres is simply the diameter of one of the spheres. The quantity B is therefore four times the volume occupied by a molecule. Comparing (13.46) with (13.9), it also follows that the van der Waal's constants are given by $a = 0$ $b = B$.

If the interaction between molecules is given by the Sutherland potential, the second virial coefficient becomes

$$B = \left(\frac{2\pi\sigma^3}{3}\right)\left[1 + \left(\frac{3}{\sigma^3}\right)\int_\sigma^\infty r^2\left\{1 - \exp\left[\left(\frac{\epsilon}{kT}\right)\left(\frac{\sigma}{r}\right)^n\right]\right\}dr\right] \tag{13.47}$$

Expanding the exponential in a Taylor series and integrating, we obtain

$$B = \left(\frac{2\pi\sigma^3}{3}\right)\left[1 - \sum_{j=1}^\infty \frac{1}{j!}\left(\frac{3}{nj-3}\right)\left(\frac{\epsilon}{kT}\right)^j\right] \tag{13.48}$$

If $\epsilon \ll kT$

$$B \approx \left(\frac{2\pi\sigma^3}{3}\right)\left[1 - \frac{\epsilon}{kT}\left(\frac{3}{n-3}\right)\right] \tag{13.49}$$

Comparing this with (13.9), we obtain for the van der Waal's coefficients

$$a = \frac{2\pi\sigma^3\epsilon}{3}\left(\frac{3}{n-3}\right) \tag{13.50}$$

$$b = \frac{2\pi\sigma^3}{3} \tag{13.51}$$

In a similar fashion, we obtain for the inverse power potential

$$B = \frac{2\pi}{3}\left(\frac{c}{kT}\right)^{3/n} \Gamma\left(\frac{n-3}{3}\right) \qquad n > 3 \qquad (13.52)$$

For $n < 3$ the expression for the static pressure p_s diverges. The Coulomb potential between ions is an example of such a potential. The difficulty with the divergent integrals could be avoided by noting that the integration should correctly be carried out over the volume of the container rather than all space, in which case the pressure would depend on the shape and size of the container. However, for such potentials, the assumption that only two-body interactions are important is at least questionable.

HIGHER ORDER VIRIAL COEFFICIENTS

The previous derivation of the second virial coefficient was based on the assumption that the probability of three-body interactions was negligible. If the density of the gas becomes sufficiently large, this assumption is no longer valid and our analysis must be extended to include three-body interactions and, if necessary, interactions of higher order. By considering the behavior of a system of three molecules in a container of volume V which is weakly coupled to a large set of similar systems, we can in principle easily extend our previous result to handle three-body systems. The evaluation of the resulting integrals is proportionately more difficult.

Consideration of systems of three particles will lead us to both the second and third virial coefficients. If we calculate the second and third virial coefficients using a rigid sphere potential, we find

$$B(T) = \frac{2\pi\sigma^3}{3} \qquad (13.53)$$

$$C(T) = \left(\frac{5}{8}\right)\left(\frac{2\pi\sigma^3}{3}\right)^2 \qquad (13.54)$$

This does not agree with the result obtained by expansion of the van der Waal's equation, as can be seen by comparing (13.53) and (13.54) with Eq. (13.9) and (13.10). We conclude that the van der Waal's equation is not valid when the density of the gas is such that we must use the third virial coefficient.

THE VIRIAL EQUATION

In the preceding sections we have devised a systematic approach for obtaining the virial coefficients of a gas in which the interaction between particles is expressible in terms of a potential $u(r)$. In the present section we wish to outline an alternative technique for obtaining the same results by a method which is mathematically simpler but physically a little more obscure. In a later chapter we will again rederive the same results using even more powerful techniques which are applicable to gases in which the interaction between particles is quite arbitrary.

Let us assume we have a gas of particles whose configuration is describable by a set of generalized coordinates q_i. Let p_i be the corresponding generalized momenta. We now consider the quantity

$$G = \sum_i p_i q_i \qquad (13.55)$$

The time rate of change of G is given by

$$\dot{G} = \sum_i \dot{p}_i q_i + \sum_i p_i \dot{q}_i \qquad (13.56)$$

If we average (13.56) over the time $t = 0$ to $t = \tau$ we obtain

$$\frac{1}{\tau} \int_0^\tau \left(\frac{dG}{dt}\right) dt = \frac{1}{\tau} \left\{ \int_0^\tau \sum_i \dot{p}_i q_i \, dt + \int_0^\tau \sum_i p_i \dot{q}_i \, dt \right\} \qquad (13.57)$$

or

$$\frac{G(\tau) - G(0)}{\tau} = \sum_i \overline{\dot{p}_i q_i} + \sum_i \overline{p_i \dot{q}_i} \qquad (13.58)$$

where the bar indicates a time average. The function G is bounded since the coordinates q_i and momenta p_i are finite, and therefore if we make τ large enough, the left-hand side of (13.58) will vanish. We showed in Chapter 10, Eq. (10.37) for conservative systems that $\sum p_i \dot{q}_i = 2K$, where K is the kinetic energy. It follows that for τ very large

$$\overline{K} = -\tfrac{1}{2} \sum_i \overline{\dot{p}_i q_i} \qquad (13.59)$$

This result is known as the virial theorem and the right-hand side of (13.59) is known as the virial of Clausius.

Let us now consider a finite volume V of a gas. Let $\mathbf{x}(i)$, $\mathbf{v}(i)$, and $\mathbf{F}(i)$ be the position, velocity, and force respectively, associated with the ith particle. In terms of these variables the virial theorem can be written

$$\tfrac{1}{2} \sum_{i=1}^N \sum_{j=1}^3 \overline{m[v_j(i)]^2} = -\tfrac{1}{2} \sum_{i=1}^N \sum_{j=1}^3 \overline{F_j(i) x_j(i)} \qquad (13.60)$$

There are two types of forces acting on the particles, forces due to the wall $\mathbf{F}'(i)$ and forces due to the intermolecular attractions or repulsions $\mathbf{F}''(i)$. For the forces due to the wall

$$-\tfrac{1}{2} \sum_i \sum_j \overline{F_j'(i) x_j(i)} = -\tfrac{1}{2} \sum_{j=1}^3 \oint (-p) x_j n_j \, dS \qquad (13.61)$$

where p is the pressure. Making use of Green's theorem (Appendix 8) we have

$$\oint x_j n_j \, dS = \int (\partial x_j / \partial x_j) dV = V \qquad (13.62)$$

and therefore

$$-\tfrac{1}{2} \sum_i \sum_j \overline{F_j'(i)x_j(i)} = 3pV/2 \qquad (13.63)$$

Let us now consider the contribution to the virial due to the interaction between a pair of molecules with positions $x(1)$ and $x(2)$ respectively, separated by a distance $r = |x(1) - x(2)|$ having an intermolecular potential $u(r)$. We have

$$-\tfrac{1}{2} \sum_{j=1}^{3} \overline{\{[-\partial u(r)/\partial x_j(1)]x_j(1) + [-\partial u(r)/\partial x_j(2)]x_j(2)\}}$$

$$= \tfrac{1}{2} \sum_{j=1}^{3} \overline{\frac{\partial u}{\partial r} \left\{ \frac{[x_j(1) - x_j(2)]x_j(1)}{r} - \frac{[x_j(1) - x_j(2)]x_j(2)}{r} \right\}}$$

$$= \tfrac{1}{2}\overline{(\partial u/\partial r)r} \qquad (13.64)$$

If we consider two-body interactions only, then the probability of finding particle one in $dx(1)$ and particle two in $dx(2)$ is $\exp(-u/kT)/V^2$, so that

$$\overline{(\partial u/\partial r)r} = \frac{\iint r \, exp\,(-u/kT)dx(1)dx(2)}{V^2}$$

$$= (4\pi/V) \int r^3 \exp(-u/kT)dr \qquad (13.65)$$

and since there are $N(N-1)/2 \approx N^2/2$ pairs of particles

$$-\tfrac{1}{2} \sum_i \sum_j \overline{F_j''(i)x_j(i)} = \tfrac{1}{2}(N^2/2)(4\pi/V) \int r^3 \exp(-u/kT)dr \qquad (13.66)$$

If we substitute (13.63) and (13.66) in (13.60) and let $\tfrac{1}{2} \sum_i \sum_j \overline{m[v_j(i)]^2} = \tfrac{3}{2}NkT$

we obtain

$$pV = NkT - (2\pi N^2/3V) \int_0^\infty r^3(\partial u/\partial r) \exp(-u/kT)dr \qquad (13.67)$$

which agrees with the result we have already obtained.

CONCLUSION

Experimental measurements of the pressure of a gas as a function of its volume and temperature will lead to values for the virial coefficients. These values together with the theoretical results given in the preceding sections will enable one to obtain a considerable amount of information about the nature of the intermolecular interaction. On the other hand, a theoretical investigation of the interaction of molecules using known information about their electronic and atomic structure will lead to predictions about the macroscopic behavior. The continual interplay between these levels of investigation ultimately leads us to more knowledge about the behavior of a particular type of molecule, and a greater theoretical understanding of the basic structure of molecules in general.

PROBLEMS

1. Consider two molecules which interact according to the Lennard-Jones (6–12) potential energy function. What is the force of interaction when the molecules are at a separation of $r = 2\sigma$? at a separation of $r = 0.9\sigma$?

2. Values of the second virial coefficient for xenon are given below. Using these data, determine reasonable values for the parameters in the rigid sphere potential, the square well potential, and the Sutherland potential. The coefficient of viscosity of xenon at 20°C and 1 atm is 2.246×10^7 dyn sec/cm². Determine the radius of a xenon atom using the correct hard sphere expression for the coefficient of viscosity. Compare it with the above results.

$T°K$	B_0 (liters/mole)	$T°K$	B_0 (liters/mole)
289.80	−0.1378	448.20	−0.0526
298.15	−0.1302	473.21	−0.0454
323.15	−0.1106	498.23	−0.0391
348.15	−0.0945	523.25	−0.0332
373.16	−0.0812	548.26	−0.0280
398.17	−0.0701	573.28	−0.0235
423.18	−0.0607		

3. Consider a two-dimensional gas consisting of N point masses contained within a "box" of dimensions $L \times L$. Imagine the "box" to be a frictionless plate on which the points are free to slide.

   (a) Suppose the point masses interact and the interparticle potential is given by $u(r)$ where r is the distance between the particles. Assuming only two-body interactions and neglecting any effect due to the finite dimensions of the box, find the equation of state, i.e., the pressure as a function of density and temperature [and of course $u(r)$].

   (b) Suppose the gas is a collection of smooth elastic disks of radius r (i.e., we have a rigid disk interparticle potential). Find the equation of state.

4. Calculate the second virial coefficient using the square well potential and the Lennard-Jones 6–12 potential.

5. Calculate the time-average kinetic energy and potential energy for a one-dimensional harmonic oscillator, and compare the results with the prediction of the virial theorem.

Chapter 14

THE FAILURE
OF CLASSICAL
STATISTICAL MECHANICS

INTRODUCTION

In Chapter 12 we derived the classical Boltzmann distribution function for an assembly of weakly interacting systems, and applied this distribution to the problem of finding the specific heat of a polyatomic gas. As pointed out at the end of Chapter 12, the theoretical results obtained are not entirely in agreement with the experimental data. In the present chapter we want to investigate this disagreement and also some other problems where the classical Boltzmann distribution leads us into difficulties.

THE SPECIFIC HEAT OF DIATOMIC GASES

If we apply the equipartition theorem, which was derived in Chapter 12 to determine the specific heat of hydrogen (H_2) we would predict a specific heat per molecule of $7k/2$, since hydrogen has three translational, two rotational, and one vibrational degree of freedom.

The experimental curve for the specific heat of gaseous hydrogen is shown in Figure 14.1. We have not plotted the very low temperature behavior of the specific heat, since at sufficiently low temperatures ($20.4°K$ at atmospheric pressure) the hydrogen liquefies, and the theory which we have developed so far makes no claim to be able to handle the liquid state.

From the experimental evidence it is apparent that our theory is not entirely adequate. For $T > 5000°K$ the experimental results agree with the theoretical predictions for a diatomic molecule. But for $T < 50°K$ the experi-

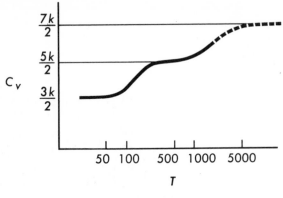

Fig. 14.1

mental data gives a value for the specific heat which would be theoretically correct for a gas of monatomic molecules rather than diatomic molecules.

The error in theory can be shown to be a basic failure in classical mechanics. The motion of a molecule cannot accurately be described by Newton's law. The laws of motion of classical mechanics must be replaced by new laws. In Chapter 15 we will investigate these new laws which form the basis of the quantum theory of matter.

THE SPECIFIC HEAT OF SOLIDS

Another potential application of the classical Boltzmann distribution is to the specific heat of solids.

A very simple and yet fruitful picture of a solid, due to Einstein, can be had by imagining each atom to be contained in a little cell and bound to its lattice site by a set of springs as shown in Figure 14.2. For an isotropic solid the springs are all identical.

If atom i is displaced from its equilibrium position in the x, y, or z direction it will oscillate about the equilibrium position with a frequency ν, and amplitude $A(i)$. Let the total energy of the atom, potential plus kinetic, be $\epsilon(i)$.

If there were no coupling between the atoms, each atom could oscillate independently, and any initial distribution of energies $\epsilon(i)$ would remain fixed. Let us assume, however, that there is a small coupling between atoms, just enough to allow a slow exchange of energy between the atoms without seriously affecting the motion of the atoms. We might, for instance, imagine neighboring atoms to be coupled together by a spring with a spring constant very much less than the spring constant of the springs binding the atoms to their lattice sites. Now if an initial distribution of energies is set up, it will not necessarily remain fixed. The total energy will redistribute itself among

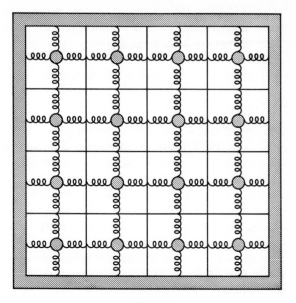

Fig. 14.2

the atoms until some sort of equilibrium is established. The equilibrium distribution should be the Boltzmann distribution.

The total energy of an atom is

$$\epsilon = \sum_{i=1}^{3} \left[\left(\frac{p_i^2}{2m} \right) + \left(\frac{\kappa x_i^2}{2} \right) \right] \tag{14.1}$$

Applying the Boltzmann distribution, and making use of the equipartition theorem we obtain $3kT$ for the average energy of an atom, and $3k$ for the specific heat per molecule.

The actual specific heat per molecule of copper is shown in Figure 14.3.

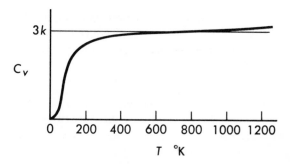

Fig. 14.3

Again at high temperatures, the agreement between experiment and theory is good, but at low temperatures there is a complete disagreement.

This gross disagreement can be shown, as previously, to be due to a failure in classical mechanics, and not to the crudeness of our model. Refinement of our model will not at this stage alter the disagreement.

BLACK BODY RADIATION

Still another failure of classical statistical mechanics was in its application to black body radiation. Historically, the attempt to solve the dilemma which we are about to consider led to one of the first major breakthroughs in the development of quantum mechanics.

Consider a cubical metal box of unit volume. Assume the walls to be perfect conductors. Such a box is able to contain electromagnetic energy, since any electromagnetic radiation within the box will simply be reflected back and forth inside the box, and will not escape.

If we choose an appropriate set of generalized coordinates q_i and momenta p_i, it can be shown (see Appendix 11) that the Hamiltonian associated with the electromagnetic field within the box can be written in the form

$$H = \sum_i \left(\frac{p_i^2}{2m} + \frac{m\omega_i^2 q_i^2}{2} \right) \tag{14.2}$$

Equation (14.2) represents the Hamiltonian of a collection of simple harmonic oscillators of angular frequency ω_i. It can further be shown that a particular pair of p_i and q_i simply corresponds to a standing electromagnetic wave. We will refer to such a standing wave as a normal mode.

It is thus possible to describe the electromagnetic field within the box in terms of a set of independent normal modes. The amplitudes of the normal modes will depend on the field.

The amplitude of a traveling electromagnetic wave of wavelength λ and velocity c can be written in the form

$$A = A_0 \cos [\mathbf{k} \cdot \mathbf{r} - \omega t + \phi] \tag{14.3}$$

where $\mathbf{k}$ is a vector of magnitude $2\pi/\lambda$ directed along the direction of propagation and $\omega = kc$. If such a wave is introduced into a hollow metal cube of unit volume it will be reflected back and forth off the wall and will generate a standing wave if

$$k_i = n_i \pi \tag{14.4}$$

where n_i is a positive integer. Since electromagnetic waves are transverse waves with two independent orientations, there are two distinct normal modes associated with each set of values of n_1, n_2, n_3. The angular frequency corresponding to a particular mode is

$$\omega = kc = (n_1^2 + n_2^2 + n_3^2)^{1/2} \pi c \tag{14.5}$$

If we plot a point in n_1, n_2, n_3 space for each possible normal mode and define $n_{n_1 n_2 n_3} dn_1 dn_2 dn_3$ as the number of waves or points for which n_1 is between n_1 and $n_1 + dn_1$, n_2 between n_2 and $n_2 + dn_2$ and n_3 is between n_3 and $n_3 + dn_3$, we obtain

$$n_{n_1 n_2 n_3} = 2 \quad n_1 > 0 \quad n_2 > 0 \quad n_3 > 0$$
$$= 0 \quad \text{otherwise} \tag{14.6}$$

The corresponding density $n_{k_1 k_2 k_3}$ in $\mathbf{k}$ space is

$$n_{k_1 k_2 k_3} = n_{n_1 n_2 n_3} \left| J\left(\frac{n_1,\, n_2,\, n_3}{k_1,\, k_2,\, k_3}\right) \right| = 2\pi^{-3} \tag{14.7}$$

and the density n_k in k space is

$$n_k = \int_0^{\pi/2} \int_0^{\pi/2} n_{k_1 k_2 k_3} k^2 \sin\theta d\theta d\phi = \left(\frac{k}{\pi}\right)^2 \tag{14.8}$$

The integration in (14.8) is over octant one only since $n_{k_1 k_2 k_3}$ is zero unless $k_1 > 0$, $k_2 > 0$, $k_3 > 0$. Finally the density n_ν in $\nu \equiv \omega/2\pi$ space is

$$n_\nu = n_k \left| J\left(\frac{k}{\nu}\right) \right| = \frac{8\pi\nu^2}{c^3} \tag{14.9}$$

If the electromagnetic energy in our cubical cavity is originally divided among the normal modes in some arbitrary fashion, then the energy will maintain the initial distribution.

Suppose, however, a small foreign object of temperature T which is capable of absorbing and emitting radiation is introduced into the cavity. The radiation in the cavity will now come into thermal equilibrium with the object. Since the Hamiltonian associated with a normal mode is that of a simple harmonic oscillator, each mode will receive on the average an amount of energy kT. Since there is an infinite number of normal modes, each desiring kT of energy, the small foreign object will not be able to quench the thermal thirst of the cavity, and will be quickly drained of all its energy. The cavity thus acts as an object of infinite heat capacity. This is an obviously non-sensical result, since if it were true, all the energy in the universe would be quickly disappearing into these heat sinks. If we define $E_\nu d\nu$ as the energy density of the radiation with frequency between ν and $\nu + d\nu$ then according to the classical analysis

$$E_\nu = n_\nu kT = \frac{8\pi\nu^2 kT}{c^3} \tag{14.10}$$

If the actual distribution of electromagnetic energy within the cavity is measured we find that it agrees quite well with the analytical expression

$$E_\nu = \frac{8\pi\nu^2 kT}{c^3} \left\{ \frac{(h\nu/kT)}{\exp(h\nu/kT) - 1} \right\} \tag{14.11}$$

where h is Planck's constant.

Equation (14.10) agrees with (14.11) in the low-frequency limit where $\exp(h\nu/kT) \approx 1 + (h\nu/kT)$, but is in gross disagreement in the high-frequency region.

THE SPECIFIC HEAT OF METALS

In deriving the specific heat of polyatomic molecules and solids we have been implicitly assuming that atoms are point particles, and molecules are systems of point particles. But atoms are not point particles, they are complex structures with a large number of degrees of freedom. If this is so, we would expect each of the internal degrees of freedom of an atom to share in the partition of energy according to the equipartition theorem, with the result that the predicted specific heat would be far greater than that predicted on the basis of point atoms. For some reason we can neglect the internal degrees of freedom.

The difficulty becomes more apparent in the case of metals. The electrons in the atoms of a metal can no longer be overlooked, for they are obviously free to move around, and have some sort of existence independent of the atoms. Many of the electronic properties of a metal can, as a matter of fact, be explained by assuming that the metal consists of a box of free electrons. This model is called the free electron model. If the free electron model is valid, we would classically expect the heat capacity of a metal containing N_a atoms and N_e electrons to be at least

$$C = N_a(3k) + N_e(3k/2) \tag{14.12}$$

Experimentally, one does find an electronic contribution to the specific heat, but it is temperature dependent and at ordinary temperatures is only about 1 percent of the classically predicted value. As in the preceding cases we have examined, the failure is in the classical theory and not in the model.

CONCLUSION

In the preceding sections we have studied a number of problems in which classical statistical mechanics provides answers which are incorrect or at best partially correct. The error in classical theory can in each one of these cases be traced to a failure of classical mechanics. In Chapter 15, we will investigate the new mechanics, quantum mechanics.

Using quantum mechanics, it will be shown that the division of phase space into cells of equal size as was done in deriving the Boltzmann distribution is not entirely arbitrary. Quantum mechanics provides us with a set of rules for dividing phase space into cells, and quantum statistics a rule for determining the a priori probability which we must assign to each cell. We cannot, as in classical statistics, allow the cell size to become infinitestimally small.

It will turn out in most cases that the cells are of volume h^s where s is the number of degrees of freedom of the system and h a constant called Planck's constant. The exact shape of the cells will vary. Whenever the quantities we are attempting to measure are of the same order of magnitude as the corresponding dimension of these finite-sized cells, or whenever the density of particles in phase space becomes of the same order of magnitude as the density of these cells, we will encounter difficulties.

We will leave any further comment on the subject of quantum mechanics for Chapter 15.

PROBLEMS

1. We have used the Einstein model to discuss the specific heat of a solid. A better model is the Debye model. In its simplest form this model consists of the following assumptions:
   (1) a solid is a continuous medium which can be set in vibration;
   (2) the medium is nondispersive, i.e., a wave of any frequency will travel with the same velocity v_0; (3) both transverse and longitudinal waves can be propagated in the medium; (4) the behavior of the medium can be completely described in terms of the $3N$ normal modes of motion having the lowest frequencies, where N is the number of atoms in the solid.
   Using the Debye model, what would the classical specific heat of a solid be?

2. The representative point in phase space of a simple harmonic oscillator moves in an elliptical orbit. Suppose that a simple harmonic oscillator could have only those energies for which the area under the ellipse was a multiple of the constant h, and that each of these energies was a priori equally probable. Show that the average energy of the simple harmonic oscillator would then be

$$\bar{\epsilon} = \frac{h\nu}{\exp(h\nu/kT) - 1}$$

where ν is the frequency of the oscillator.

Chapter 15

QUANTUM MECHANICS

INTRODUCTION

In Chapter 14 we have seen that the predictions of statistical mechanics do not fully agree with the experimental facts. The main source of difficulty is the failure of classical mechanics to adequately describe the behavior of the systems we have been considering.

In classical mechanics the state of a system at a particular time is completely specified by giving its generalized coordinates q and generalized momenta p at that instant. If in addition to knowing the state of the system at some instant of time we also know the Hamiltonian $H(p, q, t)$, then we can, by making use of Hamilton's equation, predict what the state of the system will be at any future time, or what is equivalent, we can solve for q and p as functions of time.

Experiment on the atomic level shows that the classical definition of a state, and the equations of motion connecting states are only valid under certain limiting conditions. The correct laws governing the dynamics of mechanical systems constitute the basis of quantum mechanics. The fundamental principles of quantum mechanics can be conveniently stated in a series of postulates. In the following section we will consider these postulates.

THE FUNDAMENTAL POSTULATES OF QUANTUM MECHANICS

In classical mechanics the state of a system is defined if we know q and p. In quantum mechanics we replace the idea of a state by a state function.

Postulate I: For a given mechanical system at a given instant of time, there exists a function $\Psi(q)$ which describes the state of that system as completely as possible. The function Ψ, which is called the state function or wave

162

function, has the following properties: (1) it may be complex, (2) it is a continuous, single-valued, and finite function of q and t, (3) its first derivatives with respect to q_i are single-valued, continuous, and finite, (4) $\int \Psi^* \Psi dq = 1$ where Ψ^* is the complex conjugate of Ψ.

It follows from Postulate I that if we know the function $\Psi(q)$ at some instant of time, we should be able to determine every mechanical property of the system at that time. It is not immediately obvious how we are to extract information concerning the system from the function $\Psi(q)$. This will be the concern of Postulates II and III. However, before we consider these postulates it will be helpful to define a few terms.

Definition I: An operator $\hat{A}$ is an entity which acting upon a function $f_1(x)$ converts it into some other function $f_2(x)$. We can express this symbolically by writing

$$\hat{A}f_1(x) = f_2(x) \tag{15.1}$$

Typical operations are differentiation, integration, and multiplication by some function $g(x)$. The corresponding operators are d/dx, $\int dx$, and $g(x)$.

Definition II: A linear operator $\hat{A}$ is an operator which for arbitrary functions $f_1(x)$ and $f_2(x)$ and arbitrary constants c_1 and c_2 satisfies the condition

$$\hat{A}(c_1 f_1 + c_2 f_2) = c_1 \hat{A} f_1 + c_2 \hat{A} f_2 \tag{15.2}$$

Definition III: An Hermitian operator $\hat{A}$ is an operator which for arbitrary complex functions $f_1(x)$ and $f_2(x)$ satisfies the condition

$$\int f_1^* \hat{A} f_2 dx = \int (\hat{A} f_1)^* f_2 dx \tag{15.3}$$

Definition IV: A set of functions $f_n(x)$ is said to be complete with respect to a particular class of functions if any arbitrary function $f(x)$ belonging to the class can be expressed as a linear combination of the $f_n(x)$, i.e., if there exists a set of constants c_n such that

$$f(x) = \sum_n c_n f_n(x) \tag{15.4}$$

Having introduced the notion of an operator we can now consider Postulates II and III.

Postulate II: With every measurable property of a system there is associated an operator $\hat{A}$ which can operate on the state function $\Psi(q)$. The operator $\hat{A}$ has the following properties: (1) it is linear; (2) it is Hermitian; (3) there exists a set of functions ϕ_n which satisfy the equation $\hat{A}\phi_n = a_n\phi_n$, where the a_n are constants, and the ϕ_n constitute a complete set of functions with respect to the class of functions made up of all acceptable wave functions Ψ for the system. The actual form of the operator corresponding to a given observable must be obtained by trial.

Although we cannot give a universal rule for obtaining the appropriate operator $\hat{A}$ corresponding to a particular observable, there are a few rules which allow one to write down the correct operator for a large number of observables.

Suppose the observable in which we are interested corresponds classically to the function $A(\mathbf{q}, \mathbf{p})$. We first convert to Cartesian coordinates $\mathbf{x}$, and the corresponding momenta which we will for convenience designate by the same letter $\mathbf{p}$. If the resulting function can then be written in the form

$$A(\mathbf{x}, \mathbf{p}) = f_1(\mathbf{p}) + f_2(\mathbf{x}) + \tfrac{1}{2}\sum_i [p_i g_i(\mathbf{x}) + g_i(\mathbf{x}) p_i] \qquad (15.5)$$

where f_1, f_2, and the g_i are arbitrary functions, then the corresponding operator is obtained by replacing p_i by $-i\hbar\dfrac{\partial}{\partial x_i}$ in the above form of the observable $A(\mathbf{x}, \mathbf{p})$.

Postulate III: If a series of measurements of the observable corresponding to the operator $\hat{A}$ is carried out on a set of identical systems all in the state $\Psi(\mathbf{q})$, the average value of these measurements will be given by

$$<\hat{A}> = \int \Psi^* \hat{A} \Psi dq \qquad (15.6)$$

The quantity $<\hat{A}>$ is called the expectation value.

In Postulate I we introduced the state function $\Psi(\mathbf{q})$. In Postulates II and III we provided the connection between the state function and the measurable properties of a system. The only thing needed now is the equation of motion which will enable us to predict the state of a system at some future time if we know it at some initial time. We need an equation which will enable us to solve for Ψ as a function of $\mathbf{q}$, and t if we know Ψ as a function of $\mathbf{q}$ at some time t_0. The correct equation of motion is provided by Postulate IV.

Postulate IV: The state function $\Psi(\mathbf{q}, t)$ obeys the following equation

$$\hat{H}\Psi(\mathbf{q}, t) = i\hbar \frac{\partial \Psi(\mathbf{q}, t)}{\partial t} \qquad (15.7)$$

where $\hat{H}$ is the operator corresponding to the classical Hamiltonian. The above equation is called the time-dependent Schrodinger's equation.

SOME USEFUL THEOREMS

As we shall see, the preceding postulates are sufficient to enable us to describe and predict the behavior of a dynamical system in a manner which is consistent with the results of experiment and observation. Before applying these postulates to a specific problem, it will be helpful to derive a number of useful theorems which follow from the postulates.

Theorem I: If a system is in a state $\Psi(\mathbf{q})$, then the probability of finding the system in the range between $\mathbf{q}$ and $\mathbf{q} + d\mathbf{q}$ is given by $\Psi^*(\mathbf{q})\Psi(\mathbf{q})d\mathbf{q}$.

Proof: If $P(\mathbf{q})d\mathbf{q}$ is the probability of finding the system between $\mathbf{q}$ and $\mathbf{q} + d\mathbf{q}$, then the expectation value of the quantity $A(\mathbf{q})$ is given by

$$<A(\mathbf{q})> = \int A(\mathbf{q})P(\mathbf{q})d\mathbf{q} \tag{15.8}$$

But from Postulate III

$$<A(\mathbf{q})> = \int \Psi^*A(\mathbf{q})\Psi d\mathbf{q} = \int A(\mathbf{q})\Psi^*\Psi d\mathbf{q} \tag{15.9}$$

Equating (15.8) and (15.9) we obtain

$$\int A(\mathbf{q})P(\mathbf{q})d\mathbf{q} = \int A(\mathbf{q})\Psi^*\Psi d\mathbf{q} \tag{15.10}$$

Since A is arbitrary, it follows that $P = \Psi^*\Psi$.

Theorem II: The wave function Ψ may be multiplied by any complex constant C, for which $C^*C = 1$, without changing its physical significance.

Proof: The expectation value of the observable corresponding to $\hat{A}$ is, from Postulate III, $<\hat{A}> = \int \Psi^*A\Psi d\mathbf{q}$. Multiplying Ψ by C has the effect of multiplying $<\hat{A}>$ by C^*C. If $C^*C = 1$ then $<\hat{A}>$ remains unchanged. It follows that no physical observable is altered if we multiply Ψ by C provided $C^*C = 1$.

Theorem III: If $\hat{A}$ is an operator corresponding to a physical observable, then it is possible to obtain a complete set of orthonormal functions ψ_n which are solutions of the equation

$$\hat{A}\psi_n = a_n\psi_n \tag{15.11}$$

The ψ_n are called eigenfunctions of the operator $\hat{A}$. The a_n are called eigenvalues of the operator $\hat{A}$ and are always real. If there is more than one eigenfunction corresponding to the same eigenvalue, that eigenvalue is said to be degenerate.

Proof: A set of functions ψ_n is an orthonormal set if

$$\int \psi_n^*\psi_m d\mathbf{q} = \delta_{nm} \tag{15.12}$$

Suppose ψ_n and ψ_m are two solutions of Eq. (15.11). Then

$$\hat{A}\psi_n = a_n\psi_n \tag{15.13}$$

$$\hat{A}\psi_m = a_m\psi_m \tag{15.14}$$

If we multiply (15.13) by ψ_m^* and integrate over $\mathbf{q}$ we obtain

$$\int \psi_m^*\hat{A}\psi_n d\mathbf{q} = a_n \int \psi_m^*\psi_n d\mathbf{q} \tag{15.15}$$

If we multiply (15.14) by $\psi_n{}^*$, take the complex conjugate, and integrate over $\mathbf{q}$ we obtain

$$\int (\psi_n{}^*\hat{A}\psi_m)^* d\mathbf{q} = a_m{}^* \int \psi_n \psi_m{}^* d\mathbf{q} \tag{15.16}$$

Since $\hat{A}$ is Hermitian

$$\int (\psi_n{}^*\hat{A}\psi_m)^* d\mathbf{q} \equiv \int \psi_n (\hat{A}\psi_m)^* d\mathbf{q}$$

$$\equiv \int (\hat{A}\psi_m)^* \psi_n d\mathbf{q} = \int \psi_m{}^* \hat{A}\psi_n d\mathbf{q} \tag{15.17}$$

Substituting (15.17) in (15.16) and subtracting the result from (15.15) we obtain

$$(a_n - a_m{}^*) \int \psi_n{}^* \psi_m d\mathbf{q} = 0 \tag{15.18}$$

Consider first the case in which $n = m$. Unless $\psi_n \equiv 0$, $\int \psi_n{}^*\psi_n d\mathbf{q} > 0$ and therefore $a_n = a_n{}^*$. The eigenvalues a_n are therefore always real. We can, as a result, rewrite (15.18)

$$(a_n - a_m) \int \psi_n{}^* \psi_m d\mathbf{q} = 0 \tag{15.19}$$

If $n \neq m$ and $a_n \neq a_m$ then

$$\int \psi_n{}^* \psi_m d\mathbf{q} = 0$$

and ψ_n and ψ_m are orthogonal.

If two or more functions ψ_n correspond to the same value of a_n they may not be orthogonal. However, it is always possible to choose linear combinations of these functions which are orthogonal. We will not prove the latter point.

We shall, however, always assume that we have chosen our ψ_m in such a way that they are orthogonal.

If ψ_n is a solution of (15.11), then $c\psi_n$ is a solution. It is therefore always possible to choose ψ_n in such a way that

$$\int \psi_n{}^* \psi_n d\mathbf{q} = 1 \tag{15.20}$$

Gathering our results, we have

$$\int \psi_n{}^* \psi_m d\mathbf{q} = \delta_{nm} \tag{15.21}$$

This result, together with the fact that the ψ_n constitute a complete set, proves our theorem.

Theorem IV: If one measurement is made on the observable corresponding to the operator $\hat{A}$, the result will be one of the eigenvalues a_n.

Proof: From Postulate III

$$<\hat{A}^n> = \int \Psi^* \hat{A}^n \Psi d\mathbf{q} \tag{15.22}$$

From Theorem III we can expand Ψ in the eigenfunctions ψ_i of the operator $\hat{A}$, i.e.,

$$\Psi = \sum_i c_i \psi_i \tag{15.23}$$

Substituting (15.23) in (15.22) we obtain

$$\begin{aligned}
<\hat{A}^n> &= \sum_i \sum_j c_i^* c_j \int \psi_i^* \hat{A}^n \psi_j d\mathbf{q} \\
&= \sum_i \sum_j c_i^* c_j (a_j)^n \int \psi_i^* \psi_j d\mathbf{q} \\
&= \sum_i c_i^* c_i (a_i)^n
\end{aligned} \tag{15.24}$$

The only way this can be true for all values of n, is if the only result of a measurement is one of the a_i.

Theorem V: If a system is in a state Ψ and we expand Ψ in a series of eigenfunctions ψ_i of the operator $\hat{A}$, i.e.,

$$\Psi = \sum_i c_i \psi_i \tag{15.25}$$

then, assuming no degeneracy, $c_i^* c_i$ represents the probability that a measurement of the observable corresponding to $\hat{A}$ will yield the eigenvalue a_i corresponding to the eigenfunction ψ_i.

Proof: Let P_i represent the probability that a measurement of the observable corresponding to $\hat{A}$ will yield the value a_i. Then

$$<\hat{A}^n> = \sum_i P_i (a_i)^n \tag{15.26}$$

In the proof of Theorem IV we have shown that

$$<\hat{A}^n> = \sum_i c_i^* c_i (a_i)^n \tag{15.27}$$

equating (15.26) and (15.27) we have

$$\sum_i P_i (a_i)^n = \sum_i c_i^* c_i (a_i)^n \tag{15.28}$$

The only way this can be true for all values of n is if

$$P_i = c_i^* c_i \tag{15.29}$$

Theorem VI: If two quantum mechanical operators $\hat{A}$ and $\hat{B}$ have the same set of eigenfunctions, then they commute. Conversely, if they commute then it is possible to find a common set of eigenfunctions for them.

Proof: Suppose

$$\hat{A}\psi_n = a_n\psi_n \qquad (15.30)$$

$$\hat{B}\psi_n = b_n\psi_n \qquad (15.31)$$

Operate on (15.30) with $\hat{B}$ and on (15.31) with $\hat{A}$ and subtract the result. We obtain

$$\hat{B}\hat{A}\psi_n - \hat{A}\hat{B}\psi_n = \hat{B}a_n\psi_n - \hat{A}b_n\psi_n$$
$$= a_n\hat{B}\psi_n - b_n\hat{A}\psi_n = a_nb_n\psi_n - b_na_n\psi_n = 0 \qquad (15.32)$$

It follows that

$$(\hat{B}\hat{A} - \hat{A}\hat{B})\psi_n = 0 \qquad (15.33)$$

But this must be true for each ψ_n, and since the ψ_n constitute a complete set, it follows that

$$\hat{A}\hat{B} = \hat{B}\hat{A} \qquad (15.34)$$

Suppose $\hat{A}\hat{B} = \hat{B}\hat{A}$ and $\hat{A}\psi_n = a_n\psi_n$, then $\hat{B}\hat{A}\psi_n = \hat{B}a_n\psi_n$, and therefore

$$\hat{A}(\hat{B}\psi_n) = a_n(\hat{B}\psi_n) \qquad (15.35)$$

It follows that $\hat{B}\psi_n$ is any linear combination of the eigenfunctions of $\hat{A}$ corresponding to the eigenvalue a_n. If we let $\hat{B}\psi_n = b_n\psi_n$ then the ψ_n are simultaneously eigenfunctions for $\hat{B}$ and $\hat{A}$.

Theorem VII: If a single measurement of the observable A or B is made on each member of a set of identical systems all in the same initial state Ψ, and if we designate by ΔA and ΔB the root-mean-square deviation of the measurements from the expectation values $<\hat{A}>$ and $<\hat{B}>$, then

$$\Delta A \Delta B \geq |\tfrac{1}{2} < \hat{A}\hat{B} - \hat{B}\hat{A} >|$$

We will not prove this theorem in general but will simply consider the case in which A and B are the position x and momentum p of a particle constrained to move in one dimension. For this case $\hat{x} = x$, $\hat{p} = -i\hbar d/dx$, and $\hat{x}\hat{p} - \hat{p}\hat{x} = i\hbar$, and therefore we wish to prove

$$\Delta x \Delta p \geq \hbar/2 \qquad (15.36)$$

Suppose a, b, and c are arbitrary constants, then

$$|\Psi' + (ax + b + ic)\Psi|^2 \geq 0 \qquad (15.37)$$

where Ψ' is the derivative of Ψ with respect to x. From (15.37) it follows that

$$[\Psi' + (ax + b + ic)\Psi]^* [\Psi' + (ax + b + ic)\Psi]$$
$$= \Psi^{*'}\Psi' + ax(\Psi\Psi^{*'} + \Psi^*\Psi') + b(\Psi\Psi^{*'} + \Psi^*\Psi')$$
$$+ ic(\Psi\Psi^{*'} - \Psi^*\Psi') + a^2x^2\Psi^*\Psi + 2abx\Psi^*\Psi$$
$$+ (b^2 + c^2)\Psi^*\Psi \geq 0 \tag{15.38}$$

If we integrate (15.38) and make use of the following series of results which one obtains by integration by parts

$$\int \Psi^{*'}\Psi' dx = -\int \Psi^*\Psi'' dx = <\hat{p}^2>/\hbar^2 \tag{15.39}$$

$$\int x(\Psi^*\Psi' + \Psi^{*'}\Psi)dx = \int x(\Psi^*\Psi)'dx = -\int \Psi^*\Psi dx = -1 \tag{15.40}$$

$$\int (\Psi^*\Psi' + \Psi^{*'}\Psi)dx = \int (\Psi^*\Psi)'dx = 0 \tag{15.41}$$

$$\int (\Psi\Psi^{*'} - \Psi^*\Psi')dx = -2\int \Psi^*\Psi' dx = (2/i\hbar)<\hat{p}> \tag{15.42}$$

We obtain

$$(1/\hbar^2) <\hat{p}^2> - a + (2c/\hbar) <\hat{p}> + a^2<\hat{x}^2>$$
$$+ 2ab<\hat{x}> + (b^2 + c^2) \geq 0 \tag{15.43}$$

If we set $a = 1/2(\Delta x)^2$, $b = -<\hat{x}>/2(\Delta x)^2$ and $c = -<\hat{p}>/\hbar$ where

$$\Delta x = [<(\hat{x} - <\hat{x}>)^2>]^{1/2} = [<\hat{x}^2> - <\hat{x}>^2]^{1/2} \tag{15.44}$$

$$\Delta p = [<\hat{p}^2> - <\hat{p}>^2]^{1/2} \tag{15.45}$$

then we obtain

$$(\Delta p)^2/\hbar^2 - 1/4(\Delta x)^2 \geq 0 \tag{15.46}$$

which reduces to (15.36).

Theorem VIII: If Ψ_a and Ψ_b are solutions of Schrodinger's equation, then any linear combination of Ψ_a and Ψ_b is also a solution.

The proof of this theorem can readily be seen by simply substituting the function $a\Psi_a + b\Psi_b$ in Schrodinger's equation and making use of the linear character of the operator $\hat{H}$.

TIME-INDEPENDENT SCHRODINGER'S EQUATION

Suppose we consider a system in which H is not a function of time. We can then solve Schrodinger's equation

$$\hat{H}\Psi = i\hbar\frac{\partial \Psi}{\partial t} \tag{15.47}$$

by the technique of separation of variables. Let us assume a solution of the form

$$\Psi(\mathbf{q}, t) = \psi(\mathbf{q})T(t) \tag{15.48}$$

Substituting (15.48) in (15.47) and dividing by Ψ we obtain

$$\frac{\hat{H}\psi}{\psi} = \frac{i\hbar T'}{T} \tag{15.49}$$

where $T' \equiv dT/dt$. The left-hand side of (15.49) is a function of $\mathbf{q}$ only and the right-hand side is a function of t only. The only way this can be true is if both sides are equal to the same constant. There is in general a whole set of constants which will work. We shall designate a member of this set by the symbol E_n. For each value of E_n there is a different solution for $T(t)$. We will designate the solution corresponding to E_n by $T_n(t)$. For each value of E_n there is one or more solutions for ψ. We designate these solutions $\psi_{n(j)}$ where j takes on as many values as is necessary to label each distinct ψ corresponding to the same E_n. If we let Z_n be the number of distinct ψ's corresponding to the same E_n, then j runs from 1 to Z_n.

Equating (15.49) to E_n, we obtain

$$\hat{H}\psi_{n(j)} = E_n\psi_{n(j)} \tag{15.50}$$

$$T_n' = -\frac{i}{\hbar}E_nT_n \tag{15.51}$$

Equation (15.50) is just the eigenvalue equation for the Hamiltonian, and is called the time-independent Schrodinger equation. It follows from Theorem IV that for systems in which H is equal to the total energy E, the values E_n are possible measurements for the energy. We refer to the values of E_n as energy levels. If $Z_n = 1$, we say that the energy level E_n is nondegenerate. If $Z_n > 1$, we say that the energy level is degenerate.

Solving (15.51) we obtain

$$T_n = A_n \exp(-iE_nt/\hbar) \tag{15.52}$$

where A_n is a constant. Since T_n will always appear as a factor in the product $T_n\psi_{n(j)}$, we can incorporate the constant A_n into the corresponding constant in $\psi_{n(j)}$ or what is equivalent, set $A_n = 1$. We thus have

$$T_n = \exp(-iE_nt/\hbar) \tag{15.53}$$

The solutions to (15.47) can now be written

$$\Psi_{n(j)} = \psi_{n(j)} \exp(-iE_nt/\hbar) \tag{15.54}$$

Any linear combination of the $\Psi_{n(j)}$ will also be a solution. We can therefore write the general solution in the form

$$\Psi(\mathbf{q}, t) = \sum_n \sum_{j=1}^{z_n} c_{n(j)} \psi_{n(j)} \exp(-iE_n t/\hbar) \tag{15.55}$$

where the $c_{n(j)}$ are arbitrary constants. We still have the freedom to adjust the functions $\psi_{n(j)}$ so as to constitute a complete orthonormal set of functions, and we assume this always to be done. The $\psi_{n(j)}$ are then the eigenfunctions for the Hamiltonian operator.

If instead of labeling the energy levels E_n from 0 to ∞, we had labeled the states $\psi_{n(j)}$ from 0 to ∞, the expression (15.55) would become

$$\Psi(\mathbf{q}, t) = \sum_n c_n \psi_n \exp(-iE_n t/\hbar) \tag{15.56}$$

where now the energy levels E_n are not all necessarily distinct.

Because of its notational simplicity we usually prefer the form (15.56) to the form (15.55). The reader should remember that when (15.56) occurs, the sum is over possible states ψ_n and not over possible energy levels.

From Theorem V it follows (assuming no degeneracy) that

$$[c_n \exp(-iE_n t/\hbar)]^* [c_n \exp(-iE_n t/\hbar)] \equiv c_n{}^* c_n \tag{15.57}$$

represents the probability that if the system is in the state Ψ a measurement of the energy will give E_n and therefore

$$\sum c_n{}^* c_n = 1 \tag{15.58}$$

We will in general be dealing with a large number of macroscopically identical systems and will consequently be interested in the average value of $c_n{}^* c_n$ rather than its specific value for a particular system. Instead of assuming that $c_n{}^* c_n$ can take on all values consistent with the condition $\sum c_n{}^* c_n = 1$, we shall assume that for a particular system it can assume only the values 0 or 1. Since $\sum c_n{}^* c_n = 1$, it follows that we are assuming that each system is in one of the set of states

$$\Psi_n = \psi_n \exp(-iE_n t/\hbar) \tag{15.59}$$

Although the above assumption is convenient, commonly made, and leads to results in agreement with experiment, it does not follow from the postulates we have set up. We are essentially introducing a new postulate called the postulate of random phases. This postulate will be considered in detail in Chapter 23.

It is customary also to suppress the time dependence in (15.59) and simply say that the system is in the state ψ_n. We thus envisage the system to be in a definite state ψ_n with a definite energy E_n. If disturbed, the system can jump to another state ψ_m with energy E_m.

THE SOLUTION OF SCHRODINGER'S EQUATION FOR A NUMBER OF SIMPLE SYSTEMS

Let us consider a few simple applications of Schrodinger's time-independent equation to systems of frequent occurrence in statistical mechanics.

The Particle in a Box: Consider a particle constrained to move in the one-dimensional potential

$$
\begin{aligned}
V &= \infty & x &< 0 \\
V &= 0 & 0 &< x < L \\
V &= \infty & x &> L
\end{aligned}
\tag{15.60}
$$

The classical Hamiltonian is simply

$$
H = \frac{p^2}{2m} + V(x)
\tag{15.61}
$$

The corresponding quantum mechanical operator is

$$
\hat{H} = -\frac{\hbar^2}{2m}\frac{d^2}{dx^2} + V(x)
\tag{15.62}
$$

Schrodinger's equation for the region $0 \leq x \leq L$ is

$$
-\frac{\hbar^2}{2m}\frac{d^2\psi_n}{dx^2} = E_n\psi_n
\tag{15.63}
$$

Outside the box the wave function vanishes, and therefore

$$
\psi_n(0) = \psi_n(L) = 0
\tag{15.64}
$$

The following set of functions constitute a complete set of orthonormal functions satisfying (15.63) together with the boundary condition (15.64)

$$
\psi_n = \left(\frac{2}{L}\right)^{1/2} \sin\left(\frac{n\pi x}{L}\right) \qquad n = 1, 2, 3
\tag{15.65}
$$

The corresponding eigenvalues are

$$
E_n = \frac{n^2 h^2}{8mL^2}
\tag{15.66}
$$

Rigid Diatomic Molecule: Consider a rigid diatomic molecule free to rotate about its center of mass. The orientation of the molecule can be completely specified in terms of the spherical coordinates θ and ϕ. The Hamiltonian operator is

$$
\hat{H} = -\frac{\hbar^2}{2I}\left(\frac{1}{\sin\theta}\frac{\partial}{\partial\theta}\sin\theta\frac{\partial}{\partial\theta} + \frac{1}{\sin^2\theta}\frac{\partial^2}{\partial\phi^2}\right)
\tag{15.67}
$$

where I is the moment of inertia about an axis passing through the center of mass and normal to the line joining the masses. The eigenfunctions of this operator are the surface spherical harmonics, and the eigenvalues are

$$E_n = \frac{n(n+1)\hbar^2}{2I} \tag{15.68}$$

The eigenvalues are degenerate. For each value of n there are $2n + 1$ eigenfunctions, i.e.,

$$Z_n = (2n+1) \tag{15.69}$$

The Simple Harmonic Oscillator: Consider a mass m on a spring with spring constant κ. Let x be the displacement of the mass from its equilibrium position. The Hamiltonian operator is

$$\hat{H} = -\frac{\hbar^2}{2m}\frac{d^2}{dx^2} + \frac{m\omega^2 x^2}{2} \tag{15.70}$$

The eigenfunctions are products of $\exp(-m\omega x^2/2\hbar)$ and Hermite polynomials. The eigenvalues are

$$E_n = (n + \tfrac{1}{2})\hbar\omega \tag{15.71}$$

THE *WKB* APPROXIMATION

If a particle of energy $E(x, p)$ is contained in a one-dimensional potential well $V(x)$ and if

$$\frac{m\hbar\,|dV/dx|}{[2m(E-V)]^{3/2}} \ll 1 \tag{15.72}$$

then it can be shown that the allowed values of p are those satisfying the condition

$$\oint p\,dx = (n + \tfrac{1}{2})h \tag{15.73}$$

where n is an integer. Except for the factor $1/2$, this is just the Wilson-Sommerfeld condition. The derivation of (15.73) starting from Schrodinger's equation is discussed in detail in most books on quantum mechanics. It is a particular application of the so-called *WKB* approximation.

PROBLEMS

1. Show that the angular momentum operator $L_z = -i\hbar(\partial/\partial\phi)$ is Hermitian.
2. Show that complex conjugation is not a linear operator.
3. Show that the operator which associates the square of a function with the function is not linear.

4. A one-dimensional harmonic oscillator is in a state such that at $t = 0$
$$\psi(x) = A \exp(-x^2/2a^2) \exp(ip_0x/\hbar)$$
Find
(a) A^*A
(b) $<x>$
(c) $<(x - <x>)^2>^{1/2}$
(d) the expectation value of the potential energy
(e) $<\hat{p}>$
(f) the expectation value of the kinetic energy

5. Show that $-i\hbar\partial/\partial x_i$ is a linear Hermitian operator.

6. A particle of mass m moves in a conservative force field. Find the operator that corresponds to the angular momentum of the particle about the z axis.

7. The classical Hamiltonian for a rigid body rotating about a fixed axis is given by $H = p_\phi^2/2I$ where I is the moment of inertia. Find the energy eigenfunction and eigenvalues.

8. Given: A one-dimensional system in the state $\Psi(x, t)$. The probability density is given by $\Psi^*\Psi$. Show that the probability current is given by
$$I = (i\hbar/2m)\left\{ \Psi\frac{\partial\Psi^*}{\partial x} - \Psi^*\frac{\partial\Psi}{\partial x} \right\}$$

9. A particle of mass m moves in a field described by the potential function
$$V(r) = -V_0 \qquad\qquad 0 \leq r \leq a$$
$$V(r) = 0 \qquad\qquad r > a$$

Obtain an equation from which it is possible to calculate the allowed energies and corresponding wave functions for those states in which there is spherical symmetry. Show that there is no bound state of this type unless $V_0a^2 > h^2/32m$ and that there is just one bound state if $h^2/32m < V_0a^2 < 9h^2/32m$.

10. Given: A particle mass m moving in a conservative force field $V(x, y, z)$. Show that
$$\frac{d<x>}{dt} = \frac{<p_x>}{m}$$
$$\frac{d<p_x>}{dt} = -\left\langle\frac{\partial V}{\partial x}\right\rangle$$

11. Find the number of energy eigenstates per unit volume of phase space for a free particle in a box.

16

QUANTUM STATISTICS
OF INDEPENDENT
DISTINGUISHABLE SYSTEMS

INTRODUCTION

In Chapter 15 we briefly pointed out some of the failures of classical statistical mechanics. As we shall see in this chapter and in Chapter 17, there are two sources of difficulty. In the first place a molecule in a box obeys quantum mechanical rather than classical equations of motion. In the second place the interaction between molecules in the same box cannot be neglected since even if classically the interaction between the molecules is weak, there are quantum effects which cannot be ignored.

In this chapter we will consider the first difficulty. In later chapters we will consider the second difficulty.

A MODEL

In the present section we wish to review in detail some of the assumptions which were implicit in deriving the classical Boltzmann distribution.

In deriving the classical Boltzmann distribution we assumed that the interactions between molecules had no other effect than to occasionally kick a molecule abruptly from one trajectory in phase space to another. Between collisions each molecule was assumed to follow the trajectory which it would if there were no other molecules present. We also assumed that the volume occupied by the molecules was negligible compared to the volume of the container.

As discussed in Chapter 13, these assumptions are equivalent to assuming that the distribution function for a gas of particles contained in a volume V is the same as the distribution function (reduced to a common $\mathbf{p}$, $\mathbf{q}$ space) which would be associated with a collection of particles, each of which was contained in a separate volume V and which, except for some mechanism by which they could exchange energy, were isolated from one another. Such a model is symbolically represented in Figure 16.1. The total energy E and the

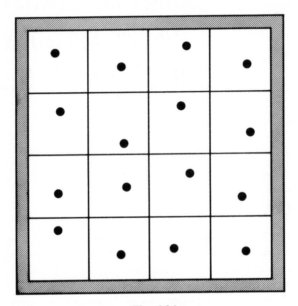

Fig. 16.1

total number of molecules N is assumed to remain constant. There are a number of situations where this model provides a good representation of the actual state of affairs. In this chapter we will work with this model.

THE BASIC POSTULATE OF QUANTUM STATISTICS

Consider a collection of N molecules, contained in separate compartments of volume V, as shown in Figure 16.1. We assume that the total energy of the N molecules is E and that the molecules can exchange energy with one another, but otherwise are entirely independent. We shall refer to these molecules as independent and distinguishable.

In classical mechanics the state of an individual molecule is specified by giving a set of generalized coordinates and momenta. In quantum mechanics we must instead specify what quantum state $\psi_n(\mathbf{q})$ it is in.

In classical statistical mechanics we started off with the basic assumption that equal regions in phase space were a priori equally probable. To obtain the equilibrium distribution, we then divided phase space into cells of equal size, determined the most probable distribution of the molecules among these cells, and proceeded to the limit as the cell size became infinitesimally small.

The above procedure cannot be carried out in quantum mechanics. By Theorem VII it is impossible to simultaneously specify both $\mathbf{q}$ and $\mathbf{p}$, and therefore we cannot proceed to the limit as the cell size becomes infinitesimally small. There is a lower limit to the size of our cell. Suppose the molecule is a point particle in the state $\Psi(\mathbf{x})$. Let Δp_i be the root-mean-square deviation of a measurement of p_i from the expectation value $<p_i>$ and Δx_i the root-mean-square deviation of a measurement of x_i from the expectation value $<x_i>$; then the best we can hope to do is to specify that $\mathbf{x}$ and $\mathbf{p}$ fall somewhere within a volume roughly of the order of $\prod_i \Delta p_i \Delta x_i$

where i in the present case goes from one to three. But from Theorem VII

$$\prod_i \Delta p_i \Delta x_i \geq (\hbar/2)^3 \qquad (16.1)$$

and therefore we have a lower limit on the size of our cells in phase space.

We must therefore replace our classical procedure by the correct quantum mechanical approach. We are guided in our search by the fact that in the classical limit we expect the quantum mechanical results to go over to the classical results, since as we have seen, the classical distribution gives good agreement with a large portion of the experimental data. In discussing the *WKB* approximation we obtained the result for a particle in a one-dimensional potential

$$\oint p\,dq = (n + \tfrac{1}{2})h \qquad (16.2)$$

But the $\oint p\,dq$ is just the area in phase space enclosed by the representative point of the particle, as the particle executes one cycle. It follows that the allowed quantum mechanical states characterized by different values of n divide phase space into equal areas h, at least in the limit in which the *WKB* approximation is valid. This suggests that instead of assigning equal a priori probability to equal regions in phase space, we should assign equal a priori probabilities to each quantum state.

We therefore assume each quantum state of a system is a priori equally probable. This is one of the basic postulates of quantum statistics. The strongest justification of this assumption is its agreement with the experimental data. We have not proved it. We have only given a plausibility argument. In later chapters, when we have developed a little more sophisticated machinery, we will strengthen the plausibility of this assumption, but we will not prove it.

THE BOLTZMANN DISTRIBUTION

We can now derive the correct quantum mechanical distribution for the model with which we are working. The derivation proceeds exactly as did the derivation of the classical Boltzmann distribution, except instead of talking about cells we talk about quantum states, and we do not of course try to pass over to a continuous distribution in phase space. We obtain as our final result

$$N_i = \exp(\alpha - \beta\epsilon_i) \qquad (16.3)$$

where N_i is the number of molecules in the quantum state i, ϵ_i is the energy of a molecule in the state i, and α and β are constants which can be determined from the conditions

$$\Sigma N_i = N \qquad (16.4)$$

$$\Sigma N_i\epsilon_i = E \qquad (16.5)$$

We can, as in the classical case, use (16.5) to identify β as $1/kT$. This together with (16.4) enables us to write (16.3)

$$N_i = \frac{N \exp(-\epsilon_i/kT)}{\displaystyle\sum_i \exp(-\epsilon_i/kT)} \qquad (16.6)$$

This is the correct quantum mechanical distribution for a set of systems which can exchange energy with one another but are otherwise isolated and independent. It is not, as we shall see in Chapter 19, rigorously correct for a gas of identical molecules contained within the same box. However, distribution (16.6), if applied with discretion, is perfectly adequate to handle a dilute gas except in the limit of extremely low temperatures.

It should be remembered that the sum in the denominator is a sum over all quantum states and not over all levels. If we wish to deal with levels rather than states, then

$$N_{i(j)} = \frac{N \exp(-\epsilon_i/kT)}{\displaystyle\sum_i \sum_{j=1}^{Z_i} \exp(-\epsilon_i/kT)} \qquad (16.7)$$

where Z_i is the degeneracy of the ith level. If we then define N_i as the number of particles in the ith level we have

$$\frac{N_i}{N} = \frac{\displaystyle\sum_{j=1}^{Z_i} \exp(-\epsilon_i/kT)}{\displaystyle\sum_i \sum_{j=1}^{Z_i} \exp(-\epsilon_i/kT)} = \frac{Z_i \exp(-\epsilon_i/kT)}{\displaystyle\sum_i Z_i \exp(-\epsilon_i/kT)} \qquad (16.8)$$

THE PARTITION FUNCTION

In using the Boltzmann distribution to study the equilibrium properties of a collection of molecules which are independent and isolated, a quantity often encountered is the molecule or system partition function q which we define

$$q = \sum_i \exp(-\epsilon_i/kT) \qquad (16.9)$$

where the sum is over states and not levels.

Many of the properties of such a collection of molecules can be expressed in terms of q. For example, the average energy of a molecule is given by

$$<\epsilon> = kT^2\frac{\partial}{\partial T}(\ln q) \qquad (16.10)$$

THE EINSTEIN MODEL OF A SOLID

In discussing the specific heat of solids, in Chapter 14, we introduced the Einstein model of a solid. In the Einstein model, each atom is assumed to be bound to its lattice site by a set of springs. If the atom is displaced in the x, y, or z direction and released it will, in the case of an isotropic solid, oscillate with frequency ν. The various atoms are assumed to be weakly coupled together with just enough coupling to allow energy to be exchanged between one atom and another without otherwise disturbing the motion of the atom.

We have in the Einstein model an example of a collection of systems which satisfy the conditions discussed in the preceding section. We can therefore use the Boltzmann distribution.

The energy levels of a three-dimensional simple harmonic oscillator are given by

$$\epsilon_{n_1 n_2 n_3} = (n_1 + \tfrac{1}{2})h\nu + (n_2 + \tfrac{1}{2})h\nu + (n_3 + \tfrac{1}{2})h\nu \qquad (16.11)$$

where n_1, n_2, and n_3 are integers ranging from 0 to ∞. The distribution of atoms among the various oscillator states is thus

$$N_{n_1 n_2 n_3} = \frac{N \exp(-\epsilon_{n_1 n_2 n_3}/kT)}{\sum_{n_1} \sum_{n_2} \sum_{n_3} \exp(-\epsilon_{n_1 n_2 n_3}/kT)} \qquad (16.12)$$

where $N_{n_1 n_2 n_3}$ is the number of atoms in the oscillator state characterized by the values n_1, n_2, n_3.

The average energy of an atom is

$$<\epsilon> = kT^2\frac{\partial}{\partial T}(\ln q) \qquad (16.13)$$

where
$$q = \sum_{n_1} \sum_{n_2} \sum_{n_3} \exp\left(\frac{-\epsilon_{n_1 n_2 n_3}}{kT}\right)$$

$$= \exp\left(\frac{-3h\nu}{2kT}\right)\left[\sum_n \exp\left(\frac{-nh\nu}{kT}\right)\right]^3$$

$$= \exp\left(\frac{-3h\nu}{2kT}\right)\left[1 - \exp\left(\frac{-h\nu}{kT}\right)\right]^{-3} \tag{16.14}$$

Substituting (16.14) in (16.13) we obtain

$$<\epsilon> = 3\left[\frac{h\nu}{2} + \frac{h\nu}{\exp(h\nu/kT) - 1}\right] \tag{16.15}$$

The specific heat per atom of the solid is

$$c_V = \partial <\epsilon>/\partial T = 3k\left\{\frac{(h\nu/kT)^2 \exp(h\nu/kT)}{[\exp(h\nu/kT) - 1]^2}\right\} \tag{16.16}$$

If $kT \gg h\nu$ then $\exp(h\nu/kT) \approx 1 + (h\nu/kT) \approx 1$ and therefore

$$c_V \approx 3k \tag{16.17}$$

If $kT \ll h\nu$ then $\exp(h\nu/kT) - 1 \approx \exp(h\nu/kT)$ and therefore

$$c_V \approx 3k(h\nu/kT)^2 \exp(-h\nu/kT) \tag{16.18}$$

According to (16.16) the specific heat per atom is $3k$ at high temperatures, and approaches zero at low temperature in the manner given by Eq. (16.18). Classically, the theoretical value of the specific heat is $3k$ at all temperatures. Experimentally, the specific heat falls off to zero as the temperature approaches zero, but not quite, according to Eq. (16.18).   By introducing quantum statistics, we have overcome the gross disagreement between the classical theoretical results and the experimental results.   The remaining disagreement can be shown to be due to the inadequacies of the Einstein model, rather than any error in theory.   We will not, however, refine our model of a solid since our main aim is to understand the basic principles of quantum statistics, not to proliferate applications.

BLACK BODY RADIATION

In Chapter 13, we saw that the radiation in a cavity could be broken down into a set of normal modes, the equation of motion of a normal mode being that of a simple harmonic oscillator.   The number of normal modes with frequency between ν and $\nu + d\nu$ in a cubical cavity of unit volume was given by $n_\nu d\nu$ where

$$n_\nu = 8\pi\nu^2/c^3 \tag{16.19}$$

Each of these normal modes is independent and distinguishable.

According to the quantum mechanical Boltzmann distribution, the average energy of a simple harmonic oscillator which can exchange energy with an object at temperature T is

$$<\epsilon> = \frac{h\nu}{2} + \frac{h\nu}{\exp(h\nu/kT) - 1} \tag{16.20}$$

It follows that the energy per unit volume contained in the normal modes with frequency between ν and $\nu + d\nu$ is $E_\nu d\nu$ where

$$E_\nu = n_\nu <\epsilon> = \frac{4\pi h\nu^3}{c^3} + \frac{8\pi h\nu^3/c^3}{\exp(h\nu/kT) - 1} \tag{16.21}$$

The first term in (16.21) is a constant, and since all we can measure is a change in energy, it represents an immeasurable zero point energy which we will neglect.

The last term in (16.21) agrees very closely with the experimental data.

THE SPECIFIC HEAT OF IDEAL DIATOMIC GASES

In comparing the experimental and theoretical values for the specific heats of diatomic gases, we saw in Chapter 14 that the classical theory gave a good fit to the experimental data for the translational degrees of freedom in the gas region, but broke down in handling the vibrational and rotational degrees of freedom. In the present section we will therefore concentrate on the vibrational and rotational degrees of freedom. In discussing the specific heat of metals we will take up the translational degrees of freedom, and we will find that the aforementioned agreement is partly fortuitous and that our theory needs to be further refined before we can properly handle the translational degrees of freedom at all densities and temperatures.

The rotational and vibrational degrees of freedom of the molecules are independent and distinguishable modes of motion and we can apply the Boltzmann distribution.

The average energy of a simple harmonic oscillator is, as we have seen in the preceding section,

$$<\epsilon> = \frac{h\nu}{2} + \frac{h\nu}{\exp(h\nu/kT) - 1} \tag{16.22}$$

The vibrational degree of freedom therefore contributes

$$c_{vib} = \frac{\partial <\epsilon>}{\partial T} = k\left\{\frac{(h\nu/kT)^2 \exp(h\nu/kT)}{[\exp(h\nu/kT) - 1]^2}\right\} \tag{16.23}$$

to the specific heat per molecule.

The energy levels of a rigid two-dimensional rotator with moment of inertia I are given by

$$\epsilon_n = n(n + 1)\hbar^2/2I \tag{16.24}$$

with a degeneracy $Z_n = 2n + 1$. Using the Boltzmann distribution, we obtain for the average energy

$$<\epsilon> = \frac{\sum\limits_{n=0}^{\infty} \sum\limits_{j=1}^{Z_n} \epsilon_n \exp(-\epsilon_n/kT)}{\sum\limits_{n=0}^{\infty} \sum\limits_{j=1}^{Z_n} \exp(-\epsilon_n/kT)}$$

$$= kT^2 \frac{\partial}{\partial T}\left[\ln \sum_{n=0}^{\infty} (2n + 1)\exp(-\epsilon_n/kT)\right] \tag{16.25}$$

The two rotational degrees of freedom therefore contribute

$$c_{rot} = \frac{\partial <\epsilon>}{\partial T} = \frac{\partial}{\partial T}\left\{kT^2 \frac{\partial}{\partial T}\left[\ln \sum_{n=0}^{\infty} (2n + 1)\exp\left(-\frac{n(n + 1)\hbar^2}{2IkT}\right)\right]\right\} \tag{16.26}$$

to the specific heat per molecule.

If we now let the translational specific heat per molecule be $3k/2$, then the total specific heat per molecule for a diatomic gas is

$$c_V = (3k/2) + k\left\{\frac{(h\nu/kT)^2 \exp(h\nu/kT)}{[\exp(h\nu/kT) - 1]^2}\right\}$$

$$+ k\left\{\frac{\partial}{dT}\left[T^2 \frac{\partial}{\partial T}\left[\ln \sum_{n=0}^{\infty} (2n + 1)\exp\left(-\frac{n(n + 1)\hbar^2}{2IkT}\right)\right]\right]\right\} \tag{16.27}$$

By proper choice of ν and I we can get (16.27) to fit the experimental specific heat data for heteronuclear diatomic molecules such as HD or NO. The values of ν and I so obtained can also be shown to agree well with the same information obtained by other experiments. Equation (16.27) does not, however, give completely correct results for the rotational contribution to the specific heat of H_2. The difficulty can be shown to be due to the fact that for homonuclear diatomic molecules we cannot neglect the effect of the nuclear spins on the specific heat. The difficulty lies in our model of the diatomic molecule rather than in the theory and we will therefore not pursue the subject further.

From the above results it is apparent that we can use the specific heat data to tell us something about the actual structure of molecules. Knowledge of ν provides us with information about the binding force between atoms and knowledge of I provides us with information about the spacing of atoms in a molecule.

THE SPECIFIC HEAT OF METALS

So far the Boltzmann distribution $C \exp(-\epsilon_i/kT)$ has been able to provide very good agreement between theory and experiment. We will now take up a situation where it fails.

Consider a collection of point particles of mass m in a cubic box of volume V. The energy levels for a single particle in a box are

$$\epsilon_{n_1 n_2 n_3} = \frac{(n_1^2 + n_2^2 + n_3^2)h^2}{8mV^{2/3}} \tag{16.28}$$

where n_1, n_2, and n_3 are positive integers. If we use a Boltzmann distribution, then we obtain for the average energy of a particle

$$<\epsilon> = \frac{\sum_{n_1} \sum_{n_2} \sum_{n_3} \epsilon_{n_1 n_2 n_3} \exp(-\epsilon_{n_1 n_2 n_3}/kT)}{\sum_{n_1} \sum_{n_2} \sum_{n_3} \exp(-\epsilon_{n_1 n_2 n_3}/kT)}$$

$$= 3kT^2 \frac{\partial}{\partial T}\left[\ln \sum_{n=1}^{\infty} \exp\left(-\frac{n^2 h^2}{8mV^{2/3}kT}\right)\right] \tag{16.29}$$

For $T \gg h^2/8mV^{2/3}k$

$$<\epsilon> \approx 3kT^2 \frac{\partial}{\partial T}\left[\ln \int_0^{\infty} \exp\left(-\frac{n^2 h^2}{8mV^{2/3}kT}\right)dn \right]$$

$$= \frac{3kT}{2} \tag{16.30}$$

Therefore, as long as $T \gg h^2/8mV^{2/3}k$, we obtain the usual classical result. For 1 cubic centimeter of hydrogen, $h^2/8mV^{2/3}k \sim 10^{-14}$. Long before we arrive at this temperature hydrogen liquefies, and we can no longer neglect the interaction of the molecules. We therefore expect the classical result to be applicable to gaseous hydrogen at ordinary temperatures, and this agrees with experiment.

But suppose we consider the electrons in a metal to be a gas of free electrons as discussed in Chapter 14. For 1 cubic centimeter of an electron gas $h^2/8mV^{2/3}k \sim 10^{-11}$. We would therefore expect the classical result also to be valid for an electron gas at ordinary temperatures. But, as we have seen in Chapter 14, at ordinary temperatures the electronic specific heat in a metal is much less than $3k/2$.

We might suspect that the error lies in assuming the electrons in a metal to be free, i.e., essentially noninteracting, since the Coulomb force between electrons is a strong and long-range force. We cannot at this stage refute this argument. But we shall see in succeeding chapters that the Coulomb interaction is not the source of our difficulties.

The fundamental error lies in assuming that two particles which are contained in the same box of volume V can be represented by a model in which we have two particles each in a separate box of volume V. Even if there is no classical force between these particles, there will be quantum mechanical effects which cannot be ignored.

These effects will manifest themselves when the density of particles in phase space becomes of the same order of magnitude as the density of the cells. To get some idea of the densities and temperatures at which this occurs, consider a box of volume V containing N particles at a temperature T. The average momentum p of the particles will be of the same order of magnitude as $(2m\bar{\epsilon})^{1/2} = (3mkT)^{1/2}$ where $\bar{\epsilon}$ is the average energy. The total volume in momentum space occupied by the molecules will be of the order of $4\pi\bar{p}^3/3 \sim (4\pi/3)(3mkT)^{3/2}$. The total volume in phase space occupied by the molecules will thus be of the order of $(4\pi V/3)(3mkT)^{3/2}$ and thus the density of representative points in phase space will be of the order of

$$[N/(4\pi V/3)(3mkT)^{3/2}] \sim n/(mkT)^{3/2}$$

The density of cells in the phase space for a particle in a box is of the order of $1/h^3$. We therefore expect quantum effects to become significant if

$$n/(mkT)^{3/2} > 1/h^3 \tag{16.31}$$

or

$$n > (mkT/h^2)^{3/2} \tag{16.32}$$

Letting $T_0 = 300°K$ and m_e the mass of an electron and noting that $(m_e kT_0/h^2) \sim 10^{12}$ cm^{-2} = 10^{16} m^{-2} we have

$$n > (mT/m_e T_0)^{3/2} \, 10^{18} \text{ cm}^{-3} \tag{16.33}$$

The density of electrons in a metal is of the order of 10^{22} cm^{-3}, and therefore we expect quantum effects at ordinary temperatures.

The density of hydrogen at atmospheric pressure and $T = 300°K$ is of the order of 10^{16} cm^{-3} and $(mT/m_e T_0)^{3/2} \sim 10^6$. For hydrogen gas we are well above the range where we have to worry about quantum effects.

CONCLUSION

Classically, the correct distribution for a collection of identical systems which are able to exchange energy with one another but are otherwise independent and distinguishable is

$$\phi(\mathbf{p}, \mathbf{q}) = C \exp[-\epsilon(\mathbf{p}, \mathbf{q})/kT] \tag{16.34}$$

Quantum mechanically we obtain

$$N_i = C \exp(-\epsilon_i/kT) \tag{16.35}$$

If $kT \gg |\epsilon_{i+1} - \epsilon_i|$ then the discrete distribution can be replaced by the continuous distribution (16.34).

The distribution (16.35) is rigorously correct for independent and distinguishable systems. If, however, we are dealing with a collection of systems in the same box, e.g., a gas, it must be used with caution.

In the first place, the interaction between the particles may not be negligible. As the density increases, this difficulty becomes increasingly more significant.

In the second place, if our systems are identical, then even if there is no classical force of interaction between them, there will be quantum mechanical effects which cannot be neglected, and which become particularly significant at high densities and/or low temperatures. Gases in which these quantum mechanical effects appear are then said to be quantum degenerate.

PROBLEMS

1. Prove that the specific heat per molecule is given by

$$c_V = (1/kT^2)(\overline{\epsilon^2} - \overline{\epsilon}^2)$$

2. What fraction of diatomic molecules have rotational energy greater than kT?

3. Consider 1000 diatomic molecules at a temperature equal to $h\nu/2k$. Find the number in each of the three lowest vibrational energy states.

4. Calculate the rotational specific heat of hydrogen at 34°K, 85°K and 283°K, given that

$$\theta_r = h^2/8\pi^2 Ik = 85°K$$

5. Calculate the constant volume specific heat of carbon dioxide at 1200°K. Carbon dioxide has three fundamental vibration frequencies with wave numbers (ν/c) of 667.5 cm^{-1} (double), 1388 cm^{-1}, and 2350 cm^{-1}.

6. The potential energy V between the two atoms in a hydrogen molecule is given by the following (empirical) expression, where r is the distance between the atoms and D, a and r_0 are constants with the values given below:

$$V = D\{\exp[-2a(r - r_0)] - 2\exp[-a(r - r_0)]\}$$

Calculate the quantum of energy required to set the molecule:
   (a) rotating (this may be taken to be $\hbar^2/2I$, where $\hbar$ is Planck's constant and I is the moment of inertia of the molecule);
   (b) vibrating (this is $\hbar\omega$, where ω is the angular frequency of vibration).

Hence estimate the temperatures at which rotation and vibration begin to contribute to the specific heat of hydrogen gas. $[D = 7 \times 10^{-12}$ erg; $a = 2 \times 10^8$ cm^{-1}; $r_0 = 8 \times 10^{-9}$ cm]

7. Show that the energy per photon in black body radiation is 2.701 kT.

8. A material is composed of atoms having a magnetic moment μ which may be oriented in the direction of, or opposite to, a field B with energy $-\mu B$ and $+\mu B$ respectively. Find the paramagnetic moment and Curie constant.

9. According to quantum theory and in agreement with experiment, when atoms of silver vapor, which have a magnetic moment μ, are in a magnetic field, the molecules align themselves either parallel or antiparallel to the field, and in no other orientation. Find the relative number of atoms of silver vapor aligned parallel and antiparallel to a magnetic field of flux density 0.1 Wb/m^2, at a temperature of 1000°K.

10. Derive the Stefan-Boltzmann radiation law for a
    (a) three-dimensional space
    (b) two-dimensional space.

11. Derive the Einstein specific heat for a two-dimensional crystal.

12. We have used the Einstein model to discuss the specific heat of a solid. A better model is the Debye model. In its simplest form this model consists in the following assumptions: (1) a solid is a continuous medium which can be set in vibration; (2) the medium is nondispersive, i.e., a wave of any frequency will travel with the same velocity v_0; (3) both transverse and longitudinal waves can be propagated in the medium; (4) the behavior of the medium can be described in terms of the $3N$ normal modes of motion having the lowest frequencies, where N is the number of atoms in the solid. Using the Debye model, derive an expression for the specific heat of a solid, and show that at low temperatures the specific heat is proportional to T^3.

13. Consider a two-dimensional isotropic elastic sheet to have $2N$ degrees of freedom. Apply the method of Debye to develop an equation for the specific heat of this system, and show that near 0°K it reduces to a T-square law.

14. In the Debye model one assumes the dispersion relation for photons to be of the form $\nu = Ak$ where k is the wave number. With this assumption, the specific heat at low temperatures is proportional to T^3. Suppose we had assumed a dispersion relation of the form $\nu = Ak^2$. Show that at low temperatures the specific heat would then be proportional to $T^{3/2}$.

Chapter 17

QUANTUM STATISTICS OF DEPENDENT SYSTEMS

INTRODUCTION

In using classical statistical mechanics to study the properties of an ideal gas of N particles in a volume V we assumed that each molecule could be treated as if it were moving independently of the other molecules in the container. Implicitly we were assuming that if we had a collection of containers each of volume V and each containing a single molecule weakly coupled to the other molecules, then the average behavior of one of these isolated molecules could be used to describe the average behavior of one of the molecules in an actual gas.

In studying the properties of a real gas of N particles in a volume V, we found in Chapter 13 that it was possible to introduce the effect of molecular interactions to a first approximation by considering the behavior of a collection of weakly coupled containers of volume V, each with two rather than one molecule in it, and assuming that the average behavior of any two particles in the actual gas was the same as the average behavior of one of these independent pairs.

The natural extension of these ideas is to construct a collection of weakly coupled boxes of volume V, each having N molecules in it, and then to assume that the average properties of an actual gas of N molecules in a volume V is the same as the average properties of one of the members of this collection. As before, the boxes are so coupled that energy can be exchanged. Other than for this exchange of energy, the motion of the molecules in one box is unaffected by the motion of the molecules in any other box. This situation is schematically represented in Figure 17.1.

Classically, the interaction between two molecules contained within the same box is negligible except when the molecules come within very close range. Quantum mechanically however, a molecule in a box cannot be thought of as

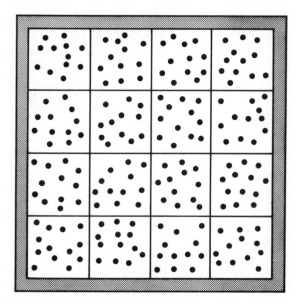

Fig. 17.1

occupying a specific position. If we calculate the expectation value for the position of a molecule which is in a particular energy state, we obtain a function which has nonzero values throughout the box. It follows that we can never entirely neglect the quantum mechanical interaction between two particles in the same box, and the model which we used in the preceding chapter is not completely correct, even for a dilute gas. We will therefore work in this section with the model depicted in Figure 17.1, which in principle takes into account all interactions within the gas, and should be valid not only for gases but for any assembly of N particles whether in the gaseous, liquid, or solid state.

THE GIBBS CANONICAL DISTRIBUTION

We have introduced a number of concepts which we will make frequent use of in the chapters which follow, and it will be profitable to pause and define a few terms before we go any further.

We will refer to one of the N particles which make up a gas as a system. We shall refer to the gas as a whole as an assembly. We shall refer to the collection of gases represented in Figure 17.1 as an ensemble. We will always deal with ensembles containing a large number of assemblies. As we shall see later, the ensemble we have been dealing with is a so-called canonical ensemble, but until we learn more about different kinds of ensembles we will simply use the word ensemble. Thus a set of systems is an assembly, and a set of identical assemblies an ensemble.

We define E_i as the energy eigenvalue of an assembly considered as a single entity in the eigenstate i; N_i as the number of assemblies in the assembly state i; $\mathcal{E}$ as the total energy in the ensemble; M as the number of systems in the ensemble; N as the number of systems in an assembly, and $\mathcal{N}$ as the number of assemblies in the ensemble. It follows that

$$\Sigma \, N_i = \mathcal{N} \tag{17.1}$$

$$\Sigma \, N_i E_i = \mathcal{E} \tag{17.2}$$

$$N\mathcal{N} = M \tag{17.3}$$

To find the distribution of assemblies among the different assembly states, we simply apply the Boltzmann distribution to the ensemble. The assembly now takes the place of a molecule, and can, if desired, be thought of as a monstrous macromolecule. We then have

$$\frac{N_i}{\mathcal{N}} = \frac{\exp(-E_i/kT)}{\sum\limits_{i} \exp(-E_i/kT)} \tag{17.4}$$

In order to distinguish the distribution (17.4) from the Boltzmann distribution for which the energy levels are usually system energy levels and where we are interested in the distribution of systems among system states, we shall refer to the distribution (17.4) as the Gibbs canonical distribution. We will sometimes refer to this distribution as simply the canonical distribution, or the Gibbs distribution.

The Gibbs distribution (17.4) gives us the probability that a particular assembly in the ensemble will be in the assembly state i. We can, if desired, view all of the assemblies except the one of interest as constituting a huge heat bath in which the assembly of interest is immersed and which maintains this assembly at a temperature T. The Gibbs distribution can then be interpreted as the probability that an assembly which is maintained at a temperature T will be in the assembly state i.

The Gibbs distribution is the fundamental distribution of equilibrium statistical mechanics or more correctly, one of a set of equivalent fundamental distributions. All the equilibrium properties of an assembly can in principle be derived from this distribution, which is not only valid for assemblies of weakly interacting systems such as a dilute gas, but is also valid for dense gases, liquids, solids, and quantum degenerate gases.

Although the Gibbs distribution is in principle the answer to all of our problems, it is, as we shall see in the following chapters, not easy to apply in practice, except in a number of simple cases. We will consider one of these simple cases later in this chapter, and reserve the more difficult problems for the succeeding chapters.

THE ASSEMBLY PARTITION FUNCTION

In using the Gibbs distribution to study the equilibrium properties of an assembly we can usually express the desired result in terms of the assembly partition function Q which we define

$$Q = \sum_i \exp\{-E_i/kT)$$ (17.5)

This function is also referred to as the canonical partition function. For example, if we wish to find the average energy of an assembly, we have

$$\bar{E} = \frac{\sum\limits_i E_i \exp(-E_i/kT)}{\sum\limits_i \exp(-E_i/kT)}$$

$$= kT^2 \frac{\partial}{\partial T}(\ln Q)$$ (17.6)

We shall later show that it is possible to express any thermodynamic function in terms of the assembly partition function. It follows that if we know Q we can evaluate any thermodynamic property of the system. However, we will for the time being consider each case separately.

RADIATION IN A CAVITY

In Chapter 13 we saw that the radiation in a cavity could be broken down into a set of normal modes, the equation of motion of a normal mode being that of a simple harmonic oscillator.

In Chapter 16 we used the Boltzmann distribution to evaluate the equilibrium distribution of energy among the various normal modes. In the present chapter we wish to reconsider the same problem, using the Gibbs distribution.

If we consider the radiation in a cavity to constitute an assembly, then the energy eigenvalues are given by

$$E_{n_1 n_2 \ldots n_i \ldots} = (n_1 + \tfrac{1}{2})h\nu_1 + (n_2 + \tfrac{1}{2})h\nu_2 + \ldots + (n_i + \tfrac{1}{2})h\nu_i + \ldots$$ (17.7)

where the n_i are integers which run from 0 to ∞, and the ν_i the frequencies associated with the normal modes. Each set of n_i which we designate $\{n_i\}$

characterizes a particular eigenstate. Equation (17.7) can be expressed more simply as

$$E(n_i) = \sum_i (n_i + \tfrac{1}{2})h\nu_i \qquad (17.8)$$

If $N(n_i)$ is the probability that an assembly in an ensemble of assemblies is in the state $\{n_i\}$, then using the Gibbs distribution we have

$$N(n_i) = \frac{N \exp[-\sum_i (n_i + \tfrac{1}{2})h\nu_i/kT]}{\sum_{\{n_i\}} \exp[-\sum_i (n_i + \tfrac{1}{2})h\nu_i/kT]} \qquad (17.9)$$

where $\sum_{\{n_i\}}$ represents a sum over all possible sets of n_i. The average energy of an assembly is

$$\bar{E} = kT^2 \frac{\partial}{\partial T}(\ln Q) \qquad (17.10)$$

where the assembly partition function Q is given by

$$Q = \sum_{\{n_i\}} \exp[-\sum_i (n_i + \tfrac{1}{2})h\nu_i/kT] \qquad (17.11)$$

Equation (17.11) can be rewritten

$$Q = \sum_{\{n_i\}} \prod_i \exp[-(n_i + \tfrac{1}{2})h\nu_i/kT] \qquad (17.12)$$

It can be shown that as long as there is no restriction on the n_i

$$\sum_{\{n_i\}} \prod_i [\ ] = \prod_i \sum_{n_i=0}^{\infty} [\ ] \qquad (17.13)$$

The reader can convince himself of (17.13) most easily by considering a few simple examples.

Using the relation (17.13) in (17.12) we obtain

$$Q = \prod_i \sum_{n_i} \exp[-(n_i + \tfrac{1}{2})h\nu_i/kT]$$

$$= \prod_i [\exp(-h\nu_i/2kT)][1 - \exp(-h\nu_i/kT)]^{-1} \qquad (17.14)$$

Substituting (17.14) in (17.10) we obtain

$$\bar{E} = \sum_i \frac{h\nu_i}{2} + \sum_i \frac{h\nu_i}{\exp(h\nu_i/kT) - 1} \qquad (17.15)$$

The first term on the right-hand side of (17.15) is infinite. It is, however, constant and therefore cannot be measured directly since we ordinarily observe only changes in energy. We will therefore neglect it and simply write

$$\bar{E} = \sum_i \frac{h\nu_i}{\exp(h\nu_i/kT) - 1} \qquad (17.16)$$

In the continuous approximation, there are, as we have shown earlier, $(8\pi\nu^2/c^3)d\nu$ normal modes with frequency between ν and $\nu + d\nu$ in a unit volume. It follows that

$$\bar{E} \approx \int \frac{8\pi\nu^2}{c^3} \left[\frac{h\nu}{\exp(h\nu/kT) - 1} \right] d\nu \tag{17.17}$$

This result agrees with the result which we previously obtained, and with the experimental results.

CONCLUSION

The fundamental distribution of equilibrium statistical mechanics is the Gibbs distribution which is given by Eq. (17.4). All of the equilibrium properties of an assembly, whether in the gaseous, liquid, or solid state, can in principle be derived from this distribution.

We will in the following chapters apply the Gibbs distribution to a number of different problems, and in particular to assemblies of identical and essentially noninteracting particles contained in the same box.

Before we can tackle the latter problem it will be necessary to discuss the quantum mechanical description of a collection of identical particles. This will be the main objective of Chapter 18.

18

THE QUANTUM MECHANICS OF AN ASSEMBLY OF IDENTICAL PARTICLES

INTRODUCTION

In Chapter 15 we were concerned with the quantum mechanics of a single isolated system. In this chapter we will be concerned with the quantum mechanics of an assembly of identical systems.

We will restrict ourselves to a discussion of the simplest type of systems. At first glance the simplest system would seem to be a point mass without any internal structure. It is found, however, that even the so-called fundamental particles cannot be treated as structureless point masses, but can be handled by assuming that they are point masses with a certain intrinsic angular momentum.

Before discussing in detail the properties of an assembly of identical particles, we will therefore find it necessary to briefly consider the topic of angular momentum.

INTRINSIC ANGULAR MOMENTUM

The wave function of a structureless point mass is a function of x, y, z, and t. Let us suppose that in addition to its translational degrees of freedom, a particle possesses an intrinsic angular momentum, and that the effect of this additional property can be included in the wave function by introducing a new variable σ so that the wave function now is a function of x, y, z, σ, and t. In order to extract information from a wave function it is necessary to define operators corresponding to physical quantities. The addition of a functional dependence of the wave function on the variable σ is therefore meaningless until we define operators which when they operate on Φ, considered as a function of σ, provide us with some measurable information about the angular momentum.

Let $\hat{S}_x$, $\hat{S}_y$, and $\hat{S}_z$ be the operators corresponding to the x, y, and z components of intrinsic angular momentum. Instead of specifying the exact form of these operators, it is possible to provide the same information in the following set of commutation relations

$$\hat{S}_x\hat{S}_y - \hat{S}_y\hat{S}_x = i\hbar\,\hat{S}_z \qquad (18.1)$$

$$\hat{S}_y\hat{S}_z - \hat{S}_z\hat{S}_y = i\hbar\,\hat{S}_x \qquad (18.2)$$

$$\hat{S}_z\hat{S}_x - \hat{S}_x\hat{S}_z = i\hbar\,\hat{S}_y \qquad (18.3)$$

Using the above commutation relations, it is possible to show that the only allowed values of the total intrinsic angular momentum are $\sqrt{s(s+1)}\,\hbar$ where $s = 0$, $1/2$, 1, $3/2$, ...

We shall assume that the particles with which we are dealing have a fixed value of total intrinsic angular momentum characterized by a particular value of s. For the sake of brevity we often say simply that the intrinsic angular momentum or spin is s.

It can further be shown from the commutation relations alone that $\hat{S}^2$ commutes with $\hat{S}_x$, $\hat{S}_y$, and $\hat{S}_z$. It is therefore possible to find a set of eigenfunctions which are simultaneously eigenfunctions of $\hat{S}^2$ and any one of the components $\hat{S}_x$, $\hat{S}_y$, or $\hat{S}_z$. Since $\hat{S}_x$, $\hat{S}_y$, and $\hat{S}_z$ do not commute, it is not possible to find a set of eigenfunctions which are simultaneously eigenfunctions of all four of the above operators.

It can finally be shown that if we have a particle with fixed intrinsic angular momentum $\sqrt{s(s+1)}\,\hbar$ which is in an eigenstate which is simultaneously an eigenstate of $\hat{S}^2$ and $\hat{S}_z$, then the only possible eigenvalues of the operator $\hat{S}_z$ are $-s\hbar$, $(-s+1)\hbar$, ..., $(s-1)\hbar$, $s\hbar$. We assume without proof that these eigenvalues are nondegenerate.

For a particle with intrinsic angular momentum $\sqrt{s(s+1)}\,\hbar$ there are therefore $(2s+1)$ independent spin eigenfunctions which we designate χ_1, χ_2, ..., χ_{2s+1}.

For convenience we shall assume that a particle is always in a specific spatial eigenstate $\psi_n(x, y, z)$, and in a particular angular momentum eigenstate $\chi_m(\sigma)$, and that, neglecting the time dependence, we can write the resulting state function

$$\phi_i \equiv \phi_{nm}(x, y, z, \sigma) = \psi_n(x, y, z)\chi_m(\sigma) \qquad (18.4)$$

SYMMETRY

Let us consider an assembly consisting of two identical and noninteracting particles contained in a box. The Hamiltonian for the system is

$$H = \sum_{i=1}^{3} \frac{p_i^2(1)}{2m} + \sum_{i=1}^{3} \frac{p_i^2(2)}{2m} \tag{18.5}$$

Let us define

$$\hat{H}(1) = -\frac{\hbar^2}{2m} \sum_{i=1}^{3} \frac{\partial^2}{\partial x_i^2(1)} \tag{18.6}$$

$$\hat{H}(2) = -\frac{\hbar^2}{2m} \sum_{i=1}^{3} \frac{\partial^2}{\partial x_i^2(2)} \tag{18.7}$$

$$\phi(1, 2) = \phi[x(1), \sigma(1), x(2), \sigma(2)] \tag{18.8}$$

Schrodinger's equation for the assembly then takes the form

$$[\hat{H}(1) + \hat{H}(2)]\phi(1, 2) = E\phi(1, 2) \tag{18.9}$$

If we interchange 1 and 2 in (18.9), noting that $\hat{H}(1) + \hat{H}(2) = \hat{H}(2) + \hat{H}(1)$, we obtain $[\hat{H}(1) + \hat{H}(2)]\phi(2, 1) = E\phi(2, 1)$. Thus if $\phi(1, 2)$ is a solution of (18.9), then $\phi(2, 1)$ is also a solution. It follows that any linear combination of $\phi(1, 2)$ and $\phi(2, 1)$ is a solution, i.e.,

$$a\phi(1, 2) + b\phi(2, 1) \equiv \phi(12) \tag{18.10}$$

is a solution.

Although any linear combination (18.10) is a solution to (18.9), it turns out that not all of these solutions are physically permissible. It is found experimentally that if we have two identical particles contained in the same box, then there is no way of experimentally distinguishing between the two particles. For our assembly of two particles it follows that all physical predictions such as expectation values must be symmetric in the exchange of the coordinates of the two particles, i.e., they must be independent of which particle we label particle 1 and which we label 2. In particular

$$|\phi(12)| = |\phi(21)| \tag{18.11}$$

It follows from (18.11) that

$$\phi(21) = e^{i\theta}\phi(12) \tag{18.12}$$

If we interchange 1 and 2 in Eq. (18.12), the equation remains valid, and we obtain

$$\phi(12) = e^{i\theta}\phi(21) \tag{18.13}$$

Substituting (18.13) on the right-hand side of (18.12) we obtain

$$\phi(21) = e^{i2\theta}\phi(21) \tag{18.14}$$

It follows that $e^{i2\theta} = 1$ or $2\theta = n(2\pi)$ where n is an integer. Thus $e^{i\theta} = \pm 1$, and (18.12) becomes

$$\phi(21) = \pm\, \phi(12) \tag{18.15}$$

Substituting (18.10) in (18.15) we have

$$(a \pm b)[\phi(1, 2) \pm \phi(2, 1)] = 0 \tag{18.16}$$

It follows that if $\phi(1, 2) \neq \pm\, \phi(2, 1)$ then

$$a = \pm b \tag{18.17}$$

Thus if $\phi(1, 2)$ is a solution to (18.9) it is not necessarily a physically permissible solution. However, the solution

$$\phi(12) = a[\phi(1, 2) \pm \phi(2, 1)] \tag{18.18}$$

is a physically permissible solution.

The constant a can be determined from the normalization condition. It will not necessarily be the same for the two cases.

Since interchanging 1 and 2 in (18.18) has no effect on the physical properties of the assembly, we can drop the argument (12). We will, however, distinguish between the two cases by writing

$$\phi(+) = \text{const}\,[\phi(1, 2) + \phi(2, 1)] \tag{18.19}$$

$$\phi(-) = \text{const}\,[\phi(1, 2) - \phi(2, 1)] \tag{18.20}$$

We call (18.19) a symmetric wave function since interchanging the coordinates of the two particles leaves the wave function unchanged. We call (18.20) an antisymmetric wave function since interchanging the coordinates of the two particles changes the sign of the wave function.

THE STATE FUNCTIONS FOR AN ASSEMBLY OF TWO IDENTICAL PARTICLES

In order to solve (18.9) we use the technique of separation of variables. Let us assume

$$\phi(1, 2) = \phi_i(1)\phi_j(2) \tag{18.21}$$

where ϕ_i and ϕ_j are at this point arbitrary functions of the variables 1 and 2 respectively. Substituting (18.21) in (18.9) and dividing by $\phi_i(1)\phi_j(2)$ we obtain

$$\frac{\hat{H}(1)\phi_i(1)}{\phi_i(1)} + \frac{\hat{H}(2)\phi_j(2)}{\phi_j(2)} = E \tag{18.22}$$

The first term on the left-hand side is a function of the coordinates 1 only, and the second term a function of the coordinates 2 only. The only way that this can be true is if each term is separately equal to a constant. Thus

$$\frac{\hat{H}(1)\phi_i(1)}{\phi_i(1)} = \epsilon_i \tag{18.23}$$

$$\frac{\hat{H}(2)\phi_j(2)}{\phi_j(2)} = \epsilon_j \tag{18.24}$$

$$\epsilon_i + \epsilon_j = E \tag{18.25}$$

Equations (18.23) and (18.24) are formally identical, and are just the Schrodinger equation for a single particle, having eigenfunctions ϕ_n and eigenvalues ϵ_n.

Thus the functions

$$\phi_{ij}(1, 2) = \phi_i(1)\phi_j(2) \tag{18.26}$$

are solutions to (18.9), where ϕ_i and ϕ_j are solutions to the one-particle Schrodinger equation. As stated in the previous section, (18.26) is a mathematically valid solution to (18.9), but not necessarily a physically permissible solution. From (18.26) we obtain two physically permissible solutions,

$$\phi_{ij}(+) = a_{ij}[\phi_i(1)\phi_j(2) + \phi_i(2)\phi_j(1)] \tag{18.27}$$

$$\phi_{ij}(-) = b_{ij}[\phi_i(1)\phi_j(2) - \phi_i(2)\phi_j(1)] \tag{18.28}$$

The a_{ij} can be shown to be equal to $(1/\sqrt{2})^{1+\delta_{ij}}$ where δ_{ij} is the Kronecker delta, and the b_{ij} can be shown to be equal to $1/\sqrt{2}$. There is an infinite number of solutions of the form (18.27) and (18.28) since i and j can assume an infinite number of values. The actual wave function will be a linear combination of these solutions. We shall assume for convenience however, that the system of two particles is always in a state corresponding to a specific value of i and a specific value of j (see Chapter 23).

If our assembly of two particles is in the state (18.27) or (18.28) and we wish to calculate the expectation value of the energy, we find

$$<H> = \epsilon_i + \epsilon_j = E \tag{18.29}$$

where ϵ_i and ϵ_j are the eigenvalues corresponding to the eigenfunctions ϕ_i and ϕ_j.

Since there is no physical difference between the wave functions ϕ_{ij} and ϕ_{ji}, we can describe the state of the two particles by simply saying we have one particle in the state i and one particle in the state j. Or we can construct an energy level diagram as shown in Figure 18.1.

If the state i and j are the same state then

$$\phi_{ii}(+) = 2a_{ii}\phi_i(1)\phi_i(2) \tag{18.30}$$

$$\phi_{ii}(-) = 0 \tag{18.31}$$

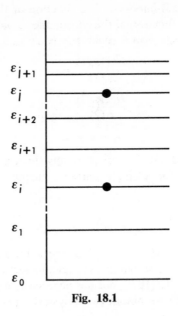

ε_{j+1}

ε_j

ε_{i+2}

ε_{i+1}

ε_i

ε_1

ε_0

Fig. 18.1

A wave function which is identically zero everywhere is physically meaningless. We therefore conclude that if the wave function is antisymmetric we cannot have two particles in the same state. This is the same result we would obtain using the Pauli exclusion principle. The Pauli exclusion principle is thus a consequence of the required antisymmetry of the wave function.

AN ASSEMBLY OF N INDEPENDENT IDENTICAL PARTICLES

The results of the preceding section can be extended to a system of N identical noninteracting particles.

Let us first define a quantity of $e_{i_1 i_2 \ldots i_N}$, as follows: $e_{i_1 \ldots i_N} = +1$ if $i_1 \ldots i_N$ is an even permutation of the numbers $1, 2, \ldots N$; $e_{i_1 \ldots i_N} = -1$ if $i_1 \ldots i_N$ is an odd permutation of the numbers $1, 2 \ldots N$; $e_{i_1 \ldots i_N} = 0$ if one or more indices are repeated.

The physically admissible wave functions of an assembly of N identical noninteracting particles can be shown to assume the form

$$\phi_{i_1 i_2 \ldots i_N}(+) = a_{i_1 \ldots i_N} \sum_{j_1=1}^{N} \ldots \sum_{j_N=1}^{N} |e_{j_1 \ldots j_N}| \phi_{i_1}(j_1) \ldots \phi_{i_N}(j_N) \qquad (18.32)$$

$$\phi_{i_1 i_2 \ldots i_N}(-) = b_{i_1 \ldots i_N} \sum_{j_1=1}^{N} \ldots \sum_{i_N=1}^{N} e_{j_1 \ldots j_N} \phi_{i_1}(j_1) \ldots \phi_{i_N}(j_N)$$

$$= b_{i_1 \ldots i_N} \begin{vmatrix} \phi_{i_1}(1) \ldots & \phi_{i_1}(N) \\ \cdot & \cdot \\ \cdot & \cdot \\ \cdot & \cdot \\ \phi_{i_N}(1) \ldots & \phi_{i_N}(N) \end{vmatrix} \tag{18.33}$$

We can show that $b_{i_1 \ldots i_N} = 1/\sqrt{N!}$

The assembly energy corresponding to the state $\phi_{i_1 i_2 \ldots i_N}$ is

$$E_{i_1 i_2 \ldots i_N} = \epsilon_{i_1} + \epsilon_{i_2} + \ldots + \epsilon_{i_N} \tag{18.34}$$

To illustrate the preceding formulae let us assume that we have an assembly of three particles which are in the single particle states 5, 7, and 9. The two possible wave functions are

$$\begin{aligned}
\phi_{579}(\pm) = (1/\sqrt{6})[&\phi_5(1)\phi_7(2)\phi_9(3) \\
\pm &\phi_5(1)\phi_7(3)\phi_9(2) \pm \phi_5(2)\phi_7(1)\phi_9(3) \\
+ &\phi_5(2)\phi_7(3)\phi_9(1) + \phi_5(3)\phi_7(1)\phi_9(2) \\
\pm &\phi_5(3)\phi_7(2)\phi_9(1)]
\end{aligned} \tag{18.35}$$

and the assembly energy is

$$E_{579} = \epsilon_5 + \epsilon_7 + \epsilon_9 \tag{18.36}$$

Suppose in Eq. (18.33) $i_j = i_k$ then the jth and kth rows in the determinant would be identical, and the determinant would vanish. It follows that if the wave function is antisymmetric we can have only one particle to a state.

We could just as easily have described the state of the assembly by giving the occupation numbers n_i of the various single particle states. The corresponding wave function could be written $\phi_{n_1 n_2 \ldots n_i \ldots}$ and the assembly energy level

$$E_{n_1 n_2 \ldots n_i \ldots} = \sum_{i=1}^{\infty} n_i \epsilon_i \tag{18.37}$$

SPIN AND SYMMETRY

The intrinsic angular momentum of a particle is, as we have seen, given by $\sqrt{s(s+1)}\hbar^2$.

It is found experimentally that the wave function of an assembly of identical particles for which s is an integer will always be symmetric, and the wave function of an assembly of identical particles for which s is half of an odd integer will be antisymmetric.

Examples of "particles" with half odd integer values of s are (1) electrons, (2) protons, (3) neutrons, and (4) atoms, ions, nuclei, or molecules made up of an odd number of electrons, neutrons, and protons.

Examples of "particles" with integer values of s are (1) photons and (2) atoms, ions, nuclei, or molecules made up of an even number of electrons, neutrons, and protons.

Chapter 19

QUANTUM STATISTICS OF INDEPENDENT INDISTINGUISHABLE SYSTEMS

INTRODUCTION

In Chapter 17 we saw that an assembly in equilibrium at a temperature T can be described by the Gibbs distribution.

$$P_i = \frac{N_i}{N} = \frac{\exp(-E_i/kT)}{Q} \tag{19.1}$$

$$Q = \sum_i \exp(-E_i/kT) \tag{19.2}$$

where the summation is over all possible states of the assembly.

In this chapter we wish to apply this distribution to a description of an assembly of identical and independent particles. Those readers encountering the Fermi-Dirac and Bose-Einstein statistics for the first time will find it profitable to read Chapter 5 in conjunction with the present chapter.

FERMI-DIRAC STATISTICS

Let us consider an assembly of N identical noninteracting particles for which the intrinsic angular momentum s is half an odd integer, e.g., a gas of electrons. The possible states of the assembly are given by $\phi_{n_1 n_2 \ldots n_i \ldots}(-)$ where n_i is the occupation number of the ith single-particle state. Since j is half an odd integer, n_i can assume only the values 0 or 1. The corresponding energy is $\sum_i n_i \epsilon_i$.

Applying the Gibbs distribution to the above assembly, we get

$$P_{\ldots n_i \ldots} = \frac{N_{\ldots n_i \ldots}}{\mathcal{N}} = \frac{\exp[-\sum_i n_i \epsilon_i / kT]}{\sum_{\{n_i\}} \exp[-\sum_i n_i \epsilon_i / kT]} \tag{19.3}$$

where the summation in the denominator is over the set of all n_i satisfying the two conditions

$$n_i = 0 \quad \text{or} \quad 1 \tag{19.4}$$

$$\sum n_i = N \tag{19.5}$$

To determine the average number of particles in an assembly in the jth single particle state, we average over the ensemble

$$n_j = \sum_{\{n_i\}} n_j P_{\ldots n_i \ldots} = -kT \frac{\partial}{\partial \epsilon_j} \ln Q \tag{19.6}$$

where the partition function Q is given by

$$Q = \sum_{\{n_i\}} \exp[-\sum_i n_i \epsilon_i / kT]$$

$$= \sum_{\{n_i\}} \prod_i \exp(-n_i \epsilon_i / kT) \tag{19.7}$$

The evaluation of the partition function Q is not an easy task because of the restrictions on the n_i. We will find in Chapter 21 that n_j can be evaluated quite easily if we make use of the grand canonical ensemble rather than the canonical ensemble which we are using in this chapter. We have therefore relegated the evaluation of Q and n_j to Appendix 12 and simply quote the result,

$$n_j = \frac{1}{\exp[(\epsilon_j - \mu)/kT] + 1} \tag{19.8}$$

where μ is a function of N and T which can be determined from the condition

$$\sum n_j = N \tag{19.9}$$

In what follows we will drop the average sign on n_j and simply write n_j. The distribution (19.8) is called the Fermi-Dirac distribution.

The energy levels of a particle in a box are given by

$$\epsilon_{n_1 n_2 n_3} = (n_1^2 + n_2^2 + n_3^2) h^2 / 8m V^{2/3} \tag{19.10}$$

where the n_1, n_2, and n_3 are positive integers and should not be confused with the occupation numbers n_i with which we have been dealing. Since the particles have an intrinsic angular momentum s, each level has a degeneracy of $2s + 1$.

Substituting (19.10) in (19.8) we obtain

$$n_{n_1 n_2 n_3} = \frac{2s + 1}{\exp[(\epsilon_{n_1 n_2 n_3} - \mu)/kT] + 1} \tag{19.11}$$

This is the same distribution which we obtained in Chapter 5 by a slightly different approach. If, as in Chapter 5, we replace the discrete distribution by a continuous distribution, we obtain

$$f_\epsilon = \frac{C\epsilon^{1/2}}{\exp[(\epsilon - \mu)/kT] + 1} \tag{19.12}$$

where
$$C = (2s + 1)2\pi(2m/h^2)^{3/2} \tag{19.13}$$

and $f_\epsilon d\epsilon$ is the number of particles per unit volume with energy between ϵ and $\epsilon + d\epsilon$.

THE ELECTRONIC SPECIFIC HEAT IN METALS

If we apply Fermi-Dirac statistics to the electrons in a metal, then, as was shown in Chapter 5, the distribution f_ϵ at ordinary temperatures differs only slightly from its value at $T = 0$. For many properties of the electron gas in a metal, we can assume the distribution is the same as the distribution at $T = 0$. If we want to know the specific heat however, we have to worry about the exact dependence of the average energy on temperature.

To obtain the dependence of $\bar\epsilon$ on temperature we will take advantage of the fact that at ordinary temperatures μ is approximately equal to μ_0.

Let us consider an integral of the form

$$I(y) = \int_0^\infty g'(x)h(x - y)dx \tag{19.14}$$

where
$$g'(x) \equiv dg(x)/dx \tag{19.15}$$

$$h(x - y) = [\exp(x - y) + 1]^{-1} \tag{19.16}$$

$$y \gg 1 \tag{19.17}$$

$$g(0) = 0 \tag{19.18}$$

$$[g(x)h(x - y)]_{x=\infty} = 0 \tag{19.19}$$

Integrating (19.14) by parts we obtain

$$I(y) = -\int_0^\infty g(x)h'(x-y)dx$$

$$= -\int_{-y}^\infty g(x+y)h'(x)dx \qquad (19.20)$$

But $h'(x) \approx 0$ for $x < -y$ since $y \gg 1$, and therefore

$$I(y) \approx -\int_{-\infty}^\infty g(x+y)h'(x)dx \qquad (19.21)$$

If we expand $g(x+y)$ around $x = 0$ we obtain

$$g(x+y) = e^{x\delta}g(y) \qquad (19.22)$$

where

$$\delta = \partial/\partial y \qquad (19.23)$$

$$e^{x\delta} = 1 + x\delta + \tfrac{1}{2}x^2\delta^2 + \ldots \qquad (19.24)$$

Thus

$$I(y) \approx -\int_{-\infty}^\infty e^{x\delta}h'(x)dx\, g(y)$$

$$= +\int_{-\infty}^\infty e^{x\delta}e^x[e^x+1]^{-2}dx\, g(y) \qquad (19.25)$$

Letting $z = e^x$ we obtain

$$I(y) = \int_0^\infty [z^\delta/(z+1)^2]dz\, g(y)$$

$$= [\pi\delta \csc \pi\delta]g(y)$$

$$= [1 + (\pi^2/6)\delta^2 + (7\pi^4/360)\delta^4 + \ldots]g(y) \qquad (19.26)$$

We can use this result to evaluate a number of integrals involving the Fermi-Dirac distribution:

$$\frac{N}{V} = \int_0^\infty \frac{C\epsilon^{1/2}d\epsilon}{\exp[(\epsilon - \mu)/kT] + 1}$$

$$= \left(\frac{2C}{3}\right)(kT)^{3/2}\int_0^\infty \frac{d}{dx}[x^{3/2}]h\left(x - \frac{\mu}{kT}\right)dx$$

$$= \left(\frac{2C}{3}\right)(\mu)^{3/2}\left[1 + \frac{\pi^2}{8}\left(\frac{kT}{\mu}\right)^2 + \ldots\right] \qquad (19.27)$$

$$\bar{\epsilon} = \frac{V}{N}\int \frac{C\epsilon^{3/2}}{\exp[(\epsilon - \mu)/kT] + 1}$$

$$= \frac{V}{N}\left(\frac{2C}{5}\right)\mu^{5/2}\left[1 + \frac{5\pi^2}{8}\left(\frac{kT}{\mu}\right)^2 + \ldots\right] \qquad (19.28)$$

If we set $(N/V) = (2C/3)\mu_0^{3/2}$ in (19.27) and let $1 + (\pi^2/8)(kT/\mu)^2 + \ldots \approx 1 + (\pi^2/8)(kT/\mu_0)^2$ we obtain

$$\mu_0 \approx \mu\left[1 + \left(\frac{\pi^2}{8}\right)\left(\frac{kT}{\mu_0}\right)^2\right]^{2/3} \approx \mu\left[1 + \left(\frac{\pi^2}{12}\right)\left(\frac{kT}{\mu_0}\right)^2\right] \tag{19.29}$$

or

$$\mu \approx \mu_0\left[1 - \left(\frac{\pi^2}{12}\right)\left(\frac{kT}{\mu_0}\right)^2\right] \tag{19.30}$$

From (19.30) we see that as long as $kT \ll \mu_0$ there is only a slight dependence of μ on T.

Substituting (19.30) in (19.28) we obtain

$$
\begin{aligned}
\bar{\epsilon} &\approx \frac{V}{N}\left(\frac{2C}{5}\right)\left\{\mu_0\left[1 - \frac{\pi^2}{12}\left(\frac{kT}{\mu_0}\right)^2\right]\right\}^{5/2}\left\{1 + \frac{5\pi^2}{8}\left(\frac{kT}{\mu_0}\right)^2\right\} \\
&\approx \frac{V}{N}\left(\frac{2C}{5}\right)\mu_0^{5/2}\left[1 - \frac{5\pi^2}{24}\left(\frac{kT}{\mu_0}\right)^2 + \frac{5\pi^2}{8}\left(\frac{kT}{\mu_0}\right)^2\right] \\
&= \frac{V}{N}\left(\frac{2C}{5}\right)\mu_0^{5/2}\left[1 + \frac{5\pi^2}{12}\left(\frac{kT}{\mu_0}\right)^2\right] \\
&= \left(\frac{3\mu_0}{5}\right)\left[1 + \frac{5\pi^2}{12}\left(\frac{kT}{\mu_0}\right)^2\right]
\end{aligned}
\tag{19.31}
$$

The electronic specific heat per electron is thus

$$c_V = \frac{\partial\bar{\epsilon}}{\partial T} = \frac{\pi^2 k^2 T}{2\mu_0} \tag{19.32}$$

If we compare this with the classical result $(c_V)_{\text{class.}} = 3k/2$ we have

$$\frac{c_V}{(c_V)_{\text{class.}}} = \left(\frac{\pi^2}{3}\right)\left(\frac{kT}{\mu_0}\right) \tag{19.33}$$

At ordinary temperatures kT is of the order of one-fortieth of an electron volt, while for ordinary metals μ_0 is of the order of several electron volts. The electronic contribution to the specific heat is therefore of the order of one-hundredth of the expected classical value.

BOSE-EINSTEIN STATISTICS

Let us now consider an assembly of N identical particles for which the intrinsic angular momentum s is an integer. The possible states of the assembly are $\phi_{n_1 n_2 \ldots n_i \ldots}(+)$ where n_i is the occupation number of the ith single particle state, which may assume any value from 0 to N.

Using the Gibbs distribution we have

$$P_{\ldots n_i \ldots} = \frac{\exp(-\sum_i n_i\epsilon_i/kT)}{\sum\limits_{\{n_i\}}^{*} \exp(-\sum_i n_i\epsilon_i/kT)} \tag{19.34}$$

where the summation in the denominator is over the set of all n_i satisfying the condition

$$\Sigma\, n_i = N \tag{19.35}$$

We have used the asterisk in (19.34) to emphasize the fact that the summation is not over the same sets of n_i as in the Fermi-Dirac case where in addition to the condition (19.35), the occupation numbers were restricted to 0 or 1.

To determine $\bar{n}_j$, the average occupation number of the jth single particle state, we proceed exactly as in the Fermi-Dirac case and obtain

$$\bar{n}_j = -kT \frac{\partial}{\partial \epsilon_j}(\ln Q^*) \tag{19.36}$$

where

$$Q^* = \underset{\{n_i\}}{\Sigma^*} \prod_i \exp(-n_i\epsilon_i/kT) \tag{19.37}$$

The quantity $\bar{n}_j$ can be evaluated in the same way as the corresponding quantity for Fermi statistics is derived in Appendix 12. We obtain

$$\bar{n}_j = \frac{1}{\exp[(\epsilon_j - \mu)/kT] - 1} \tag{19.38}$$

where μ is a function of N and T which can be determined in principle from the condition

$$\Sigma\, \bar{n}_j = N \tag{19.39}$$

The distribution (19.38) is called the Bose-Einstein distribution.

In the continuous case we obtain

$$f_\epsilon = \frac{C\epsilon^{1/2}}{\exp[(\epsilon - \mu)/kT] - 1} \tag{19.40}$$

$$C = (2s + 1)(2\pi)(2m/h^2)^{3/2} \tag{19.41}$$

where $f_\epsilon d\epsilon$ is the number of particles per unit volume with energy between ϵ and $\epsilon + d\epsilon$.

BOSE-EINSTEIN CONDENSATION

We have assumed in the preceding sections in dealing with the Fermi-Dirac distribution and the Bose-Einstein distribution that because of the closeness of the energy levels we could always replace the discrete distribution by a continuous distribution. As long as the change in occupation number from state to state is small compared to the number of particles in the states, then this is a valid procedure. If, however, the temperature in an ideal Bose gas is lowered to zero, the particles will begin to crowd into a few levels, and the above condition will be violated.

Consider the Bose-Einstein distribution in the form

$$n_i = \frac{1}{\exp[(\epsilon_i - \mu)/kT] - 1} \tag{19.42}$$

Let us for convenience assume that $\epsilon_0 = 0$. Then

$$n_0 = \frac{1}{\exp(-\mu/kT) - 1} \tag{19.43}$$

Since n_0 can never be negative, $\alpha = \mu/kT$ must always be negative. For large values of the temperature we expect n_0 to approach 0, in which case α will be large and negative. As the temperature approaches zero, n_0 will increase, therefore α and μ must increase. Let α_0 and μ_0 be the values of α and μ at $T = 0$. At $T = 0$, $n_0 = N$ and therefore α_0 is a very small negative number, and $\mu_0 = 0$.

For temperatures very near zero $\mu \approx 0$. However, if we set $\mu = 0$ in (19.43) we get an indeterminate value for n_0. We do not encounter this difficulty with the occupation numbers of the other levels. As long as $\mu \approx 0$ we in fact get a good approximation to $n_i(i \neq 0)$ by letting $\mu = 0$. If we set $\mu = 0$ in the expression for $n_i(i \neq 0)$ and study the change in n_i with temperature we find that the relative difference between the occupation numbers of adjacent levels is not great. We therefore assume that the continuous distribution

$$f_\epsilon = \frac{C\epsilon^{1/2}}{\exp[(\epsilon - \mu)/kT] - 1} \tag{19.44}$$

is valid for all levels except the ϵ_0 level. This level must be treated separately.

It follows that if we integrate f_ϵ over all values of ϵ we do not get the density. We have instead

$$N/V = n_0 + \int_0^\infty f_\epsilon d\epsilon \tag{19.45}$$

where n_0 is, as before, the number of particles in the ϵ_0 level.

We would now like to use (19.45) to find the temperature dependence of μ. We will obviously have to make some more assumptions since we do not know the temperature dependence of n_0.

Making use of the distribution (19.44), we obtain

$$\int f_\epsilon d\epsilon = \int C\epsilon^{1/2}[\exp(\beta\epsilon - \alpha) - 1]^{-1} d\epsilon$$

$$= -\frac{\partial}{\partial\alpha}\left\{\int C\epsilon^{1/2} \ln[1 - \exp(\alpha - \beta\epsilon)] d\epsilon\right\}$$

$$= -\frac{\partial}{\partial\alpha}\left\{C\beta^{-3/2} \int x^{1/2} \ln[1 - \exp(\alpha - x)] dx\right\}$$

$$= \frac{\partial}{\partial \alpha} \left\{ C\beta^{-3/2} \int x^{1/2} \sum_{n=1}^{\infty} \frac{\exp[n(\alpha - x)]}{n} dx \right\}$$

$$= \frac{\partial}{\partial \alpha} \left\{ C\beta^{-3/2} \sum_{n=1}^{\infty} \frac{\exp(n\alpha)}{n} \int x^{1/2} \exp(-nx) dx \right\}$$

$$= \frac{\partial}{\partial \alpha} \left\{ C\beta^{-3/2} (\pi^{1/2}/2) \sum_{n=1}^{\infty} \frac{\exp(n\alpha)}{n^{5/2}} \right\}$$

$$= \tfrac{1}{2} \pi^{1/2} C\beta^{-3/2} \sum_{n=1}^{\infty} \frac{\exp(n\alpha)}{n^{3/2}} \tag{19.46}$$

Substituting (19.46) in (19.45) we obtain

$$N/V = n_0 + n' \tag{19.47}$$

where

$$n' = (2s + 1)(2\pi mkT/h^2)^{3/2} \sum_{n=1}^{\infty} \exp(n\alpha)/n^{3/2} \tag{19.48}$$

The maximum value n' can have occurs if $\alpha = 0$. Therefore n' will always be less than the value obtained by setting $\alpha = 0$, i.e.,

$$n' < 2.612(2s + 1)(2\pi mkT/h^2)^{3/2} \tag{19.49}$$

We now ask at what value of T will the right-hand side of (19.49) be equal to N/V. Let this value be T_0. Solving, we find that

$$T_0 = \frac{(N/V)^{2/3} h^2}{[(2s + 1)(2.612)]^{2/3} 2\pi mk} \tag{19.50}$$

For temperatures below T_0, n' must be appreciably less than N/V and therefore the value of n_0 must be very large and consequently α must be very small. We shall therefore assume that below T_0 we can set $\alpha = 0$ in (19.47). Setting $\alpha = 0$ in (19.47) we obtain

$$N/V = n_0 + (N/V)(T/T_0)^{3/2} \tag{19.51}$$

For temperatures above T_0, α must decrease in order to keep $n' \leq N/V$. But if α becomes significantly different from zero, then n_0 becomes very small. We therefore assume for temperatures above T_0 that $n_0 = 0$.

Gathering results, we have for $T < T_0$

$$\alpha = 0 \tag{19.52}$$

$$n_0 = (N/V)[1 - (T/T_0)^{3/2}] \tag{19.53}$$

while for $T > T_0$

$$(N/V) = (2s + 1)(2\pi mkT/h^2)^{3/2} \sum_{n=1}^{\infty} (\exp n\alpha/n^{3/2}) \qquad (19.54)$$

$$n_0 = 0 \qquad (19.55)$$

From (19.53) we note that, as the temperature is lowered, beginning at $T = T_0$ the molecules fall rapidly into the ground state. There is a sort of condensation into this state. This phenomenon is known as a Bose-Einstein condensation.

The temperature T_0 at which the Bose-Einstein condensation begins to occur depends on the density of the gas. If we consider liquid helium to be a gas we would obtain a value of about 3.14°K for T_0.

It is found experimentally that liquid helium does undergo a rather unusual transition at 2.19°K. Below this temperature the liquid helium displays the properties of a superfluid. It is generally agreed that this transition in liquid helium is associated with a Bose-Einstein condensation. The disagreement between the theoretical and experimental value is surprisingly small, considering that we have neglected intermolecular interactions.

CONCLUSION

Applying the Gibbs canonical distribution to an assembly of identical and independent particles contained in the same volume, we have found that particles with half odd integer spin obey Fermi-Dirac statistics while particles with integer spin obey Bose-Einstein statistics. An alternate derivation of these same results, together with more applications, can be found in Chapter 5. A third derivation will be given in Chapter 21.

PROBLEMS

1. Show that for tungsten at 2900°K μ differs from μ_0 by less than one-tenth of one percent ($\mu_0 = 9.0$ eV).
2. Compute values for the Fermi energy (μ_0) of silver and copper.
3. Calculate the electronic contribution to the specific heat of tungsten. Let $\mu_0 = 9.0$ eV and $T = 3000$°K.
4. Derive an approximate expression for the paramagnetic spin susceptibility of a free electron gas.
5. If $g(\epsilon)$ is the density of states for an electron gas, show that for $kT \ll \mu_0$ the heat capacity is given by

$$C = \pi^2 k^2 T g(\mu_0)/3$$

even if $g(\epsilon)$ is a complicated function of ϵ.

6. In a metal the allowed energy states of electrons do not form a continuum but fall into bands. If the metal contains N positive ions, then each band contains $2N$ states. Call the energies of these states ϵ_i.

   (a) Show that, if all the ϵ_i in a band are occupied by electrons, then these electrons contribute nothing to the low-temperature thermal properties of the metal.

   (b) If $2N - N'$ of these states are occupied, show that the contribution to the thermal properties of these electrons is the same as that of a gas of N' electrons in a band with energies $(-\epsilon_i)$ and chemical potential $(-\mu)$, where μ is the chemical potential of the actual electrons.

7. Derive the specific heat for an ideal Bose-Einstein gas.

8. Discuss a perfect gas of monatomic atoms obeying Bose-Einstein statistics in two dimensions. Does an Einstein condensation phenomenon occur?

Chapter 20

THE DENSITY MATRIX

INTRODUCTION

An assembly in equilibrium at a temperature T can be described by the Gibbs distribution

$$P_i = \frac{\exp(-E_i/kT)}{\sum\limits_i \exp(-E_i/kT)} \tag{20.1}$$

where P_i is the probability that the assembly is in the assembly state i, and the summation is over all assembly states. More correctly, P_i is the probability that if a measurement is made on the energy that the energy will be the energy corresponding to the eigenfunction ψ_i.

In order to employ this distribution, it would appear that we need to know the eigenvalues E_i. As we shall see in this chapter, it is sufficient in principle to know the Hamiltonian of the assembly, and have at our disposal any set of complete orthonormal functions in the assembly space.

MATRICES

Before taking up the subject of the density matrix, it will be helpful to first discuss the general idea of matrices in quantum mechanics, at least to the extent that they will be needed in the following sections.

Let $\hat{A}$ be some quantum mechanical operator having a complete orthonormal set of eigenfunctions ϕ_n, and corresponding eigenvalues a_n. Let $\{\psi_n\}$ be some other complete set of orthonormal eigenfunctions in the same space.

The functions ψ_i can be expressed as a linear combination of the ϕ_i and the functions ϕ_i can be expressed as a linear combination of the ψ_i. Thus

$$\phi_n = \sum_j b_{nj}\psi_j \tag{20.2}$$

$$\psi_i = \sum_m c_{im}\phi_m \tag{20.3}$$

211

The following properties of the c_{in} and b_{ni} will be found useful and will be derived:

$$c_{in} = b_{ni}{}^* \tag{20.4}$$

$$\sum_n c_{in}{}^* c_{jn} = \delta_{ij} \tag{20.5}$$

$$\sum_i c_{in}{}^* c_{im} = \delta_{nm} \tag{20.6}$$

where $c_{in}{}^*$ and $b_{ni}{}^*$ are the complex conjugate of c_{in} and b_{ni} respectively.

To prove (20.4) we first multiply (20.3) by $\phi_n{}^*$ and integrate

$$\int \psi_i \phi_n{}^* dq = \sum_m c_{im} \int \phi_n{}^* \phi_m dq = c_{in} \tag{20.7}$$

Now take the complex conjugate of (20.2), multiply by ψ_i, and integrate

$$\int \phi_n{}^* \psi_i dq = \sum_j b_{nj}{}^* \int \psi_j{}^* \psi_i dq = b_{ni}{}^* \tag{20.8}$$

Equating (20.7) and (20.8) we obtain (20.4). To prove (20.5) we note that

$$\sum_n c_{in}{}^* c_{jn} = \sum_n c_{in}{}^* c_{jn} \int \phi_n{}^* \phi_n dq$$

$$= \sum_n \sum_m c_{in}{}^* c_{jm} \int \phi_n{}^* \phi_m dq$$

$$= \int \sum_n c_{in}{}^* \phi_n{}^* \sum_m c_{jm} \phi_m dq = \int \psi_i{}^* \psi_j dq = \delta_{ij} \tag{20.9}$$

To prove (20.6) we note that (20.5) is also true for the b_{ni}, i.e.,

$$\sum_i b_{ni}{}^* b_{mi} = \delta_{nm} \tag{20.10}$$

Substituting (20.4) in (20.10) we obtain (20.6).

The set of numbers

$$A_{ij} = \int \psi_i{}^* \hat{A} \psi_j dq \tag{20.11}$$

constitute a matrix, which we shall refer to as the matrix associated with the operator $\hat{A}$ in the $\{\psi_i\}$ representation.

We will obtain a different matrix for each set of $\{\psi_i\}$. If we consider the matrix elements in the $\{\phi_i\}$ representation where the $\{\phi_i\}$ are the eigenfunctions of $\hat{A}$ we obtain

$$A_{ij} = a_i \delta_{ij} \tag{20.12}$$

where the a_i are the eigenvalues corresponding to the eigenfunctions ϕ_i. In this representation the matrix is diagonal.

Although the matrix A_{ij} will differ from representation to representation, the trace of A_{ij}, i.e., the sum of the diagonal terms, will remain invariant. To show this we note that in the $\{\psi_i\}$ representation

$$
\begin{aligned}
Tr[A_{ij}] &= \sum_i \int \psi_i{}^* \hat{A} \psi_i d\mathbf{q} \\
&= \sum_i \sum_m \sum_n c_{im}{}^* c_{in} \int \phi_m{}^* \hat{A} \phi_n d\mathbf{q} \\
&= \sum_i \sum_m \sum_n c_{im}{}^* c_{in} a_n \delta_{mn} \\
&= \sum_i \sum_n c_{in}{}^* c_{in} a_n \\
&= \sum_n a_n \sum_i c_{in}{}^* c_{in} = \sum_n a_n
\end{aligned}
\tag{20.13}
$$

Since the ψ_i are arbitrary and the Σa_n is simply the invariant sum of the eigenvalues of $\hat{A}$, we have proved our original statement.

THE DENSITY MATRIX

Consider an ensemble of assemblies. Let ψ_i be the energy eigenfunctions for an assembly and E_i the corresponding eigenvalues. Let P_i be the probability that an assembly will be in the state ψ_i. We then define the density matrix in the $\{\psi_i\}$ representation as

$$
\rho_{ij} = P_i \delta_{ij}
\tag{20.14}
$$

A more general definition of the density matrix will be given in Chapter 23. In most practical cases it will, however, reduce to the definition (20.14). An operator is defined when all its matrix elements with respect to a complete set of eigenfunctions are known. The relation (20.14) therefore defines an operator $\hat{\rho}$.

Using the canonical distribution, we obtain for the density matrix

$$
\rho_{ij} = \frac{\exp(-E_i/kT)\delta_{ij}}{\sum_i \exp(-E_i/kT)}
\tag{20.15}
$$

We now define the operator

$$
\exp\left(-\frac{\hat{H}}{kT}\right) \equiv 1 - \frac{\hat{H}}{kT} + \frac{1}{2!}\left(\frac{\hat{H}}{kT}\right)^2 - \frac{1}{3!}\left(\frac{\hat{H}}{kT}\right)^3 + \cdots
\tag{20.16}
$$

The eigenvalues of this operator can easily be shown to be $\exp(-E_i/kT)$ and the eigenfunctions simply ψ_i, i.e.,

$$
\exp(-\hat{H}/kT)\psi_i = \exp(-E_i/kT)\psi_i
\tag{20.17}
$$

It is apparent that the density operator $\hat{\rho}$ is simply

$$\hat{\rho} = \frac{\exp(-\hat{H}/kT)}{Tr[\exp(-\hat{H}/kT)]} \tag{20.18}$$

Suppose now we wish to calculate the probability that if a measurement is made of an observable whose operator is $\hat{A}$, having eigenfunctions ϕ_i, the result will be the eigenvalue a_n corresponding to the eigenfunction ϕ_n. If the assembly is in the state ψ_i and we express ψ_i as a linear combination of the ϕ_i, we obtain

$$\psi_i = \sum_j c_{ij}\phi_j \tag{20.19}$$

The probability that a measurement of $\hat{A}$ will give a_n is then simply $c_{in}{}^*c_{in}$. But the probability that the assembly is in the state ψ_i is P_i. Therefore the probability that the measurement of A will yield a_n is just

$$\sum_i P_i c_{in}{}^*c_{in} = \sum_i\sum_j P_i\delta_{ij}c_{jn}{}^*c_{in}$$

$$= \sum_i\sum_j \rho_{ij}c_{in}c_{jn}{}^*$$

$$= \sum_i\sum_j c_{in}c_{jn}{}^*\int \psi_i{}^*\hat{\rho}\psi_j d\mathbf{q}$$

$$= \int (\sum_i c_{in}\psi_i{}^*)\hat{\rho}(\sum_j c_{jn}{}^*\psi_j)d\mathbf{q}$$

$$= \int \phi_n{}^*\hat{\rho}\phi_n d\mathbf{q} \tag{20.20}$$

The right-hand side of (20.20) is just the nn component of $\hat{\rho}$ in the ϕ_i representation which we can write ρ_{nn}'. Therefore the probability that a measurement on $\hat{A}$ will give a_n is just

$$\rho_{nn}' = \int \phi_n{}^*\hat{\rho}\phi_n d\mathbf{q} \tag{20.21}$$

Now suppose we wish to calculate the average value of A. This will be simply

$$\overline{<\hat{A}>} = \sum_n a_n\rho_{nn}'$$

$$= \sum_n \int \phi_n{}^*\hat{\rho}a_n\phi_n d\mathbf{q}$$

$$= \sum_n \int \phi_n{}^*\hat{\rho}\hat{A}\phi_n d\mathbf{q}$$

$$= Tr[\hat{\rho}\hat{A}] \tag{20.22}$$

We note that the average $\overline{<\hat{A}>}$ is a double average: a quantum mechanical average and a statistical mechanical average.

Since the trace of $[\hat{\rho}\hat{A}]$ is invariant, it follows that in order to determine the average value of any observable it is sufficient to know the operators $\hat{A}$ and $\hat{H}$ and any complete set of orthonormal functions. In principle, we do not need to solve the complete quantum mechanical problem, or even solve for the eigenvalues.

THE ASSEMBLY PARTITION FUNCTION

In Chapter 17 we defined the assembly partition function Q as

$$Q = \sum_i \exp(-E_i/kT) \tag{20.23}$$

According to the analysis of the preceding section

$$Q = Tr[\exp(-\hat{H}/kT)] \tag{20.24}$$

In order to determine the partition function Q it is therefore sufficient in principle to know $\hat{H}$, since we can use any complete set of orthonormal functions to calculate the trace of the matrix of an operator.

We will show in Chapter 26 that it is possible to express any thermodynamic function of the assembly in terms of the partition function Q. Therefore, if we know $\hat{H}$, we can quickly and easily write down an expression for any thermodynamic property of the system. However, explication of the resulting expressions is not easy.

THE CLASSICAL LIMIT
OF THE ASSEMBLY PARTITION FUNCTION

In the present section we wish to obtain the classical limit of the assembly partition function. Let us for simplicity initially choose our assembly to be a point particle in a one-dimensional potential $U(x)$ of the form

$$
\begin{aligned}
U(x) &= \infty & x &< 0 \\
U(x) &= \infty & x &> L \\
U(x) \text{ arbitrary} & & 0 &< x < L
\end{aligned} \tag{20.25}
$$

The Hamiltonian operator for the assembly is given by

$$\hat{H} = -\frac{\hbar^2}{2m}\frac{d^2}{dx^2} + U(x) \tag{20.26}$$

The partition function Q is given by

$$Q = \sum_n \int \phi_n{}^*(x)\exp(-\hat{H}/kT)\phi_n(x)dx \tag{20.27}$$

where the set of functions $\{\phi_i\}$ is any complete orthonormal set of functions in the space $0 < x < L$. Let us choose the ϕ_i to be the eigenfunctions for a free particle in a box, i.e.,

$$\phi_n = (2/L)^{1/2} \sin [n\pi x/L] \qquad n = 0, 1, 2, \ldots \qquad (20.28)$$

Then

$$Q = \sum_n (2/L) \int \sin(n\pi x/L) \exp(-\hat{H}/kT) \sin(n\pi x/L)dx \qquad (20.29)$$

In the limit as $L \to \infty$ we can replace the summation over n by an integration, and therefore assuming a large value of L

$$Q \approx (2/L) \int_0^\infty \int_0^L \sin(n\pi x/L) \exp(-\hat{H}/kT) \sin(n\pi x/L)dxdn \qquad (20.30)$$

If we define:

$$p \equiv nh/2L \qquad (20.31)$$

then we can rewrite (20.30) as

$$Q \approx (4/h) \int_0^\infty \int_0^L \sin(px/\hbar) \exp(-\hat{H}/kT) \sin(px/\hbar)dxdp \qquad (20.32)$$

The operator $\exp(-\hat{H}/kT)$ is defined as

$$\exp(-\hat{H}/kT) = 1 - (\hat{H}/kT) + \tfrac{1}{2}(\hat{H}/kT)^2 \qquad (20.33)$$

Furthermore

$$-\hat{H} \sin(px/\hbar) = -[(p^2/2m) + U] \sin(px/\hbar) \qquad (20.34)$$

and $\hat{H}^2 \sin(px/\hbar) = \left(-\dfrac{\hbar^2}{2m}\dfrac{d^2}{dx^2} + U\right)\left(-\dfrac{\hbar^2}{2m}\dfrac{d^2}{dx^2} + U\right) \sin(px/\hbar)$

$$= [(p^2/2m)^2 + 2U(p^2/2m) + U^2] \sin(px/\hbar)$$
$$- [(\hbar p/m)(dU/dx)] \cos(px/\hbar)$$
$$- [(\hbar^2/2m)(d^2U/dx^2)] \sin(px/\hbar) \qquad (20.35)$$

If the potential is not a rapidly varying function, then we can neglect the second and third terms in (20.35) and we obtain

$$\hat{H}^2 \sin(px/\hbar) \approx [(p^2/2m) + U]^2 \sin(px/\hbar) \qquad (20.36)$$

To the same approximation

$$\hat{H}^n \sin(px/\hbar) \approx [(p^2/2m) + U]^n \sin(px/\hbar) \qquad (20.37)$$

and

$$\exp(-\hat{H}/kT)\sin(px/\hbar) \approx \exp\left[-\dfrac{(p^2/2m) + U}{kT}\right] \sin(px/\hbar) \qquad (20.38)$$

Substituting (20.38) in (20.32) we obtain

$$Q \approx (4/h) \int_0^\infty \int_0^L \sin^2(px/\hbar) \exp\left[-\frac{(p^2/2m) + U}{kT} \right] dx \, dp$$

$$\approx (2/h) \int_0^\infty \int_0^L \exp\left[-\frac{(p^2/2m) + U}{kT} \right] dx \, dp$$

$$= (1/h) \int_{-\infty}^\infty \int_0^L \exp\left[-\frac{(p^2/2m) + U}{kT} \right] dx \, dp \qquad (20.39)$$

But the total energy for the assembly is just $E(p, x) = (p^2/2m) + U(x)$. Therefore

$$Q \approx (1/h) \iint \exp(-E/kT) dx \, dp \qquad (20.40)$$

If we had a single particle in a two-dimensional well we would have obtained

$$Q \approx (1/h^2) \iint \exp(-E/kT) d\mathbf{x} \, d\mathbf{p} \qquad (20.41)$$

and if we had had two particles in a one-dimensional well, we would have obtained

$$Q \approx (1/2h^2) \iint \exp(-E/kT) d\mathbf{x} \, d\mathbf{p} \qquad (20.42)$$

This is true even if the particles are interacting.

In general if we have N particles, each with s degrees of freedom, we obtain

$$Q \approx (1/N! h^{sN}) \iint \exp(-E/kT) d\mathbf{p} \, d\mathbf{q} \qquad (20.43)$$

Those readers who are interested in a more detailed derivation of the above result and a discussion of the conditions under which it is valid are referred to the statistical mechanics text by K. Huang, pp. 213–220 (see bibliography).

Chapter 21

ENSEMBLES

INTRODUCTION

In the preceding chapters we have found that the properties of an assembly of systems, e.g., a gas, could be derived by replacing the time average of the assembly by an average over a large number of identical assemblies which were in thermal contact but were otherwise isolated. We referred to such a collection of assemblies as a canonical ensemble.

In this chapter we will investigate a number of other ensembles from which the properties of an assembly can also be derived. As long as we are interested in the equilibrium properties of the assembly, each of the ensembles to be discussed will give the same results. We therefore choose the ensemble which is mathematically most convenient. If we are interested, however, in fluctuations in the assembly, it will make a difference which ensemble we choose.

Although the mathematics used in deriving many of the results of the preceding chapters could have been simplified if we had introduced these ensembles at an earlier stage, the over-all result for someone encountering the concepts of statistical mechanics for the first time is usually a loss in physical clarity. We have therefore attempted to develop as thoroughly as possible a single unified approach. We are now in a position to look at some of these other approaches.

ENSEMBLES

For the sake of completeness, we will review and extend some of the definitions we have previously introduced. Let us assume we are interested in the properties of a gas of molecules. We shall refer to a single molecule in the gas as a system, and to the gas as a whole as an assembly.

An ensemble is then defined as a collection of a very large number of assemblies which are essentially independent of one another but which have been made macroscopically as identical as possible. By being independent of

218

one another, we mean that in calculating the *possible* eigenstates of an assembly we do not have to worry about any interaction between the assembly of interest and any of the other assemblies. By being macroscopically identical, we mean that each assembly is characterized by the same values of some set of macroscopic parameters which uniquely determine the equilibrium state of the assembly. For example, we might assume that each assembly has the same temperature and volume, and is made up of the same number and kind of systems or we might assume that each assembly has the same energy and pressure and is made up of the same number and type of systems. For each set of parameters we choose to specify the equilibrium state of the assembly, we will have a different type of ensemble. There are therefore many different types of ensembles. We will investigate the three most commonly used ensembles, the microcanonical, the canonical, and the grand canonical ensemble.

THE MICROCANONICAL ENSEMBLE

The microcanonical ensemble is a collection of essentially independent assemblies having the same energy E, volume V, and number N of systems, where for simplicity we assume that we have only one type of system.

In Figure 21.1 we have symbolically represented a microcanonical ensemble. The individual assemblies are separated by rigid, impermeable, and well-insulated walls.

We cannot actually specify the macroscopic energy of an assembly exactly.

Fig. 21.1

The best we can do is to specify the energy within some narrow range. Let us assume the energy falls between $(E - \Delta E)$ and E.

Let P_i be the probability that an assembly is in the eigenstate I and E_i be the corresponding eigenvalue. We then obtain for the microcanonical ensemble

$$P_i = 1/Z \qquad E - \Delta E \leq E_i \leq E$$
$$P_i = 0 \qquad \text{otherwise} \qquad (21.1)$$

where Z is the number of assembly eigenstates between $E - \Delta E$ and E. This is the microcanonical distribution. As we shall see in a later chapter, all of the equilibrium properties of the assembly can be calculated if we simply know Z as a function of E, V, and N. We call Z the microcanonical partition function. As an example of an application of the microcanonical distribution, the reader is referred to Chapter 5 where the Fermi and Bose statistics were first derived. A careful analysis of the argument used there will reveal that we were implicitly employing the microcanonical distribution. The energy, volume, and density of the gas were held fixed, and we assigned equal probability to all assembly states falling within a small energy range.

THE CANONICAL ENSEMBLE

The canonical ensemble is a collection of essentially independent assemblies having the same temperature T, volume V, and number of identical systems N.

To assure ourselves that the assemblies all have the same temperature we could bring each in thermal contact with a large heat reservoir at temperature T. Alternatively, we could simply bring all of the assemblies in thermal contact with each other. Since we have a large number of assemblies, each assembly is then effectively immersed in a heat bath.

In Figure 21.2 we have symbolically represented such a canonical ensemble. The individual assemblies are separated by rigid, impermeable, but diathermal walls. Since energy can be exchanged between the assemblies, they will all arrive at a common temperature T.

Let the number of assemblies in the ensemble be N; the total energy of the ensemble be $\mathcal{E}$; the number of assemblies in the state i be N_i; the energy corresponding to the state i be E_i; the probability that an assembly will be in the state i be P_i.

We have in an earlier chapter derived the canonical distribution. We will now simply briefly review the results.

A microstate for the ensemble is defined as a particular arrangement of the N assemblies among the assembly states. Since each assembly state is a priori equally probable, each microstate is a priori equally probable. A macrostate is defined as a particular set of the occupation numbers N_i. The thermodynamic probability $W(N_i)$ for a macrostate is defined as the number of distinct microstates associated with it. The a priori probability of a macrostate will be proportional to $W(N_i)$. From Appendix 2 we obtain

$$W(N_i) = \mathcal{N}!/\Pi N_i! \tag{21.2}$$

If we maximize ln $W(N_i)$ subject to the constraints

$$\Sigma N_i E_i = \mathcal{E} \tag{21.3}$$

$$\Sigma N_i = \mathcal{N} \tag{21.4}$$

we find

$$N_i = \frac{\mathcal{N} \exp(-\beta E_i)}{\sum\limits_i \exp(-\beta E_i)} \tag{21.5}$$

We can, as was done earlier, identify β as $1/kT$, and since $P_i = N_i/\mathcal{N}$, we have

$$P_i = \frac{\exp(-E_i/kT)}{\sum\limits_i \exp(-E_i/kT)} \tag{21.6}$$

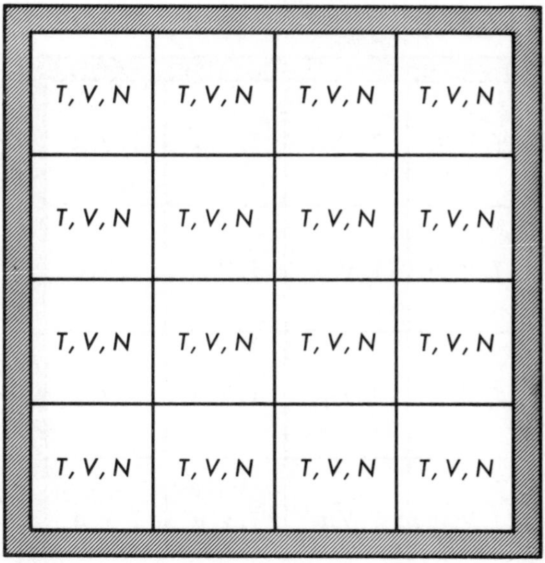

T, V, N	T, V, N	T, V, N	T, V, N
T, V, N	T, V, N	T, V, N	T, V, N
T, V, N	T, V, N	T, V, N	T, V, N
T, V, N	T, V, N	T, V, N	T, V, N

Fig. 21.2

This is the canonical distribution. We have employed this distribution extensively, and practically exclusively, in the preceding chapters.

We will in a later chapter show that all of the equilibrium properties of an assembly can be calculated if we can evaluate $\sum\limits_i \exp(-E_i/kT)$ as a function of T, V, and N. We call this sum the canonical partition function and designate it by the symbol Q, i.e.,

$$Q = \sum_i \exp(-E_i/kT) \qquad (21.7)$$

THE GRAND CANONICAL DISTRIBUTION

The grand canonical ensemble is a collection of essentially independent assemblies having the same temperature T, volume V, and chemical potential μ. In Chapter 22 we will discuss the chemical potential in greater detail. For our purposes, it is sufficient to know that if two gases of the same species are allowed to exchange molecules freely with one another, their chemical potentials will equalize. In the grand canonical ensemble we then effectively have a collection of assemblies each occupying a separate volume V, but which can exchange energy and molecules with one another.

In Figure 21.3 we have symbolically represented a grand canonical ensemble. The individual assemblies are separated by rigid, permeable, diathermal walls.

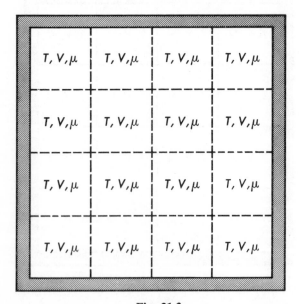

Fig. 21.3

The eigenstates of an assembly will depend on the number of systems in the assembly. Since in the microcanonical and canonical ensemble the number of systems was held fixed, we did not need to worry about this fact.

In the grand canonical ensemble we do. We therefore designate a particular eigenstate as ψ_{ni} where by this we mean it is the ith energy eigenstate of an assembly with n systems in it.

Let the number of assemblies in the ensemble be $\mathcal{N}$; the number of systems in the ensemble be $\mathcal{M}$; the number of assemblies in the state ψ_{ni} be N_{ni}; the energy corresponding to the state ψ_{ni} be E_{ni}; and the probability that an assembly will be in the state ψ_{ni} be P_{ni}.

The thermodynamic probability $W(N_{ni})$ will be given by

$$W(N_{ni}) = \mathcal{N}! / \prod_n \prod_i N_{ni}! \tag{21.8}$$

To find the most probable macrostate $\{N_{ni}\}$ we maximize $\ln W(N_{ni})$ subject to the constraints

$$\sum_n \sum_i N_{ni} E_{ni} = \mathcal{E} \tag{21.9}$$

$$\sum_n \sum_i N_{ni} = \mathcal{N} \tag{21.10}$$

$$\sum_n \sum_i n N_{ni} = \mathcal{M} \tag{21.11}$$

Carrying out the maximization using Stirling's approximation and the method of Lagrange multipliers, we obtain

$$N_{ni} = \frac{\mathcal{N} \exp(\alpha n - \beta E_{ni})}{\sum_n \sum_i \exp(\alpha n - \beta E_{ni})} \tag{21.12}$$

If we assume that n can assume only the value N, then we will obtain the canonical ensemble. We can consequently identify $\beta = 1/kT$. Then if we simply define $\mu \equiv \alpha kT$, we have for $P_{ni} \equiv N_{ni}/\mathcal{N}$,

$$P_{ni} = \frac{\exp\left(\dfrac{\mu n - E_{ni}}{kT}\right)}{\sum_n \sum_i \exp\left(\dfrac{\mu n - E_{ni}}{kT}\right)} \tag{21.13}$$

We will in a later chapter show that μ is the chemical potential, but it is sufficient for the present to consider it to be a parameter which can be determined from the condition (21.11).

If there were two species of molecules in our gas or assembly, then we would have obtained

$$P_{n_a n_b i} = \frac{\exp\left(\dfrac{\mu_a n_a + \mu_b n_b - E_{n_a n_b i}}{kT}\right)}{\sum_{n_a} \sum_{n_b} \sum_i \exp\left(\dfrac{\mu_a n_a + \mu_b n_b - E_{n_a n_b i}}{kT}\right)} \tag{21.14}$$

The distribution (21.13) or (21.14) is called the grand canonical distribution. As an example of the use of the grand canonical distribution, we will in the next section rederive the Fermi-Dirac and Bose-Einstein distributions using this distribution.

In a later chapter we will show that all of the equilibrium properties of the assembly can be calculated if we know $\sum_n \sum_i \exp[(\mu n - E_{ni})/kT]$ as a function of μ, T, V. We call this sum the grand canonical partition function and designate it $\mathcal{Q}$, i.e.,

$$\mathcal{Q} = \sum_n \sum_i \exp\left(\frac{\mu n - E_{ni}}{kT}\right) \qquad (21.15)$$

FERMI-DIRAC AND BOSE-EINSTEIN STATISTICS

Let us assume that our assembly consists of a gas of very weakly interacting particles. Let ϵ_i be the energy associated with the ith single-particle energy state; n_i the occupation number of this state; and n the total number of particles in the gas. The set of occupation numbers $\{n_i\}$ will determine the state of the gas as a whole. The number of particles n in the assembly will be given by

$$n = \sum_i n_i \qquad (21.16)$$

and the energy of the assembly will be

$$E_{ni} = \sum_i n_i \epsilon_i \qquad (21.17)$$

In order to calculate the average occupation number of the ith single-particle state we will employ the grand canonical distribution

$$P_{ni} = \frac{\exp\left(\dfrac{\mu n - E_{ni}}{kT}\right)}{\sum_n \sum_i \exp\left(\dfrac{\mu n - E_{ni}}{kT}\right)}$$

$$= \frac{\exp\left(\dfrac{\mu \sum_i n_i - \sum_i n_i \epsilon_i}{kT}\right)}{\sum_{\{n_i\}} \exp\left(\dfrac{\mu \sum_i n_i - \sum_i n_i \epsilon_i}{kT}\right)} \qquad (21.18)$$

where the summation in the last term is over all possible sets of occupation numbers $\{n_i\}$.

The average occupation $\bar{n}_j$ can be written quite simply in terms of the grand canonical partition function defined by Eq. (21.15):

$$\bar{n}_j = \sum_{\{n_i\}} n_j P_{ni} = -kT \frac{\partial}{\partial \epsilon_j}(\ln \mathcal{Q}) \qquad (21.19)$$

where

$$\mathcal{Q} = \sum_{\{n_i\}} \exp\left(\frac{\mu \sum_i n_i - \sum_i n_i \epsilon_i}{kT}\right) \qquad (21.20)$$

In order to find $\bar{n}_i$ we must evaluate $\mathcal{Q}$. We note first that it is possible to rewrite (21.20) as

$$\mathcal{Q} = \sum_{\{n_i\}} \prod_i \exp\left[\frac{(\mu - \epsilon_i)n_i}{kT}\right] \qquad (21.21)$$

we now define

$$x_i \equiv \exp\left[\frac{\mu - \epsilon_i}{kT}\right] \qquad (21.22)$$

and note that $\sum_{\{n_i\}} \prod_i$ can be replaced by $\prod_i \sum_{n_i}$. This relation is most easily verified by considering a few simple cases. With these changes $\mathcal{Q}$ becomes

$$\mathcal{Q} = \prod_i \sum_{n_i} x_i^{n_i} \qquad (21.23)$$

If our assembly wave function is antisymmetrical, then the occupation numbers n_i can assume only the values 0 or 1, and the grand canonical partition function becomes

$$\mathcal{Q} = \prod_i \sum_{n_i=0}^{1} x_i^{n_i} = \prod_i (1 + x_i) \qquad (21.24)$$

and the average occupation number

$$
\begin{aligned}
\bar{n}_i &= -kT \frac{\partial}{\partial \epsilon_i}[\ln \mathcal{Q}] = -kT \frac{\partial}{\partial x_i}[\ln \mathcal{Q}]\frac{\partial x_i}{\partial \epsilon_i} \\
&= -kT \frac{\partial}{\partial x_i}\left[\sum_j \ln(1 + x_j)\right]\frac{\partial x_i}{\partial \epsilon_i} \\
&= \frac{1}{\exp[(\epsilon_i - \mu)/kT] + 1} \qquad (21.25)
\end{aligned}
$$

which is just the Fermi-Dirac distribution which we have already derived several different ways, and discussed at length.

If our assembly wave function is symmetrical, then the occupation numbers n_i can assume any value and therefore

$$\mathcal{Q} = \prod_i \sum_{n_i=0}^{\infty} x_i^{n_i} = \prod_i \frac{1}{1 - x_i} \tag{21.26}$$

$$\bar{n}_i = -kT\frac{\partial}{\partial \epsilon_i}(\ln \mathcal{Q}) = kT\frac{\partial}{\partial x_i}\left[\sum_j \ln(1 - x_j)\right]\frac{\partial x_i}{\partial \epsilon_i}$$

$$= \frac{1}{\exp[(\epsilon_i - \mu)/kT] - 1} \tag{21.27}$$

which is just the familiar Bose-Einstein distribution.

In the course of the text we have derived the Fermi and Bose statistics using the microcanonical, the canonical, and the grand canonical distribution functions. The derivation in terms of the grand canonical distribution function is certainly mathematically the easiest of the three derivations, but it is also the least employed, since it is apparently physically the most obscure.

THE DENSITY MATRIX

The notion of the density matrix introduced in Chapter 20 can be used with the microcanonical and grand canonical distributions as well as the canonical distribution.

Consider an ensemble of assemblies. Let ψ_i be the energy eigenfunctions for an assembly and E_i the corresponding eigenvalues. Let P_i be the probability that an assembly will be in the state ψ_i. We then define the density matrix as

$$\rho_{ij} = P_i\delta_{ij} \tag{21.29}$$

A more general definition of the density matrix will be given in Chapter 23. In most practical cases it will, however, reduce to the definition given by Eq. (21.29). Since an operator is defined when all of its matrix elements are defined, Eq. (21.29) defines an operator $\hat{\rho}$. The average value of an observable, A, is, as shown previously, given in terms of $\hat{\rho}$ by

$$\overline{<\hat{A}>} = Tr[\hat{\rho}\hat{A}] \tag{21.30}$$

The density operator $\hat{\rho}$ for the microcanonical ensemble is

$$\hat{\rho} = 1/Z \quad E - \Delta E < E_i < E$$
$$\hat{\rho} = 0 \quad \text{otherwise} \tag{21.31}$$

where Z is the number of assembly states between $E - \Delta E$ and E.

The operator $\hat{\rho}$ for the canonical ensemble is

$$\hat{\rho} = \frac{\exp(-\hat{H}/kT)}{Tr[\exp(-\hat{H}/kT)]} \tag{21.32}$$

The operator $\hat{\rho}$ for the grand canonical ensemble is

$$\hat{\rho} = \frac{\exp\left(\dfrac{\mu n - \hat{H}}{kT}\right)}{Tr\left[\exp\left(\dfrac{\mu n - \hat{H}}{kT}\right)\right]} \tag{21.33}$$

THE CLASSICAL LIMIT OF THE PARTITION FUNCTIONS

We can use the results of the preceding section to calculate the classical limit of the partition functions Z, Q, and $\mathcal{Q}$ exactly as we did in Chapter 20 for the canonical partition function. We obtain

$$Z = (1/N!h^{3N}) \int\int_{E-\Delta E}^{E} d\mathbf{p}d\mathbf{q} \tag{21.34}$$

$$Q = (1/N!h^{3N})\int\int \exp(-E/kT)d\mathbf{p}d\mathbf{q} \tag{21.35}$$

$$\mathcal{Q} = \sum_{n}(1/n!h^{3n})\exp(\mu n/kT)\int\int \exp(-E/kT)d\mathbf{p}d\mathbf{q} \tag{21.36}$$

where the integration $d\mathbf{p}d\mathbf{q}$ is over the phase space for the *assembly*.

Chapter 22

FLUCTUATIONS

INTRODUCTION

If a gas is enclosed in a rigid, impermeable, and well-insulated box, the values of the energy E, volume V, and number of molecules N will remain fixed. However, it is possible for the pressure to fluctuate about some average value. If we are dealing with a gas in equilibrium containing a large number of molecules, the relative fluctuation in the pressure of the gas will be small and we can describe the state of the gas by assigning it some average pressure. If, on the other hand, we are dealing with a gas containing only a few molecules, the pressure fluctuations may be significant.

Which variables will fluctuate, and exactly how they will fluctuate will depend on the environment—for example, the pressure fluctuations in a gas which is maintained at a constant T, V, and N will not necessarily be the same as the pressure fluctuations in a gas which is maintained at a constant E, V, and N. The various ensembles which we discussed in the preceding chapter were defined in terms of the environment in which the assembly of interest was placed, and as a consequence are particularly well suited for the investigation of fluctuations under various environments.

The study of fluctuations is important for a number of reasons. A study of fluctuations will tell us why and under what conditions they can be ignored in many problems. On the other hand, there are many phenomena which depend on fluctuations. The scattering of light from the atmosphere, for example, depends on the local fluctuations in the density of the atmosphere.

FLUCTUATIONS IN ENERGY IN A SYSTEM AT CONSTANT T, V, N

Suppose we are interested in the fluctuations in the energy of a gas consisting of a fixed number of molecules N, in a rigid box of volume V, immersed in a heat bath at temperature T.

228

To solve this problem we should use the canonical distribution

$$P_i = \frac{\exp(-E_i/kT)}{\sum\limits_i \exp(-E_i/kT)} \tag{22.1}$$

since this is the distribution which is appropriate to an assembly having constant T, V, and N. We can obtain a quantitative measure of the importance of the fluctuations by calculating the relative dispersion $\sigma_E/\bar{E}$, where σ_E, the dispersion, is defined by the relation

$$\sigma_E^2 = \overline{(E - \bar{E})^2} \equiv \overline{E^2} - \bar{E}^2 \tag{22.2}$$

Evaluating $\bar{E}$ using (22.1) and multiplying the result by $\sum \exp(-E_i/kT)$, we obtain

$$\bar{E} \sum \exp(-E_i/kT) = \sum E_i \exp(-E_i/kT) \tag{22.3}$$

The energy levels E_i are functions of V and N. Therefore if we differentiate (22.3) with respect to T, holding V and N fixed, we obtain

$$(\partial \bar{E}/\partial T)_{V, N} \sum \exp(-E_i/kT) + (\bar{E}/kT^2)\sum E_i \exp(-E_i/kT)$$
$$= (1/kT^2)\sum E_i^2 \exp(-E_i/kT) \tag{22.4}$$

Multiplying (22.4) by $kT^2/\sum \exp(-E_i/kT)$, we obtain

$$kT^2(\partial \bar{E}/\partial T)_{V, N} + \bar{E}^2 = \overline{E^2} \tag{22.5}$$

the specific heat per molecule c_V is given by

$$c_V = (1/N)(\partial \bar{E}/\partial T)_{V, N} \tag{22.6}$$

Substituting (22.6) in (22.5) and rearranging, we obtain

$$\sigma_E^2 = \overline{E^2} - \bar{E}^2 = kT^2 N c_V \tag{22.7}$$

and therefore the relative dispersion is

$$\sigma_E/\bar{E} = T(kNc_V)^{1/2}/\bar{E} \tag{22.8}$$

For ordinary thermodynamic systems this is very small. Consider a monatomic ideal gas in which case $c_V = 3k/2$, and $E = 3NkT/2$ and therefore

$$\sigma_E/\bar{E} = (2/3N)^{1/2} \sim (1/N)^{1/2} \tag{22.9}$$

In 1 liter of an ideal gas there are on the order of 10^{22} molecules and the relative dispersion is of the order of 10^{-11}.

FLUCTUATIONS IN DENSITY IN A SYSTEM AT CONSTANT μ, V, T

Suppose we are interested in the fluctuations in the number of molecules in a region V, which is at a temperature T and chemical potential μ.

To solve this problem, the appropriate distribution is the grand canonical distribution

$$P_{ni} = \frac{\exp\left(\dfrac{\mu n - E_{ni}}{kT}\right)}{\displaystyle\sum_{n}\sum_{i} \exp\left(\dfrac{\mu n - E_{ni}}{kT}\right)} \tag{22.10}$$

If we multiply (22.10) by n and sum over n and i we obtain

$$n\sum_{n}\sum_{i} \exp\left(\frac{\mu n - E_{ni}}{kT}\right) = \sum_{n}\sum_{i} n \exp\left(\frac{\mu n - E_{ni}}{kT}\right) \tag{22.11}$$

The energy level E_{ni} will be a function of V only. Therefore if we differentiate (22.11) with respect to μ, holding V and T fixed, and divide by

$$\sum_{n}\sum_{i} \exp[(\mu n - E_{ni})/kT]$$

we obtain

$$(\partial \bar{n}/\partial \mu)_{T, V} + (\bar{n}^2/kT) = (\overline{n^2}/kT) \tag{22.12}$$

The relative dispersion in n is therefore

$$\sigma_n/\bar{n} = [\overline{n^2} - \bar{n}^2]^{1/2}/\bar{n} = [kT(\partial \bar{n}/\partial \mu)_{T, V}]^{1/2}/\bar{n} \tag{22.13}$$

Letting $\bar{n} = N$ we have

$$\sigma_n/\bar{n} = [kT(\partial N/\partial \mu)_{T, V}]^{1/2}/N \tag{22.14}$$

From thermodynamics it is possible to show that

$$(\partial N/\partial \mu)_{T, V} = -(N^2/V^2)/(\partial V/\partial p)_{T, N} \tag{22.15}$$

Therefore

$$\sigma_n/\bar{n} = -[kT(\partial V/\partial p)_{T, N}]^{1/2}/V \tag{22.16}$$

For ordinary thermodynamic systems this is very small. For an ideal gas $pV = NkT$ and therefore

$$\sigma_n/\bar{n} = (1/N)^{1/2} \tag{22.17}$$

Chapter 23

THE POSTULATE
OF RANDOM PHASES

INTRODUCTION

In the preceding chapters we have assumed that in an ensemble of identical assemblies, each assembly was in a definite energy eigenstate ψ_i.

In reality, if we had an ensemble of very weakly coupled assemblies, such as we have considered previously when discussing the canonical ensemble, then at any instant of time it is unlikely that a particular assembly chosen at random would be in a definite energy eigenstate. The actual state of the assembly would probably be a linear combination of a large number of energy eigenstates.

In the present chapter we wish to consider why and under what conditions we can make the assumption that the assemblies are in definite energy eigenstates.

THE POSTULATE OF RANDOM PHASES

Let us designate the actual ensemble at some time t as ensemble R. In this ensemble the assembly states are linear combinations of the assembly energy eigenstates. We would now like to construct a second ensemble, which we will call ensemble X, in such a way that the assemblies are all in definite energy eigenstates, and yet such that the properties of ensemble X are as close as possible to the properties of ensemble R.

Let Ψ_n represent the state function of the nth assembly in an arbitrary ensemble. In ensemble R the state of an assembly is a linear combination of the ψ_i, and we have

$$\Psi_n = \sum_j d_{nj}\psi_j \tag{23.1}$$

In ensemble X each assembly is in one of the eigenstates ψ_i and therefore

$$\Psi_n = \psi_{in} \tag{23.2}$$

However, before ensemble X can be completely described, we need to know how many assemblies are in each of the assembly states ψ_i. Let us therefore designate P_i as the probability that an assembly in ensemble X is in state ψ_i.

Suppose now we wish to calculate the average energy of the assemblies in each of the ensembles. The expectation value of the energy in the nth assembly in an arbitrary ensemble is

$$<\hat{H}>_n = \int \Psi_n{}^*\hat{H}\Psi_n d\mathbf{q} \tag{23.3}$$

If we average over the N assemblies, we obtain

$$\overline{<\hat{H}>} = (1/N)\sum_{n=1}^{N} <\hat{H}>_n = (1/N)\sum_{n=1}^{N} \int \Psi_n{}^*\hat{H}\Psi_n d\mathbf{q} \tag{23.4}$$

The average value of the energy in ensemble R is therefore

$$\overline{<\hat{H}>} = (1/N)\sum_{n=1}^{N} \sum_j \sum_k d_{nj}{}^*d_{nk} \int \psi_j{}^*\hat{H}\psi_k d\mathbf{q}$$

$$= (1/N)\sum_{n=1}^{N} \sum_j d_{nj}{}^*d_{nj}E_j \tag{23.5}$$

while the average value of the energy in ensemble X is

$$\overline{<\hat{H}>} = (1/N)\sum_{n=1}^{N} \int \psi_{in}{}^*\hat{H}\psi_{in} d\mathbf{q}$$

$$= (1/N)\sum_{n=1}^{N} E_{in} = \sum_i P_i E_i \tag{23.6}$$

If we choose

$$P_i = (1/N)\sum_{n=1}^{N} d_{ni}{}^*d_{ni} \tag{23.7}$$

then we will obtain the same value for $\overline{<\hat{H}>}$ with ensemble X as with ensemble R.

Suppose next we wish to determine the average value of the observable whose operator is $\hat{A}$. Let ϕ_i be the eigenfunctions associated with this operator and A_i the corresponding eigenvalues. The functions ψ_i can be expressed as a linear combination of the ϕ_i and the ϕ_i can be expressed as a linear combination of the ψ_i. Thus

$$\phi_i = \sum_j b_{ij}\psi_j \tag{23.8}$$

$$\psi_j = \sum_i c_{ji}\phi_i \tag{23.9}$$

Furthermore, the quantity $c_{ji}{}^*c_{ji}$ can, from Theorem V, Chapter 15, be interpreted as the probability that if the assembly is in the state ψ_j that a measurement of $\hat{A}$ will yield the eigenvalue A_i corresponding to the eigenfunction ϕ_i. We will for convenience designate this quantity P_{ji}, i.e.,

$$P_{ji} = c_{ji}{}^*c_{ji} \qquad (23.10)$$

We are now ready to calculate the average value $\overline{<\hat{A}>}$. For ensemble X we obtain

$$\overline{<\hat{A}>} = (1/N)\sum_{n=1}^{N} \int \Psi_n{}^*\hat{A}\Psi_n d\mathbf{q}$$

$$= (1/N)\sum_{n=1}^{N} \int \psi_{in}{}^*\hat{A}\psi_{in} d\mathbf{q}$$

$$= (1/N)\sum_{n=1}^{N} \sum_j \sum_k c_{inj}{}^*c_{ink} \int \phi_j{}^*\hat{A}\phi_k d\mathbf{q}$$

$$= (1/N)\sum_{n=1}^{N} \sum_j c_{inj}{}^*c_{inj}A_j$$

$$= \sum_i P_i \sum_j c_{ij}{}^*c_{ij}A_j$$

$$= \sum_i \sum_j P_i P_{ij}A_j \qquad (23.11)$$

For ensemble R we obtain

$$\overline{<\hat{A}>} = (1/N)\sum_{n=1}^{N} \sum_j \sum_k d_{nj}{}^*d_{nk} \int \psi_j{}^*\hat{A}\psi_k d\mathbf{q}$$

$$= (1/N)\sum_{n=1}^{N} \sum_j \sum_k \sum_l \sum_m d_{nj}{}^*d_{nk}c_{jl}{}^*c_{km} \int \phi_l{}^*\hat{A}\phi_m d\mathbf{q}$$

$$= (1/N)\sum_{n=1}^{N} \sum_j \sum_k \sum_l d_{nj}{}^*d_{nk}c_{jl}{}^*c_{kl}A_l$$

$$= (1/N)\sum_{n=1}^{N} \sum_j \sum_k \sum_l d_{nj}{}^*d_{nk}c_{jl}{}^*c_{kl}A_l(1 - \delta_{jk})$$

$$+ (1/N)\sum_{n=1}^{N} \sum_j \sum_k \sum_l d_{nj}{}^*d_{nk}c_{jl}{}^*c_{kl}A_l\delta_{jk} \qquad (23.12)$$

The last term in (23.12) can be written

$$(1/N)\sum_{n=1}^{N} \sum_j \sum_k \sum_l d_{nj}{}^*d_{nk}c_{jl}{}^*c_{kl}A_l\delta_{jk}$$

$$= (1/N) \sum_{n=1}^{N} \sum_j \sum_l d_{nj}{}^* d_{nj} c_{jl}{}^* c_{jl} A_l$$

$$= \sum_j \sum_l P_j c_{jl}{}^* c_{jl} A_l$$

$$= \sum_j \sum_l P_j P_{jl} A_l \qquad (23.13)$$

This term alone gives the same result we obtained for $\overline{<\hat{A}>}$ using ensemble X. It follows that the average value (23.12) which was obtained using ensemble R will be the same as the average value (23.11) which was obtained using ensemble X, only if

$$(1/N) \sum_{n=1}^{N} \sum_j \sum_k \sum_l d_{nj}{}^* d_{nk} c_{jl}{}^* c_{kl} A_l (1 - \delta_{jk}) = 0 \qquad (23.14)$$

A sufficient condition for this is

$$(1/N) \sum_{n=1}^{N} d_{nj}{}^* d_{nk} (1 - \delta_{jk}) = 0 \qquad (23.15)$$

The d_{nj} are complex numbers which we can write in the form

$$d_{nj} = r_{nj} \exp[i\phi_{nj}] \qquad (23.16)$$

where the r_{nj} are real numbers. Therefore the condition (23.15) can be written

$$(1/N) \sum_{n=1}^{N} r_{nj} r_{nk} \exp[i(\phi_{nk} - \phi_{nj})](1 - \delta_{jk}) = 0 \qquad (23.17)$$

If the phase angles ϕ_{ni} are completely random over the ensemble R, then the expression (23.17) will vanish. We have no reason to assume that the phases are not random and therefore in the absence of any information to the contrary we postulate random phases.

We conclude that ensemble R and ensemble X will exhibit the same statistical properties if

(1) $P_i = (1/N) \sum_{n=1}^{N} d_{ni}{}^* d_{ni}$ and   (2) $(1/N) \sum_{n=1}^{N} d_{nj}{}^* d_{nk} (1 - \delta_{jk}) = 0$.

We can always construct X in such a way that condition (1) is true, and if the phases of the d_{nj} are random, then condition (2) will be satisfied.

THE DENSITY MATRIX

In an earlier chapter we defined the density matrix as

$$\rho_{ij} = P_i \delta_{ij} \qquad (23.18)$$

where P_i was the probability that an assembly was in the state ψ_i. From the analysis of the present chapter

$$P_i = (1/N) \sum_{n=1}^{N} d_{ni}^* d_{ni} \tag{23.19}$$

and therefore

$$\rho_{ij} = (1/N) \sum_{n=1}^{N} d_{ni}^* d_{ni} \delta_{ij} \tag{23.20}$$

A more general definition, frequently used, is

$$\rho_{ij} = (1/N) \sum_{n=1}^{N} d_{nj}^* d_{ni} \tag{23.21}$$

If the random phase approximation is made both definitions yield the same results.

Chapter 24

A SUMMARY OF THE POSTULATES
OF STATISTICAL MECHANICS

INTRODUCTION

In deriving the results of classical statistical mechanics and quantum statistical mechanics we have taken a crooked path, and have at times hurried ourselves along by making expeditious assumptions.

The most logical development of statistical mechanics would have been to (1) state all the hypotheses needed, then (2) derive the fundamental formulae of quantum statistics, and finally (3) obtain the classical formulae as limiting cases of the quantum formulae. This course of action is fraught with perils for the student. In the first place, a tremendous amount of mathematical machinery would have been necessary to obtain the simplest of results, and consequently the student would probably have lost a good deal of physical insight on the way. In the second place, many students would have become so intrigued or even possibly confused by the hypotheses and the machinery that they never would have gone beyond the foundations.

In this chapter we would like to review the major hypotheses made along the way as an aid in consolidating what gains have been made.

THE ERGODIC HYPOTHESIS

In studying the equilibrium properties of an assembly we are not interested in its state at one instant of time, we are interested in its average behavior over a period of time. The state of a given mass of gas can, for example, be determined by the readings on a manometer and thermometer. The numbers recorded do not, however, represent the instantaneous state of the gas. Even the most refined thermometers and manometers are sluggish compared with the rapidity with which the assembly state changes, and such devices successfully record only time average values.

To evaluate the time average of an assembly having a large number of degrees of freedom is a discouraging undertaking. To avoid this difficulty, we construct, usually in our imagination, a large number of replicas of the assembly being studied. These replicas are made macroscopically as identical as possible with the original assembly. The collection of assemblies is called an ensemble. We then assume that if we take the average of some assembly property over the entire ensemble at some instant of time we will obtain the same result as if we had considered the time average of an individual assembly in the ensemble.

The hypothesis that the time average of some property of an assembly in equilibrium will be the same as the instantaneous ensemble average is known as the ergodic hypothesis.

This hypothesis is not rigorously true. It is possible for one of the assemblies to behave in a pathological fashion. However, if an assembly is picked at random, experiment seems to bear out the fact that the odds are overwhelming that it will exhibit the same time average properties as would be expected if we averaged instantaneously over the entire ensemble.

THE POSTULATE OF RANDOM PHASES

The state of an assembly in an ensemble can be written as a linear combination of the energy eigenfunctions ψ_i. Suppose Ψ_n is the state of the nth assembly in the ensemble. Then

$$\Psi_n = \sum_j d_{nj}\psi_j \qquad (24.1)$$

where the d_{nj} are complex numbers satisfying the condition $\sum_j d_{nj}{}^*d_{nj} = 1$.

We have assumed in the ensembles with which we were dealing that

$$d_{nj} = \delta_{i_n j} \qquad (24.2)$$

where $\delta_{i_n j}$ is the Kronecker delta. This is the same as saying that each assembly is in a definite energy eigenstate. This assumption will not get us into trouble as long as the phases of the d_{nj} over all the members of the ensemble are random, i.e., as long as the phases of $d_{1j}, d_{2j}, d_{3j}, \ldots$ are random. We therefore assume that the phases are random. This hypothesis is known as the postulate of random phases, and has been discussed in detail in Chapter 23.

THE POSTULATE OF EQUAL A PRIORI PROBABILITY OF EIGENSTATES

In determining the average properties of the assemblies in an ensemble in which each assembly was in one or another of the energy eigenstates, we assumed that every state which was consistent with the constraints was equally likely to be found.

The assumption that in the absence of any other information to the contrary we should assume that each eigenstate is equally probable is known as the postulate of equal a priori probability of eigenstates.

In the limit in which classical statistics is valid, it is found that those eigenstates which are most important in calculating the average properties of the assembly divide phase space into cells of equal size. In classical statistical mechanics we therefore replace the eigenstates by equal regions in phase space, and assume that equal regions in phase space must be assigned a priori equal probabilities. It should be noted that in classical statistical mechanics the assumption of equal a priori probabilities for equal regions in phase space takes the place of both the assumption of random phases and the assumption of equal a priori probabilities of eigenstates.

CONCLUSION

The validity of the preceding postulates is amply borne out by the success of the resulting theory. An immense amount of mathematical investigation has, however, gone into an attempt to probe deeper into these postulates and put them on a more fundamental footing.

For example, it is possible to increase the plausibility of the quantum postulates of random phase and equal a priori probability of eigenstates by an analysis similar to the analysis which we made in attempting to justify the corresponding classical postulate of equal a priori probability for equal regions in phase space. In the classical case, Liouville's equation told us that the representative points for the assemblies in an ensemble move in phase space like an incompressible fluid. We therefore found no reason to prefer one region of phase space over another. The quantum mechanical analog of Liouville's equation derived below provides the same sort of plausibility argument for the two postulates of quantum statistics.

Consider an ensemble of assemblies. Let $\hat{H}$ be the Hamiltonian operator; let Ψ_n be the state function for the nth assembly in the ensemble; and let ϕ_i be a complete orthonormal set of functions. Schrodinger's equation for the nth assembly is

$$\hat{H}\Psi_n = i\hbar\frac{\partial}{\partial t}\Psi_n \tag{24.3}$$

The state function Ψ_n can be expressed as a linear combination of the ϕ_i. Thus

$$\Psi_n = \sum_i a_{ni}(t)\phi_i(\mathbf{q}) \tag{24.4}$$

Substituting (24.4) in (24.3); multiplying by $\phi_j{}^*$; and integrating over **q**, we obtain

$$i\hbar\frac{\partial a_{nj}}{\partial t} = \sum_i a_{ni}H_{ji} \tag{24.5}$$

Taking the complex conjugate of (24.5) we obtain

$$i\hbar\frac{\partial a_{nj}{}^*}{\partial t} = -\sum_i a_{ni}{}^*H_{ji}{}^* \tag{24.6}$$

We define the density matrix in the ϕ_i representation as

$$\rho_{ij} = (1/N)\sum_{n=1}^{N} a_{nj}{}^*a_{ni} \tag{24.7}$$

Taking the derivative of (24.7) with respect to time we obtain

$$\frac{\partial \rho_{ij}}{\partial t} = (1/N)\sum_{n=1}^{N}\left(\frac{\partial a_{nj}{}^*}{\partial t}a_{ni} + a_{nj}{}^*\frac{\partial a_{ni}}{\partial t}\right) \tag{24.8}$$

Substituting (24.5) and (24.6) in (24.8) and noting that $H_{ji}{}^* = H_{ij}$ we obtain

$$\frac{\partial \rho_{ij}}{\partial t} + \frac{i}{\hbar}\sum_k (H_{ik}\rho_{kj} - \rho_{ik}H_{kj}) = 0 \tag{24.9}$$

Equation (24.9) is the quantum mechanical analogue of Liouville's equation. If our ensemble is uniform, i.e., if the phases of the assembly are completely random and if every eigenstate has equal probability, then

$$\rho_{nm} = \rho_0\delta_{nm} \tag{24.10}$$

where ρ_0 is a constant. If we substitute (24.10) in (24.9) we find

$$\partial\rho_{nm}/\partial t = 0 \tag{24.11}$$

The uniform ensemble is thus independent of time. In the classical case, a uniform distribution of representative points in phase space will also be independent of time. The classical result suggests the plausibility of assigning equal a priori probabilities to equal regions in phase space. The quantum mechanical result suggests the plausibility of assigning equal a priori probability to eigenstates and also assuming random phases.

In the classical case, the uniform distribution will be the same in any phase space, since the Jacobian for the transformation is one. In the quantum mechanical case, if the ensemble is uniform in one representation it will be the same in all representations.

Those readers wishing to pursue this subject in greater detail will find a good treatment in the text *The Principles of Statistical Mechanics* by Tolman (see bibliography).

Another equation which is frequently used in attempting to justify the postulates of statistical mechanics is the master equation. If we assume the random phase approximation; define $P_n(t)$ as the probability that at time t the system is in the state ψ_n; and define W_{nm} as the transition probability per second from the state n to the state m, we can write

$$dP_n(t)/dt = \sum_n [W_{nm}P_m(t) - W_{mn}P_n(t)] \qquad (24.12)$$

This is called the master equation. A great deal of work has gone into solving this equation and improving the assumptions on which it is based.

The preceding remarks were meant to be directive rather than definitive. It is hoped that any reader who is seriously interested in learning something about the foundations of statistical mechanics will turn to those authors who are actively working on the problem.

Chapter 25

THERMODYNAMICS

INTRODUCTION

The physical properties of a gas or any other material system may be viewed from either a microscopic or a macroscopic point of view. From the microscopic or molecular point of view, a gas is composed of a large number of rapidly moving particles. From the macroscopic point of view, a gas is a continuum. A complete description of the microscopic state of the gas would require an immense number of variables, and yet only a few parameters are required to describe the macroscopic state of the gas. In the preceding chapters we have bridged the gap between the microscopic and the macroscopic in a number of particular cases by judiciously averaging over the microscopic motions.

It is possible to study the behavior of matter from a completely macroscopic point of view with little or no reference to its microscopic structure. Laws can be established and predictions made in complete ignorance of the atomic structure of matter. Mechanics, electrodynamics, hydrodynamics, optics, thermodynamics, and other disciplines can be studied in depth with no reference to atoms or molecules.

In the present chapter we would like to *review* the basic laws of macroscopic thermodynamics. Once established, they can be used to derive innumerable useful results with no reference at all to the molecular structure of matter. In the following chapter we will then show in detail how we can tie in our statistical mechanical results with thermodynamics, so that all of the powerful techniques of thermodynamics can be systematically exploited in calculating the macroscopic properties of a system starting from a microscopic theory.

EQUILIBRIUM STATES

Suppose we have a collection of identical boxes whose walls are rigid, impermeable, and well insulated. If we introduce some gas into one of the boxes and allow it to come to equilibrium we will be able to make numerous macroscopic measurements on the gas. We can, for example, put a thermometer or manometer in the gas and note the readings on the scales, or we could weigh the gas. Now suppose we ask some other person to put the same species of gas in the other boxes in such a way as to make the various measurements on each of the gases as identical as possible. He will find that by matching a few of the macroscopic measurements he is able to prepare the gases in such a way that a third person will be unable to tell the difference between the gases by any macroscopic measurement. We conclude that there are macroscopic states of the gas which can be specified with a few variables. We call such states equilibrium states.

For more complicated systems more variables may be required. For example, if the molecules in the gas had an electric dipole moment, and were in an electric field, some additional variables such as the field strength would be required. Or if the gas were a mixture of variable composition, we would need some parameter to indicate the relative composition. We will, for simplicity, restrict ourselves to a simple, homogeneous, isotropic substance, consisting of one type of molecule, with no external fields acting on it. For concreteness we will refer to it as a gas. The extension to more elaborate systems will introduce additional complexity but will not introduce any new principles. We will also assume that there will be no effects due to the walls or shape of the container. We can summarize our results in a postulate.

Postulate I: There exist states of a gas called equilibrium states that macroscopically are characterized by a relatively small number of variables.

THE INTERNAL ENERGY

From a microscopic point of view a gas is composed of a large number N of particles obeying the laws of mechanics. If the gas is contained in a rigid, impermeable, and well-insulated box of volume V and is not acted upon by any external forces, the total energy E of the gas will remain constant.

We have found from a microscopic point of view that the parameters E, V, and N are sufficient to specify the equilibrium state of a gas. It would be convenient if we could divorce the parameters E and N from any reference to molecules; then we could use E, V, and N as a complete set of thermodynamic variables. This can be accomplished if we can simply devise a scheme for measuring E and N macroscopically.

As far as N is concerned, we could just as well have talked about the number of grams of the gas as the number of molecules. We simply define N as the number of molecules for convenience. A measurement of the mass of the gas is therefore equivalent for our purposes to measuring N. The number N can therefore be regarded as a macroscopic parameter.

As far as E is concerned, we do not need to know its exact value. What we need to be able to calculate is the difference in energy between two different states of the gas. We can do this quite simply, at least in principle, by taking the gas from the one state to the other in such a way that the exact increase in energy of the system can be measured. We could allow the gas to do work by slowly changing its volume, or we could put energy into the gas in some measurable fashion such as inserting a resistor of negligible mass in the gas and allowing a known current to pass through the resistor for a definite length of time.

One type of energy exchange we must avoid is heat transfer due to collisions of the molecules with the wall since we cannot at this stage directly measure such an energy transfer. We avoid this difficulty by keeping the walls well insulated during any of the above processes. We shall refer to all those processes in which we can directly measure the input of energy to the gas as work.

With a means at our disposal for measuring the energy macroscopically, or at least the difference in energy between two states, we can define energy and justify its conservation on a strictly macroscopic level. We summarize this result in the following postulate.

Postulate II: There exists a state function E called the internal energy. The difference between the internal energy in one state and the internal energy in another state is equal to the work required to bring the system, while thermally insulated, from the one state to the other. The work required is independent of the source of work and the path through which the system passes from the initial to the final state. The internal energy has a lower bound.

Once we know how to measure E, we can measure the flow of energy due to heat transfer. Suppose we strip off the insulation from our gas and take the gas from state 1 to state 2. Let E_1 and E_2 be the initial and final energies; W_{12} the work done on the gas in the process; and Q_{12} the heat transferred to the gas, then

$$E_2 - E_1 = Q_{12} + W_{12} \tag{25.1}$$

Knowing W_{12}, E_1, and E_2, we can solve for Q_{12}. It is customary to write the above relation in differential form as follows:

$$dE = đQ + đW \tag{25.2}$$

where the bar on the differential in dQ and dW is used to indicate that there is no function Q or W of which dQ or dW is the differential, since Q_{12} and W_{12} depend on the path taken in going from state 1 to state 2.

As mentioned at the beginning of this section, the parameters E, V, and N are sufficient to completely specify the macroscopic state of a simple gas. Since they can be interpreted as macroscopic parameters, we have a complete set of thermodynamic variables. We can summarize this fact in the following postulate.

Postulate III: The equilibrium state of a simple gas is completely characterized macroscopically by the energy E, volume V, and number of molecules N.

There are, of course, other complete sets of variables besides E, V, and N which could be used to specify the state of a gas. They will be considered later.

The various parameters used to describe the macroscopic state of a gas can be divided into two types: extensive parameters and intensive parameters. Suppose we have two identical gases A which are in identically the same state and which are separated by a wall of negligible thickness. If the wall is removed we have a single system AA. A parameter X such that $X_{AA} = 2X_A$ is called an extensive parameter. A parameter I such that $I_{AA} = I_A$ is called an intensive parameter. The parameters E, V, and N are all extensive parameters. The pressure and density are examples of intensive parameters.

ENTROPY

Suppose now we have two simple gases 1 and 2 which are separated and surrounded by rigid, impermeable, and well-insulated walls as shown in Figure 25.1. We will refer to the combined system as a composite gas.

Fig. 25.1

The state of gas 1 is determined by the parameters E_1, V_1, and N_1; the state of gas 2 is determined by the parameters E_2, V_2, and N_2; and the state of the composite gas is determined by the parameters E_1, E_2, V_1, V_2, N_1, and N_2.

The external walls maintain the energy, volume, and number of molecules in the composite gas fixed, i.e.,

$$E_1 + E_2 = E_T = \text{const} \tag{25.3}$$

$$V_1 + V_2 = V_T = \text{const} \tag{25.4}$$

$$N_1 + N_2 = N_T = \text{const} \tag{25.5}$$

The insulation, rigidity, and impermeability of the outside walls which maintain the above conditions are called external constraints.

The insulation, rigidity, and impermeability of the wall separating the two gases are called internal constraints. These constraints together with the external constraints maintain E_1, E_2, V_1, V_2, N_1, and N_2 fixed.

By removing one or more of the internal constraints we can cause the equilibrium states of the individual gases, and consequently the equilibrium state of the composite gas to change. There are many possible final states which are consistent with the conditions (25.3), (25.4), and (25.5). The basic problem of thermodynamics is to determine which of these final states will eventually result when one or more of the internal constraints is removed.

Let us consider first how we solved this problem on the microscopic level. Quantum mechanically a gas of N particles contained in a volume V and having an energy between $E - \Delta E$ and E can exist in a large number of different states ψ_i. Each one of these states is assumed to be equally probable, and is called a microstate. The various microstates can be arranged into groups of states all of which exhibit essentially the same macroscopic properties. The state of the gas corresponding to one of these groups of states is called a macrostate. The thermodynamic probability W of a particular macrostate is then defined as the number of microstates associated with it. The actual probability of a given macrostate will be proportional to the thermodynamic probability. We now assume that the properties of the gas will be essentially the same as the properties associated with the most probable macrostate. Let us designate by W^* the thermodynamic probability of the most probable macrostate. W^* will be a function of E, V, and N.

Let us now consider two gases forming a composite gas. Let us assume initially that the two gases are separated by a rigid, impermeable, and well-insulated wall. If W_1 and W_2 are the thermodynamic probabilities associated with particular macrostates of the two component gases, then $W_T = W_1 W_2$ will be the thermodynamic probability associated with the corresponding macrostate for the composite gas. In equilibrium the properties of the composite system will be the same as those of the most probable macrostate.

Let W_T^* be the thermodynamic probability associated with this state, then

$$W_T^*(E_1, V_1, N_1, E_2, V_2, N_2) = W_1^*(E_1, V_1, N_1)W_2^*(E_2, V_2, N_2) \qquad (25.6)$$

If one or more of the internal constraints is removed, the value of W_T^* will assume the maximum value consistent with the remaining constraints. The function W^* therefore tells us everything that we can know thermodynamically about a gas, since knowing W^* for a particular system is equivalent to knowing as much as can be known about how the system will interact thermodynamically with its surroundings.

The function $W^*(E, V, N)$ is neither an intensive nor extensive variable since $W_T^* = W_1^* W_2^*$. It is therefore more convenient to deal with the function

$$S(E, V, N) = k\ln W^* \qquad (25.7)$$

which we call the entropy. The quantity k is at this point an arbitrary constant. The entropy is an extensive variable. Its value for the composite gas is given by

$$S_T = k\ln W_T^* = k\ln W_1^* W_2^* = k\ln W_1^* + k\ln W_2^* = S_1 + S_2 \qquad (25.8)$$

The word "entropy" can be loosely translated from the Greek to mean *evolution*, and we can think of the entropy as the function which tells us how a system will thermodynamically evolve in a known environment.

For each equilibrium state W^* has a single value. The entropy S will therefore be a single-valued function of E, V, and N. From the nature of W^* we also expect S to be continuous and to have continuous derivatives.

On the macroscopic level we can state the above results as follows:

Postulate IV: For every gas there exists a function S, called the entropy, which has the following properties:
1. For a simple gas, S is a single-valued continuous, and differentiable function of E, V, and N.
2. For a composite gas S is the sum of the values of S for the component gases.
3. If an internal constraint is removed in an isolated composite gas, then the values assumed by the extensive variables E_1, V_1, N_1, E_2, V_2, and N_2 will be those values, consistent with the remaining internal and external constraints, which maximize the entropy of the composite gas.

CONDITIONS OF EQUILIBRIUM

Let us suppose we have a composite system as described at the beginning of the preceding section. If the insulation is stripped off the internal wall, then we can determine the equilibrium state by maximizing $S_T = S_1(E_1V_1N_1) + S_2(E_2V_2N_2)$ while holding V_1, V_2, N_1, N_2, and $E_1 + E_2$ constant. Using the method of Lagrange multipliers (Appendix 6) we obtain

$$(\partial S_1/\partial E_1)_{V_1, N_1} = (\partial S_2/\partial E_2)_{V_2, N_2} \tag{25.9}$$

If we replace the wall by a diathermal piston which is free to move, then we have to maximize S_T while holding N_1, N_2, $V_1 + V_2$, and $E_1 + E_2$ constant. Using the method of Lagrange multipliers we obtain (25.9) plus the additional condition

$$(\partial S_1/\partial V_1)_{E_1, N_1} = (\partial S_2/\partial V_2)_{E_2, N_2} \tag{25.10}$$

If the wall is rigid but permeable then energy and particles can be exchanged and we must maximize S_T while holding V_1, V_2, $N_1 + N_2$, and $E_1 + E_2$ constant. We again obtain (25.9) plus the additional condition

$$(\partial S_1/\partial N_1)_{E_1, V_1} = (\partial S_2/\partial N_2)_{E_2, V_2} \tag{25.11}$$

For convenience we define

$$(\partial S/\partial E)_{V, N} \equiv 1/T \tag{25.12}$$

$$(\partial S/\partial V)_{E, N} \equiv p/T \tag{25.13}$$

$$(\partial S/\partial N)_{E, V} \equiv -\mu/T \tag{25.14}$$

We call T, the temperature; p, the pressure; and μ, the chemical potential. At the moment these quantities are merely defined in terms of the entropy, which is a function we do not yet know how to measure. In a later section we shall see how they are measured.

In terms of T, p, and μ, our equilibrium conditions are

$$\frac{1}{T_1} = \frac{1}{T_2} \tag{25.15}$$

$$\frac{p_1}{T_1} = \frac{p_2}{T_2} \tag{25.16}$$

$$\frac{\mu_1}{T_1} = \frac{\mu_2}{T_2} \tag{25.17}$$

QUASISTATIC PROCESSES

Suppose we have a gas in equilibrium in the state (E_1, V_1, N_1) which we call state 1, and we wish to change it to the state (E_2, V_2, N_2) which we call state 2.

We could, if desired, rapidly change the volume from V_1 to V_2, let some gas escape till the number of molecules was N_2, and then dump the system into a heat bath till the gas had arrived at E_2. During this process the equilibrium of the gas would be destroyed and the intermediate states could not be described by the parameters E, V, and N. The gas would pass from state 1 to state 2 through a series of nonequilibrium states.

If, on the other hand, we change the volume slowly, allow the gas to seep out slowly, and bring the gas in contact with the heat bath by means of a very poor heat conductor, the intermediate states of the gas will be very close to equilibrium states. If the gas passes from the state 1 to the state 2 through a succession of equilibrium states we call the process quasistatic.

MEASUREMENT OF ENTROPY AND TEMPERATURE

Postulate IV tells us that the entropy function exists. In the present section we will determine how the entropy can be measured.

We note first that in a quasistatic process

$$dS = (\partial S/\partial E)_{V, N} dE + (\partial S/\partial V)_{E, N} dV + (\partial S/\partial N)_{E, V} dN \qquad (25.18)$$

Substituting (25.12), (25.13), and (25.14) in (25.18) and rearranging, we obtain

$$dE = TdS - pdV + \mu dN \qquad (25.19)$$

For a gas containing a fixed number of molecules N

$$dE = TdS - pdV \qquad (25.20)$$

If we define p' as the force per unit area exerted by the gas on the walls, then we can show that the work done on the gas in a quasistatic change of volume is $dW = -p'dV$. Substituting this in Eq. (25.2) we have

$$dE = dQ - p'dV \qquad (25.21)$$

Comparing (25.20) and (25.21) we find

$$TdS = dQ \qquad (25.22)$$

$$p = p' \qquad (25.23)$$

The pressure p can thus be identified as the force per unit area exerted by the gas on the wall, and the quantity TdS as the heat transferred to the gas during a quasistatic process. If we can devise a scheme to measure T then we can obtain S, at least within an additive constant.

We note first that two gases have the same temperature if, when they are brought in contact by a diathermal wall, there is no change in the state of either gas. We can therefore arrange all gases into sets of gases having the same temperature, and can treat each set as a large heat reservoir at a fixed temperature.

Let us consider two of these reservoirs whose temperatures we label T_1 and T_2 respectively. We now take a gas through the following cyclic process: (1) adiabatic compression from T_1 to T_2, (2) isothermal expansion at T_2, (3) adiabatic expansion from T_2 to T_1, (4) isothermal compression at T_1 back to the original state. The only heat transferred to the gas is transferred during the two isothermal processes. Let Q_1 and Q_2 be the heat transferred to the gas during the isothermal processes at T_1 and T_2 respectively. Since the process is cyclic the net entropy change of the gas must be zero, and therefore

$$\frac{Q_1}{T_1} + \frac{Q_2}{T_2} = 0 \tag{25.24}$$

By measuring Q_1 and Q_2 we can solve for the ratio T_2/T_1. It follows that if we know the temperature of one reservoir we can find the temperature of all other reservoirs. The absolute Kelvin scale of temperature is obtained by assigning the number 273.16 to the temperature of a mixture of pure ice, water, and water vapor in mutual equilibrium. Once we have established the temperatures of the various reservoirs it is possible to construct and calibrate simple thermometers which enable the temperature to be easily measured.

THE NERNST POSTULATE

We have not yet recorded all of the general facts concerning $S = k\ln W^*$ which can be found from a microscopic analysis. If we examine the specific values of W^* for quite general types of system we find that there are certain characteristics of W^* which seem to be true for any type of system.

In the first place if V and N are held fixed, then as E approaches its minimum value E_0 the number of accessible states decreases to the point where $S = k\ln W^*$ becomes negligibly small compared to its value for higher E, and we can assume that it vanishes, i.e., $S(E_0, V, N) = 0$. We note that this is found to be true for all values of V and N.

Next, a study of the specific forms of W^* will reveal that if V and N are held fixed, W^* always increases with increasing E. It follows that $(\partial S/\partial E)_{V, N} > 0$ or the temperature is always positive. This can most easily be understood by thinking in terms of phase space. As the energy is increased, the accessible region in phase space is increased, and therefore the number of accessible states is increased. If there is an upper bound to the energy this will not be true, but we shall exclude these cases from our consideration.

Finally it will be found to be quite generally true that if V and N are held fixed, then W^* increases in such a fashion that at the minimum of energy $T = 0$.

We can summarize these results in the following postulates:

Postulate V: The temperature $T \equiv (\partial E/\partial S)_{V, N}$ is always positive and at the minimum value of the energy for arbitrary V and N is zero.

Postulate VI: The entropy of any system vanishes in the states for which the temperature is zero.

The latter postulate is known as the Nernst postulate. It should be noted in this postulate that we are not just assigning a specific value of the entropy to a single state. The generality of this result rests with the facts: (1) the entropy is zero for a whole set of states, namely, all those states for which $T = 0$ irrespective of the values of any other parameters of which S may be a function; (2) it refers to any system.

THE THREE LAWS OF THERMODYNAMICS

Using Postulate IV it is possible to derive the following theorem.

Theorem I: It is impossible to construct a device that, operating in a cycle, will produce no other effect than the transfer of heat from a cooler to a hotter body.

The usual starting point of thermodynamics is Postulate II, Theorem I, and Postulate VI, which are respectively referred to as the first, second, and third law of thermodynamics. The remaining postulates are implicitly understood or can be derived from these three laws. The advantage in starting with the three laws of thermodynamics lies in the fact that their connection with experiment is immediately apparent. However, this advantage is, in the opinion of the author, far outweighed by the analytic clarity and consequent ease of application afforded by starting with Postulates I–VI. The reader who wishes to see a development of thermodynamics starting from the Postulates I–VI is referred to the thermodynamics textbook by Callen (see bibliography). We have for the sake of additional clarity rearranged his postulates, and added postulates which were implicitly understood. The most complete postulational formulation has been carried out by L. Tisza.[1]

FUNDAMENTAL EQUATIONS

If we know the entropy S of a gas as a function of E, V, and N, then we know everything that can be known thermodynamically about the gas. If we know S as a function of some other set of variables, for example T, V, and N, we do not necessarily have the same amount of information about the system as is contained in the function $S(E, V, N)$. The equation $S = S(E, V, N)$ is therefore called a fundamental equation.

Since S is a monotonically increasing function of E, we can invert the function $S(E, V, N)$ to obtain $E(S, V, N)$, a single-valued, continuous, and differentiable function of S, V, and N. If we know E as a function of S, V, and N, we also know everything that can be known thermodynamically about the system, and therefore $E = E(S, V, N)$ is also a fundamental equation.

Starting with $E = E(S, V, N)$ or $S = S(E, V, N)$, it is possible to generate a whole set of fundamental equations by making Legendre transformations

[1] *Annals of Physics*, vol. 13, p. 1, 1961.

of the functions $E(S, V, N)$ or $S(E, V, N)$ (Appendix 9). There are seven possible Legendre transformations of $E(S, V, N)$. One of these, however, is identically zero. There are therefore six functions in addition to $E(S, V, N)$ which contain the same information as $E(S, V, N)$. Of these, we are particularly interested in the following four:

$$F(T, V, N) = E - (\partial E/\partial S)_{V, N} S = E - TS \tag{25.25}$$

$$G(T, p, N) = E - (\partial E/\partial S)_{V, N} S - (\partial E/\partial V)_{S, N} V = E - TS + pV \tag{25.26}$$

$$H(S, p, N) = E - (\partial E/\partial V)_{S, N} V = E + pV \tag{25.27}$$

$$I(T, V, \mu) = E - (\partial E/\partial S)_{V, N} S - (\partial E/\partial N)_{S, V} N = E - TS - \mu N \tag{25.28}$$

F is called the Helmholtz free energy; G the Gibbs free energy; H the enthalpy; and I the grand canonical potential. The letters F, G, and H are in common use for the first three functions. There is no letter or name usually assigned to the grand canonical potential. We have taken the liberty therefore of assigning it the letter I.

In electrostatics if we know the potential we can calculate the electric forces. The potential therefore contains a complete description of the force field. In thermodynamics if we know $E(S, V, N)$ $F(T, V, N)$, $G(T, p, N)$, $H(S, p, N)$, $I(T, V, \mu)$ or any of the other Legendre transformations of $E(S, V, N)$, we have a complete thermodynamic description of the system. We therefore sometimes call these functions thermodynamic potentials.

We frequently have need of the first derivatives of the various thermodynamic potentials. Recalling that

$$dE = TdS - PdV + \mu dN \tag{25.29}$$

we have $(\partial E/\partial S)_{V, N} = T$; $(\partial E/\partial V)_{S, N} = -p$; $(\partial E/\partial N)_{S, V} = \mu$. To obtain the first derivatives of $F(T, V, N)$ we note that

$$\begin{aligned} dF = d(E - TS) &= dE - TdS - SdT \\ &= (TdS - pdV + \mu dN) - TdS - SdT \\ &= -SdT - pdV + \mu dN \end{aligned} \tag{25.30}$$

Similarly

$$dG = -SdT + Vdp + \mu dN \tag{25.31}$$

$$dH = TdS + Vdp + \mu dN \tag{25.32}$$

$$dI = -SdT - pdV - Nd\mu \tag{25.33}$$

THE EQUATIONS OF STATE

The thermodynamic potential $E(S, V, N)$ is a homogeneous function of degree one in the variables S, V, and N, i.e.,

$$E(\lambda S, \lambda V, \lambda N) = \lambda E(S, V, N) \tag{25.34}$$

Applying Euler's theorem (Appendix 10), we obtain

$$E = (\partial E/\partial S)_{V, N}S + (\partial E/\partial V)_{S, N}V + (\partial E/\partial N)_{S, V}N$$
$$= TS - pV + \mu N \tag{25.35}$$

It follows that if we know $T(S, V, N)\, p(S, V, N)$ and $\mu(S, V, N)$ we can obtain $E(S, V, N)$. The three equations $T = T(S, V, N)$, $p = p(S, V, N)$ and $\mu = \mu(S, V, N)$, which are called equations of state, are therefore equivalent to knowing the fundamental equation $E = E(S, V, N)$. From the definition of F and Eq. (25.35) we obtain $F = E - TS = -pV + \mu N$. It follows that if we know $p(T, V, N)$ and $\mu(T, V, N)$ we can obtain $F(T, V, N)$. Similarly

$$G = E - TS + pV = \mu N \tag{25.36}$$

$$H = E + pV = TS + \mu N \tag{25.37}$$

$$I = E - TS - \mu N = -pV \tag{25.38}$$

$$S = (1/T)E + (p/T)V - (\mu/T)N \tag{25.39}$$

and therefore if we know $\mu(T, p, N)$ we can obtain $G(T, p, N)$; if we know $T(S, p, N)$ and $\mu(S, p, N)$ we can obtain $H(S, p, N)$; if we know $p(T, V, \mu)$ we can obtain $I(T, V, \mu)$; and if we know $\frac{1}{T}(E, V, N)$, $\frac{p}{T}(E, V, N)$, and $\frac{\mu}{T}(E, V, N)$ we can obtain $S(E, V, N)$.

CONCLUSION

When we discussed ensembles in Chapter 21, it was pointed out that the different ensembles corresponded to different choices of thermodynamic variables used to specify the state of an assembly. In the following chapter, when we study the link between statistical mechanics and thermodynamics we will find that an ensemble characterized by a particular set of variables will provide us with the fundamental equation appropriate to the same set of variables. Thus the microcanonical ensemble will yield $S = S(E, V, N)$; the canonical ensemble will yield $F = F(T, V, N)$; and the grand canonical ensemble will yield $I = I(T, V, \mu)$.

PROBLEMS

1. A given system is such that the quasistatic adiabatic change in the volume at constant mole numbers is found to change the pressure in accordance with the equation $p = \text{const } V^{-5/3}$.

A small paddle wheel is installed in the system. The shaft of the paddle wheel extends through the walls of the system and can be driven at 240 rps by an external motor. The viscous torque on the paddle wheel is then 10^4 cm dyn. If the motor is thus permitted to do work on the system while the volume is kept constant and the system is adiabatically enclosed, the pressure is found to increase at a rate

$$dp/dt = 2T\omega/3V$$

where T is the viscous torque and ω is the angular velocity of the paddle wheel.

Find the internal energy of any equilibrium state with arbitrary pressure p and volume V. Choose the state $p = 32$ atm, $V = 1$ liter as the fiducial state.

2. The fundamental equation of system A is

$$S_A = C(N_A V_A E_A)^{1/3}$$

where C is a constant. The fundamental equation of system B is

$$S_B = C(N_B V_B E_B)^{1/3}$$

Assume that the two systems are enclosed by a rigid, adiabatic, impermeable wall and are separated from one another by a rigid, impermeable, and diathermal wall. Assume $V_A = 9$ cm^3, $V_B = 4$ cm^3, $N_A = 3$ moles, $N_B = 2$ moles, and $E_A + E_B = 20$ cal. When the composite system has come to equilibrium what are the internal energies of each of the two subsystems?

3. Two particular systems have the following equations of state

$$1/T_A = 3RN_A/2E_A \qquad p_A/T_A = RN_A/V_A$$
$$1/T_B = 5RN_B/2E_B \qquad p_B/T_B = RN_B/V_B$$

The two systems are contained in a closed cylinder separated by a movable diathermal piston. Initially $N_A = 0.5$ moles, $N_B = 0.75$ moles, $T_A = 200°$K, $T_B = 300°$K, $V_A + V_B = 20$ liters. What is the energy, volume, pressure, and temperature of each system in equilibrium?

4. The fundamental equation for an ideal monatomic gas in the entropy representation is

$$S = NR\ln(E^{3/2}VN^{-5/2}) + NC$$

where C is a constant. Find the fundamental equation in the Helmholtz free energy representation.

5. Using the fundamental equation given in problem 4 derive the ideal gas law.

6. The fundamental equation for an ideal monatomic gas is given in problem 4. Show that in an adiabatic quasistatic process $pV^{5/3}$ is a constant.

7. The fundamental equation of an ideal diatomic gas is

$$S = NR\ln(E^{5/2}VN^{-7/2}) + NC$$

An ideal diatomic gas is contained in a cylinder which is closed by a frictionless and weightless piston backed by a spring whose restoring force is proportional to the displacement. Initially the gas occupies 100 cm³, the temperature is 300°K, the pressure is 1 atm, and the spring is exerting no force. The temperature is now raised to 400°K and the volume increases to 150 cm³. Compute the work done against both the spring and the external atmosphere. How much heat was supplied to the gas?

8. A certain solid obeys the equation

$$V = V_0 - Ap + BT$$

and its internal energy is given by

$$E = CT - BpT$$

where A, B, C, and V_0 are constants.
(a) Find the enthalpy of the solid.
(b) Find the heat capacities c_V and c_p.

9. Two reservoirs of 1000 cal/deg heat capacity and constant volume are initially at 1200°K and 300°K. An engine is used to obtain the greatest amount of work possible from these reservoirs.
(a) What is the total change in entropy?
(b) What is the final temperature?
(c) How much work is obtained?

10. Prove that for a perfect gas of structureless particles the entropy change between any two temperatures when the pressure is kept constant is 5/3 times the corresponding entropy change when the volume is kept constant.

26

THE CONNECTION BETWEEN STATISTICAL MECHANICS AND THERMODYNAMICS

INTRODUCTION

In the present chapter we will show how starting with a microscopic analysis of a particular assembly we can obtain one or another of the fundamental equations of thermodynamics. Once this connection is made, all of the techniques of thermodynamics can be used in evaluating the equilibrium properties of the assembly. We will start with the canonical ensemble, not because it is the most logical starting place, but because the canonical ensemble is probably the most familiar of the ensembles.

THE CANONICAL ENSEMBLE

The thermodynamic probability associated with a particular macrostate $\{N_i\}$ of the canonical ensemble is

$$W(N_i) = \mathcal{N}!/\Pi N_i! \tag{26.1}$$

The entropy of the ensemble is given by

$$S = k \ln W^* \tag{26.2}$$

where W^* is the maximum value of $W(N_i)$ consistent with the constraints $\Sigma N_i = \mathcal{N}$ and $\Sigma N_i E_i = \mathcal{E}$.

The average entropy of one of the assemblies in the ensemble is

$$S = S/\mathcal{N} \tag{26.3}$$

To determine S we note first that

$$
\begin{aligned}
(1/\mathcal{N})\ln W(N_i) &= (1/\mathcal{N})\ln \mathcal{N}! - (1/\mathcal{N})\Sigma \ln N_i! \\
&\approx (1/\mathcal{N})\{\mathcal{N}\ln \mathcal{N} - \mathcal{N}\} - (1/\mathcal{N})\{\Sigma N_i \ln N_i - \Sigma N_i\} \\
&= (1/\mathcal{N})\{\Sigma N_i \ln \mathcal{N} - \Sigma N_i\} - (1/\mathcal{N})\{\Sigma N_i \ln N_i - \Sigma N_i\} \\
&= -\Sigma(N_i/\mathcal{N})\ln(N_i/\mathcal{N}) \\
&= -\Sigma_i P_i \ln P_i
\end{aligned}
\tag{26.4}
$$

where P_i is the probability that an assembly chosen at random is in the state ψ_i. If we maximize $\ln W(N_i)$ subject to the appropriate constraints we obtain

$$
P_i = \exp(-\beta E_i)/Q \tag{26.5}
$$

$$
Q = \Sigma_i \exp(-\beta E_i) \tag{26.6}
$$

The assembly energy level E_i is a function of V and N and therefore Q is a function of β, V, and N.

Combining Eqs. (26.2), (26.3), (26.4), (26.5), and (26.6) we obtain

$$
\begin{aligned}
S &= -k\Sigma_i P_i \ln P_i \\
&= -k\Sigma_i P_i(-\beta E_i - \ln Q) \\
&= k\beta \bar{E} + k\ln Q
\end{aligned}
\tag{26.7}
$$

and therefore

$$
dS = k\beta d\bar{E} + k\bar{E}d\beta + kd(\ln Q) \tag{26.8}
$$

Noting that

$$
\begin{aligned}
d\ln Q &= -\left(\Sigma_i E_i P_i\right)d\beta - \beta\left[\Sigma_i P_i(\partial E_i/\partial V)_N\right]dV - \beta\left[\Sigma_i P_i(\partial E_i/\partial N)_V\right]dN \\
&= -\bar{E}d\beta - \beta\left[\Sigma_i P_i(\partial E_i/\partial V)_N\right]dV - \beta\left[\Sigma_i P_i(\partial E_i/\partial N)_V\right]dN
\end{aligned}
\tag{26.9}
$$

substituting (26.9) in (26.8) and letting $\bar{E} = E$ we obtain

$$
dS = k\beta dE - k\beta\left[\Sigma_i P_i(\partial E_i/\partial V)_N\right]dV - k\beta\left[\Sigma_i P_i(\partial E_i/\partial N)_V\right]dN \tag{26.10}
$$

It follows that

$$
1/T = (\partial S/\partial E)_{V,N} = k\beta \tag{26.11}
$$

$$
p/T = (\partial S/\partial V)_{E,N} = -k\beta\Sigma_i P_i(\partial E_i/\partial V)_N \tag{26.12}
$$

$$
-\mu/T = (\partial S/\partial N)_{E,V} = -k\beta\Sigma_i P_i(\partial E_i/\partial N)_V \tag{26.13}
$$

and therefore

$$
\beta = 1/kT \tag{26.14}
$$

$$p = -\sum_i P_i (\partial E_i / \partial V)_N \qquad (26.15)$$

$$\mu = \sum_i P_i (\partial E_i / \partial N)_V \qquad (26.16)$$

Substituting (26.14) in (26.7) we obtain

$$S = \frac{E}{T} + k \ln Q(T, V, N) \qquad (26.17)$$

Rearranging, we have

$$E - TS = -kT \ln Q \qquad (26.18)$$

But $E - TS$ is just the Helmholtz free energy and therefore we have

$$F(T, V, N) = -kT \ln Q \qquad (26.19)$$

$$Q = \sum_i \exp[-E_i(V, N)/kT] \qquad (26.20)$$

The Helmholtz free energy F expressed as a function of T, V, and N contains a complete thermodynamic description of the assembly. It follows that if we know the canonical partition function $Q(T, V, N)$ we can immediately write down the fundamental equation $F = F(T, V, N)$ At this point the job of statistical mechanics ends and thermodynamics takes over.

The evaluation of $Q(T, V, N)$ can in principle be further simplified by recalling that

$$Q = Tr[\exp(-\hat{H}/kT)] \qquad (26.21)$$

THE GRAND CANONICAL ENSEMBLE

To obtain the connection between thermodynamics and the grand canonical ensemble, we proceed exactly as we did for the canonical ensemble.

We obtain first

$$S = -k \sum_n \sum_i P_{ni} \ln P_{ni} \qquad (26.22)$$

$$P_{ni} = \exp(\alpha n - \beta E_{ni})/\mathcal{Q} \qquad (26.23)$$

$$\mathcal{Q} = \sum_n \sum_i \exp(\alpha n - \beta E_{ni}) \qquad (26.24)$$

Substituting (26.23) and (26.24) in (26.22) and noting that E_{ni} is a function of V only we obtain

$$S = -k \alpha \bar{n} + k \beta \bar{E} + k \ln \mathcal{Q} \qquad (26.25)$$

$$dS = k \beta d\bar{E} - k \beta \left[\sum_n \sum_i P_{ni}(dE_{ni}/dV) \right] dV - k \alpha dN \qquad (26.26)$$

From (26.26) we obtain directly

$$\beta = 1/kT \tag{26.27}$$

$$\alpha = \mu/kT \tag{26.28}$$

$$p = -\sum_n \sum_i P_{ni}(dE_{ni}/dV) \tag{26.29}$$

Substituting these results in (26.25) and rearranging we have

$$E - TS - \mu N = -kT \ln \mathcal{Q}(T, V, \mu) \tag{26.30}$$

But $E - TS - \mu N = -pV$ is just the grand canonical potential and therefore

$$I(T, V, \mu) = -p(T, V, \mu)V = -kT \ln \mathcal{Q} \tag{26.31}$$

$$\mathcal{Q} = \sum_n \sum_i \exp\left[\frac{\mu n - E_{ni}(V)}{kT}\right] \tag{26.32}$$

Since $I = I(T, V, \mu)$ is a fundamental equation we have a complete thermodynamic description of the assembly. It follows that if we know the grand canonical partition function $\mathcal{Q}(T, V, \mu)$ we can immediately write down the fundamental equation $I = I(T, V, \mu)$ and turn the result over to the thermodynamicist.

THE MICROCANONICAL ENSEMBLE

For the microcanonical ensemble we obtain

$$S = -k\sum_i P_i \ln P_i \tag{26.33}$$

$$P_i = 1/Z \qquad E - \Delta E \leq E_i \leq E$$
$$P_i = 0 \qquad \text{otherwise} \tag{26.34}$$

where Z is the number of assembly eigenstates between $E - \Delta E$ and E. The quantity Z is called the microcanonical partition function. If we substitute (26.34) in (26.33) we obtain

$$S = -kZ(1/Z)\ln(1/Z) = k\ln Z \tag{26.35}$$

It would appear from (26.35) that S is a function of E, V, N and ΔE. It can be shown, however, that the entropy is relatively insensitive to the choice of ΔE. Let $(\Delta E)_1$ and $(\Delta E)_2$ be two values of ΔE, both of which are very much less than E. Let S_1, S_2, Z_1, and Z_2 be the respective values of S and Z. Then

$$\frac{Z_1}{Z_2} \approx \frac{(\Delta E)_1}{(\Delta E)_2} \tag{26.36}$$

and

$$S_1 - S_2 = k\ln Z_1 - k\ln Z_2 \approx k\ln\frac{(\Delta E)_1}{(\Delta E)_2} \tag{26.37}$$

Experimentally the entropy is of the order of kN. Therefore unless $(\Delta E)_1/(\Delta E)_2$ is of the order of e^N, the difference $S_1 - S_2$ is negligible. For a gas containing 10^{17} particles e^N is a very large number. The entropy S as given by (26.35) will therefore to a high degree of approximation be a function of E, V, and N.

Since $S = S(E, V, N)$ is a fundamental equation, it provides a complete thermodynamic description of the assembly. It follows that if we know $Z(E, V, N)$ we can immediately write down the fundamental equation $S = S(E, V, N)$ and turn the result over to the thermodynamicist. Whether we interpret Z as the degeneracy of the level $E_i = E$, or as the number of states with energy between $E - \Delta E$ and E, we will get essentially the same result.

THE IDEAL GAS

As an example of an application of the formulae of the preceding section, let us show, using the microcanonical, canonical, and grand canonical ensembles, that for an ideal monatomic gas

$$pV = NkT \tag{26.38}$$

$$E = 3NkT/2 \tag{26.39}$$

The classical limit for the canonical partition function is given by

$$Q = (1/h^{3N}N!)\int\int \exp(-E/kT)d\mathbf{p}d\mathbf{q} \tag{26.40}$$

For a gas of point particles, the most convenient set of generalized coordinates are Cartesian coordinates. The energy is then

$$E = (1/2m)\sum_{i=1}^{N}\sum_{j=1}^{3}p_j^2(i) \equiv (1/2m)\sum_{i=1}^{3N}p_i^2 \tag{26.41}$$

where $p_j(i)$ is the jth component of momentum of the ith particle.

Substituting (26.41) in (26.40) and integrating over $\mathbf{x}$ we obtain

$$Q = (1/h^{3N}N!)V^N\left[\int \exp(-p^2/2mkT)dp\right]^{3N}$$

$$= (V^N/N!)(2\pi mkT/h^2)^{3N/2} \tag{26.42}$$

The Helmholtz free energy is therefore

$$F = -kT\ln Q = -kT\ln\left\{\frac{V^N}{N!}\left(\frac{2\pi mkT}{h^2}\right)^{3N/2}\right\} \tag{26.43}$$

Recalling that

$$dF = -SdT - pdV + \mu dN \tag{26.44}$$

we obtain $\qquad\qquad p = -(\partial F/\partial V)_{T, N} = NkT/V$ $\qquad\qquad$ (26.45)

$$S = -(\partial F/\partial T)_{V, N} = (3Nk/2) + k\ln Q \qquad (26.46)$$

Combining (26.46) and (26.43) we obtain

$$E = F + TS = 3NkT/2 \qquad (26.47)$$

Equations (26.45) and (26.47) are the desired result.

The classical limit of the grand canonical partition function is

$$\mathcal{Q} = \sum_n (1/h^{3n}n!)\exp(\mu n/kT)\iint \exp(-E/kT)d\mathbf{p}d\mathbf{q}$$

$$= \sum_n (1/n!)\exp(\mu n/kT)\{V^n(2\pi mkT/h^2)^{3n/2}\}$$

$$= \sum_n A^n/n! = \exp(A) \qquad (26.48)$$

where $\qquad A = [\exp(\mu/kT)](2\pi mkT/h^2)^{3/2}V$

The grand canonical potential is therefore given by

$$I(T, V, \mu) = -p(T, V, \mu)V = -kT\ln\mathcal{Q} = -kTA \qquad (26.49)$$

Recalling that

$$dI = -SdT - pdV - Nd\mu \qquad (26.50)$$

we obtain

$$S = -(\partial I/\partial T)_{V, \mu} = (5kA/2) - (\mu A/T) \qquad (26.51)$$

$$p = -(\partial I/\partial V)_{T, \mu} = kTA/V \qquad (26.52)$$

$$N = -(\partial I/\partial \mu)_{T, V} = A \qquad (26.53)$$

and therefore

$$pV = NkT \qquad (26.54)$$

$$E = TS - pV + \mu N = 3NkT/2 \qquad (26.55)$$

The classical limit of the microcanonical partition function is

$$Z = (1/h^{3N}N!) \int\int\limits_{E-\Delta E}^{E} d\mathbf{p}d\mathbf{q}$$

$$= (1/h^{3N}N!)V^N \int\limits_{E-\Delta E}^{E} d\mathbf{p} \qquad (26.56)$$

Since $E = \sum_i p_i^2/2m$, the integral in (26.56) is just the "volume" contained between the $3N$ dimensional hypersphere of radius $(2mE)^{1/2}$ and the $3N$

dimensional hypersphere of radius $[2m(E - \Delta E)]^{1/2}$. The volume of an n dimensional hypersphere of radius R is

$$V_n(R) = c_n R^n \tag{26.57}$$

where

$$c_n = \pi^{n/2}/\Gamma\left(\frac{n+2}{2}\right) \tag{26.58}$$

We will for convenience assume that n is always an even number, in which case

$$c_n = \pi^{n/2}/(n/2)! \tag{26.59}$$

The microcanonical partition function is therefore

$$Z = \frac{V^N \pi^{3N/2}}{h^{3N} N! (3N/2)!} \{[2mE]^{3N/2} - [2m(E - \Delta E)]^{3N/2}\} \tag{26.60}$$

and the entropy

$$S = kN\ln V - k\ln N! - k\ln[(3N/2)!]$$
$$+ \frac{3Nk}{2}\ln\left(\frac{2m\pi E}{h^2}\right) + k\ln\left[1 - \left(1 - \frac{\Delta E}{E}\right)^{3N/2}\right] \tag{26.61}$$

As long as ΔE is less than or equal to E but not so small as to be of the order of roughly e^{-N}, the last term in (26.61) will be negligible. Dropping this term and making use of Stirling's approximation, we obtain

$$S = Nk\ln(E^{3/2}VN^{-5/2}) + (5Nk/2) + (3Nk/2)\ln(4m\pi/3h^2) \tag{26.62}$$

This equation is called the Sackur Tetrode equation.

Recalling that

$$dS = (1/T)dE + (p/T)dV - (\mu/T)dN \tag{26.63}$$

we have

$$1/T = (\partial S/\partial E)_{V,N} = 3Nk/2E \tag{26.64}$$

$$p/T = (\partial S/\partial V)_{E,N} = Nk/V \tag{26.65}$$

which again are the same results we have obtained previously.

PROBLEMS

1. Two identical perfect gases with the same pressure p and number of particles N but with different temperatures T_1 and T_2 are in two vessels with volumes V_1 and V_2. The vessels are then connected. Find the change in entropy.

2. Find the work done on a perfect gas during an adiabatic compression.

3. (a) Find the canonical partition function for a two-dimensional monatomic gas, i.e., one whose molecules can move freely in a plane but are confined within an area A.

   (b) Find the equation of state of the gas from its Helmholtz function.

4. A film of (i) He^3 atoms, (ii) He^4 atoms, is adsorbed as a monolayer on the surface of a solid. Assume that the atoms form a two-dimensional ideal gas, and work out the thermodynamic properties subject to the continuous spectrum approximation. Illustrate graphically the temperature dependence of the heat capacity at constant area. The number of atoms per unit area should be treated as a given constant.

5. Show that the absolute value of the entropy of a monatomic van der Waals gas is

$$S = NR[(5/2) - \ln(NR) + i + (3/2)\ln T + \ln(V - Nb)]$$

   The constant i is called the chemical constant.

6. (a) Calculate the grand partition function $\mathcal{Q}(T, V, \mu)$ for a two-dimensional ideal Bose gas.

   (b) Find the average number of particles per unit area as a function of μ and T.

   (c) Show that there is no Bose-Einstein condensation for a two-dimensional ideal Bose gas.

7. Consider a classical system of N noninteracting diatomic molecules enclosed in a box of volume V at temperature T. The Hamiltonian for a single molecule is taken to be

$$H(\mathbf{p}_1, \mathbf{p}_2, \mathbf{r}_1, \mathbf{r}_2) = \frac{1}{2m}(p_1^2 + p_2^2) + \tfrac{1}{2}\kappa |\mathbf{r}_1 - \mathbf{r}_2|^2$$

   where $\mathbf{p}_1, \mathbf{p}_2, \mathbf{r}_1, \mathbf{r}_2$ are the momenta and coordinates of the two atoms in a molecule. Find

   (a) the Helmholtz free energy of the system;

   (b) the specific heat at constant volume;

   (c) the mean square molecular diameter $<|\mathbf{r}_1 - \mathbf{r}_2|^2>$.

8. The carbon dioxide molecule has fundamental vibrational frequencies of 667.3, 667.3, 1388.3, and 2439.3 wave numbers (cm^{-1}). The moment of inertia is 71.67×10^{-40} g cm^2. Compute the rotational, vibrational, and translational contributions to the Gibbs function, Helmholtz function, entropy, and enthalpy at

   (a) 30°F

   (b) 500°F

   (c) 4000°F.

9. Calculate the thermodynamic functions E, F, G, H, S, c_V, c_p for argon and and nitrogen at 300°K and 1000°K. Disregard nuclear spin and elec-

tronic contributions. For nitrogen, use $h\nu/k = 3336.6°K$ and $\hbar^2/2Ik = 2.847°K$ for calculating the vibrational and rotational contributions, respectively.

10. A perfect gas of structureless particles has its temperature raised from 390°K to 400°K. Show that if this is done at constant volume the increase in entropy of the gas is 0.43 R (per mole), while if it is done at constant pressure the increase in entropy is 0.72 R (per mole).

11. Show that if P is the pressure and V the volume of an assembly of point masses obeying either the Fermi-Dirac or Bose-Einstein statistics, then $PV = 2E/3$, where E is the energy of the assembly. Prove that in the analogous case of radiation $PV = E/3$ and comment on the difference.

12. A system has probability P_1 of being in any one of a group of g_1 degenerate and equiprobable quantum states, and probability P_2 of being in any one of a group of g_2 degenerate and equiprobable quantum states where $P_1 + P_2 = 1$. Show clearly why $-k(P_1\ln P_1 + P_2\ln P_2)$ is not a correct expression for the entropy of the system (unless $g_1 = g_2 = 1$). By using a canonical distribution for temperature T show that the correct expression for the entropy yields

$$S = k\left\{\ln g_1 + \ln\left[1 + \frac{g_2}{g_1}\exp(-x)\right] + x \left/ \left[1 + \frac{g_2}{g_1}\exp x\right]\right.\right\}$$

where xkT is the gap between the two energies. Verify the above expression for the entropy by deriving the free energy from the partition function, and then using $S = -\partial F/\partial T$. Show that as $T \to 0$, $S \to k\ln g_1$, as expected, since the upper level becomes in fact unavailable in this limit.

13. (a) Two dilute nonreacting gases A, B, occupy volumes V_A, V_B, and consist of N_A and N_B identical molecules respectively. They are at the same temperature and initially separated. Both gases may later occupy the total volume $V \equiv V_A + V_B$. If $p \equiv V_A/V$, $q \equiv N_A/N$ where $N \equiv N_A + N_B$, and if any difference between the molecular mass of A and B is neglected, show that the increase in the entropy total system is

$$S_1 = -kN[q\ln p + (1 - q)\ln(1 - p)]$$

or

$$S_2 = kN\{q\ln(q/p) + (1 - q)\ln[(1 - q)/(1 - p)]\}$$

depending on whether the molecules of A are distinguishable from those of B or not.

(b) Show that $S_1 \geq kN\ln 2$, $S_2 \geq 0$, and $S_1 - S_2 \geq kN\ln 2$, the minimum values being reached for $p = q = 1/2$ in the case of S_1, for $p = q$ in the case of S_2, and for $q = 1/2$ in the case of $S_1 - S_2$.

(c) Does the entropy change drop abruptly from S_1 to S_2 as the molecules of A are gradually made identical with those of B?

14. A gas consists of a mixture of $N/2$ molecules of mass M_1 and N_2 molecules of mass M_2, in a volume V at temperature T. Set up the partition function, assuming that the molecular rotation and vibration can be neglected and that the molecules of each kind are indistinguishable from each other (but distinguishable from those of the other kind). Calculate the entropy, internal energy, and pressure of the mixture.

15. Write the equations for the thermodynamic properties of a Debye solid, including the Gibbs function, enthalpy, internal energy U, Helmholtz function, and pressure.

16. Show that for the ideal Fermi gas of N particles the Helmholtz free energy at low temperatures is given by

$$F = \frac{3\mu_0}{5}\left[1 - \frac{5\pi^2}{12}\left(\frac{kT}{\mu_0}\right)^2 + \cdots\right]$$

17. Prove the expressions for the entropy:

$$S = k\ln Q + T\left[\frac{\partial}{\partial T}(\ln Q)\right]_{V,\,N}$$

$$S = k\ln \mathfrak{Q} + T\left[\frac{\partial}{\partial T}(\ln \mathfrak{Q})\right]_{V,\,\mu}$$

18. When a crystal is stretched along one of its axes, the frequency of lattice vibrations in the direction of the stretch is changed, becoming $\omega_s = \omega_0[1 + (\alpha/2L_0^2)(L - L_0)^2]$, where L_0 is the equilibrium length. Use the Einstein model, with energy

$$E_v = (YA/2L_0)(L - L_0)^2 + \sum_{i=1}^{2N}\hbar\omega_0 n_i + \sum_{j=1}^{N}\hbar\omega_s n_j$$

to set up a canonical ensemble for this case (Y is Young's modulus of elasticity, A is the cross section of the crystal perpendicular to the tension, so that AL_0 is the crystal volume). Calculate the equation of state for elongation, $J = (\partial F/\partial L)_T$, for temperatures larger than $(\hbar\omega_0/k)$. If α is positive does the temperature rise or fall when the crystal is stretched adiabatically?

19. Suppose that the particles of an ideal gas have the relativistic dependence of energy on momentum

$$\epsilon = c(p_x^2 + p_y^2 + p_z^2 + m_0^2c^2)^{1/2}$$

Find the energy, Helmholtz function, and equation of state for this ideal gas in the extreme relativistic range where $m_0c \ll p_j$.

20. A dilute gas consisting of molecules with a permanent electric dipole moment is brought into a uniform electric field. Find the free energy of the system and calculate the average electric dipole moment per unit volume of the gas.

21. Work out the grand canonical ensemble for a gas of point atoms, each with spin magnetic moment μ which can have magnetic energy $+(1/2)\mu H$ or $-(1/2)\mu H$ in a magnetic field H in addition to its kinetic energy. Obtain expressions for the grand canonical potential. Using the grand canonical potential obtain the magnetization. How much heat is given off by the gas when the magnetic field is reduced from H to zero isothermally at constant volume?

22. (a) An $[w]$ oscillator of frequency ν is defined to be a system with energy levels $E_j = (w/2 + j)h\nu$ of degeneracies $g_j \equiv (w + j - 1)!/j!(w - 1)!$, where $j = 1, 2, \ldots$. Show that the degeneracies are such that for $w = 2$ or 3 the $[w]$ oscillator is an isotropic two- or three-dimensional oscillator so that the $[w]$ oscillator represents a generalization to w dimensions.

    (b) Determine the partition function and the main thermodynamic functions of a system of N independent, identical but distinguishable $[w]$ oscillators.

23. An evacuated vessel containing a little metallic sodium is heated; it becomes filled with sodium vapor, which consists of Na atoms, together with some diatomic molecules, Na_2, in equilibrium with the free atoms. Derive an expression for the condition of the equilibrium $2Na \rightleftarrows Na_2$ in terms of the partition functions of the atoms and molecules, assuming that sodium consists of a single isotope.

24. Consider a system that has only two accessible states, a ground state of energy zero and an excited state of energy ϵ. If this system were in equilibrium with a heat bath of temperature T, calculate F, E, S and c_V. Sketch a plot of c_V versus T.

25. A system consists of a box of volume V and a variable number of indistinguishable particles each of mass m. Each particle can be "created" by the expenditure of energy γ; once created it becomes a member of a perfect gas of point particles within the volume V. The allowed energies of the system are therefore $N\gamma$ plus the kinetic energies of N particles inside V, for $N = 0, 1, 2, \ldots$. Show that the Helmholtz function for this system (canonical ensemble) is

$$F = kT\ln\left[\sum_{N=0}^{\infty} (V^N X^N / N!)\right] = -kTVX$$

where $X = (2\pi mkT/h^2)^{3/2}e^{-\gamma/kT}$. Calculate the probability that N particles are present in the box and thence obtain an expression for $\bar{N}$, the mean number of free particles present as a function of γ, T, and V. Also calculate S, c_V, and P from F and express these quantities as functions of $\bar{N}$, T, and V.

Chapter 27

THE QUANTUM THEORY
OF REAL GASES

INTRODUCTION

In Chapter 13 we discussed the virial expansion for a one-component classical gas, and derived an expression for the second virial coefficient in terms of the intermolecular potential.

In the present chapter we wish to reconsider the problem of real gases, making use of the more sophisticated techniques which we have developed in the last few chapters.

THE VIRIAL EXPANSION FOR A ONE-COMPONENT GAS

The grand canonical partition function $\mathcal{Q}$ for a one-component gas of volume V, temperature T, and chemical potential μ is given by

$$\mathcal{Q} = \sum_n Q_n \lambda^n \tag{27.1}$$

where

$$Q_n(T, V) = \sum_i \exp(-E_{ni}/kT) \tag{27.2}$$

$$\lambda = \exp(\mu/kT) \tag{27.3}$$

The quantity Q_n is just the canonical partition function for a gas or assembly of n molecules at temperature T and volume V. When $n = 0$ the assembly has only one state and its energy is zero. It follows that

$$Q_0 = 1 \tag{27.4}$$

If we know the grand canonical partition function we can obtain the grand canonical potential $I(T, V, \mu)$ from the relation

$$I = -pV = -kT\ln\mathcal{Q} = -kT\ln\left(\sum_n Q_n\lambda^n\right) \tag{27.5}$$

The potential $I(T, V, \mu)$ is a fundamental potential, and therefore contains a complete thermodynamic description of the assembly. As we shall see, it is possible to get a good approximation to the potential $I(T, V, \mu)$ in terms of only the first few values of Q_n. Remembering that

$$dI = -SdT - pdV - Nd\mu \tag{27.6}$$

we can write

$$N = -\left(\frac{\partial I}{\partial \mu}\right)_{T, V} = -\left(\frac{\partial I}{\partial \lambda}\right)_{T, V}\left(\frac{\partial \lambda}{\partial \mu}\right)_{T, V} = \frac{\sum_n nQ_n\lambda^n}{\sum_n Q_n\lambda^n} \tag{27.7}$$

As the temperature is increased or the density decreases, the interaction between the particles will become less significant, and the behavior of the gas will approximate the behavior of an ideal gas. In this limit λ approaches zero. Dividing (27.7) by V and taking the limit as λ approaches zero, we obtain

$$\lim_{\lambda \to 0}\left\{\frac{\sum_n nQ_n\lambda^n}{V\sum_n Q_n\lambda^n}\right\} = \lim_{\lambda \to 0}\left\{\frac{Q_1\lambda}{V}\right\} = \frac{N}{V} \tag{27.8}$$

We see that the function

$$z = \frac{Q_1\lambda}{V} \tag{27.9}$$

will, in the ideal gas limit, be approximately equal to the density. It will serve us as a convenient expansion parameter.

If we rearrange Eq. (27.5) slightly and express λ in terms of z we obtain

$$\exp\left(\frac{pV}{kT}\right) = \sum_n \frac{Z_n z^n}{n!} \tag{27.10}$$

where

$$Z_n(T, V) = \frac{Q_n n! V^n}{[Q_1]^n} \tag{27.11}$$

Equation (27.10) provides us with an expansion of $\exp(pV/kT)$ in powers of z. We would like to obtain an expansion of p/kT in powers of z. Let us assume we have such an expansion which we write

$$p/kT = \sum_{j=1}^{\infty} b_j z^j \tag{27.12}$$

The coefficients in the expansion (27.12) can be obtained by comparison of (27.12) with (27.10). To facilitate this we rewrite (27.12)

$$\exp(pV/kT) = \exp\left(V\Sigma_j b_j z^j\right) = \prod_{j\geq 1} \exp(Vb_j z^j) \tag{27.13}$$

Expanding the exponential in a power series we obtain

$$\exp(pV/kT) = \prod_{j\geq 1} \Sigma_{m_j} (Vb_j z^j)^{m_j}/m_j!$$

$$= [1 + Vb_1 z + \tfrac{1}{2}(Vb_1 z)^2 + \tfrac{1}{6}(Vb_1 z)^3 + \ldots]$$
$$[1 + (Vb_2 z^2) + \tfrac{1}{2}(Vb_2 z^2)^2 + \ldots]$$
$$[1 + (Vb_3 z^3) + \tfrac{1}{2}(Vb_3 z^3)^2 + \ldots] \tag{27.14}$$

If we equate like powers of z in (27.14) and (27.10) we obtain

$$Z_1 = Vb_1 \tag{27.15}$$

$$\tfrac{1}{2}Z_2 = Vb_2 + \tfrac{1}{2}(Vb_1)^2 \tag{27.16}$$

$$\tfrac{1}{6}Z_3 = Vb_3 + (Vb_1)(Vb_2) + \tfrac{1}{6}(Vb_1)^3 \tag{27.17}$$

Solving for b_1, b_2, and b_3 and noting that $z_1 = V$ we obtain

$$b_1 = 1 \tag{27.18}$$

$$b_2 = \frac{Z_2 - Z_1^2}{2Z_1} \tag{27.19}$$

$$b_3 = \frac{Z_3 - 3Z_1 Z_2 + 2Z_1^3}{6Z_1} \tag{27.20}$$

We have succeeded in obtaining an expansion of p/kT in powers of z. What we would really like is an expansion of p/kT in powers of the density. In order to accomplish this we seek first an expansion of z in powers of the density N/V.

From (27.5) and (27.7) it follows that

$$N = -\left(\frac{\partial I}{\partial \mu}\right)_{T, V} = \left[\frac{\partial}{\partial \mu}(pV)\right]_{T, V} \tag{27.21}$$

Substituting (27.12) in (27.21) we obtain

$$\frac{N}{V} = \left[\frac{\partial}{\partial z}\left(kT\sum_{j=1}^{\infty} b_j z^j\right)\right]_{T, V}\left(\frac{\partial z}{\partial \mu}\right)_{T, V} = \sum_{j=1}^{\infty} jb_j z^j \tag{27.22}$$

To invert this series we express z as a power series in (N/V), i.e.,

$$z = (N/V) + a_2(N/V)^2 + a_3(N/V)^3 + \ldots \tag{27.23}$$

Substituting (27.23) in (27.22) and equating coefficients of like powers of (N/V) on the two sides of the equation, we obtain

$$a_2 = -2b_2 \tag{27.24}$$

$$a_3 = -3b_3 - 4a_2b_2 = -3b_3 + 8b_2^2 \tag{27.25}$$

Substituting (27.23), (27.24), (27.25), (27.18), (27.19) and (27.20) in (27.12) we obtain

$$\frac{p}{kT} = \frac{N}{V}\left[1 + B\left(\frac{N}{V}\right) + C\left(\frac{N}{V}\right)^2 + \ldots\right] \tag{27.26}$$

where

$$B = \frac{Z_1^2 - Z_2}{2Z_1} \tag{27.27}$$

$$C = \frac{Z_2(Z_2 - Z_1^2)}{Z_1^2} + \frac{Z_1^3 - Z_3}{3Z_1} \tag{27.28}$$

We have succeeded in expanding p/kT in powers of the density, and have obtained expressions for the second and third virial coefficients B and C. It is a simple matter in principle to extend the series to higher powers of the density and to obtain the higher virial coefficients.

The results we have obtained are valid for any one-component gas that possesses a virial expansion. In the following section we shall apply our results to a classical gas in which the intermolecular potential is a function only of the separation between the molecules.

An investigation of the series (27.26) will show that the rth virial coefficient will be a function of $Z_1, Z_2, Z_3, \ldots, Z_r$, and therefore a function of $Q_1, Q_2, Q_3, \ldots Q_r$. As pointed out earlier, Q_r is the canonical partition function for a gas of r molecules. It follows that if we wish to evaluate the rth virial coefficient we do not have to consider the interactions between more than r molecules at once. Thus to obtain the second virial coefficient we need to consider binary interactions; to obtain the third virial coefficient we need to consider binary and ternary interactions; etc. This is in agreement with the general conclusion of Chapter 13.

THE SECOND VIRIAL COEFFICIENT FOR A ONE-COMPONENT CLASSICAL MONATOMIC GAS

The energy of a gas of n identical interacting particles of mass m can be written

$$E = \sum_{j=1}^{3} \sum_{i=1}^{n} (1/2m)p_j^2(i) + U[\mathbf{x}(1), \mathbf{x}(2) \ldots \mathbf{x}(n)]$$

$$\equiv (1/2m)\sum_{i=1}^{3n} p_i^2 + U(\mathbf{x}) \tag{27.29}$$

where we are using the same notation introduced in Chapter 10. The classical limit for the canonical partition function of such a gas is

$$Q_n = \frac{1}{h^{3n}n!} \int\int \exp\left[\frac{-\sum\limits_{i=1}^{3n}(p_i^2/2m) - U(\mathbf{x})}{kT}\right] d\mathbf{x}d\mathbf{p} \qquad (27.30)$$

Integrating over the momenta, we obtain

$$Q_n = \frac{1}{n!}\left(\frac{2\pi mkT}{h^2}\right)^{3n/2} \int \exp\left(-\frac{U}{kT}\right) d\mathbf{x} \qquad (27.31)$$

If $n = 1$ and there are no external fields, then $U = U[\mathbf{x}(1)] = 0$ and

$$Q_1 = (2\pi mkT/h^2)^{3/2}V \qquad (27.32)$$

The quantities Z_n which we introduced in the preceding section are given by

$$Z_n(T, V) = \frac{Q_n n! V^n}{(Q_1)^n} = \int \exp\left(-\frac{U}{kT}\right) d\mathbf{x} \qquad (27.33)$$

In this form they are referred to as configuration integrals.

We now assume: (a) the potential energy of interaction between atom i and atom j is a function only of their distance apart $|\mathbf{x}(i) - \mathbf{x}(j)| \equiv x_{ij}$; (b) the potential energy of the gas is a sum of pair potentials, i.e.

$$U(\mathbf{x}) = \sum\sum_{i<j} u(x_{ij}) \qquad (27.34)$$

The first few values of Z_n are then given by:

$$Z_1 = V \qquad (27.35)$$

$$Z_2 = \int\int \exp[-u(x_{12})/kT]d\mathbf{x}(1)d\mathbf{x}(2) \qquad (27.36)$$

$$Z_3 = \int\int\int \exp\{-[u(x_{12}) + u(x_{13}) + u(x_{23})]/kT\}d\mathbf{x}(1)d\mathbf{x}(2)d\mathbf{x}(3) \qquad (27.37)$$

We can now write down expression for the second and third virial coefficients in terms of $u(x_{ij})$. We will consider only the second virial coefficient B. Substituting (27.35) and (27.36) in (27.27) we obtain

$$B = \frac{V^2 - \int\int \exp[-u(x_{12})/kT]d\mathbf{x}(1)d\mathbf{x}(2)}{2V}$$

$$= (1/2V)\int\int\{1 - \exp[-u(x_{12})/kT]\}d\mathbf{x}(1)d\mathbf{x}(2) \qquad (27.38)$$

If we introduce the spherical coordinates r, θ, ϕ which locate particle two with respect to particle one, we obtain

$$B = (1/2V)\int d\mathbf{x}(1) \int\int\int \{1 - \exp[-u(r)/kT]\} r^2 \sin\theta dr d\theta d\phi$$

$$= 2\pi \int \{1 - \exp[-u(r)/kT]\} r^2 dr \tag{27.39}$$

This is the same result as Eq. (13.38). A detailed evaluation of B starting from (27.39) for a number of different potentials is carried out in Chapter 13.

PROBLEMS

1. For nonspherical molecules, a potential of the form

$$u(r, \theta_1, \theta_2, \phi_2 - \phi_1) = u_1(r) + u_2(r)[\cos^2\theta_1 + \cos^2\theta_2]$$

may be used. Show that for this potential the classical second virial coefficient is given by

$$B(T) = -2\pi N \int_0^\infty \left[\frac{kT}{u_2} \exp\left(-\frac{u_1}{kT}\right)\left(\frac{\sqrt{\pi}}{2}\mathrm{erf}\sqrt{\frac{u_2}{kT}}\right)^2 - 1 \right] r^2 dr$$

KINETIC THEORY

In Part I we investigated the properties of a collection of independent point masses. We were able, using arguments which were at times admittedly weak, to derive some exact equilibrium properties, and some approximate non-equilibrium or transport properties for such a collection.

In Part II, by introducing a number of statistical postulates, we were able to derive rigorous and quite general formulae for the equilibrium properties of assemblies of interacting molecules.

In Part III we wish to rigorously develop the equilibrium and non-equilibrium properties of a collection of independent point masses from a kinetic point of view. Although the type of system we can handle using kinetic arguments is more restricted than the type of system discussed in Part II we can, for these systems, handle more properties with fewer basic assumptions.

The only preceding material necessary to follow the development in Part III is that contained in Chapters 1, 2 and 3 of Part I, and Chapters 10 and 11 in Part II. Those students encountering kinetic theory for the first time will, however, find it helpful to also read Chapters 4, 6, 7, 8 and 9 in Part I.

Chapter 28

COLLISIONS

In order to study the properties of gases from a detailed kinetic point of view, it will be necessary to consider in some detail the dynamic interaction of two molecules.

TWO-BODY INTERACTION

The dynamical state of a system at some instant of time is determined if we know the generalized coordinates and the generalized momenta or velocities at that time. Furthermore, if the system has a Lagrangian and it is known as a function of the generalized coordinates and velocities, then we can immediately obtain the equations of motion. Knowing the Lagrangian, we can therefore predict what the dynamical state of the system will be at any future time.

Let us consider a system consisting of two point masses m and M which are located at x and X respectively and are moving with velocities v and V respectively. Let us assume that the only force acting is a force whose magnitude is a function of the distance between the masses, and whose direction is along the line joining the two masses. Such a force is derivable from a potential of the form $U(|x - X|)$.

For such a system there is a Lagrangian, and in terms of x, v, X, and V, it is simply

$$L = \tfrac{1}{2}mv^2 + \tfrac{1}{2}MV^2 - U(|x - X|) \qquad (28.1)$$

If the Lagrangian of a system can be broken up into a sum of terms, such that each term is a function of some subset of the generalized coordinates and the corresponding generalized velocities, and if the subsets are mutually exclusive, then the equations governing the dynamical behavior of the subsets would be completely independent. If, for example, the above Lagrangian could be written as

$$L = L_1(\mathbf{x}, \mathbf{v}) + L_2(\mathbf{X}, \mathbf{V})$$

then the motion of the two particles would be entirely independent.

Although the motions of the two particles discussed above are not independent, if we choose as generalized coordinates the coordinates of the center of mass, and the coordinates of the relative position of one of the masses with respect to the other, then it is possible to separate the Lagrangian into independent terms.

Let $\mathbf{s}$ represent the location of the center of mass, and $\mathbf{w}$ the velocity of the center of mass. Then

$$\mathbf{s} = \frac{m\mathbf{x} + M\mathbf{X}}{m + M} \tag{28.2}$$

$$\mathbf{w} = \frac{m\mathbf{v} + M\mathbf{V}}{m + M} \tag{28.3}$$

Let $\mathbf{r}$ represent the relative position of the mass m with respect to the mass M, and $\mathbf{u}$ the corresponding velocity. Then

$$\mathbf{r} = \mathbf{x} - \mathbf{X} \tag{28.4}$$

$$\mathbf{u} = \mathbf{v} - \mathbf{V} \tag{28.5}$$

For convenience, we further define M^* as the total mass, and m^* as the reduced mass. Thus

$$M^* = m + M \tag{28.6}$$

$$m^* = \frac{mM}{m + M} \tag{28.7}$$

If we solve (28.3) and (28.5) for $\mathbf{v}$ and $\mathbf{V}$, we obtain

$$\mathbf{v} = \mathbf{w} + (m^*/m)\mathbf{u} \tag{28.8}$$

$$\mathbf{V} = \mathbf{w} - (m^*/M)\mathbf{u} \tag{28.9}$$

In terms of $\mathbf{u}, \mathbf{r}, \mathbf{w}$, and $\mathbf{s}$, the Lagrangian (28.1) becomes

$$L = \tfrac{1}{2}M^*w^2 + \tfrac{1}{2}m^*u^2 - U(r) \tag{28.10}$$

The Lagrangian (28.10) can be broken into two independent terms

$$L_1 = \tfrac{1}{2}M^*w^2 \tag{28.11}$$

$$L_2 = \tfrac{1}{2}m^*u^2 - U(r) \tag{28.12}$$

The Lagrangian L_1 determines the motion of the center of mass. It is the Lagrangian of a particle of mass M^* which is acted upon by no forces. Consequently the center of mass moves with constant velocity. The Lagrangian L_2 determines the motion of particle two with respect to particle one.

It is the Lagrangian of a particle of mass m^* moving in the potential U. To an observer fixed on the mass M, the mass m is a distance r away and it moves as if it were a mass m^* in the potential $U(r)$ obeying the ordinary equation of motion.

It follows that if we can solve this one-body problem, our results can easily be generalized to handle the corresponding two-body interaction. We shall therefore consider in detail the interaction of a single particle of mass m^* with a static potential field U.

Although we have assumed a potential $U(|\mathbf{x} - \mathbf{X}|)$, our result would have been equally valid if the potential had been a generalized potential of the form $U(\mathbf{x} - \mathbf{X}, \mathbf{v} - \mathbf{V})$.)

SCATTERING CROSS SECTION

Let us assume that we have a potential $U(r)$ such that

$$U(r) \neq 0 \qquad r < b_m \qquad (28.13)$$

$$U(r) = 0 \qquad r > b_m \qquad (28.14)$$

Now let us assume that we have a particle of mass m^* moving in the positive z direction toward the region $r < b_m$ as shown in Figure 28.1. Let b be the distance between the z axis and the trajectory of the particle before it enters the shaded region $r < b_m$. The quantity b is called the impact parameter. The particle will enter the shaded region if $b < b_m$ and will emerge at some

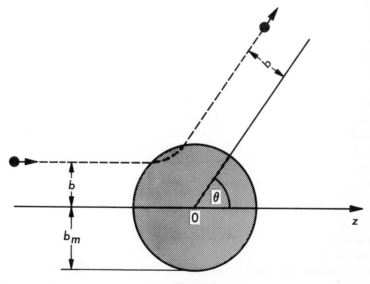

Fig. 28.1

angle θ, with velocity $\mathbf{v}'$. Since the force acting on the particle is conservative, it follows that $v' = v$. Since the direction of the force lies in the plane determined by $\mathbf{v}$ and the $0z$ axis, it follows that the motion always remains in this plane. Finally, since the force is directed toward 0, it follows that there is no torque exerted about 0 and consequently the angular momentum with respect to 0 is conserved. The magnitude of the angular momentum before the collision is m^*bv and after the collision is $m^*b'v'$. Since $v = v'$, it follows that $b = b'$.

In Figure 28.2, we show the collision as seen by an observer looking in the positive direction along the z axis. The circle with the cross in it represents

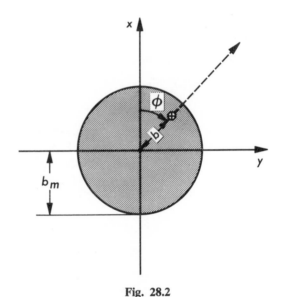

Fig. 28.2

the trajectory before collision. The arrow represents the component of velocity in the xy plane after collision.

As the particle moves along before collision in the positive z direction, it sees a target of cross-sectional area πb_m^2. If $b < b_m$, it will hit the target, i.e., encounter the potential U, and be scattered off at some angle θ. The quantity πb_m^2 is called the total scattering cross section and is designated by the letter σ. Thus

$$\sigma = \pi b_m^2 \tag{28.15}$$

It is possible that the quantity b_m may depend on the speed of the incoming particle, in which case $\sigma = \sigma(v)$. Since most potential fields extend out to infinity, the total scattering cross section would in most cases be infinite. There is, however, usually some radius beyond which the potential is negligible, and we can neglect scattering for impact parameters greater than this radius.

In order to experimentally measure $\sigma(v)$, a uniform beam of particles all moving with velocity **v** may be allowed to fall on a set of N identical targets. If A is the cross-sectional area of the beam, and all of the N targets fall within the beam width, the fraction of the particles in the beam which are scattered is given by $N\sigma/A$. If we know N and A and measure $N\sigma/A$, we can determine σ.

For the potentials which we will encounter there will be a one-to-one correspondence between the set of impact parameters b and the set of scattering angles θ. Therefore if we know b, we can determine θ and if we know θ, we can determine b. This correspondence can be given by a functional relationship $b = b(\theta)$.

In addition to the total scattering cross section, we will have occasion to make frequent use of the differential scattering cross section. In order to understand this cross section, let us again consider a view of the target as seen by an observer looking in the positive z direction as shown in Figure 28.3.

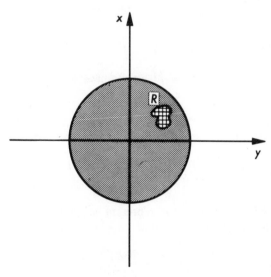

Fig. 28.3

If the particle which strikes the target falls somewhere within the cross-hatched region R, there is a corresponding range of values of θ and ϕ within which the scattered particle must lie. Conversely, for a given range of values of θ and ϕ after collision, there is a corresponding range of values of b and ϕ before collision.

We now define $\sigma(v, \theta)$ $\sin\theta d\theta d\phi$ as the area in Figure 28.3 which corresponds to scattering into the solid angle $\sin\theta d\theta d\phi$ or equivalently to scattering with θ between θ and $\theta + d\theta$ and ϕ between ϕ and $\phi + d\phi$. The quantity $\sigma(v, \theta)$ is called the differential scattering cross section. Since the solid angle $\sin\theta d\theta d\phi$ is dimensionless, $\sigma(v, \theta)$ has the dimensions of area just as does the total cross section $\sigma(v)$. The quantity $\sigma(v, \theta)$ $\sin\theta d\theta d\phi$ is that portion of the total scattering cross section $\sigma(v)$ which corresponds to scattering into the solid angle $\sin\theta d\theta d\phi$. If we integrate $\sigma(v, \theta)$ over all allowed solid angles, we will obtain the total cross section. Thus

$$\sigma(v) = \int_0^{2\pi} \int_{\theta_0}^{\pi} \sigma(v, \theta) \sin\theta d\theta d\phi \qquad (28.16)$$

The angle ϕ ranges from 0 to 2π. However the angle θ ranges from $\theta = \theta_0$, which is the value of θ for $b = b_m$, to $\theta = \pi$ which is the value of θ for a head-on collision, on the assumption that $U(0) = \infty$. Unless otherwise indicated, we shall assume that $\theta_0 = 0$.

Let us let A_R be the area of some arbitrary range R in Figure 28.3. The area A_R is given by either

$$A_R = \iint_R bdbd\theta \qquad (28.17)$$

or from the definition of $\sigma(v, \theta)$ by

$$A_R = \iint_{R'} \sigma(v, \theta) \sin\theta d\theta d\phi \qquad (28.18)$$

where R' is the range in θ, ϕ coordinates corresponding to the range R in b, ϕ coordinates. Equating (28.17) and (28.18), we have

$$\iint_R bdbd\phi = \iint_{R'} |J(b/\theta)| b(\theta)d\theta d\phi = \iint_{R'} \sigma(v, \theta) \sin\theta d\theta d\phi \qquad (28.19)$$

Since R and the corresponding R' represent an arbitrary range, we can equate the integrands and have, noting that $|J(b/\theta)| = |db/d\theta|$

$$\sigma(v, \theta) = \frac{b(\theta) |db/d\theta|}{\sin \theta} \qquad (28.20)$$

Consequently if we know b as a function of θ we can determine $\sigma(v, \theta)$.

SOME USEFUL CROSS SECTIONS

In the present section we will derive several useful cross sections.

Hard Sphere Cross Section: Suppose a smooth sphere of radius r collides with a rigid elastic sphere of radius R. The trajectory of the incident sphere is shown in Figure 28.4. From Figure 28.4 it is apparent that

$$b = (r + R)\sin[(\pi - \theta)/2] \qquad (28.21)$$

If we substitute (28.21) in (28.20) we obtain

$$\sigma(v, \theta) = (r + R)^2/4 \qquad (28.22)$$

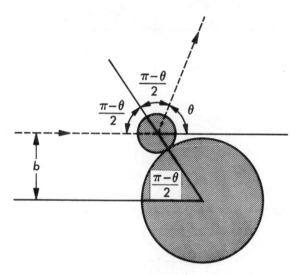

Fig. 28.4

Coulomb Cross Section: Suppose a point particle of mass m, charge $Z_1 e$, and initial velocity $\mathbf{v}$ collides with a fixed point charge $Z_2 e$. A typical trajectory is shown by the dotted line in Figure 28.5. During the collision the mass m receives an impulse in the x direction of $\int_{-\infty}^{\infty} F_x dt$ and its x component of momentum is changed an amount $2mv\cos[(\pi - \theta)/2]$. Equating these two quantities and changing the variable of integration from t to ϕ we have

$$2mv\cos\left(\frac{\pi - \theta}{2}\right) = \int_{\frac{\pi-\theta}{2}}^{-\left(\frac{\pi-\theta}{2}\right)} \left(\frac{F_x}{d\phi/dt}\right) d\phi \qquad (28.23)$$

The initial angular momentum is $-mvb$. The angular momentum at the point (r, ϕ) is $mr^2 d\phi/dt$. Since angular momentum is conserved about the origin, these two quantities are equal, and we have

$$d\phi/dt = -bv/r^2 \qquad (28.24)$$

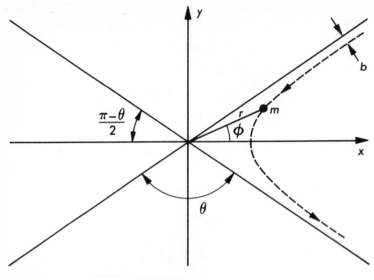

Fig. 28.5

The force on the mass m in the x direction is in mks units

$$F_x = (Z_1Z_2e^2/4\pi\epsilon_0 r^2)\cos\phi \tag{28.25}$$

Substituting (28.24) and (28.25) in (28.23) we obtain

$$b = \frac{Z_1Z_2e^2\cot(\theta/2)}{4\pi\epsilon_0 mv^2} \tag{28.26}$$

Substituting (28.26) in (28.20) we obtain

$$\sigma(v, \theta) = \left[\frac{Z_1Z_2e^2}{8\pi\epsilon_0 mv^2\sin^2(\theta/2)}\right]^2 \tag{28.27}$$

THE SCATTERING PROBABILITY

Let us consider two particles of masses m and M and velocities $\mathbf{v}$ and $\mathbf{V}$ respectively which we know are contained within a certain unit volume, as shown in Figure 28.6.

We then define $W(\mathbf{v}, \mathbf{V}; \mathbf{v}', \mathbf{V}')d\mathbf{v}'d\mathbf{V}'$ as the probability per unit time that the two particles contained within the unit volume will (1) undergo a collision and (2) end up with their final velocities in the ranges $d\mathbf{v}'$ and $d\mathbf{V}'$ respectively.

As we shall show, it is possible to write down a simple expression for $W(\mathbf{v}, \mathbf{V}; \mathbf{v}', \mathbf{V}')$ in terms of the differential scattering cross section. The resulting expression will be extremely helpful in describing the interaction of the molecules in a gas, and in obtaining results which are valid not only for a gas

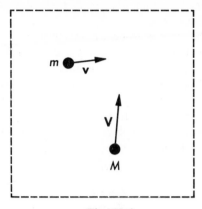

Fig. 28.6

of hard spheres, but for a gas in which the intermolecular potential is quite arbitrary.

The probability that a collision will take place in a unit time can be obtained by following essentially the same procedure which was used in Chapter 6 to evaluate the probability of a collision between two hard spheres.

We first transform to a system which is moving with velocity $\mathbf{V}$, in which case the mass m is moving with a velocity $\mathbf{u} = \mathbf{v} - \mathbf{V}$ and the mass M is at rest as shown in Figure 28.7.

Let $\sigma(u)$ represent the total scattering cross section in relative coordinates, i.e., it is the cross section for a collision as seen by an observer sitting on M, and observing the particle m approaching at a velocity $\mathbf{u}$. The particle m as seen by this observer will behave as if it was a mass $m^* = mM/(m + M)$

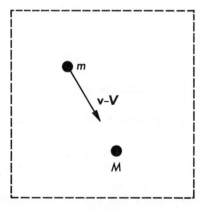

Fig. 28.7

moving in a stationary potential $U(|\mathbf{x} - \mathbf{X}|)$ where $\mathbf{x}$ and $\mathbf{X}$ are the positions of m and M respectively.

We may imagine the mass m to be a point mass, and the mass M to be a sphere of cross-sectional area $\sigma(u)$. If the mass m enters the sphere, a collision will take place. Alternatively, we may imagine the mass m to be a sphere of cross-sectional area $\sigma(u)$, and the mass M to be a point mass. In this case the mass m will sweep out an area $u\sigma(u)$ in one second, and the probability that it will encounter the point mass M will be simply $u\sigma(u)$ since both masses are somewhere within the same unit volume. The probability that in a unit time the two particles will collide is thus

$$u\sigma(u) \tag{28.28}$$

The area $\sigma(u)$ is the total scattering cross section. The area $\sigma(u, \theta)$ $\sin\theta d\theta d\phi$ is the cross section for scattering into the solid angle $\sin\theta d\theta d\phi$ where θ and ϕ determine the orientation of $\mathbf{u}'$ with respect to $\mathbf{u}$. It follows that the probability that in a unit time a collision will take place and the final relative velocity will lie in the solid angle $\sin\theta d\theta d\phi$ is obtained by simply replacing the area $\sigma(u)$ by the area $\sigma(u, \theta) \sin\theta d\theta d\phi$ in (28.28). Doing this, we obtain

$$u\sigma(u, \theta) \sin\theta d\theta d\phi \tag{28.29}$$

where θ and ϕ determine the orientation of $\mathbf{u}'$ with respect to $\mathbf{u}$.

A complete description of a collision between two point masses is provided if we know $\mathbf{v}, \mathbf{V}, \mathbf{v}', \mathbf{V}'$, the velocities before and after collision respectively. However, not all of these twelve collision parameters are independent. The conservation of energy and momentum provide us with a set of four equations which reduce the number of independent parameters to eight. It follows that if $\mathbf{v}, \mathbf{V}, \theta$ and ϕ are known, the remaining parameters can be determined by employing the conservation equations. The expression (28.29) together with the equations of energy and momentum conservation therefore provide us with as complete a description as possible of the collision of the two particles discussed above. Since all that is known about the positions of the two particles is that they are contained within the same unit volume, this description must necessarily be in the form of a probability. We will find it convenient to introduce the conservation equations explicitly into our expression (28.29) so as to incorporate the entire description of the collision into a single mathematical expression.

In order to accomplish this we will make use of the Dirac delta function which was introduced in Chapter 3. The Dirac delta function is the density function which is associated with a single point particle. For a single particle located on the x axis at $x = a$, the density in one dimension is written $\delta(x - a)$. It follows that $\delta(x - a)dx$ represents the probability that the particle will be found between x and $x + dx$. Analogously in three dimensions, the density associated with a distribution consisting of a single particle located at $x = a$ is given by $\delta(x - a)$ and $\delta(x - a)dx$ represents the probability that the particle will be found in the range dx. For other properties of the Dirac delta function, the reader is referred to Chapter 3.

Using the notation introduced in the first section of this chapter, the conservation of momentum and energy in the collision can be written

$$mv + MV = mv' + MV' \tag{28.30}$$

$$\tfrac{1}{2}m^*u^2 + \tfrac{1}{2}M^*w^2 = \tfrac{1}{2}m^*(u')^2 + \tfrac{1}{2}M^*(w')^2 \tag{28.31}$$

where the unprimed quantities refer to values of the velocities before collision, and the primed quantities to velocities after collision.

Dividing equation (28.30) by $M^* = m + M$, we obtain

$$w = w' \tag{28.32}$$

Combining (28.32) and (28.31) we obtain

$$u = u' \tag{28.33}$$

Thus the conservation of energy and momentum in the collision are equivalent to stating that the velocity of the center of mass is the same before and after collision, and the relative speed before and after the collision is the same.

It follows that if the relative speed before collision of two particles which collide is u, the probability that the final relative speed lies between u' and $u' + du'$, is given by

$$\delta(u' - u)du' \tag{28.34}$$

and if the velocity of the center of mass before collision is w, the probability that the velocity of the center of mass after collision will be in the range dw' is given by

$$\delta(w' - w)dw' \tag{28.35}$$

The three probabilities (28.29), (28.34), and (28.35) are independent. It follows that the probability that the two particles will (1) collide, and (2) end up with relative speed in du', center of mass velocity in dw' and be scattered into the solid angle $\sin\theta d\theta d\phi$ will be

$$[u\sigma(u, \theta)\sin\theta d\theta d\phi]\,[\delta(u' - u)du]\,[\delta(w' - w)dw'] \tag{28.36}$$

To obtain the quantity $W(\mathbf{v}, \mathbf{V}; \mathbf{v}', \mathbf{V}')$, it is only necessary to change the variables of integration in (28.36), i.e.,

$$W(\mathbf{v}, \mathbf{V}; \mathbf{v}', \mathbf{V}')$$

$$= [u\sigma(u, \theta)\sin\theta]\,[\delta(u' - u)]\,[\delta(w' - w)]\left| J\!\left(\frac{u', \theta, \phi, w_1', w_2', w_3'}{v_1', v_2', v_3', V_1', V_2', V_3'}\right)\right| \tag{28.37}$$

The evaluation of the Jacobian is greatly simplified if we break the transformation into a succession of simpler transformations. Let $u_1{}^*, u_2{}^*, u_3{}^*$ be the components of $\mathbf{u}'$ with respect to a set of axes having the z axis oriented along $\mathbf{u}$. The quantities (u_1', u_2', u_3'), (w_1', w_2', w_3'), etc., are all components with respect to the original set of axes which we chose to describe the problem.

The original transformation can now be broken down as follows

$$J\left(\frac{u', \theta, \phi, w_1', w_2', w_3'}{v_1', v_2', v_3', V_1', V_2', V_3'}\right) = J_1 J_2 J_3 \tag{28.38}$$

where

$$J_1 = J\left(\frac{u', \theta, \phi, w_1', w_2', w_3'}{u_1{}^*, u_2{}^*, u_3{}^*, w_1', w_2', w_3'}\right) = J\left(\frac{u', \theta, \phi}{u_1{}^*, u_2{}^*, u_3{}^*}\right) \tag{28.39}$$

$$J_2 = J\left(\frac{u_1{}^*, u_2{}^*, u_3{}^*, w_1', w_2', w_3'}{u_1', u_2', u_3', w_1', w_2', w_3'}\right) = J\left(\frac{u_1{}^*, u_2{}^*, u_3{}^*}{u_1', u_2', u_3'}\right) \tag{28.40}$$

$$J_3 = J\left(\frac{u_1', u_2', u_3', w_1', w_2', w_3'}{v_1', v_2', v_3', V_1', V_2', V_3'}\right) = J\left(\frac{\mathbf{u}', \mathbf{w}'}{\mathbf{v}', \mathbf{V}'}\right) \tag{28.41}$$

The transformation J_1, is simply a transformation from spherical to rectangular coordinates since θ and ϕ measure the orientation of $\mathbf{u}'$ with respect to $\mathbf{u}$. Therefore

$$J_1 = 1/(u')^2 \sin\theta \tag{28.42}$$

The transformation J_2 represents a simple rotation of rectangular axes, and thus

$$J_2 = 1 \tag{28.43}$$

To evaluate the transformation J_3, we recall

$$\mathbf{u}' = \mathbf{v}' - \mathbf{V}' \tag{28.44}$$

$$\mathbf{w}' = \frac{m\mathbf{v}' + M\mathbf{V}'}{m + M} \tag{28.45}$$

and we find

$$J_3 = 1 \tag{28.46}$$

Combining our results and substituting them into (28.37), we obtain

$$W(\mathbf{v}, \mathbf{V}; \mathbf{v}', \mathbf{V}') = u\sigma(u, \theta)\delta(u' - u)\delta(\mathbf{w}' - \mathbf{w})/(u')^2 \tag{28.47}$$

In order to emphasize the fact that θ is the angle between $\mathbf{u}'$ and $\mathbf{u}$ and not the angle between $\mathbf{u}'$ and the z axis, we will write $\sigma(u, \theta)$ as $\sigma(u, \mathbf{u} \cdot \mathbf{u}')$. Furthermore, since $\delta(u' - u)$ is zero unless $u = u'$, we can replace u' by u. We thus obtain finally

$$W(\mathbf{v}, \mathbf{V}; \mathbf{v}', \mathbf{V}') = \sigma(u, \mathbf{u} \cdot \mathbf{u}')\delta(u' - u)\delta(\mathbf{w}' - \mathbf{w})/u \tag{28.48}$$

We will find it convenient in what follows to write

$$W(\mathbf{v}, \mathbf{V}; \mathbf{v}', \mathbf{V}') = S(\mathbf{u}, \mathbf{u}')\delta(\mathbf{w}' - \mathbf{w}) \tag{28.49}$$

where

$$S(\mathbf{u}, \mathbf{u}') = \sigma(u, \mathbf{u} \cdot \mathbf{u}')\delta(u' - u)/u \tag{28.50}$$

The probability that the two particles will collide and end up with their relative velocity in $d\mathbf{u}'$ and their center of mass velocity in $d\mathbf{w}'$ can be readily obtained from (28.49) and is simply

$$W(\mathbf{v}, \mathbf{V}; \mathbf{v}', \mathbf{V}') \left| J\left(\frac{\mathbf{v}', \mathbf{V}'}{\mathbf{u}', \mathbf{w}'}\right) \right| d\mathbf{u}'d\mathbf{w}'$$

$$= W(\mathbf{v}, \mathbf{V}; \mathbf{v}', \mathbf{V}')d\mathbf{u}'d\mathbf{w}' = [S(\mathbf{u}, \mathbf{u}')d\mathbf{u}'] \, [\delta(\mathbf{w}' - \mathbf{w})d\mathbf{w}'] \qquad (28.51)$$

The quantity $\delta(\mathbf{w}' - \mathbf{w})d\mathbf{w}'$ is the probability that if the two particles collide they will end up with center of mass velocity in $d\mathbf{w}'$. It follows that $S(\mathbf{u}, \mathbf{u}')d\mathbf{u}'$ is the probability that they collide and end up with relative velocity in $d\mathbf{u}'$.

SYMMETRY

It is often possible to make use of the quantity $W(\mathbf{v}, \mathbf{V}; \mathbf{v}', \mathbf{V}')$ without knowing the specific form of the differential scattering cross section $\sigma(u, \mathbf{u} \cdot \mathbf{u}')$, but by simply making use of some of its symmetry properties. We note first that

$$\delta(\mathbf{w}' - \mathbf{w}) = \delta(-\mathbf{w}' + \mathbf{w}) = \delta(\mathbf{w} - \mathbf{w}') \qquad (28.52)$$

Thus we can interchange $\mathbf{w}$ and $\mathbf{w}'$, or change the sign of both without affecting the value of $W(\mathbf{v}, \mathbf{V}; \mathbf{v}', \mathbf{V}')$.

Similarly

$$S(\mathbf{u}, \mathbf{u}') = S(\mathbf{u}', \mathbf{u}) = S(-\mathbf{u}, -\mathbf{u}') \qquad (28.53)$$

Thus we can interchange $\mathbf{u}$ and $\mathbf{u}'$ or change the sign of both without affecting the value of $W(\mathbf{v}, \mathbf{V}; \mathbf{v}', \mathbf{V}')$.) The symmetry of S depends on the fact that we are restricting ourselves to elastic collisions, i.e., $u = u'$, and are assuming that the interaction potential is spherically symmetric, i.e., $\sigma(u, \mathbf{u} \cdot \mathbf{u}')$ depends only on the angle θ between $\mathbf{u}'$ and $\mathbf{u}$ and not on the angle ϕ.

Interchanging $\mathbf{v}$ with $\mathbf{v}'$ and $\mathbf{V}$ with $\mathbf{V}'$ in $W(\mathbf{v}, \mathbf{V}; \mathbf{v}', \mathbf{V}')$ is equivalent to interchanging $\mathbf{u}$ with $\mathbf{u}'$ and $\mathbf{w}$ with $\mathbf{w}'$; and changing the signs of $\mathbf{v}$, $\mathbf{V}$, $\mathbf{v}'$ and $\mathbf{V}'$ is equivalent to changing the sign of $\mathbf{u}$, $\mathbf{u}'$, $\mathbf{w}$ and $\mathbf{w}'$. Thus

$$W(\mathbf{v}, \mathbf{V}; \mathbf{v}', \mathbf{V}') = W(\mathbf{v}', \mathbf{V}'; \mathbf{v}, \mathbf{V})$$
$$= W(-\mathbf{v}, -\mathbf{V}; -\mathbf{v}', -\mathbf{V}') \qquad (28.54)$$

If the masses of the two particles had been the same, then we could also simultaneously interchange $\mathbf{v}$ with $\mathbf{V}$ and $\mathbf{v}'$ with $\mathbf{V}'$ without affecting W.

SUMMARY

In the previous sections we have shown that if two particles of masses m and M, and velocities $\mathbf{v}$ and $\mathbf{V}$ respectively are contained within the same unit volume, then the probability that in a unit time they will (1) collide, and

(2) have their final velocities in $d\mathbf{v}'$ and $d\mathbf{V}'$ respectively is given by $W(\mathbf{v}, \mathbf{V}; \mathbf{v}', \mathbf{V}')d\mathbf{v}'d\mathbf{V}'$ where

$$W(\mathbf{v}, \mathbf{V}; \mathbf{v}', \mathbf{V}') = S(\mathbf{u}, \mathbf{u}')\delta(\mathbf{w}' - \mathbf{w}) \tag{28.55}$$

$$S(\mathbf{u}, \mathbf{u}') = \sigma(u, \mathbf{u} \cdot \mathbf{u}')\delta(u' - u)/u \tag{28.56}$$

$$\mathbf{u} = \mathbf{v} - \mathbf{V} \tag{28.57}$$

$$\mathbf{u}' = \mathbf{v}' - \mathbf{V}' \tag{28.58}$$

$$\mathbf{w} = \frac{m\mathbf{v} + M\mathbf{V}}{m + M} \tag{28.59}$$

$$\mathbf{w}' = \frac{m\mathbf{v}' + M\mathbf{V}'}{m + M} \tag{28.60}$$

and $\sigma(u, \mathbf{u} \cdot \mathbf{u}')$ is the differential scattering cross section in relative coordinates.

Thus if we know the differential scattering cross section associated with the interaction between two particles, and we know that they are contained within the same unit volume, and moving with the velocities $\mathbf{v}$ and $\mathbf{V}$, the quantity $W(\mathbf{v}, \mathbf{V}; \mathbf{v}', \mathbf{V}')$ tells us as much as we can know about what is likely to happen.

Knowledge of $W(\mathbf{v}, \mathbf{V}; \mathbf{v}', \mathbf{V}')$ should therefore enable us to determine the macroscopic properties of a gas whose particles interact by means of binary collisions. We shall see in the following chapters that the equilibrium properties of a gas depend only on the symmetry of $W(\mathbf{v}, \mathbf{V}; \mathbf{v}', \mathbf{V}')$, but the nonequilibrium properties depend on the specific nature of the cross section $\sigma(u, \mathbf{u} \cdot \mathbf{u}')$.

PROBLEMS

1. Consider the small-angle scattering in a field described by the potential $u(r) = cr^{-n}$ where n is a positive integer and c a constant. Show that for small deflections, the scattering angle is given by

$$\theta \approx \frac{n|c|\int_0^{\pi/2} \cos^n\alpha \, d\alpha}{Eb^n}$$

where b is the impact parameter and E the incident kinetic energy.

2. Consider the two-dimensional scattering of a smooth elastic disk of radius r off a fixed smooth elastic disk of radius R. What is the total scattering cross section in two dimensions? (Note: the dimensions of this cross section will be length.) What is the differential scattering cross section, $\sigma(v, \theta)$ where $\sigma(v, \theta)d\theta$ is the effective cross sectional length of the target for scattering between θ and $\theta + d\theta$?

3. A unit volume contains n hard, smooth, elastic spheres of radius r and mass m, and N hard, smooth, elastic spheres of radius R. Assuming a Maxwellian distribution, show that the number of collisions per unit time between spheres of mass m and spheres of mass M is

$$nN\pi(r + R)^2 \left(\frac{8kT}{\pi}\right)^{1/2}\left(\frac{m + M}{mM}\right)$$

4. For the mixture of hard spheres discussed in problem 3 show that the fraction of the collisions in which the kinetic energy associated with the component of the relative velocity along the line of centers exceeds a certain value ϵ_0 is

$$\exp(-\epsilon_0/kT)$$

5. Calculate the differential scattering cross section for the scattering of a rigid elastic sphere of mass m, radius r, and speed v off of a rigid elastic sphere of mass M and radius R, which is initially at rest.

6. A box contains two species of atoms of masses M and m respectively. The velocity distribution of each is Maxwellian. Show that the fraction of collisions between these two types of atoms for which the relative speed u exceeds a certain value u_0 is given by

$$\frac{\displaystyle\int_{u_0}^{\infty} u^3 \sigma(u) \exp(-\lambda^* u^2)\,du}{\displaystyle\int_{0}^{\infty} u^3 \sigma(u) \exp(-\lambda^* u^2)\,du}$$

where $\lambda^* = mM/2(m + M)kT$.

Chapter 29

THE BOLTZMANN
TRANSPORT EQUATION

In the present chapter we will derive the Boltzmann transport equation which determines the behavior of a collection of point masses which are interacting by means of binary collisions. In later chapters we will make use of this equation to study the equilibrium and nonequilibrium properties of gases.

THE BOLTZMANN TRANSPORT EQUATION

Let us consider a mixture of point masses of masses m and M. The dynamical state of a particular particle of mass m is determined by its position $\mathbf{x}$ and momentum $\mathbf{p}$, and can be represented by a point in the phase space $\mathbf{x}$—$\mathbf{p}$. The dynamical state of the set of masses m is represented by a set of points whose density in the phase space $\mathbf{x}$—$\mathbf{p}$ is given by $\phi(\mathbf{x}, \mathbf{p})$. Similarly, the dynamical state of a particular particle of mass M is determined by its position $\mathbf{X}$ and momentum $\mathbf{P}$, and can be represented by a point in the phase space $\mathbf{X}$—$\mathbf{P}$. The dynamical state of the set of masses M is represented by a set of points whose density in the phase space $\mathbf{X}$—$\mathbf{P}$ is given by $\Phi(\mathbf{X}, \mathbf{P})$.

In Chapter 11 we have seen that in the absence of collisions, the phase space density ϕ will satisfy Liouville's equation, which can be written

$$\frac{\partial \phi}{\partial t} = -\sum_i p_i \frac{\partial \phi}{\partial p_i} - \sum_i \dot{x}_i \frac{\partial \phi}{\partial x_i} \qquad (29.1)$$

If we let $\mathbf{F}$ be the force on a particle of mass m due to the presence of external fields, then from Newton's law we have

$$\mathbf{F} = \dot{\mathbf{p}} \qquad (29.2)$$

Substituting (29.2) in (29.1) and noting that $\dot{x}_i = p_i/m$, we obtain

$$\frac{\partial \phi}{\partial t} = -\sum_i F_i \frac{\partial \phi}{\partial p_i} - \sum_i \frac{p_i}{m} \frac{\partial \phi}{\partial x_i} \tag{29.3}$$

The first term on the right-hand side of (29.3) represents the change in phase space density ϕ at the point $(\mathbf{x}, \mathbf{p})$ due to the external forces. The second term on the right-hand side of (29.3) represents a change in the density which would be present even in the absence of external forces.

Equation (29.3) represents the change in the density ϕ at the point $(\mathbf{x}, \mathbf{p})$ in the absence of collisions. It is not valid if the masses are colliding with one another. If the masses are colliding then we must add a term, or terms, to take account of the collisions. Let us designate $(D\phi/Dt)_{11}$ as the change in the density ϕ at the point $(\mathbf{x}, \mathbf{p})$ due to collisions of the particles of mass m among one another, and $(D\phi/Dt)_{12}$ as the change in the density ϕ due to collisions of the particles of mass m with the particles of mass M. The change in the density ϕ at the point $(\mathbf{x}, \mathbf{p})$ is then given by

$$\frac{\partial \phi}{\partial t} = -\sum_i F_i \frac{\partial \phi}{\partial p_i} - \sum_i \frac{p_i}{m} \frac{\partial \phi}{\partial x_i} + \left(\frac{D\phi}{Dt}\right)_{11} + \left(\frac{D\phi}{Dt}\right)_{12} \tag{29.4}$$

Instead of working in $\mathbf{x}$—$\mathbf{p}$ space, we will find it convenient to work in $\mathbf{x}$—$\mathbf{v}$ space. The transition from momenta to velocities is easy to carry out by noting that

$$\mathbf{p} = m\mathbf{v} \tag{29.5}$$

The density $f(\mathbf{x}, \mathbf{v})$ in $\mathbf{x}$—$\mathbf{v}$ space is related to the density $\phi(\mathbf{x}, \mathbf{p})$ in $\mathbf{x}$—$\mathbf{p}$ space by the relation

$$f(\mathbf{x}, \mathbf{v})|J(\mathbf{v}/\mathbf{p})| = (1/m^3)f(\mathbf{x}, \mathbf{v}) = \phi(\mathbf{x}, \mathbf{p}) \tag{29.6}$$

Substituting (29.5) and (29.6) in (29.4) and rearranging, we obtain

$$\frac{\partial f}{\partial t} + \sum_i \frac{F_i}{m} \frac{\partial f}{\partial v_i} + \sum_i v_i \frac{\partial f}{\partial x_i} = \left(\frac{Df}{Dt}\right)_{11} + \left(\frac{Df}{Dt}\right)_{12} \tag{29.7}$$

A similar expression holds for the density $F(\mathbf{X}, \mathbf{V})$ of the particles of mass M. Thus

$$\frac{\partial F}{\partial t} + \sum_i \frac{\mathscr{F}_i}{M} \frac{\partial F}{\partial V_i} + \sum_i V_i \frac{\partial F}{\partial X_i} = \left(\frac{DF}{Dt}\right)_{22} + \left(\frac{DF}{Dt}\right)_{21} \tag{29.8}$$

Equations (29.7) and (29.8) are called the Boltzmann transport equations. As we shall see in the next section, they are a pair of coupled integro-differential equations. If instead of two types of particles, there had been three types of particles, we would have had three instead of two coupled equations. The generalization to three or more types of particles is straightforward.

THE COLLISION TERM

Before it is possible to exploit the Boltzmann transport equations to determine the distribution function f, it will be necessary to obtain explicit expressions for the collision terms $(Df/Dt)_{11}$, $(Df/Dt)_{12}$, $(DF/Dt)_{21}$ and $(DF/Dt)_{22}$. Let us start with $(Df/Dt)_{12}$, the change in the density f at a point in x—v space due to collisions of particles of mass m with particles of mass M. Consider a "volume" element $dxdv$ in the six-dimensional x—v space, as represented schematically by the shaded region in Figure 29.1.

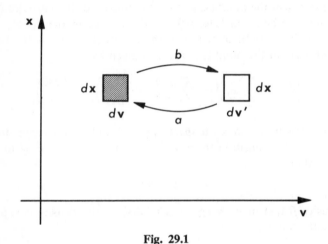

Fig. 29.1

If a particle whose dynamical state is represented by a point in the "volume" element $dxdv$ undergoes a collision, its velocity will be abruptly changed while its position remains essentially unchanged. The point representing the particle in x—v space will suddenly disappear from the "volume" element $dxdv$ and appear in some other "volume" element $dxdv'$. Actually, the transition from one volume element to another will be continuous, but we shall assume that the change in velocity occurs rapidly with little change in the position.

We would now like to calculate the rate "b" at which points go from $dxdv$ to $dxdv'$ due to collisions with particles of mass M, and the rate "a" at which points go from $dxdv'$ to $dxdv$ due to collisions with particles of mass M.

Consider two particles of masses m and M and velocities v and V respectively contained within the volume dx. The probability per unit time that they will undergo a collision and end up with their velocities in $d\mathbf{v}'$ and $d\mathbf{V}'$ respectively is given from the last chapter by

$$(1/dx)W(\mathbf{v}, \mathbf{V}; \mathbf{v}', \mathbf{V}')d\mathbf{v}'d\mathbf{V}' \tag{29.9}$$

The factor $(1/dx)$ is required because $Wd\mathbf{v}'d\mathbf{V}'$ is the probability appropriate to two particles contained within the same unit volume. In the present case the two particles are contained within the volume dx.

Finally we note that there are $f(\mathbf{x}, \mathbf{v}, t)dxd\mathbf{v}$ particles of mass m in dx with velocity in $d\mathbf{v}$ and $F(\mathbf{x}, \mathbf{V}, t)dxd\mathbf{V}$ particles of mass M in dx with velocity in $d\mathbf{V}$. The probability per unit time that there will be a collision between a pair of these particles such that the final velocities of the scattered particles will lie in $d\mathbf{v}$ and $d\mathbf{V}'$ respectively is therefore

$$[f(\mathbf{x}, \mathbf{v}, t)dxd\mathbf{v}] [F(\mathbf{x}, \mathbf{V}, t)dxd\mathbf{V}] [W(\mathbf{v}, \mathbf{V}; \mathbf{v}', \mathbf{V}')d\mathbf{v}'d\mathbf{V}'/dx]$$
$$= f(\mathbf{x}, \mathbf{v}, t)F(\mathbf{x}, \mathbf{V}, t)W(\mathbf{v}, \mathbf{V}; \mathbf{v}', \mathbf{V}')d\mathbf{v}d\mathbf{v}'d\mathbf{V}d\mathbf{V}'dx \tag{29.10}$$

The rate "b" at which particles are scattered from $dxd\mathbf{v}$ to $dxd\mathbf{v}'$ is now obtained by integrating over all values of $\mathbf{V}$ and $\mathbf{V}'$ since we are interested in all collisions which take a particle from $dxd\mathbf{v}$ to $dxd\mathbf{v}'$ irrespective of what the initial and final velocities of the mass M are. Thus

$$b = \left\{ \iiint f(\mathbf{x}, \mathbf{v}, t)F(\mathbf{x}, \mathbf{V}, t)W(\mathbf{v}, \mathbf{V}; \mathbf{v}', \mathbf{V}')d\mathbf{V}d\mathbf{V}' \right\} d\mathbf{v}d\mathbf{v}'dx \tag{29.11}$$

The rate "a" at which particles are scattered from $dxd\mathbf{v}'$ to $dxd\mathbf{v}$ is similarly obtained, and is given by

$$a = \left\{ \iiint f(\mathbf{x}, \mathbf{v}', t)F(\mathbf{x}, \mathbf{V}', t)W(\mathbf{v}', \mathbf{V}'; \mathbf{v}, \mathbf{V})d\mathbf{V}d\mathbf{V}' \right\} d\mathbf{v}d\mathbf{v}'dx \tag{29.12}$$

The *net* flow of points from $dxd\mathbf{v}'$ to $dxd\mathbf{v}$ due to collision of particles of mass m with particles of mass M is then $a - b$. To obtain the net increase of points in $dxd\mathbf{v}$ from all other volume elements $dxd\mathbf{v}'$ due to collisions with particles of mass M, we simply carry out the integration over $\mathbf{v}'$, and obtain

$$\left[\frac{D[f(\mathbf{x}, \mathbf{v}, t)dxd\mathbf{v}]}{Dt} \right]_{12}$$
$$= \left\{ \iiiint f(\mathbf{x}, \mathbf{v}', t)F(\mathbf{x}, \mathbf{V}', t)W(\mathbf{v}', \mathbf{V}'; \mathbf{v}, \mathbf{V})d\mathbf{v}'d\mathbf{V}d\mathbf{V}' \right.$$
$$\left. - \iiint f(\mathbf{x}, \mathbf{v}, t)F(\mathbf{x}, \mathbf{V}, t)W(\mathbf{v}, \mathbf{V}; \mathbf{v}', \mathbf{V}')d\mathbf{v}'d\mathbf{V}d\mathbf{V}' \right\} dxd\mathbf{v} \tag{29.13}$$

Dividing by $dxd\mathbf{v}$ and suppressing the variables $\mathbf{x}$ and t, we obtain

$$(Df/Dt)_{12} = A - B \tag{29.14}$$

where $\qquad A = \iiint f(\mathbf{v}')F(\mathbf{V}')W(\mathbf{v}',\mathbf{V}';\mathbf{v},\mathbf{V})d\mathbf{v}'d\mathbf{V}d\mathbf{V}'$ $\qquad$ (29.15)

$$B = \iiint f(\mathbf{v})F(\mathbf{V})W(\mathbf{v},\mathbf{V};\mathbf{v}',\mathbf{V}')d\mathbf{v}'d\mathbf{V}d\mathbf{V}' \qquad (29.16)$$

Up to this point, we have made no assumptions about the form of W. We will now make use of the symmetry which follows from assuming elastic collisions, and a spherically symmetric interaction potential, that is

$$W(\mathbf{v},\mathbf{V};\mathbf{v}',\mathbf{V}') = W(\mathbf{v}',\mathbf{V}';\mathbf{v},\mathbf{V}) \qquad (29.17)$$

Substituting (29.17) in (29.16), we obtain

$$(Df/Dt)_{12} = \iiint [f(\mathbf{v}')F(\mathbf{V}') - f(\mathbf{v})F(\mathbf{V})]W(\mathbf{v},\mathbf{V};\mathbf{v}',\mathbf{V}')d\mathbf{v}'d\mathbf{V}d\mathbf{V}' \qquad (29.18)$$

Equation (29.18) can easily be generalized. Let f_i be the distribution of particles of type i, f_j be the distribution of particles of type j. Then the rate of change of f_i due to collisions of particles of type i with particles of type j is simply

$$(Df_i/Dt)_{ij} = \iiint [f_i(\mathbf{v}')f_j(\mathbf{V}') - f_i(\mathbf{v})f_j(\mathbf{V})][W_{ij}(\mathbf{v},\mathbf{V};\mathbf{v}',\mathbf{V}')d\mathbf{v}'d\mathbf{V}d\mathbf{V}' \qquad (29.19)$$

The subscripts must appear on W_{ij} since W depends on the collision cross section which will be different for different pairs. The value of W_{ij} does not, however, depend on the ordering of the pairs and therefore

$$W_{ij}(\mathbf{v},\mathbf{V};\mathbf{v}',\mathbf{V}') = W_{ji}(\mathbf{V},\mathbf{v};\mathbf{V}',\mathbf{v}') \qquad (29.20)$$

Equation (29.18) is not the usual form of the collision term which one finds in the literature. For the sake of comparison, we will obtain the usual expression from (29.18).

From the preceding chapter

$$W(\mathbf{v},\mathbf{V};\mathbf{v}',\mathbf{V}') = \sigma(u,\mathbf{u}\cdot\mathbf{u}')\delta(u'-u)\delta(\mathbf{w}'-\mathbf{w})/u \qquad (29.21)$$

and $\qquad\qquad\qquad d\mathbf{v}'d\mathbf{V}' = d\mathbf{u}'d\mathbf{w}' \qquad (29.22)$

Substituting (29.22) and (29.21) in (29.18) and integrating over u' and $\mathbf{w}'$ one obtains

$$(Df/Dt)_{12} = \iiint \{f[\mathbf{v}'(\theta,\phi,\mathbf{V})]F[\mathbf{V}'(\theta,\phi,\mathbf{V})]$$
$$-f(\mathbf{v})F(\mathbf{V})\}u\sigma(u,\theta)\sin\theta d\theta d\phi d\mathbf{V} \qquad (29.23)$$

The functions $\mathbf{v}'(\theta,\phi,\mathbf{v})$ and $\mathbf{V}'(\theta,\phi,\mathbf{v})$ are obtained from the conservations of energy and momentum. Equation (29.23) is the usual form of the collision term found in most texts. We shall never have occasion to use it, but have included it to facilitate comparison of results with other authors.

SUMMARY

In the preceding sections we have shown that the distribution functions f and F for a mixture of two gases interacting by means of elastic collisions are determined from the Boltzmann transport equations

$$\frac{\partial f}{\partial t} + \sum_i \frac{F_i}{m}\frac{\partial f}{\partial v_i} + \sum_i v_i \frac{\partial f}{\partial x_i} = \left(\frac{Df}{Dt}\right)_{11} + \left(\frac{Df}{Dt}\right)_{12} \tag{29.24}$$

$$\frac{\partial F}{\partial t} + \sum_i \frac{\mathcal{F}_i}{M}\frac{\partial F}{\partial V_i} + \sum_i V_i \frac{\partial F}{\partial X_i} = \left(\frac{DF}{Dt}\right)_{22} + \left(\frac{DF}{Dt}\right)_{21} \tag{29.25}$$

$$(Df_i/Dt)_{ij} = \int\int\int [f_i(\mathbf{v'})f_j(\mathbf{V'}) - f_i(\mathbf{v})f_j(\mathbf{V})]$$
$$W_{ij}(\mathbf{v}, \mathbf{V}; \mathbf{v'}, \mathbf{V'})d\mathbf{v'}d\mathbf{V}d\mathbf{V'} \tag{29.26}$$

$$f_1 \equiv f \tag{29.27}$$

$$f_2 \equiv F \tag{29.28}$$

In the following chapters we will consider solutions of these equations.

PROBLEMS

1. Show that if

   $$f(\mathbf{v}) = n(\lambda/\pi)^{3/2} \exp(-\lambda v^2)$$
   and
   $$F(\mathbf{V}) = N(\Lambda/\pi)^{3/2} \exp(-\Lambda V^2)$$

   where $\lambda = m/2kT$ and $\Lambda = M/2kT$, then the collision term in the Boltzmann transport equation vanishes.

2. Multiply the Boltzmann transport equation by m, integrate over $\mathbf{v}$, and show that one obtains the continuity equation $(\partial\rho/\partial t) + \nabla\cdot(\rho\mathbf{v}) = 0$ where $\rho = nm$.

3. Assume that the distribution function for the electrons in a slightly ionized gas can be approximated by the form

   $$f(\mathbf{v}) = f_0(\mathbf{v}) + v_x g(v, t) \quad \text{where}$$
   $$f_0(\mathbf{v}) = n(\lambda/\pi)^{3/2} \exp(-\lambda v^2) \quad \text{and} \quad \lambda = m/2kT$$

   and assume that the collision term in the Boltzmann transport equation can be approximated by

   $$Df/Dt = \nu(f_0 - f)$$

where v is the collision frequency which is assumed to be constant. Show that in the presence of a constant electric field iE, the current density J is given by

$$J = ne^2E/mv$$

4. Show that in the presence of an oscillating electric field of magnitude $E\cos\omega t$ that the current density J in problem 3 is given by

$$J = \frac{ne^2E(v\cos\omega t + \omega\sin\omega t)}{m(\omega^2 + v^2)}$$

Chapter 30

THE EQUILIBRIUM PROPERTIES OF A GAS

INTRODUCTION

In the present chapter, we will present a rigorous kinetic theory derivation of the Maxwell-Boltzmann distribution for a gas of point masses.

Let us consider a gas of N point particles contained within a static potential $U(\mathbf{x})$. We shall assume that the only forces acting on the particles are due to this potential and to collisions of the particles with one another. We shall furthermore assume that the potential at infinity is greater than the total energy, potential plus kinetic, of all the particles, and that the topology of the potential is such that the particles can freely collide with one another. The particles contained within an isolated box with perfectly reflecting walls would constitute such a situation. If the particles were divided between two separate boxes, they would obviously not satisfy the above criteria.

Since our potential is static, if we wish equilibrium to be established it will be necessary to assume also that the velocity of the center of mass is at rest.

With these assumptions, we expect

$$\lim_{x_i \to \pm\infty} f(\mathbf{x}, \mathbf{v}, t) = 0 \qquad (30.1)$$

$$\lim_{v_i \to \pm\infty} f(\mathbf{x}, \mathbf{v}, t) = 0 \qquad (30.2)$$

The distribution function f is determined by solving the Boltzmann transport equation, which, since there is only one type of particle, assumes the form

$$\frac{\partial f}{\partial t} + \sum_i \frac{F_i}{m} \frac{\partial f}{\partial v_i} + \sum_i v_i \frac{\partial f}{\partial x_i}$$

$$= \iiint [f(\mathbf{v}')f(\mathbf{V}') - f(\mathbf{v})f(\mathbf{V})]W(\mathbf{v}, \mathbf{V}; \mathbf{v}', \mathbf{V}')dv'd\mathbf{V}d\mathbf{V}' \qquad (30.3)$$

THE BOLTZMANN H-THEOREM

As an initial step in the solution of Eq. (30.3), we will make use of some ingenious results due to Boltzmann.

We first multiply Eq. (30.3) by $[\ln f(\mathbf{x}, \mathbf{v}, t) + 1]$ and integrate the result over $\mathbf{v}$ and $\mathbf{x}$ and obtain

$$A_1 + A_2 + A_3 = A_4 \tag{30.4}$$

$$A_1 \equiv \iint [\ln f + 1](\partial f/\partial t) d\mathbf{v} d\mathbf{x} \tag{30.5}$$

$$A_2 \equiv \sum_i \iint (F_i/m)(\ln f + 1)(\partial f/\partial v_i) d\mathbf{v} d\mathbf{x} \tag{30.6}$$

$$A_3 \equiv \sum_i \iint v_i [\ln f + 1](\partial f/\partial x_i) d\mathbf{v} d\mathbf{x} \tag{30.7}$$

$$A_4 \equiv \iiiint [\ln f(\mathbf{v}) + 1] [f(\mathbf{v}')f(\mathbf{V}') - f(\mathbf{v})f(\mathbf{V})] \\ W(\mathbf{v}, \mathbf{V}; \mathbf{v}', \mathbf{V}') d\mathbf{v} d\mathbf{v}' d\mathbf{V} d\mathbf{V}' d\mathbf{x} \tag{30.8}$$

Let us consider the above quantities term by term. Noting that

$$(\ln f + 1)(\partial f/\partial t) = \partial(f \ln f)/\partial t$$

we obtain

$$A_1 = \frac{d}{dt}\iint f \ln f d\mathbf{v} d\mathbf{x} \tag{30.9}$$

Similarly rearranging A_2 and A_3 and integrating we have

$$A_2 = \sum_i \iint \frac{F_i}{m} \frac{\partial}{\partial v_i} [f \ln f] d\mathbf{v} d\mathbf{x}$$

$$= \sum_i \int \frac{F_i}{m}\left\{ \iiint \left[f \ln f \right]_{v_i = -\infty}^{v_i = +\infty} dv_j dv_k \right\} d\mathbf{x} = 0 \tag{30.10}$$

$$A_3 = \sum_i \iint v_i \frac{\partial}{\partial x_i} [f \ln f] d\mathbf{v} d\mathbf{x}$$

$$= \sum_i \int v_i \left\{ \iiint \left[f \ln f \right]_{x_i = -\infty}^{x_i = +\infty} dx_j dx_k \right\} d\mathbf{v} = 0 \tag{30.11}$$

where $i \neq j \neq k \neq i$.

If we interchange $\mathbf{v}'$ with $\mathbf{V}'$ and $\mathbf{v}$ with $\mathbf{V}$ in (30.8), recalling that $W(\mathbf{v}, \mathbf{V}; \mathbf{v}', \mathbf{V}') = W(\mathbf{V}, \mathbf{v}; \mathbf{V}', \mathbf{v}')$ for collisions between particles of the same mass, and then add the result to (30.8) we obtain

$$A_4 = \frac{1}{2}\iiiint \{\ln[f(\mathbf{v})f(\mathbf{V})] + 2\} \\ [f(\mathbf{v}')f(\mathbf{V}') - f(\mathbf{v})f(\mathbf{V})]W(\mathbf{v}, \mathbf{V}; \mathbf{v}', \mathbf{V}') d\mathbf{v} d\mathbf{v}' d\mathbf{V} d\mathbf{V}' d\mathbf{x} \tag{30.12}$$

If we interchange $\mathbf{v}$ with $\mathbf{v}'$ and $\mathbf{V}$ with $\mathbf{V}'$ in (30.12), recalling that $W(\mathbf{v},\mathbf{V};\mathbf{v}',\mathbf{V}') = W(\mathbf{v}',\mathbf{V}';\mathbf{v},\mathbf{V})$, and then add the result to (30.12) we obtain

$$A_4 = \frac{1}{4}\int\int\int\int\int\int \ln\left[\frac{f(\mathbf{v})f(\mathbf{V})}{f(\mathbf{v}')f(\mathbf{V}')}\right]$$
$$[f(\mathbf{v}')f(\mathbf{V}') - f(\mathbf{v})f(\mathbf{V})]$$
$$W(\mathbf{v},\mathbf{V};\mathbf{v}',\mathbf{V}')d\mathbf{v}d\mathbf{v}'d\mathbf{V}d\mathbf{V}'d\mathbf{x} \qquad (30.13)$$

Substituting (30.13), (30.11), (30.10), and (30.9) in (30.4), we obtain

$$\frac{dH}{dt} = \frac{1}{4}\int\int\int\int\int\int \left[\ln\left(\frac{G}{F}\right)\right][F - G]W d\mathbf{v}d\mathbf{v}'d\mathbf{V}d\mathbf{V}'d\mathbf{x} \qquad (30.14)$$

$$H \equiv \int\int\int f\ln f d\mathbf{v}d\mathbf{x} \qquad (30.15)$$

$$F \equiv f(\mathbf{v}')f(\mathbf{V}') \qquad (30.16)$$

$$G \equiv f(\mathbf{v})f(\mathbf{V}) \qquad (30.17)$$

$$W \equiv W(\mathbf{v},\mathbf{V};\mathbf{v}',\mathbf{V}') \qquad (30.18)$$

The quantities F and G are always greater than or equal to zero. It follows that $[\ln(G/F)][F - G]$ is always less than or equal to zero since if $F > G$ then $\ln(G/F) < 0$ and if $F < G$ then $\ln(G/F) > 0$. Furthermore, W is always greater than or equal to zero since it is a probability. The integrand in (30.14) is therefore always negative or zero and consequently

$$\frac{dH}{dt} \leq 0 \qquad (30.19)$$

The function H is called the Boltzmann H function. Since f is always positive, and $\int\int\int f d\mathbf{v}d\mathbf{x}$ and $\int\int[U + \frac{1}{2}mv^2]f d\mathbf{v}d\mathbf{x}$ are constant, there are certain restrictions on its value. It has a lower limit. If at time $t = 0$ H is not constant, we then expect it to decrease until it arrives at this lower limit, at which time H remains constant and $dH/dt = 0$.

THE MAXWELLIAN DISTRIBUTION

In equilibrium $dH/dt = 0$. From (30.14) it is apparent, since the integrand is always less than or equal to zero, that a necessary and sufficient condition for dH/dt to vanish is that the integrand in (30.14) be identically equal to zero. The integrand in (30.14) will be identically equal to zero if and only if $F = G$ whenever $W \neq 0$, or equivalently if and only if $\ln F = \ln G$ whenever $W \neq 0$. We therefore have as a necessary and sufficient condition for equilibrium that

$$\ln f(\mathbf{v}) + \ln f(\mathbf{V}) = \ln f(\mathbf{v}') + \ln f(\mathbf{V}') \qquad (30.20)$$
whenever
$$W(\mathbf{v},\mathbf{V};\mathbf{v}',\mathbf{V}') \neq 0 \qquad (30.21)$$

When written in terms of the center of mass velocities, $\mathbf{w}$ and $\mathbf{w}'$, and the relative velocities $\mathbf{u}$ and $\mathbf{u}'$, Eq. (30.20) becomes

$$\ln f(\mathbf{w} + \tfrac{1}{2}u\mathbf{n}) + \ln f(\mathbf{w} - \tfrac{1}{2}u\mathbf{n}) = \ln f(\mathbf{w}' + \tfrac{1}{2}u'\mathbf{n}') + \ln f(\mathbf{w}' - \tfrac{1}{2}u'\mathbf{n}') \qquad (30.22)$$

where $\mathbf{n}$ and $\mathbf{n}'$ are unit vectors in the directions of $\mathbf{u}$ and $\mathbf{u}'$ respectively.

The scattering probability W will in general be nonzero if and only if $u = u'$ and $\mathbf{w} = \mathbf{w}'$. Setting $u = u'$ and $\mathbf{w} = \mathbf{w}'$ in (30.22), we obtain as the condition of equilibrium

$$\ln f(\mathbf{w} + \tfrac{1}{2}u\mathbf{n}) + \ln f(\mathbf{w} - \tfrac{1}{2}u\mathbf{n}) = \ln f(\mathbf{w} + \tfrac{1}{2}u\mathbf{n}') + \ln f(\mathbf{w} - \tfrac{1}{2}u\mathbf{n}') \qquad (30.23)$$

Letting $r \equiv u/2$ and $\ln f(\mathbf{v}) \equiv g(\mathbf{v})$, Eq. (30.23) becomes

$$g(\mathbf{w} + r\mathbf{n}) + g(\mathbf{w} - r\mathbf{n}) = g(\mathbf{w} + r\mathbf{n}') + g(\mathbf{w} - r\mathbf{n}') \qquad (30.24)$$

Any quantity which is conserved in a collision will satisfy Eq. (30.24). In Appendix 13 we show that the only function $g(\mathbf{v})$ which can satisfy Eq. (30.24) is a function of the form

$$g(\mathbf{v}) = \alpha[\tfrac{1}{2}mv^2] + \sum_i \beta_i(mv_i) + \gamma \qquad (30.25)$$

where α, β_i, and γ are constants with respect to $\mathbf{v}$.

Recalling that $g = \ln f$, and choosing a new set of constants n, T, and $\bar{\mathbf{v}}$ such that

$$n = \int f d\mathbf{v} \qquad (30.26)$$

$$\bar{\mathbf{v}} = (1/n) \int \mathbf{v} f d\mathbf{v} \qquad (30.27)$$

$$3kT/2 = (1/n) \int \tfrac{1}{2}m(\mathbf{v} - \bar{\mathbf{v}})^2 f d\mathbf{v} \qquad (30.28)$$

we obtain from (30.25)

$$f(\mathbf{v}) = n(\lambda/\pi)^{3/2} \exp[-\lambda(\mathbf{v} - \bar{\mathbf{v}})^2] \qquad (30.29)$$

$$\lambda = m/2kT \qquad (30.30)$$

which is the familiar Maxwellian distribution.

THE MAXWELL-BOLTZMANN DISTRIBUTION

In the preceding section we have shown that the velocity dependence of f must be given by Eq. (30.29). In all the arguments leading up to (30.29) nothing was said about the dependence of f on the position $\mathbf{x}$. It follows that the constant $\bar{\mathbf{v}}$, n, and T (or λ) are constants with respect to the velocity $\mathbf{v}$ only, and may be functions of $\mathbf{x}$. To determine the exact dependence of these constants on $\mathbf{x}$, we will go back to Eq. (30.3), the Boltzmann transport equation.

If we substitute Eq. (30.29) into Eq. (30.3), the collision term will vanish, and since in equilibrium $f \neq f(t)$, the term $\partial f/\partial t$ will also vanish. We thus have

$$\sum_i v_i \frac{\partial f(\mathbf{v}, \mathbf{x})}{\partial x_i} + \sum_i \frac{F_i(\mathbf{x})}{m} \frac{\partial f(\mathbf{v}, \mathbf{x})}{\partial v_i} = 0 \tag{30.31}$$

$$f(\mathbf{v}, \mathbf{x}) = C(\mathbf{x}) \exp\{-\lambda(\mathbf{x})[\mathbf{v} - \bar{\mathbf{v}}(\mathbf{x})]^2\} \tag{30.32}$$

$$C \equiv n(\mathbf{x})[\lambda(\mathbf{x})/\pi]^{3/2} \tag{30.33}$$

Substituting (30.32) into (30.31) and dividing by f, we obtain

$$-\frac{2\lambda}{m} \sum_i F_i(v_i - \bar{v}_i) + \sum_i v_i \frac{\partial}{\partial x_i}(\ln C)$$

$$-\sum_i \sum_j v_i(v_j - \bar{v}_j)^2 \frac{\partial \lambda}{\partial x_i} + \sum_i \sum_j 2\lambda v_i(v_j - \bar{v}_j)\frac{\partial \bar{v}_j}{\partial x_i} = 0 \tag{30.34}$$

This is an equation of the form

$$B_0 + \sum_i B_i v_i + \sum_{i \ge j} B_{ij} v_i v_j + \sum_{i \ge j \ge k} B_{ijk} v_i v_j v_k = 0 \tag{30.35}$$

The only way this equation can be valid for all values of v_1, v_2, and v_3 is for $B_0 = B_i = B_{ij} = B_{ijk} = 0$. For Eq. (30.34) to be valid we therefore have

$$\sum_i F_i \bar{v}_i = 0 \tag{30.36}$$

$$-\left(\frac{2\lambda}{m}\right)F_i + \frac{\partial}{\partial x_i}(\ln C) - \frac{\partial \lambda}{\partial x_i}\sum_j \bar{v}_j^2 - 2\lambda \sum_j \bar{v}_j \frac{\partial \bar{v}_j}{\partial x_i} = 0 \tag{30.37}$$

$$2\left[\bar{v}_j \frac{\partial \lambda}{\partial x_i} + \bar{v}_i \frac{\partial \lambda}{\partial x_j}\right] + 2\lambda\left[\frac{\partial \bar{v}_j}{\partial x_i} + \frac{\partial \bar{v}_i}{\partial x_j}\right] = 0 \tag{30.38}$$

$$\frac{\partial \lambda}{\partial x_i} = 0 \tag{30.39}$$

Equation (30.39) tells us that the temperature T is constant.

If we assume the force to be conservative, then $F_i = -\partial U/\partial x_i$. Substituting this result and Eq. (30.39) in (30.37), we obtain

$$\frac{\partial}{\partial x_i}\left[\frac{2\lambda U}{m} + \ln C - \lambda \sum_j \bar{v}_j^2\right] = 0 \tag{30.40}$$

Integrating and solving for C, we obtain

$$C = a \exp\left[-\frac{2\lambda}{m}\left(U - \frac{m\bar{\mathbf{v}}^2}{2}\right)\right] \tag{30.41}$$

where "a" is a constant.

Combining (30.38) and (30.39). we have

$$\frac{\partial \bar{v}_j}{\partial x_i} + \frac{\partial \bar{v}_i}{\partial x_j} = 0 \tag{30.42}$$

The solution to (30.42) is

$$\bar{v} = c + \omega \times x \tag{30.43}$$

where c and ω are arbitrary constants. The center of mass velocity $\bar{v}_0$ can be obtained from (30.43) by averaging $\bar{v}$ over all values of x, i.e.,

$$\bar{v}_0 = (1/N) \int \bar{v} n(x) dx$$

$$= (1/N) \int [c + \omega \times x] n(x) dx$$

$$= (c/N) \int n(x) dx + \omega \times \left[(1/N) \int x n(x) dx \right]$$

$$= c + \omega \times x_0 \tag{30.44}$$

where x_0 is the position of the center of mass. Combining (30.44) and (30.43), we obtain

$$\bar{v} = \bar{v}_0 + \omega \times (x - x_0) \tag{30.45}$$

The velocity v_P of a point r_P in an arbitrarily moving rigid body can be written

$$v_P = v_Q + \omega \times (r_P - r_Q) \tag{30.46}$$

where v_Q and r_Q are the velocity and position of some arbitrary point Q in the rigid body and ω is the angular velocity.

It follows that any motion of the gas in which the center of mass moves with a constant velocity and the gas rotates like a rigid body with a constant angular velocity ω about the center of mass is permitted by Eq. (30.45).

Since our potential $U(x)$ is static, it is necessary for equilibrium that the velocity of the center of mass be zero. For simplicity, let us furthermore assume that our origin of coordinates is located at the center of mass, i.e., $x_0 = 0$. Equation (30.46) then becomes

$$\bar{v} = \omega \times x \tag{30.47}$$

We have investigated all conditions except Eq. (30.36). The quantity $\sum_i F_i \bar{v}_i$ which can also be written $F \cdot \bar{v}$ is the average power dissipated by a particle at x. This must vanish, otherwise there would be local heating and cooling of the gas. As long as $\bar{v}$ is directed along an equipotential, $F \cdot \bar{v}$ vanishes. For many potentials, the only way to satisfy (30.36) and (30.47) simultaneously is for $\bar{v}$ to vanish. However, for an axially symmetric potential $U(x)$, the gas can be rotating about the axis of symmetry with constant angular velocity and be in equilibrium.

Gathering together all of our results, we obtain for the distribution $f(\mathbf{x}, \mathbf{v})$ with the origin located at the center of mass

$$f = a \exp\left\{ -\frac{1}{kT}\left[\frac{m}{2}(\mathbf{v} - \bar{\mathbf{v}})^2 + U - \frac{m\bar{\mathbf{v}}^2}{2} \right] \right\}$$ (30.48)

$$T = \text{const}$$ (30.49)

$$\bar{\mathbf{v}} = \omega \times \mathbf{x}$$ (30.50)

$$\bar{\mathbf{v}} \cdot \mathbf{F} = 0$$ (30.51)

The constant a can be determined from the condition that $\int\int f d\mathbf{v} d\mathbf{x} = N$.

The distribution function in a system rotating with angular velocity ω can be obtained by replacing $\mathbf{v} - \bar{\mathbf{v}}$ with $\mathbf{v}$ in (30.48). Doing this and letting r be the distance from the axis of rotation to the point $\mathbf{x}$, we obtain

$$f = a \exp\left[-\frac{1}{kT}\left(\frac{mv^2}{2} + U - \frac{m\omega^2 r^2}{2} \right) \right]$$ (30.52)

Thus in this frame of reference the distribution is the familiar Maxwell-Boltzmann distribution with an additional "effective" potential

$$U' = -m\omega^2 r^2/2$$ (30.53)

This additional potential can be thought of as due to the "centrifugal force" $m\omega^2 r$.

PROBLEMS

1. Calculate the Boltzmann H function for a monatomic gas in equilibrium and express it in terms of macroscopic properties. Compare it with the entropy of an ideal gas.
2. Find the density as a function of position for a gas comprised of N molecules contained in a cylinder of radius a and length l which is rotating about its axis with angular velocity ω.

31

THE EQUATION
OF CHANGE

Instead of attempting to solve the Boltzmann transport equation which was derived in Chapter 29, frequent use is made of the so-called "equation of change" which is obtained by multiplying the Boltzmann transport equation by some arbitrary function q and integrating over velocity.

THE EQUATION OF CHANGE

The Boltzmann transport equation for one component of a mixture of two gases is given by

$$\frac{\partial f}{\partial t} + \sum_i v_i \frac{\partial f}{\partial x_i} + \sum_i \frac{F_i}{m} \frac{\partial f}{\partial v_i} = \left(\frac{Df}{Dt}\right)_{11} + \left(\frac{Df}{Dt}\right)_{12} \tag{31.1}$$

where

$$\left(\frac{Df}{Dt}\right)_{11} = \iiint [f(\mathbf{v}')f(\mathbf{V}') - f(\mathbf{v})f(\mathbf{V})]W_{11}(\mathbf{v}, \mathbf{V}; \mathbf{v}', \mathbf{V}')dv'd\mathbf{V}d\mathbf{V}' \tag{31.2}$$

$$\left(\frac{Df}{Dt}\right)_{12} = \iiint [f(\mathbf{v}')F(\mathbf{V}') - f(\mathbf{v})F(\mathbf{V})]W_{12}(\mathbf{v}, \mathbf{V}; \mathbf{v}', \mathbf{V}')dv'd\mathbf{V}d\mathbf{V}' \tag{31.3}$$

If we multiply (31.1) by $q(\mathbf{x}, \mathbf{v}, t)$ where $q(\mathbf{x}, \mathbf{v}, t)$ is some arbitrary function of $\mathbf{x}$, $\mathbf{v}$, and t, and if we then integrate over $\mathbf{v}$, we obtain

$$A_1 + A_2 + A_3 = (\Delta q)_{11} + (\Delta q)_{12} \tag{31.4}$$

where, suppressing the arguments $\mathbf{x}$ and t, we define

$$A_1 = \int q(\mathbf{v})\left(\frac{\partial f}{\partial t}\right)dv \tag{31.5}$$

$$A_2 = \sum_i \int v_i q(\mathbf{v}) \left(\frac{\partial f}{\partial x_i} \right) d\mathbf{v} \tag{31.6}$$

$$A_3 = \sum_i \int \left(\frac{F_i}{m} \right) q(\mathbf{v}) \left(\frac{\partial f}{\partial v_i} \right) d\mathbf{v} \tag{31.7}$$

$$(\Delta q)_{11} = \iiiint q(\mathbf{v})[f(\mathbf{v}')f(\mathbf{V}') - f(\mathbf{v})f(\mathbf{V})] \\ W_{11}(\mathbf{v}, \mathbf{V}; \mathbf{v}', \mathbf{V}') d\mathbf{v} d\mathbf{v}' d\mathbf{V} d\mathbf{V}' \tag{31.8}$$

$$(\Delta q)_{12} = \iiiint q(\mathbf{v})[f(\mathbf{v}')F(\mathbf{V}') - f(\mathbf{v})F(\mathbf{V})] \\ W_{12}(\mathbf{v}, \mathbf{V}; \mathbf{v}', \mathbf{V}') d\mathbf{v} d\mathbf{v}' d\mathbf{V} d\mathbf{V}' \tag{31.9}$$

Let us consider the above expression term by term. We will use the notation $\bar{g}$ to indicate the average of a function g taken over velocities only, i.e.,

$$\bar{g} = (1/n) \int g f d\mathbf{v} \tag{31.10}$$

The first two terms in (31.4) can be rewritten

$$A_1 = \frac{\partial}{\partial t} \int q f d\mathbf{v} - \int f \frac{\partial q}{\partial t} d\mathbf{v} = \frac{\partial}{\partial t} [n\bar{q}] - n \overline{(\partial q/\partial t)} \tag{31.11}$$

$$A_2 = \sum_i \frac{\partial}{\partial x_i} \int v_i q f d\mathbf{v} - \sum_i \int v_i \frac{\partial q}{\partial x_i} f d\mathbf{v}$$

$$= \sum_i \frac{\partial}{\partial x_i} [n \overline{v_i q}] - n \overline{v_i (\partial q/\partial x_i)} \tag{31.12}$$

Integrating the third term by parts assuming that $\mathbf{F}$ is not a function of velocity, we find

$$A_3 = \sum_i \frac{F_i}{m} \iint \left\{ \left[qf \right]_{v_i=-\infty}^{v_i=+\infty} - \int \frac{\partial q}{\partial v_i} f dv_i \right\} dv_j dv_k \tag{31.13}$$

where $i \neq j \neq k \neq i$. Noting that f vanishes in the limit as $v_i \to \pm \infty$, we have

$$A_3 = -\sum_i \frac{F_i}{m} \int \frac{\partial q}{\partial v_i} f d\mathbf{v} = -\sum_i \frac{F_i}{m} [n \overline{(\partial q/\partial v_i)}] \tag{31.14}$$

The collision terms $(\Delta q)_{11}$ and $(\Delta q)_{12}$ can be written in a somewhat more useful form if we exploit the symmetries of $W(\mathbf{v}, \mathbf{V}; \mathbf{v}', \mathbf{V}')$. Interchanging $\mathbf{v}$ with $\mathbf{v}'$ and $\mathbf{V}$ with $\mathbf{V}'$ in (31.9) and noting that $W_{12}(\mathbf{v}, \mathbf{V}; \mathbf{v}', \mathbf{V}') = W_{12}(\mathbf{v}', \mathbf{V}'; \mathbf{v}, \mathbf{V})$ we obtain

$$(\Delta q)_{12} = \iiiint [q(\mathbf{v}')] [f(\mathbf{v})F(\mathbf{V}) - f(\mathbf{v}')F(\mathbf{V}')] \\ W_{12}(\mathbf{v}, \mathbf{V}; \mathbf{v}', \mathbf{V}') d\mathbf{v} d\mathbf{v}' d\mathbf{V} d\mathbf{V}' \tag{31.15}$$

Adding (31.15) to (31.9) and dividing by 2, we obtain

$$(\Delta q)_{12} = \frac{1}{2} \iiiint [q(\mathbf{v}') - q(\mathbf{v})] [f(\mathbf{v})F(\mathbf{V}) - f(\mathbf{v}')F(\mathbf{V}')]$$
$$W_{12}(\mathbf{v}, \mathbf{V}; \mathbf{v}', \mathbf{V}')dvdv'd\mathbf{V}d\mathbf{V}' \qquad (31.16)$$

Similarly

$$(\Delta q)_{11} = \frac{1}{2} \iiiint [q(\mathbf{v}') - q(\mathbf{v})] [f(\mathbf{v})f(\mathbf{V}) - f(\mathbf{v}')f(\mathbf{V}')]$$
$$W_{11}(\mathbf{v}, \mathbf{V}; \mathbf{v}', \mathbf{V}')dvdv'd\mathbf{V}d\mathbf{V}' \qquad (31.17)$$

In the case of $(\Delta q)_{11}$, we have the additional symmetry $W_{11}(\mathbf{v}, \mathbf{V}; \mathbf{v}', \mathbf{V}') = W_{11}(\mathbf{V}, \mathbf{v}; \mathbf{V}', \mathbf{v}')$. Interchanging $\mathbf{v}$ with $\mathbf{V}$ and $\mathbf{v}'$ with $\mathbf{V}'$ in (31.17) and averaging the resulting expression with (31.17), we obtain

$$(\Delta q)_{11} = \frac{1}{4} \iiiint [q(\mathbf{v}') + q(\mathbf{V}') - q(\mathbf{v}) - q(\mathbf{V})] [f(\mathbf{v})f(\mathbf{V}) - f(\mathbf{v}')f(\mathbf{V}')]$$
$$W_{11}(\mathbf{v}, \mathbf{V}; \mathbf{v}', \mathbf{V}')dvdv'd\mathbf{V}d\mathbf{V}' \qquad (31.18)$$

Gathering results, we have

$$\frac{\partial}{\partial t}[n\bar{q}] + \sum_i \frac{\partial}{\partial x_i}[n\overline{v_i q}] - n\left\{\overline{(\partial q/\partial t)} + \sum_i \overline{v_i(\partial q/\partial x_i)} + \sum_i \overline{(F_i/m)(\partial q/\partial v_i)}\right\}$$

$$= (\Delta q)_{11} + (\Delta q)_{12} \qquad (31.19)$$

$$q \equiv q(\mathbf{x}, \mathbf{v}, t) \qquad (31.20)$$

with $(\Delta q)_{11}$ and $(\Delta q)_{12}$ given by expressions (31.16) and (31.18) respectively. This is the general equation of change.

If we assume that q is a function of $\mathbf{v}$ only then Eq. (31.19) reduces to

$$\frac{\partial}{\partial t}[n\bar{q}] + \sum_i \frac{\partial}{\partial x_i}[n\overline{v_i q}] - \sum_i (F_i/m)[n\overline{(\partial q/\partial v_i)}] = (\Delta q)_{11} + (\Delta q)_{12} \qquad (31.21)$$

$$q \equiv q(\mathbf{v}) \qquad (31.22)$$

with $(\Delta q)_{11}$ and $(\Delta q)_{12}$ given by Eqs. (31.16) and (31.18) respectively.

THE COLLISION TERM

The term $(\Delta q)_{12}$ in the equation of change can be written in still another form which brings out its physical meaning a little more clearly.

Let us start with the collision term in the form

$$(Df/Dt)_{12} = \iiint f(\mathbf{v}')F(\mathbf{V}')W_{12}(\mathbf{v}', \mathbf{V}'; \mathbf{v}, \mathbf{V})dv'd\mathbf{V}d\mathbf{V}'$$

$$- \iiint f(\mathbf{v})F(\mathbf{V})W_{12}(\mathbf{v}, \mathbf{V}; \mathbf{v}', \mathbf{V}')dv'd\mathbf{V}d\mathbf{V}' \qquad (31.23)$$

If we multiply (31.23) by $q(\mathbf{v})$ and integrate over $\mathbf{v}$, we obtain

$$(\Delta q)_{12} = \iiiint q(\mathbf{v})f(\mathbf{v}')F(\mathbf{V}')W_{12}(\mathbf{v}',\mathbf{V}';\mathbf{v},\mathbf{V})d\mathbf{v}d\mathbf{v}'d\mathbf{V}d\mathbf{V}'$$

$$- \iiiint q(\mathbf{v})f(\mathbf{v})F(\mathbf{V})W_{12}(\mathbf{v},\mathbf{V};\mathbf{v}',\mathbf{V}')d\mathbf{v}d\mathbf{v}'d\mathbf{V}d\mathbf{V}' \qquad (31.24)$$

Interchanging $\mathbf{v}$ with $\mathbf{v}'$ and $\mathbf{V}$ with $\mathbf{V}'$ in the first term in (31.24), we obtain

$$(\Delta q)_{12} = \iiiint [q(\mathbf{v}') - q(\mathbf{v})]f(\mathbf{v})F(\mathbf{V})W_{12}(\mathbf{v},\mathbf{V};\mathbf{v}',\mathbf{V}')d\mathbf{v}d\mathbf{v}'d\mathbf{V}d\mathbf{V}' \qquad (31.25)$$

The quantity $[q(\mathbf{v}') - q(\mathbf{v})]$ is the change in q in a collision; $f(\mathbf{v})d\mathbf{v}$ is the number of particles of mass m per unit volume with velocity in $d\mathbf{v}$; $F(\mathbf{V})d\mathbf{V}$ is the number of particles of mass M per unit volume with velocity in $d\mathbf{V}$; $W_{12}(\mathbf{v},\mathbf{V};\mathbf{v}',\mathbf{V}')d\mathbf{v}'d\mathbf{V}'$ is the probability that two particles of masses m and M, and velocities $\mathbf{v}$ and $\mathbf{V}$ respectively which are contained in the same unit volume will collide and end up with their velocities in $d\mathbf{v}'$ and $d\mathbf{V}'$ respectively. It follows that $(\Delta q)_{12}$ is the time rate of change per unit volume, due to collisions between particles of mass m and M, of the quantity $q(\mathbf{v})$.

This can also be seen by remembering that $(Df/Dt)_{12}d\mathbf{v}d\mathbf{x}$ is the change in the number of particles in $d\mathbf{v}d\mathbf{x}$ due to collisions, so that $q(\mathbf{v})[(Df/Dt)_{12} d\mathbf{v}d\mathbf{x}]$ is the change in $q(\mathbf{v})$ due to collisions experienced by the particles in $d\mathbf{v}d\mathbf{x}$ and $[\int q(\mathbf{v})(Df/Dt)_{12}d\mathbf{v}]d\mathbf{x}$ is the change in $q(\mathbf{v})$ due to collisions experienced by the particles in $d\mathbf{x}$.

Chapter 32

THE HYDRODYNAMIC EQUATIONS

INTRODUCTION

In this chapter we wish to consider the fundamental equations of hydrodynamics from a kinetic theory viewpoint. Before embarking on this project, it will be well to briefly outline the fundamental equations and postulates of macroscopic hydrodynamics in order to facilitate comparison of the kinetic theory results with the corresponding results of the macroscopic approach. We will restrict our discussion to a simple fluid, composed of a single species of matter—for example, a gas of helium.

MACROSCOPIC HYDRODYNAMICS

The fundamental problem of hydrodynamics is to describe and predict the behavior of a fluid in motion. If the motion of the fluid is not too violent, we can divide the fluid into small elements, and consider each element to be in thermodynamic equilibrium at every instant of time. It is then possible at a particular instant of time to assign a density and temperature to each point in the fluid, which if known, determines the thermodynamic state of the element of fluid at that instant of time. However, the state of an element of the fluid is not completely determined by its thermodynamic properties. Since the element is in motion, we must describe its kinetic behavior also. The kinetic behavior of an element of fluid is described if we know its velocity. The science of hydrodynamics thus seeks to find and solve the equations which will provide the mass density ρ, temperature T, and velocity $\mathbf{v}$ of the fluid as functions of $\mathbf{x}$ and t, so that if ρ, T and $\mathbf{v}$ are known at one instant of time for a given set of boundary conditions, their values at some future time can be predicted.

Before writing down the equations which govern the behavior of the fluid, let us define a few useful quantities.

Consider an element of the fluid which at time t occupies the volume ΔV. The forces acting on the fluid element are of two types. There are forces due to external fields such as gravity which act throughout the element, and there are forces exerted on the surface of the volume element by the surrounding fluid. We refer to these two types of forces as body forces and surface forces respectively. We shall let $\mathbf{F}'(\mathbf{x})$ be the body force per unit mass at the point $\mathbf{x}$, and $\mathbf{T}(\mathbf{n}, \mathbf{X})$ be the force per unit area on a surface normal to the unit vector $\mathbf{n}$ and located at $\mathbf{x}$. The force $\mathbf{T}(\mathbf{n}, \mathbf{x})$ will be considered to be the force acting on the side of the surface into which $\mathbf{n}$ is pointing. We note that $\mathbf{T}(-\mathbf{n}, \mathbf{x}) = -\mathbf{T}(\mathbf{n}, \mathbf{x})$.

Let us now consider the forces acting on the tetrahedron shown in Figure

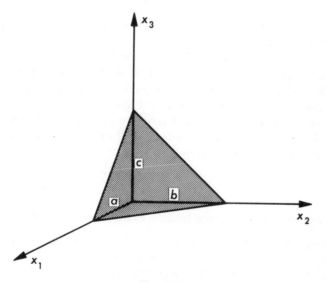

Fig. 32.1

32.1. Let $\mathbf{n}$ be a unit vector normal to the skew surface and pointing outward and let S be the area of the skew surface. Let $\mathbf{e}_i$ be a unit vector in the x_i direction. If we make the tetrahedron smaller and smaller the surface forces will eventually dominate, since they decrease as the surface area while the body forces decrease as the volume. It follows that in the limit as the tetrahedron becomes infinitesimally small the surface force will dominate and since the total force must vanish in this limit, the net surface force acting on the tetrahedron must approach zero. For an infinitesimal tetrahedron the net surface force is

$$\mathbf{T}(-\mathbf{n}, \mathbf{x})S + \mathbf{T}(\mathbf{e}_1, \mathbf{x})(n_1 S) + \mathbf{T}(\mathbf{e}_2, \mathbf{x})(n_2 S) + \mathbf{T}(\mathbf{e}_3, \mathbf{x})(n_3 S) \tag{32.1}$$

Equating this to zero, we obtain

$$\mathbf{T}(\mathbf{n}, \mathbf{x}) = \mathbf{T}(\mathbf{e}_1, \mathbf{x})n_1 + \mathbf{T}(\mathbf{e}_2, \mathbf{x})n_2 + \mathbf{T}(\mathbf{e}_3, \mathbf{x})n_3 \tag{32.2}$$

or in component form

$$T_i(\mathbf{n}, \mathbf{x}) = \sum_j T_i(\mathbf{e}_j, \mathbf{x})n_j \tag{32.3}$$

We now define

$$p_{ij} = T_i(\mathbf{e}_j, \mathbf{x}) \tag{32.4}$$

It can be shown that the quantities p_{ij} constitute a symmetric Cartesian tensor, which we call the pressure tensor. In terms of the pressure tensor, Eq. (32.3) becomes

$$T_i(\mathbf{n}, \mathbf{x}) = \sum_j p_{ij} n_j \tag{32.5}$$

It follows that if we know the pressure tensor $p_{ij}(\mathbf{x})$ we can calculate the force on any surface located at $\mathbf{x}$.

The proof that p_{ij} is a tensor follows from (32.5) and the fact that $\mathbf{T}$ and $\mathbf{n}$ are vectors. The fact that $p_{ij} = p_{ji}$ can be shown by setting the torque per unit volume due to the surface forces on a small volume element equal to zero in the limit as the volume element becomes infinitesimally small.

Suppose we consider a spherical volume of radius R. The normal component of the surface force on the outside of the sphere acting on a surface element $\mathbf{n}dS$ of the sphere is given by

$$\mathbf{T}(-\mathbf{n}, \mathbf{x}) \cdot (-\mathbf{n}dS) = \sum_i T_i(\mathbf{n}, \mathbf{x})n_i dS = \sum_i \sum_j p_{ij} n_i n_j dS \tag{32.6}$$

where

$$\mathbf{n} = \mathbf{R}/R = \mathbf{e}_1(\sin\theta \cos\phi) + \mathbf{e}_2(\sin\theta \sin\phi) + \mathbf{e}_3 \cos\theta \tag{32.7}$$

If we integrate the normal component of the surface force over the sphere, divide by the surface area of the sphere, and take the limit as the radius R approaches zero, we obtain the pressure p, i.e.,

$$p = \lim_{R \to 0} \left(\frac{\sum_i \sum_j \oint p_{ij} n_i n_j dS}{\oint dS} \right)$$

$$= \sum_i \sum_j p_{ij}(\mathbf{x}) \lim_{R \to 0} \left(\frac{\oint n_i n_j dS}{\oint dS} \right)$$

$$= \sum_i \sum_j p_{ij}(\mathbf{x}) \lim_{R \to 0} \left(\frac{\oint n_i n_j R^2 \sin\theta d\theta d\phi}{4\pi R^2} \right)$$

$$= \tfrac{1}{3} \underset{i\ j}{\Sigma\Sigma} p_{ij}\delta_{ij} = \tfrac{1}{3}(p_{11} + p_{22} + p_{33}) \tag{32.8}$$

The pressure p is an invariant, i.e., it is independent of our choice of coordinate system. This follows from the fact that $\underset{i\ j}{\Sigma\Sigma} p_{ij}\delta_{ij}$ is just the contraction of the tensor p_{ij}, and the contraction of any second-rank Cartesian tensor is an invariant.

We are now ready to write down the equations which govern the behavior of a fluid. If there are no sources or sinks within the fluid, then the equation of continuity is valid,

$$\sum_i \frac{\partial}{\partial x_i}(\rho\bar{v}_i) + \frac{\partial\rho}{\partial t} = 0 \tag{32.9}$$

This provides us with one equation in the five unknown quantities, ρ, $\bar{\mathbf{v}}$, and T.

Let us now consider the motion of an element of fluid which at time t occupies the volume ΔV. As time progresses, the fluid element moves and its shape changes but its total mass by definition remains constant.

Equating the sum of body and surface forces acting on ΔV to its time rate of change of momentum, we obtain

$$\int \mathbf{F}'\rho dV + \oint \mathbf{T}(-\mathbf{n}, \mathbf{x})dS = \int \rho(d\mathbf{v}/dt)dV \tag{32.10}$$

It should be noted that in expression (32.10), d/dt is the time rate of change as noted by an observer moving with the fluid element, i. e.

$$\frac{d}{dt} = \frac{\partial}{\partial t} + \sum_j \bar{v}_j \frac{\partial}{\partial x_j} \tag{32.11}$$

Whenever we use the notation d/dt, we will have reference to this derivative. For a further discussion of this point, the reader is referred to the discussion of Liouville's theorem in Chapter 11.

If we write Eq. (32.10) in component form, and make use of (32.5), we obtain

$$\int F_i'\rho dV - \sum_j \oint p_{ij} n_j dS = \int \rho\left(\frac{d\bar{v}_i}{dt}\right)dV \tag{32.12}$$

In Appendix 8 we show that for any single-valued, continuous and differentiable function $P(\mathbf{x})$

$$\int \left(\frac{\partial P}{\partial x_i}\right)dV = \oint P n_i dS \tag{32.13}$$

and therefore
$$\oint p_{ij}n_j dS = \int \left(\frac{\partial p_{ij}}{\partial x_j}\right) dV \tag{32.14}$$

Substituting (32.14) in (32.12) we have

$$\int F_i' \rho dV - \sum_j \int \left(\frac{\partial p_{ij}}{\partial x_j}\right) dV = \int \rho\left(\frac{d\bar{v}_i}{dt}\right) dV \tag{32.15}$$

Since Eq. (32.15) must be true for any arbitrary fluid element ΔV, we can equate the integrands, and we then obtain

$$\rho\frac{d\bar{v}_i}{dt} = \rho F_i' - \sum_j \frac{\partial p_{ij}}{\partial x_j} \tag{32.16}$$

The equations of motion (32.16) provide us with three additional equations. However, we have also introduced six additional unknowns, namely, the six independent components of p_{ij}. Altogether we now have four equations but eleven unknowns.

Let us now consider the gain and loss of energy by the element of fluid which at time t occupies the volume ΔV. We shall designate the internal energy per unit mass of the fluid by E'. By internal energy we mean the total energy of the element exclusive of the energy of motion of the center of mass and the potential energy due to the external force field $\mathbf{F}'$.

The surface and body forces acting on the element of fluid will do work on the element and will cause the kinetic energy of the center of mass and the internal energy to change. In addition to the energy changes due to body and surface forces, energy can be supplied to the fluid element by heat conduction. Let us define $\mathbf{q}$ as the energy flux density due to heat conduction.

Equating the rate of energy supplied to the element of fluid to its rate of increase of energy, we obtain

$$\int \left(\sum_i F_i'\bar{v}_i\right)\rho dV + \oint\left[\sum_i T_i(-\mathbf{n},\mathbf{x})\bar{v}_i\right]dS - \oint\sum_i q_i n_i dS$$
$$= \int \frac{d}{dt}\left(E' + \frac{1}{2}\sum_i \bar{v}_i^2\right)\rho dV \tag{32.17}$$

Substituting (32.5) in (32.17), making use of (32.13) to convert the surface integrals to volume integrals, and then equating the integrands, we obtain

$$\frac{d}{dt}\left(E + \frac{1}{2}\sum_i \bar{v}_i^2\right) = \sum_i F_i'\bar{v}_i - (1/\rho)\sum_i\left(\frac{\partial q_i}{\partial x_i}\right) - (1/\rho)\sum_i\sum_j \frac{\partial}{\partial x_i}(p_{ij}\bar{v}_j) \tag{32.18}$$

Multiplying (32.16) by $\bar{v}_i$, summing over i and subtracting the result from (32.18), we obtain

$$\frac{dE'}{dt} = -(1/\rho)\sum_i \left(\frac{\partial q_i}{\partial x_i}\right) - (1/\rho)\sum_i \sum_j p_{ij}\left(\frac{\partial \bar{v}_j}{\partial x_i}\right) \qquad (32.19)$$

Equation (32.19) provides us with one additional equation. We have, however, four additional unknowns: q_1, q_2, q_3, and E'. Altogether we now have five equations, Eq. (32.9), Eq. (32.16) and Eq. (32.19) and fifteen unknowns, ρ, $\bar{v}_1$, $\bar{v}_2$, $\bar{v}_3$, T, p_{11}, p_{12}, p_{13}, p_{23}, p_{22}, p_{33}, q_1, q_2, q_3, and E'.

Equations (32.9), (32.16) and (32.19) are the fundamental equations of hydrodynamics. However, these five equations alone do not provide us with the necessary equations to solve for ρ, $\bar{v}$, and T. There are too few equations and too many unknowns. The additional equations required are found by experiment.

Thus a thermodynamic analysis of a particular fluid will provide us with an expression for E' in terms of T and p, and for ρ as a function of T and p.

$$E' = E'(T, p) \qquad (32.20)$$

$$\rho = \rho(T, p) \qquad (32.21)$$

An analysis of the flow of heat provides us with Fourier's law of heat flow which tells us that over a broad range of conditions the rate of flow of heat is proportional to the gradient of the temperature:

$$q_i = -\kappa\left(\frac{\partial T}{\partial x_i}\right) \qquad (32.22)$$

where κ, the coefficient of thermal conductivity, depends on the nature of the fluid and must be experimentally determined. It may be a function of temperature and pressure.

Finally, suppose we have a fluid contained between two parallel plates which are perpendicular to the 1 axis and moving at constant but different speeds in the 2 direction. We then find that the shear force p_{21} is proportional to the velocity gradient $\partial \bar{v}_2/\partial x_1$. Thus in this particular case

$$p_{21} = -\mu\left(\frac{\partial \bar{v}_2}{\partial x_1}\right) \qquad (32.23)$$

where μ is an experimental constant, called the coefficient of viscosity. The coefficient of viscosity is a function of temperature and pressure. For arbitrary motion of the fluid

$$p_{ij} = p\delta_{ij} - \mu\left[\frac{\partial \bar{v}_i}{\partial x_j} + \frac{\partial \bar{v}_j}{\partial x_i} - \tfrac{2}{3}\delta_{ij}\sum_k \frac{\partial \bar{v}_k}{\partial x_k}\right] \qquad (32.24)$$

Note that p_{ij} is symmetric and $\tfrac{1}{3}\sum_i p_{ii} = p$ as we would expect. Equation (32.24) is called Stokes' hypothesis.

Equations (32.20), (32.21), (32.22), and (32.24) provide us with eleven new equations, but we have introduced three new unknowns p, κ, and μ. Altogether we now have sixteen equations and eighteen unknowns. The additional two equations needed are the dependence of κ and μ on temperature and pressure, i.e.,

$$\kappa = \kappa(T, p) \tag{32.25}$$

$$\mu = \mu(T, p) \tag{32.26}$$

We now have eighteen equations, (32.9), (32.16), (32.19), (32.20), (32.21), (32.22), (32.24), (32.25), and (32.26) in the eighteen unknowns ρ, T, $\bar{v}_1$, $\bar{v}_2$, $\bar{v}_3$, p_{11}, p_{22}, p_{33}, p_{12}, p_{13}, p_{23}, q_1, q_2, q_3, E', p, κ, μ.

If we substitute Fourier's law, and Stokes' hypothesis into Eqs. (32.9), (32.16), and (32.19), we obtain five equations in the nine unknowns ρ, $\bar{v}$, T, p, μ, κ, E'. These equations are known as the Navier-Stokes equations. The hydrodynamic properties of a fluid can be determined from the Navier-Stokes equations together with a knowledge of E', ρ, κ, and μ as functions of temperature and pressure.

In the following sections we will derive the equations of hydrodynamics from kinetic theory. We shall find that the kinetic theory provides us with a molecular interpretation of the pressure tensor p_{ij} and the heat flux vector q_i.

In a later chapter we will obtain explicit expressions for these quantities and as a result, justify Fourier's law and Stokes' hypothesis for gases. We shall also obtain equations for the coefficients κ and μ in terms of the differential scattering cross section.

THE HYDRODYNAMIC EQUATIONS OF MOTION
FROM A MOLECULAR VIEWPOINT

In Chapter 31, we derived the equation of change, which for a single component gas and for q a function of velocity only, can be written

$$\frac{\partial}{\partial t}[nq] + \sum_j \frac{\partial}{\partial x_j}[n\overline{v_j q}] - \sum_j \frac{F_j}{m}[n\overline{(\partial q/\partial v_j)}] = \frac{1}{4}\iiiint [q(\mathbf{v}) + q(\mathbf{V}) - q(\mathbf{v}') - q(\mathbf{V}')]$$

$$[f(\mathbf{v}')f(\mathbf{V}') - f(\mathbf{v})f(\mathbf{V})]W(\mathbf{v}, \mathbf{V}; \mathbf{v}', \mathbf{V}')d\mathbf{v}d\mathbf{v}'d\mathbf{V}d\mathbf{V}' \tag{32.27}$$

There are five functions $q(\mathbf{v})$ which will make the collision term in Eq. (32.27) vanish, the five quantities which are conserved in a collision, the mass m, the three components of momentum mv_i, and the energy $\frac{1}{2}mv^2$.

There are therefore five equations which can be obtained from Eq. (32.27) without having to evaluate the collision term. As we shall see, they are the five equations of hydrodynamics which were obtained in the beginning of this chapter from a macroscopic analysis.

Letting $q(\mathbf{v}) = m$ in Eq. (32.27), and noting that $nm = \rho$,

$$\frac{\partial \rho}{\partial t} + \sum_i \frac{\partial}{\partial x_i}(\rho \bar{v}_i) = 0 \tag{32.28}$$

which is just the equation of continuity.

Letting $\mathbf{q(v)} = mv_i$ in Eq. (32.27), we obtain

$$\frac{\partial}{\partial t}[\rho\bar{v}_i] + \sum_j \frac{\partial}{\partial x_j}[\rho\overline{v_i v_j}] - \rho\frac{F_i}{m} = 0 \tag{32.29}$$

But

$$\overline{v_i v_j} = \overline{(v_i - \bar{v}_i)(v_j - \bar{v}_j)} + \bar{v}_i\bar{v}_j \tag{32.30}$$

substituting (32.30) in (32.29). Then multiplying the equation of continuity (32.28) by $\bar{v}_i$ and subtracting it from (32.29), we obtain

$$\rho\left[\frac{\partial\bar{v}_i}{\partial t} + \sum_j \bar{v}_j\frac{\partial\bar{v}_i}{\partial x_j}\right] = \rho\frac{F_i}{m} - \sum_j \frac{\partial}{\partial x_j}[\rho\overline{(v_i - \bar{v}_i)(v_j - \bar{v}_j)}] \tag{32.31}$$

Comparing (32.31) with Eq. (32.16) and noting that the left-hand side of (32.31) is just $\rho(d\bar{v}_i/dt)$, we see that Eq. (32.31) is just the hydrodynamic equation of motion with the pressure tensor given by

$$p_{ij} = \rho\overline{(v_i - \bar{v}_i)(v_j - \bar{v}_j)}$$
$$\equiv m\int (v_i - \bar{v}_i)(v_j - \bar{v}_j)f d\mathbf{v} \tag{32.32}$$

Letting $q(\mathbf{v}) = \frac{1}{2}m\Sigma_j v_j^2$ in Eq. (32.27), we obtain

$$\sum_j \frac{\partial}{\partial t}[\frac{1}{2}\rho\overline{v_j^2}] + \sum_i\sum_j \frac{\partial}{\partial x_i}[\frac{1}{2}\rho\overline{v_i v_j^2}] - \sum_i \frac{F_i}{m}[\rho\bar{v}_i] = 0 \tag{32.33}$$

But

$$\overline{v_j^2} = \overline{(v_j - \bar{v}_j)^2} + \bar{v}_j^2 \tag{32.34}$$

$$\overline{v_i v_j^2} = \overline{(v_i - \bar{v}_i)(v_j - \bar{v}_j)^2} + 2\bar{v}_j\overline{(v_i - \bar{v}_i)(v_j - \bar{v}_j)} + \bar{v}_i\overline{(v_j - \bar{v}_j)^2} + \bar{v}_i\bar{v}_j^2 \tag{32.35}$$

Substituting (32.34) and (32.35) in (32.33) and rearranging terms, we find

$$\rho\frac{\partial}{\partial t}\left[\sum_j \frac{1}{2}\overline{(v_j - \bar{v}_j)^2}\right] + \rho\sum_i \bar{v}_i\frac{\partial}{\partial x_i}\left[\sum_j \frac{1}{2}\overline{(v_j - \bar{v}_j)^2}\right]$$

$$+ \sum_i\sum_j \frac{\partial}{\partial x_i}[\frac{1}{2}\rho\overline{(v_i - \bar{v}_i)(v_j - \bar{v}_j)^2}]$$

$$+ \sum_i\sum_j \frac{\partial\bar{v}_j}{\partial x_i}[\rho\overline{(v_i - \bar{v}_i)(v_j - \bar{v}_j)}]$$

$$+ \left[\frac{\partial\rho}{\partial t} + \sum_i \frac{\partial}{\partial x_i}(\rho\bar{v}_i)\right]\left[\sum_j \frac{1}{2}\bar{v}_j^2 + \sum_j \frac{1}{2}\overline{(v_j - \bar{v}_j)^2}\right]$$

$$+ \sum_i \bar{v}_i\left\{\rho\frac{\partial\bar{v}_i}{\partial t} + \rho\sum_j \bar{v}_j\frac{\partial\bar{v}_i}{\partial x_j} - \rho\frac{F_i}{m}\right.$$

$$\left. + \sum_j \frac{\partial}{\partial x_j}[\rho\overline{(v_i - \bar{v}_i)(v_j - \bar{v}_j)}]\right\} = 0 \tag{32.36}$$

From Eqs. (32.28) and (32.31) it follows that the last two terms in (32.36) vanish. We can thus write (32.36)

$$\rho\frac{d}{\partial t}\left[\sum_j \tfrac{1}{2}\overline{(v_j - \bar{v}_j)^2}\right] + \sum_i \sum_j \frac{\partial}{\partial x_i}\{\tfrac{1}{2}\rho\overline{(v_i - \bar{v}_i)(v_j - \bar{v}_j)^2}\}$$

$$+ \sum_i \sum_j \frac{\partial \bar{v}_j}{\partial x_i}\{\rho\overline{(v_i - \bar{v}_i)(v_j - \bar{v}_j)}\} = 0 \qquad (32.37)$$

where it should be remembered that

$$\frac{d}{dt} \equiv \frac{\partial}{\partial t} + \sum_i \bar{v}_i \frac{\partial}{\partial x_i}$$

Comparing (32.37) with Eq. (32.19), we see that they are identical provided the pressure tensor is given by (32.32) and the internal energy per unit mass and the thermal flux are defined by

$$E' = \tfrac{1}{2}\Sigma_j \overline{(v_j - \bar{v}_j)^2}$$

$$\equiv (1/2n)\int (\mathbf{v} - \bar{\mathbf{v}})^2 f d\mathbf{v} \qquad (32.38)$$

$$q_i = (\rho/2)\Sigma_j \overline{(v_i - \bar{v}_i)(v_j - \bar{v}_j)^2}$$

$$\equiv (m/2)\int (v_i - \bar{v}_i)(\mathbf{v} - \bar{\mathbf{v}})^2 f d\mathbf{v} \qquad (32.39)$$

If we compare (32.38) and (32.32) we see that

$$(1/m)(p_{11} + p_{22} + p_{33}) = 2nE' \qquad (32.40)$$

It follows that of the fourteen quantities ρ, $\bar{v}_i$, p_{ij}, q_i, and E' only thirteen are independent.

SUMMARY

In the preceding sections we have derived the fundamental equations of hydrodynamics,

$$\frac{\partial \rho}{\partial t} + \sum_i \frac{\partial}{\partial x_i}(\rho \bar{v}_i) = 0 \qquad (32.41)$$

$$\rho\frac{d\bar{v}_i}{dt} = \rho F_i' - \sum_j \frac{\partial p_{ij}}{\partial x_j} \qquad (32.42)$$

$$\rho\frac{dE'}{dt} = -\sum_i \frac{\partial q_i}{\partial x_i} - \sum_i \sum_j p_{ij}\frac{\partial \bar{v}_j}{\partial x_i} \qquad (32.43)$$

where ρ is the mass density, E' is the internal energy per unit mass, p_{ij} the pressure tensor, and $\mathbf{q}$ the heat flux.

In order to use these equations, we need a number of auxiliary relations. From a macroscopic point of view, these additional relations come from experiment, and consist of several equations of state, Fourier's law and Stokes' hypothesis.

$$E' = E'(T, p) \tag{32.44}$$

$$\rho = \rho(T, p) \tag{32.45}$$

$$q_i = -\kappa \frac{\partial T}{\partial x_i} \tag{32.46}$$

$$p_{ij} = p\delta_{ij} - \mu\left[\frac{\partial \bar{v}_i}{\partial x_j} + \frac{\partial \bar{v}_j}{\partial x_i} - \tfrac{2}{3}\delta_{ij}\sum_k \frac{\partial \bar{v}_k}{\partial x_k}\right] \tag{32.47}$$

where μ is the coefficient of viscosity, and κ the coefficient of thermal conductivity, both of which may be functions of T and p. We therefore also need to know

$$\mu = \mu(T, p) \tag{32.48}$$

$$\kappa = \kappa(T, p) \tag{32.49}$$

If we derive the fundamental equations of hydrodynamics from a kinetic theory point of view, we find that we are able to interpret the macroscopic parameters ρ, $\bar{v}_i$, q_i, p_{ij}, and E' as follows:

$$\rho = m\int f d\mathbf{v} \tag{32.50}$$

$$\bar{v}_i = (1/n)\int v_i f d\mathbf{v} \tag{32.51}$$

$$E' = (1/2n)\int (\mathbf{v} - \bar{\mathbf{v}})^2 f d\mathbf{v} \tag{32.52}$$

$$q_i = (m/2)\int (v_i - \bar{v}_i)(\mathbf{v} - \bar{\mathbf{v}})^2 f d\mathbf{v} \tag{32.53}$$

$$p_{ij} = m\int (v_i - \bar{v}_i)(v_j - \bar{v}_j) f d\mathbf{v} \tag{32.54}$$

Only thirteen of these parameters are independent since p_{ij} is symmetric and

$$\tfrac{1}{3}(p_{11} + p_{22} + p_{33}) = \frac{2mnE'}{3} \tag{32.55}$$

Before these results can be used it is necessary to know the distribution function f. To find f, we must solve the Boltzmann transport equation. Of course, if we could find the exact distribution function f for a particular set of boundary conditions, the hydrodynamic equations would be superfluous. Although we will not be able to completely solve the Boltzmann transport equation, we can use it to justify various approximate equations such as Fourier's law, and Stokes' hypothesis, and also to obtain explicit values for the transport coefficients. This will be taken up in later chapters after we have gained some facility in handling the collision term in the Boltzmann transport equation.

Chapter 33

THE INTERACTION BETWEEN GASES IN EQUILIBRIUM

INTRODUCTION

We have shown in Chapter 28 that if two particles of masses m and M and velocities $\mathbf{v}$ and $\mathbf{V}$ respectively are contained in the same unit volume, the probability that they will collide and end up with their velocities in $d\mathbf{v}'$ and $d\mathbf{V}'$ respectively is given by $W(\mathbf{v}, \mathbf{V}; \mathbf{v}', \mathbf{V}')d\mathbf{v}'d\mathbf{V}'$ where

$$W(\mathbf{v}, \mathbf{V}; \mathbf{v}', \mathbf{V}') = S(\mathbf{u}, \mathbf{u}')\delta(\mathbf{w}' - \mathbf{w}) \qquad (33.1)$$

$$S(\mathbf{u}, \mathbf{u}') = \sigma(u, \mathbf{u} \cdot \mathbf{u}')\delta(u' - u)/u \qquad (33.2)$$

where $\mathbf{u} = \mathbf{v} - \mathbf{V}$; $\mathbf{u}' = \mathbf{v}' - \mathbf{V}'$; $\mathbf{w} = (m\mathbf{v} + M\mathbf{V})/(m + M)$; $\mathbf{w}' = (m\mathbf{v}' + M\mathbf{V}')/(m + M)$; and $\sigma(u, \mathbf{u} \cdot \mathbf{u}') \equiv \sigma(u, \theta)$ is the differential scattering cross section in relative coordinates.

In the present chapter we will make use of this expression to derive some useful and informative expressions.

COLLISION RATES

Consider a unit volume containing molecules of mass m having a distribution function $f(\mathbf{v})$ and molecules of mass M having a distribution function $F(\mathbf{V})$. We assume the densities of both species to be constant and given by n and N respectively. We wish to find the number of collisions between the two types of molecules.

There are $f(\mathbf{v})d\mathbf{v}$ molecules of mass m with velocity in $d\mathbf{v}$ and $F(\mathbf{V})d\mathbf{V}$ molecules of mass M with velocity in $d\mathbf{V}$. The probability per unit time that a pair of these molecules will collide and end up with their velocities in $d\mathbf{v}'$ and $d\mathbf{V}'$ respectively is simply

$$[f(\mathbf{v})d\mathbf{v}]\,[F(\mathbf{V})d\mathbf{V}]\,[W(\mathbf{v},\mathbf{V};\mathbf{v}',\mathbf{V}')d\mathbf{v}'d\mathbf{V}'] \tag{33.3}$$

If we wish to find the total number of collisions, we simply integrate over the initial velocities $\mathbf{v}$ and $\mathbf{V}$, and over the final velocities $\mathbf{v}'$ and $\mathbf{V}'$. Thus if Z is the total number of collisions per second, we have

$$Z = \iiiint \!\! \int f(\mathbf{v})F(\mathbf{V})W(\mathbf{v},\mathbf{V};\mathbf{v}',\mathbf{V}')d\mathbf{v}d\mathbf{v}'d\mathbf{V}d\mathbf{V}' \tag{33.4}$$

Now let us assume that the distributions are Maxwellian, i.e.,

$$f(\mathbf{v}) = n(\lambda/\pi)^{3/2}\exp(-\lambda v^2) \tag{33.5}$$

$$F(\mathbf{V}) = N(\Lambda/\pi)^{3/2}\exp(-\Lambda V^2) \tag{33.6}$$

where
$$\lambda = m/2kT \tag{33.7}$$

$$\Lambda = M/2kT \tag{33.8}$$

Substituting (33.5) and (33.6) in (33.4) and switching to the coordinates $\mathbf{u}, \mathbf{u}', \mathbf{w}$, and $\mathbf{w}'$, i.e., relative coordinates and center of mass coordinates, we obtain

$$Z = nN(\lambda^*/\pi)^{3/2}(\Lambda^*/\pi)^{3/2}\iiiint\!\!\int \exp(-\lambda^* u^2 - \Lambda^* w^2)$$
$$S(\mathbf{u},\mathbf{u}')\delta(\mathbf{w}'-\mathbf{w})d\mathbf{u}d\mathbf{u}'d\mathbf{w}d\mathbf{w}' \tag{33.9}$$

$$\lambda^* = \lambda\Lambda/(\lambda+\Lambda) \tag{33.10}$$

$$\Lambda^* = \lambda+\Lambda \tag{33.11}$$

Integrating over $\mathbf{w}'$ and $\mathbf{w}$, and then $\mathbf{u}'$, making use of Eq. (52), Appendix 14, we have

$$Z = nN(\lambda^*/\pi)^{3/2}\int u\sigma(u)\exp(-\lambda^* u^2)d\mathbf{u} \tag{33.12}$$

where $\sigma(u) \equiv \int\!\int\sigma(u,\theta)\sin\theta d\theta d\phi \equiv 2\pi\int\sigma(u,\theta)\sin\theta d\theta$. Transforming from coordinates u_1, u_2, u_3 to u, θ, ϕ and integrating over all angles, we have

$$Z = 4\pi nN(\lambda^*/\pi)^{3/2}\int u^3\sigma(u)\exp(-\lambda^* u^2)du \tag{33.13}$$

Expression (33.13) gives us the number of collisions per unit time per unit volume for arbitrary cross section $\sigma(u)$.

If we have a single species of particles and wish to know the number of collisions per unit volume per unit time, we set $n = N$ and $m = M$ and divide by 2. We must divide by 2, otherwise, we are counting each collision twice.

REACTION RATES

According to the simplest form of the theory of reaction rates, two molecules will react chemically if and only if the kinetic energy of the relative motion in the direction of the line of centers exceeds a certain value ϵ_0, called the activation energy. Let us calculate the reaction rate R between two gases of densities n and N contained within the same unit volume.

Starting with expression (33.3), we have for the number of collisions per second in which the initial velocities are in $d\mathbf{v}$ and $d\mathbf{V}$ respectively and the final velocities in $d\mathbf{v}'$ and $d\mathbf{V}'$ respectively

$$f(\mathbf{v})F(\mathbf{V})W(\mathbf{v}, \mathbf{V}; \mathbf{v}', \mathbf{V}')d\mathbf{v}d\mathbf{v}'d\mathbf{V}d\mathbf{V}' \tag{33.14}$$

Assuming Maxwellian distributions and switching to the coordinates $\mathbf{u}$, $\mathbf{u}'$, $\mathbf{w}$ and $\mathbf{w}'$, we have for the number of collisions per second in which the initial relative velocity is in $d\mathbf{u}$ and the initial center of mass velocity in $d\mathbf{w}$ while the final relative and center of mass velocities are in $d\mathbf{u}'$ and $d\mathbf{w}'$ respectively,

$$nN(\lambda^*/\pi)^{3/2}(\Lambda^*/\pi)^{3/2}\exp(-\lambda^*u^2 - \Lambda^*w^2)$$
$$S(\mathbf{u}, \mathbf{u}')\delta(\mathbf{w}' - \mathbf{w})d\mathbf{u}d\mathbf{u}'d\mathbf{w}d\mathbf{w}' \tag{33.15}$$

Integrating over $\mathbf{w}'$ and $\mathbf{w}$, we obtain the number of collisions per second in which the initial relative velocity is in $d\mathbf{u}$ and the final relative velocity in $d\mathbf{u}'$

$$nN(\lambda^*/\pi)^{3/2}\exp(-\lambda^*u^2)S(\mathbf{u}, \mathbf{u}')d\mathbf{u}d\mathbf{u}' \tag{33.16}$$

Replacing u_1', u_2', and u_3' by u^*, θ and ϕ and integrating over u^* and ϕ where u^*, θ and ϕ are the spherical coordinates of $\mathbf{u}'$ with respect to a set of axes with polar axis along $\mathbf{u}$, we obtain

$$2\pi nN(\lambda^*/\pi)^{3/2}\exp(-\lambda^*u^2)\sigma(u, \theta)u\sin\theta du d\theta \tag{33.17}$$

Replacing $d\mathbf{u}$ by the corresponding element in spherical coordinates and integrating over all angles, we obtain

$$8\pi^2 nNu^3(\lambda^*/\pi)^{3/2}\exp(-\lambda^*u^2)\sigma(u, \theta)\sin\theta du d\theta \tag{33.18}$$

The expression (33.18) is the number of collisions per second in which the initial relative speed is in du and after collision the angle between $\mathbf{u}$ and $\mathbf{u}'$ is in $d\theta$.

The fraction of the collisions in which the initial relative speed is in du and after collision the angle between $\mathbf{u}$ and $\mathbf{u}'$ is in $d\theta$ can be obtained by dividing (33.18) by Eq. (33.13), in which case we obtain

$$\frac{u^3\exp(-\lambda^*u^2)\sigma(u, \theta)\sin\theta du d\theta}{\int_0^\pi\int_0^\infty u^3\exp(-\lambda^*u^2)\sigma(u, \theta)\sin\theta du d\theta} \tag{33.19}$$

In a collision, the molecule of mass m receives an impulse which changes its velocity. The impulse is equal to the change in momentum of the molecule and is given by $m\mathbf{v'} - m\mathbf{v}$. In terms of $\mathbf{u}$, $\mathbf{u'}$, $\mathbf{w}$, and $\mathbf{w'}$

$$m(\mathbf{v'} - \mathbf{v}) = m(\mathbf{w'} - \mathbf{w}) + m^*(\mathbf{u'} - \mathbf{u}) \qquad (33.20)$$

And since $\mathbf{w} = \mathbf{w'}$ in a collision

$$m(\mathbf{v'} - \mathbf{v}) = m^*(\mathbf{u'} - \mathbf{u}) \qquad (33.21)$$

Since the impulse is along the line of centers, the unit vector $(\mathbf{u} - \mathbf{u'})/|\mathbf{u} - \mathbf{u'}|$ is along the line of centers. Furthermore, its direction is such that in a head-on collision it is pointing in the same direction as $\mathbf{u}$. The angle between the relative velocity $\mathbf{u}$ and the line of centers is thus

$$\chi = \cos^{-1}\left[\frac{\mathbf{u} \cdot (\mathbf{u} - \mathbf{u'})}{|\mathbf{u}|\,|\mathbf{u} - \mathbf{u'}|}\right]$$

$$= \cos^{-1}\left[\frac{u^2 - uu'\cos\theta}{u(u^2 + u'^2 - 2uu'\cos\theta)^{1/2}}\right] \qquad (33.22)$$

But in an elastic collision $u = u'$, and so

$$\chi = \cos^{-1}\left(\frac{\sqrt{1 - \cos\theta}}{\sqrt{2}}\right) = \cos^{-1}\sin\frac{\theta}{2} = \frac{\pi - \theta}{2} \qquad (33.23)$$

We wish to restrict ourselves to collisions in which

$$u\cos\chi > u_0 \qquad (33.24)$$

where $\frac{1}{2}m^*u_0^2 \equiv \epsilon_0$ and $m^* \equiv mM/(m + M)$. Condition (33.24) is equivalent to the condition that

$$\sin\frac{\theta}{2} > \frac{u_0}{u} \qquad (33.25)$$

The fraction of the collisions in which the kinetic energy of relative motion along the line of centers exceeds ϵ_0, is thus

$$\frac{R}{Z} = \frac{\displaystyle\int_{u_0}^{\infty}\int_{2\sin^{-1}(u_0/u)}^{\pi} u^3 \exp(-\lambda^* u^2)\sigma(u, \theta)\sin\theta\, d\theta\, du}{\displaystyle\int_0^{\infty}\int_0^{\pi} u^3 \exp(-\lambda^* u^2)\sigma(u, \theta)\sin\theta\, d\theta\, du} \qquad (33.26)$$

or letting $x = \sin(\theta/2)$ and $y = \lambda^* u^2$ we have

$$\frac{R}{Z} = \frac{\displaystyle\int_{\epsilon_0/kT}^{\infty}\int_{(\epsilon_0/kTy)^{1/2}}^{1} xy\exp(-y)\sigma[(y/\lambda^*)^{1/2}, 2\sin^{-1}x]\,dx\,dy}{\displaystyle\int_0^{\infty}\int_0^{1} xy\exp(-y)\sigma[(y/\lambda^*)^{1/2}, 2\sin^{-1}x]\,dx\,dy} \qquad (33.27)$$

Equation (33.27) is the desired result. Suppose $\sigma(u, \theta)$ is a constant, as it would be in the case of hard spheres, then

$$\frac{R}{Z} = \frac{\int_{\epsilon_0/kT}^{\infty} \int_{(\epsilon_0/kTy)^{1/2}}^{1} xy \exp(-y)dxdy}{\int_0^{\infty} \int_0^1 xy \exp(-y)dxdy}$$

$$= \frac{\int_{\epsilon_0/kT}^{\infty} [y - (\epsilon_0/kT)] \exp(-y)dy}{\int_0^{\infty} y \exp(-y)dy} \tag{33.28}$$

Letting $y = z + (\epsilon_0/kT)$ and integrating, we obtain

$$\frac{R}{Z} = \exp(-\epsilon_0/kT) \tag{33.29}$$

The result (33.29) gives reasonable agreement for a number of simple reactions.

THE EXCHANGE OF ENERGY BETWEEN TWO GASES AT DIFFERENT TEMPERATURES

In an ionized gas we have a mixture of three or more different types of particles: electrons, ions, and neutral molecules. It is possible in a number of situations for the electrons to have a temperature higher than the temperature of the ions and neutral molecules. These hot electrons will lose energy to the ions and neutral molecules, and unless there is some mechanism maintaining the temperature difference, will cool off until they arrive at the same temperature as the ions and neutral molecules. It is often important to know the rate at which energy is passing from the electrons to the heavier particles. In the present section, we will derive an expression for the rate of exchange of energy between two gases at different temperatures.

Consider a mixture of two gases whose particle masses are m and M respectively, and whose distribution functions are $f(\mathbf{v})$ and $F(\mathbf{V})$ respectively. The number of collisions per second per unit volume between particles of mass m and particles of mass M in which the initial velocities are in $d\mathbf{v}$ and $d\mathbf{V}$ respectively and the final velocities are in $d\mathbf{v}'$ and $d\mathbf{V}'$ respectively is

$$f(\mathbf{v})F(\mathbf{V})W(\mathbf{v}, \mathbf{V}; \mathbf{v}', \mathbf{V}')d\mathbf{v}d\mathbf{v}'d\mathbf{V}d\mathbf{V}' \tag{33.30}$$

Let us let $q(\mathbf{v})$ be some arbitrary function of the velocity. The change in $q(\mathbf{v})$ in a collision is given by $q(\mathbf{v}') - q(\mathbf{v})$. The net rate of change of $q(\mathbf{v})$ per unit volume per unit time can be found by multiplying (33.30) by this change and integrating over all velocities, i.e.,

$$\Delta q = \iiiint [q(\mathbf{v}') - q(\mathbf{v})]f(\mathbf{v})F(\mathbf{V})W(\mathbf{v}, \mathbf{V}; \mathbf{v}', \mathbf{V}')d\mathbf{v}d\mathbf{v}'d\mathbf{V}d\mathbf{V}' \tag{33.31}$$

As pointed out in Chapter 14, this is exactly the same result which we obtain if we multiply the collision term in the Boltzmann transport equation by $q(\mathbf{v})$ and integrate over $\mathbf{v}$.

If we transform to the coordinates $\mathbf{u}$, $\mathbf{u}'$, $\mathbf{w}$, and $\mathbf{w}'$, and integrate over $\mathbf{w}'$, we obtain

$$\Delta q = \iiiint \left[q\left(\mathbf{w} + \frac{m^*}{m}\mathbf{u}'\right) - q\left(\mathbf{w} - \frac{m^*}{m}\mathbf{u}\right) \right]$$
$$f\left(\mathbf{w} + \frac{m^*}{m}\mathbf{u}\right) F\left(\mathbf{w} - \frac{m^*}{M}\mathbf{u}\right) S(\mathbf{u}, \mathbf{u}') d\mathbf{u} d\mathbf{w} d\mathbf{u}' \qquad (33.32)$$

Let us now assume that $q(\mathbf{v}) = mv^2/2$, that is, we are interested in the exchange of energy between the two gases, then

$$q[\mathbf{w} + (m^*/m)\mathbf{u}'] - q[\mathbf{w} - (m^*/m)\mathbf{u}]$$
$$= (m/2)[\mathbf{w} + (m^*/m)\mathbf{u}']^2 - (m/2)[\mathbf{w} + (m^*/m)\mathbf{u}]^2$$
$$= (m/2)[(2m^*/m)\mathbf{w} \cdot (\mathbf{u}' - \mathbf{u}) + (m^*/m)^2(u'^2 - u^2)] \qquad (33.33)$$

The second term in (33.33) will vanish in the integration since $S(\mathbf{u}, \mathbf{u}') = 0$ unless $u = u'$. We thus have

$$\Delta(\tfrac{1}{2}mv^2) = m^* \iiint [\mathbf{w} \cdot (\mathbf{u}' - \mathbf{u})]$$
$$f\left(\mathbf{w} + \frac{m^*}{m}\mathbf{u}\right) F\left(\mathbf{w} - \frac{m^*}{M}\mathbf{u}\right) S(\mathbf{u}, \mathbf{u}') d\mathbf{u} d\mathbf{u}' d\mathbf{w} \qquad (33.34)$$

Integrating over $\mathbf{u}'$, making use of the results of Appendix 14, we get

$$\Delta(\tfrac{1}{2}mv^2) = -m^* \iint u\mathbf{w} \cdot \mathbf{u}\sigma_m(u)$$
$$f\left(\mathbf{w} + \frac{m^*}{m}\mathbf{u}\right) F\left(\mathbf{w} - \frac{m^*}{M}\mathbf{u}\right) d\mathbf{u} d\mathbf{w} \qquad (33.35)$$

Let us now assume that $f(\mathbf{v})$ and $F(\mathbf{V})$ are Maxwellian at different temperatures, i.e.,

$$f(\mathbf{v}) = n(\lambda/\pi)^{3/2} \exp(-\lambda v^2) \qquad (33.36)$$

$$F(\mathbf{V}) = N(\Lambda/\pi)^{3/2} \exp(-\Lambda V^2) \qquad (33.37)$$

$$\lambda = m/2k\tau \qquad (33.38)$$

$$\Lambda = M/2kT \qquad (33.39)$$

then
$$f[\mathbf{w} + (m^*/m)\mathbf{u}]F[\mathbf{w} - (m^*/M)\mathbf{u}] = \psi(\mathbf{u})\Psi(\mathbf{w} - b\mathbf{u}) \qquad (33.40)$$

where
$$\psi(\mathbf{v}) = n(c/\pi)^{3/2} \exp(-cv^2) \qquad (33.41)$$

$$\Psi(\mathbf{v}) = N(a/\pi)^{3/2} \exp(-av^2) \qquad (33.42)$$

$$a = (\lambda + \Lambda) \qquad (33.43)$$

$$b = \frac{1}{M^*}\left[\frac{m\Lambda - M\lambda}{\lambda + \Lambda}\right] = \frac{m^*(\tau - T)}{mT + M\tau} \tag{33.44}$$

$$c = \frac{\lambda\Lambda}{\lambda + \Lambda} = \frac{mM}{2k(mT + M\tau)} \tag{33.45}$$

$$M^* = m + M \qquad m^* = mM/(m + M) \tag{33.46}$$

Substituting (33.40) in (33.35) we obtain

$$\Delta(\tfrac{1}{2}mv^2) = -m^*\iint u\,\mathbf{w}\cdot\mathbf{u}\,\sigma_m(u)\Psi(\mathbf{u})\Psi(\mathbf{w} - b\mathbf{u})d\mathbf{u}d\mathbf{w} \tag{33.47}$$

Letting $\mathbf{z} = \mathbf{w} - b\mathbf{u}$ we obtain

$$\Delta(\tfrac{1}{2}mv^2) = -m^*\iint u\,(\mathbf{z} + b\mathbf{u})\cdot\mathbf{u}\,\sigma_m(u)\psi(\mathbf{u})\Psi(\mathbf{z})d\mathbf{u}d\mathbf{z} \tag{33.48}$$

Integrating over $\mathbf{z}$, noting that terms odd in z_1, z_2, or z_3 vanish on integration, we obtain

$$\Delta(\tfrac{1}{2}mv^2) = -bNm^*\int u^3\sigma_m(u)\psi(\mathbf{u})d\mathbf{u} \tag{33.49}$$

Substituting (33.43) in (33.49) and gathering results, we have

$$\Delta(\tfrac{1}{2}mv^2) = -(m^*)^2N\left(\frac{\tau - T}{mT + M\tau}\right)\int u^3\sigma_m(u)\psi(\mathbf{u})d\mathbf{u} \tag{33.50}$$

where

$$\psi(\mathbf{u}) = n(c/\pi)^{3/2}\exp(-cu^2) \tag{33.51}$$

$$c = \frac{mM}{2k(mT + M\tau)} \tag{33.52}$$

$$m^* = mM/(m + M) \tag{33.53}$$

$$\sigma_m(u) = \iint(1 - \cos\theta)\sigma(u, \theta)\sin\theta d\theta d\phi \tag{33.54}$$

As one would expect, $\Delta(\tfrac{1}{2}mv^2)$ is positive if $\tau < T$ and negative if $\tau > T$. Thus the lower temperature gas always gains energy.

If the cross section $\sigma_m(u)$ is of the form

$$\sigma_m(u) = \alpha u^n \tag{33.55}$$

then (33.50) can easily be integrated. Noting that $\psi(\mathbf{u})$ is just a Maxwellian distribution with c instead of λ, we can make use of Eq. (4.27) in Chapter 4. We obtain

$$\Delta(\tfrac{1}{2}mv^2) = -(m^*)^2nN\left(\frac{\tau - T}{mT + M\tau}\right)\alpha\left[\Gamma\left(\frac{n + 3}{2}\right)\Big/c^{n/2}\Gamma\left(\frac{3}{2}\right)\right] \tag{33.56}$$

The energy gained by the gas of particles of mass M is the same as (33.50) with the sign reversed.

Chapter 34

EXPANSION OF
THE DISTRIBUTION
FUNCTION

INTRODUCTION

A collection of molecules contained in a rigid, impermeable, and well-insulated box moving with a constant velocity $\bar{\mathbf{v}}$ will quickly arrive at equilibrium, with the distribution given by the Maxwellian distribution

$$f = n(\lambda/\pi)^{3/2} \exp[-\lambda(\mathbf{v} - \bar{\mathbf{v}})^2]$$ (34.1)

where n, λ, and $\bar{\mathbf{v}}$ are constants.

If, however, the sides of the box are maintained at different temperatures, or its shape is changing, or some other set of nonequilibrium boundary conditions is established, then the distribution will no longer be Maxwellian.

If the disturbance on the boundaries is not too violent, then it is possible to divide the gas into elements whose dimensions are large compared to the mean free path, and yet small enough that the relative change in the macroscopic properties over the element are negligible. The distribution within these elements will be approximately Maxwellian. However, the values of n, λ and $\bar{\mathbf{v}}$ will differ from element to element. The distribution function for the gas is then given approximately by the local Maxwellian distribution

$$f \approx n(\mathbf{x}, t)\left[\frac{\lambda(\mathbf{x}, t)}{\pi}\right]^{3/2} \exp\{-\lambda(\mathbf{x}, t)[\mathbf{v} - \bar{\mathbf{v}}(\mathbf{x}, t)]^2\}$$ (34.2)

Although the actual distribution differs by only a small correction from the distribution function (34.2), this small difference is quite essential if we are interested in the transport properties of the gas. If, for example, we use Eq. (34.2) to calculate the heat flux vector and the pressure tensor, we find

$$q_i = (m/2)\int (v_i - \bar{v}_i)(\mathbf{v} - \bar{\mathbf{v}})^2 f d\mathbf{v} = 0 \qquad (34.3)$$

$$p_{ij} = m\int (v_i - \bar{v}_i)(v_j - \bar{v}_j) f d\mathbf{v} = nkT\delta_{ij} = p\delta_{ij} \qquad (34.4)$$

Under these conditions, all effects due to heat flow or the viscosity of the fluid vanish.

Although we cannot use the approximate distribution function (34.2) when the effects of the viscosity and heat flow are important, we can write the distribution function in the form

$$= n(\mathbf{x}, t)\left[\frac{\lambda(\mathbf{x}, t)}{\pi}\right]^{3/2} \exp\{-\lambda(\mathbf{x}, t)[\mathbf{v} - \bar{\mathbf{v}}(\mathbf{x}, t)]^2\}[1 + g(\mathbf{x}, \mathbf{v}, t)] \qquad (34.5)$$

where $g(\mathbf{x}, \mathbf{v}, t)$ is a small correction term such that $|g(\mathbf{x}, \mathbf{v}, t)| \ll 1$ for those values of $\mathbf{x}$, $\mathbf{v}$, and t for which the value of f is not negligible.

In the present chapter we will obtain a useful approximation to the correction term $g(\mathbf{x}, \mathbf{v}, t)$.

EXPANSION IN ORTHOGONAL FUNCTIONS

Let us suppose we can expand the function $(1 + g)$ in a series of the form

$$1 + g(\mathbf{x}, \mathbf{v}, t) = \sum_{i=0}^{\infty} g_i(\mathbf{v} - \bar{\mathbf{v}}, \mathbf{x}, t) \qquad (34.6)$$

where $g_0 = 1$ and the remaining g_i are at the moment undetermined. The distribution function as given by Eq. (34.5) can then be written

$$f = f_0(\mathbf{s})\sum_i g_i(\mathbf{s}) \qquad (34.7)$$

where

$$f_0(\mathbf{v}) = n(\lambda/\pi)^{3/2} \exp(-\lambda v^2) \qquad (34.8)$$

and

$$\mathbf{s} = \mathbf{v} - \bar{\mathbf{v}} \qquad (34.9)$$

and we have suppressed the dependence of g_i, n, and λ on $\mathbf{x}$ and t.

Now let us calculate the number of collisions per unit volume per unit time between a hypothetical gas whose distribution function is $f_0(\mathbf{s})g_j(\mathbf{s})$ and a second hypothetical gas whose distribution function is $f_0(\mathbf{s})g_k(\mathbf{s})$. We shall designate the number of collisions Z_{jk}. In terms of the scattering probability $W(\mathbf{v}, \mathbf{V}; \mathbf{v}', \mathbf{V}')$ we have

$$Z_{jk} = \iiiint f_0(\mathbf{s})g_j(\mathbf{s})f_0(\mathbf{S})g_k(\mathbf{S})W(\mathbf{v}, \mathbf{V}; \mathbf{v}', \mathbf{V}')d\mathbf{v}d\mathbf{V}d\mathbf{v}'d\mathbf{V}' \qquad (34.10)$$

where

$$\mathbf{S} = \mathbf{V} - \bar{\mathbf{v}} \qquad (34.11)$$

Transforming from the velocities $\mathbf{v}'$ and $\mathbf{V}'$ to the relative velocity $\mathbf{u}'$ and the center of mass velocity $\mathbf{w}'$ and integrating over $\mathbf{w}'$ and $\mathbf{u}'$, we obtain

$$Z_{jk} = \int\int f_0(\mathbf{s})g_j(\mathbf{s})f_0(\mathbf{S})g_k(\mathbf{S})u\sigma(u)d\mathbf{v}d\mathbf{V} \qquad (34.12)$$

If we transform the variable of integration from $\mathbf{v}$ and $\mathbf{V}$ to $\mathbf{s}$ and $\mathbf{S}$ and then for convenience simply relabel $\mathbf{s}$ and $\mathbf{S}$ using the symbols $\mathbf{v}$ and $\mathbf{V}$, we obtain

$$Z_{jk} = \int\int f_0(\mathbf{v})g_j(\mathbf{v})f_0(\mathbf{V})g_k(\mathbf{V})u\sigma(u)d\mathbf{v}d\mathbf{V} \qquad (34.13)$$

We cannot proceed any further in the evaluation of Z_{jk} unless we know the cross section $\sigma(u)$. There is one particular cross section which is especially simple, the cross section for which $u\sigma(u)$ is constant. A gas of particles having such a cross section is called a Maxwellian gas. Since $u\sigma(u)$ is the probability per unit time that two particles contained within the same unit volume will collide, a Maxwellian gas is a gas in which the number of collisions per second depends only on the density of the gas.

For a Maxwellian gas

$$Z_{jk} = u\sigma(u)\int\int f_0(\mathbf{v})g_j(\mathbf{v})f_0(\mathbf{V})g_k(\mathbf{V})d\mathbf{v}d\mathbf{V}$$

$$= u\sigma(u)\int g_0(\mathbf{v})g_j(\mathbf{v})f_0(\mathbf{v})d\mathbf{v}\int g_0(\mathbf{V})g_k(\mathbf{V})f_0(\mathbf{V})d\mathbf{V} \qquad (34.14)$$

If the functions $g_i(\mathbf{v})$ were orthogonal functions with respect to the weight factor $f_0(\mathbf{v})$, i.e.,

$$\int g_j(\mathbf{v})g_k(\mathbf{v})f_0(\mathbf{v})d\mathbf{v} = 0 \qquad j \neq k \qquad (34.15)$$

then for a Maxwellian gas all of the Z_{jk} would vanish except Z_{00}.

The above results suggest that if we expand the function $(1 + g)$ in Eq. (34.6) in a series of functions which are orthogonal in velocity space with respect to the weight factor $f_0(\mathbf{v})$ and the gas is not extremely different from a Maxwellian gas, then we might expect the coupling or interaction between the correction terms to be weak.

There are a number of possible choices which can be made for the set of orthogonal functions. We shall use Hermite polynomials. The Hermite polynomial $H_n(x)$ is defined by the relation

$$H_n(x) = e^{x^2}\frac{d^n}{dx^n}(e^{-x^2}) \qquad (34.16)$$

The first few polynomials are given by $H_0 = 1$; $H_1 = -2x$; $H_2 = 4x^2 - 2$; $H_3 = -8x^3 + 12x$. The Hermite polynomials satisfy the following orthogonality conditions

$$\int_{-\infty}^{\infty} e^{-x^2}H_n(x)H_m(x)dx = 2^n n!\pi^{1/2}\delta_{mn} \qquad (34.17)$$

We will be expanding three-dimensional functions in Hermite polynomials. We therefore define

$$H_{lmn}(\mathbf{x}) = H_l(x_1)H_m(x_2)H_n(x_3) \tag{34.18}$$

In terms of the three-dimensional Hermite polynomial and the distribution function $f_0(\mathbf{s})$, the orthogonality conditions are

$$\int f_0(\mathbf{v})H_{ijk}(\lambda^{1/2}\mathbf{v})H_{lmp}(\lambda^{1/2}\mathbf{v})d\mathbf{v} = \int f_0(\mathbf{s})H_{ijk}(\lambda^{1/2}\mathbf{s})H_{lmp}(\lambda^{1/2}\mathbf{s})d\mathbf{v}$$

$$= n(2)^{l+m+p}l!m!p!\delta_{li}\delta_{mj}\delta_{pk} \tag{34.19}$$

Using Hermite polynomials, we can write the distribution function

$$f = f_0(\mathbf{s}) \sum_{ijk} a_{ijk}(\mathbf{x}, t)H_{ijk}(\lambda^{1/2}\mathbf{s}) \tag{34.20}$$

The function $f_0(\mathbf{s})$ contains five arbitrary parameters n, T, and $\bar{v}_i$. Although our choice of letters for these parameters, and our previous discussion seems to imply that these are the local density, temperature, and drift velocity respectively, this need not necessarily be the case. These parameters simply determine the exact nature of the weight factor $f_0(\mathbf{s})$. If, however, we wish the actual distribution to be approximated by a few terms in the series, we should of course choose n, T, and v_i in such a way that $f_0(\mathbf{s})$ comes as close as is conveniently possible to the actual distribution. We will therefore let

$$n = \int fd\mathbf{v} \tag{34.21}$$

$$3kT/2 = (1/n)\int (ms^2/2)fd\mathbf{v} \equiv E \tag{34.22}$$

$$\bar{v}_i = (1/n)\int v_i fd\mathbf{v} \tag{34.23}$$

If we substitute the distribution function (34.20) into (34.21), (34.22) and (34.23) and make use of the orthogonality conditions we find

$$n = na_{000} \tag{34.24}$$

$$3kT/2 = (3kT/2)[a_{000} + (4/3)(a_{200} + a_{020} + a_{002})] \tag{34.25}$$

$$\bar{v}_1 = -(a_{100}/\lambda^{1/2}) + a_{000}\bar{v}_1 \tag{34.26}$$

$$\bar{v}_2 = -(a_{010}/\lambda^{1/2}) + a_{000}\bar{v}_2 \tag{34.27}$$

$$\bar{v}_3 = -(a_{001}/\lambda^{1/2}) + a_{000}\bar{v}_3 \tag{34.28}$$

Solving these equations, we have

$$a_{000} = 1 \tag{34.29}$$

$$a_{200} + a_{020} + a_{002} = 0 \tag{34.30}$$

$$a_{100} = a_{010} = a_{001} = 0 \tag{34.31}$$

In a similar fashion we can obtain relationships between the macroscopic parameters p_{ij} and q_i and the expansion coefficients a_{ijk}. Thus

$$p_{11} = m \int s_1^2 f d\mathbf{v} = (mn/2\lambda)(1 + 4a_{200}) \qquad (34.32)$$

$$p_{12} = m \int s_1 s_2 f d\mathbf{v} = (mn/\lambda)a_{110} \qquad (34.33)$$

$$q_1 = (m/2) \int s_1 s^2 f d\mathbf{v} = -(mn/\lambda^{3/2})(3a_{300} + a_{120} + a_{102}) \qquad (34.34)$$

The remaining values of p_{ij} and q_i can be easily written down from symmetry.

Recalling that $p = (1/3)\Sigma p_{ii} = nkT = mn/2\lambda$, and rearranging the above results we have

$$a_{200} = (\lambda/2mn)(p_{11} - p) \qquad (34.35)$$

$$a_{110} = (\lambda/mn)p_{12} \qquad (34.36)$$

$$(1/5)(3a_{300} + a_{120} + a_{102}) = -(\lambda^{3/2}/5mn)q_1 \qquad (34.37)$$

THE THIRTEEN-MOMENT APPROXIMATION

So far we have made no approximations. By proper choice of the parameters n, $\bar{v}_i$, T, and a_{ijk}, the function $f_0(s) \sum_{ijk} a_{ijk}H_{ijk}$ can be made equal to any arbitrary distribution function $f(\mathbf{v})$.

As a first approximation we shall assume that all the coefficients a_{ijk} are zero except those required to specify n, T, $\bar{v}_i$, p_{ij}, and q_i. This assumption, together with the conditions (34.31) leaves us with only sixteen nonvanishing coefficients: a_{000}, a_{110}, a_{101}, a_{011}, a_{200}, a_{020}, a_{002}, a_{300}, a_{120}, a_{102}, a_{210}, a_{030}, a_{012}, a_{201}, a_{021}, a_{003}. Since we have two restrictions (34.29) and (34.30), on these coefficients, only fourteen are independent.

With each component q_i there are associated three arbitrary coefficients. We can therefore introduce a number of additional conditions and still leave q_i arbitrary. We therefore assume

$$a_{300} = a_{120} = a_{102} \qquad (34.38)$$

$$a_{210} = a_{030} = a_{012} \qquad (34.39)$$

$$a_{201} = a_{021} = a_{003} \qquad (34.40)$$

We now have eight independent coefficients a_{ijk} and five independent parameters n, T, $\bar{v}_i$, which allow the thirteen parameters n, T, $\bar{v}_i$, p_{ij} and q_i to take on arbitrary values.

With the above assumption the distribution function becomes

$$f(\mathbf{v}) \approx f_0(\mathbf{s})\{1 + a_{110}H_{110}(\lambda^{1/2}\mathbf{s}) + a_{101}H_{101}(\lambda^{1/2}\mathbf{s})$$
$$+ a_{011}H_{011}(\lambda^{1/2}\mathbf{s}) + a_{200}H_{200}(\lambda^{1/2}\mathbf{s}) + a_{020}H_{020}(\lambda^{1/2}\mathbf{s})$$

$$+ a_{002}H_{002}(\lambda^{1/2}s) + a_{300}[H_{300}(\lambda^{1/2}s) + H_{120}(\lambda^{1/2}s) + H_{102}(\lambda^{1/2}s)]$$
$$+ a_{030}[H_{210}(\lambda^{1/2}s) + H_{030}(\lambda^{1/2}s) + H_{012}(\lambda^{1/2}s)]$$
$$+ a_{003}[H_{201}(\lambda^{1/2}s) + H_{021}(\lambda^{1/2}s) + H_{003}(\lambda^{1/2}s)]\} \tag{34.41}$$
$$= f_0(\mathbf{s})\left\{1 + \sum_i \sum_j \left(\frac{2\lambda^2}{mn}\right)(p_{ij} - p\delta_{ij})s_i s_j + \sum_j \left(\frac{8\lambda^3}{5mn}\right)q_i\left[s_i\left(s^2 - \frac{5}{2\lambda}\right)\right]\right\}$$

It should be noted that since $p_{ij} = p_{ji}$ the summation $\sum_i \sum_j p_{ij}s_i s_j$ contains two equal terms in $s_1 s_2$, $s_1 s_3$, and $s_2 s_3$.

The approximate distribution function (34.41) is known as the thirteen-moment approximation. By considering more coefficients we can get a better approximation. However, for our purposes the thirteen-moment approximation will suffice.

THE LINEAR APPROXIMATION

In the chapters which follow we shall restrict ourselves to distributions in which the departure from equilibrium is small. We then expect the drift velocity to be small compared to the thermal velocity,

$$|\bar{v}_i| \ll (\overline{v_i^2})^{1/2} \tag{34.42}$$

If (34.42) is true then we can approximate $\mathbf{s}$ in the correction term by

$$\mathbf{s} \equiv \mathbf{v} - \bar{\mathbf{v}} \approx \mathbf{v} \tag{34.43}$$

and the weighting factor $f_0(\mathbf{v} - \bar{\mathbf{v}})$ can be approximated by the first few terms in a Taylor expansion,

$$f_0(\mathbf{v} - \bar{\mathbf{v}}) \approx f_0(\mathbf{v}) - \sum_i \bar{v}_i \frac{\partial f_0(\mathbf{v})}{\partial v_i} = f_0(\mathbf{v})\left(1 + \sum_i 2\lambda\bar{v}_i v_i\right) \tag{34.44}$$

Making these approximations in the distribution (34.41) and dropping the product of the small correction terms, we obtain

$$f = f_0(\mathbf{x}, \mathbf{v}, t)[1 + h(\mathbf{x}, \mathbf{v}, t)] \tag{34.45}$$

where h is a small correction term given by

$$h = \sum_i a_i v_i + \sum_i \sum_j b_{ij}v_i v_j + \sum_i c_i v_i[v^2 - (5/2\lambda)] \tag{34.46}$$

with

$$a_i = 2\lambda\bar{v}_i \tag{34.47}$$

$$b_{ij} = (2\lambda^2/mn)(p_{ij} - p\delta_{ij}) \tag{34.48}$$

$$c_i = (8\lambda^3/5mn)q_i \tag{34.49}$$

This is the distribution function we shall use in the following chapters. It contains thirteen independent parameters: n, T, the three components $\bar{v}_i$, the three components q_i, and the five independent components p_{ij}.

When the departure from equilibrium is small, as we have been assuming in this section, then the correction term $h(\mathbf{x}, \mathbf{v}, t)$ will be small compared to one for those values of $\mathbf{x}$, $\mathbf{v}$ and t for which $f_0(\mathbf{x}, \mathbf{v}, t)$ is insignificant. It follows that if we have a product involving two distributions functions f and F which depart only slightly from equilibrium, then

$$fF \equiv f_0(1 + h)F_0(1 + H) = f_0F_0(1 + h + H + hH) \approx f_0F_0(1 + h + H)$$
(34.50)

i.e., we can neglect terms which are quadratic in the correction terms.

The approximations we have been making in this section constitute what is called the linear approximation. In the succeeding chapters we shall assume the linear approximation to be valid.

It should be noted that the essential difference between the approximation (34.41) and the approximation (34.45) consists in the fact that the parameters T, q_i, and p_{ij} in (34.41) are correctly interpreted as the temperature, heat flux vector, and pressure tensor, whereas in (34.45) the parameters T, q_i, and p_{ij} are only approximately equal to the temperature, heat flux vector, and pressure tensor, as can readily be seen by substituting (34.45) into equations (32.51), (32.52), and (32.53). The parameters n and $\bar{v}_i$ retain the same interpretation in either approximation. It follows that as long as we simply treat T, q_i, and p_{ij} in (34.45) as parameters whose values are to be determined from the equation of change, then it has roughly the same a priori validity as (34.41).

Chapter 35

THE TRANSPORT PROPERTIES OF A SIMPLE GAS

INTRODUCTION

In the present chapter we wish to investigate the transport properties of a one-component gas under conditions in which the departure from equilibrium is not too extreme. We will make use of Maxwell's equation of change and the approximate distribution function derived in Chapter 34. We will not discuss the problem of self-diffusion since this is most easily handled as a limiting case of mutual diffusion which will be considered in the following chapter. We will furthermore assume that there are no external forces present.

The equation of change for a one-component gas in the absence of any external fields is given by

$$\frac{\partial}{\partial t}(n\bar{q}) + \sum_i \frac{\partial}{\partial x_i}(n\overline{v_i q}) = \Delta q \tag{35.1}$$

where q is a function of velocity, and where

$$\Delta q = \frac{1}{4} \iiiint [q(\mathbf{v}') + q(\mathbf{V}') - q(\mathbf{v}) - q(\mathbf{V})]$$
$$[f(\mathbf{v})f(\mathbf{V}) - f(\mathbf{v}')f(\mathbf{V}')]W(\mathbf{v}, \mathbf{V}; \mathbf{v}', \mathbf{V}')d\mathbf{v}d\mathbf{v}'d\mathbf{V}d\mathbf{V}' \tag{35.2}$$

THE COLLISION INTEGRAL

If we make the thirteen-moment and linear approximations, then we can write the distribution function

$$f = f_0(1 + h) \tag{35.3}$$

where

$$h \approx \sum_i a_i v_i + \sum_i \sum_j b_{ij} v_i v_j + \sum_i c_i v_i [v^2 - (5/2\lambda)] \tag{35.4}$$

and

$$a_i = 2\lambda \bar{v}_i \tag{35.5}$$

$$b_{ij} = (2\lambda^2/mn)(p_{ij} - p\delta_{ij}) \tag{35.6}$$

$$c_i = (8\lambda^3/5mn)q_i \tag{35.7}$$

If we substitute (35.3) into (35.2) and note that

$$
\begin{aligned}
f(\mathbf{v})f(\mathbf{V}) &\approx f_0(\mathbf{v})f_0(\mathbf{V})[1 + h(\mathbf{v}) + h(\mathbf{V})]\\
f(\mathbf{v}')f(\mathbf{V}') &\approx f_0(\mathbf{v}')f_0(\mathbf{V}')[1 + h(\mathbf{v}') + h(\mathbf{V}')]\\
f_0(\mathbf{v})f_0(\mathbf{V})W &= n^2(\lambda/\pi)^3 \exp[-(\lambda u^2/2) - (2\lambda w^2)]W\\
&= n^2(\lambda/\pi)^3 \exp[-(\lambda u'^2/2) - (2\lambda w'^2)]W\\
&= f_0(\mathbf{v}')f_0(\mathbf{V}')W
\end{aligned}
\tag{35.8}
$$

where $\mathbf{u}$, $\mathbf{u}'$, $\mathbf{w}$, and $\mathbf{w}'$ are the relative and center of mass velocities before and after the collision, then

$$
\begin{aligned}
\Delta q \approx &- (1/4) \iiiint [q(\mathbf{v}') + q(\mathbf{V}') - q(\mathbf{v}) - q(\mathbf{V})]\\
&[h(\mathbf{v}') + h(\mathbf{V}') - h(\mathbf{v}) - h(\mathbf{V})]\\
&\qquad W(\mathbf{v}, \mathbf{V}; \mathbf{v}', \mathbf{V}')f_0(\mathbf{v})f_0(\mathbf{V})d\mathbf{v}d\mathbf{V}d\mathbf{v}'d\mathbf{V}'
\end{aligned}
\tag{35.9}
$$

Finally, if we switch from the coordinates $\mathbf{v}$, $\mathbf{v}'$, $\mathbf{V}$, $\mathbf{V}'$ to the center of mass coordinates $\mathbf{w}$ and $\mathbf{w}'$ and the relative coordinates $\mathbf{u}$ and $\mathbf{u}'$, and then integrate over $\mathbf{w}'$ we obtain

$$\Delta q = -(1/4) \iiint q^* h^* S(\mathbf{u}, \mathbf{u}')\psi'(\mathbf{u})\psi''(\mathbf{w})d\mathbf{u}d\mathbf{u}'d\mathbf{w} \tag{35.10}$$

where

$$q^* \equiv q(\mathbf{w} + \tfrac{1}{2}\mathbf{u}') + q(\mathbf{w} - \tfrac{1}{2}\mathbf{u}') - q(\mathbf{w} + \tfrac{1}{2}\mathbf{u}) - q(\mathbf{w} - \tfrac{1}{2}\mathbf{u}) \tag{35.11}$$

$$h^* \equiv h(\mathbf{w} + \tfrac{1}{2}\mathbf{u}') + h(\mathbf{w} - \tfrac{1}{2}\mathbf{u}') - h(\mathbf{w} + \tfrac{1}{2}\mathbf{u}) - h(\mathbf{w} - \tfrac{1}{2}\mathbf{u}) \tag{35.12}$$

$$\psi'(\mathbf{u}) = n(\lambda/2\pi)^{3/2} \exp(-\lambda u^2/2) \tag{35.13}$$

$$\psi''(\mathbf{w}) = n(2\lambda/\pi)^{3/2} \exp(-2\lambda w^2) \tag{35.14}$$

For convenience we will list the values of q^* which we will encounter:

$$(\text{const})^* = 0 \tag{35.15}$$

$$(\mathbf{v})^* = 0 \tag{35.16}$$

$$(v^2)^* = 0 \tag{35.17}$$

$$(v_i v_j)^* = \tfrac{1}{2}(u_i' u_j' - u_i u_j) \tag{35.18}$$

$$(v_i v^2)^* = \sum_j w_j(u_i' u_j' - u_i u_j) \tag{35.19}$$

STOKES' HYPOTHESIS

Let us assume that we have a gas which is contained between two parallel plates which are perpendicular to the 1 axis and are moving at constant but different speeds in the 2 direction. Let us furthermore assume that there is no flow of heat and the gas is in a steady state. Under these conditions, Maxwell's equation of change becomes

$$\frac{\partial}{\partial x_1}\int v_1 q f d\mathbf{v} = \Delta q \tag{35.20}$$

Since
$$\bar{v}_1 = \bar{v}_3 = q_1 = q_2 = q_3 = 0 \tag{35.21}$$

the distribution function can be written

$$f = f_0(\mathbf{v})\left(1 + a_2 v_2 + \sum_i \sum_j b_{ij} v_i v_j\right) \tag{35.22}$$

If we substitute (35.22) in (35.20) and let $q(\mathbf{v}) = v_1 v_2$ we obtain

$$\frac{\partial}{\partial x_1}\left(a_2 \int v_1^2 v_2^2 f_0 d\mathbf{v}\right) = \Delta v_1 v_2 \tag{35.23}$$

Evaluating the integral on the left-hand side of (35.23) and setting $a_2 = 2\lambda v_2$ we obtain

$$\frac{\partial}{\partial x_1}\left(\frac{n\bar{v}_2}{2\lambda}\right) = \Delta v_1 v_2 \tag{35.24}$$

If we substitute (35.22) in (35.20) and let $q(\mathbf{v}) = v_1$ we obtain

$$\frac{\partial}{\partial x_1}\left\{\int\left[v_1^2 + \sum_i b_{ii} v_1^2 v_i^2\right]f_0 d\mathbf{v}\right\} = \Delta v_1 \tag{35.25}$$

The second term in the integrand is small compared to the first and therefore

$$\frac{\partial}{\partial x_1}\left(\int v_1^2 f_0 d\mathbf{v}\right) \approx \Delta v_1 \tag{35.26}$$

Evaluating the integral and noting that $\Delta v_1 = 0$, we obtain

$$\frac{\partial}{\partial x_1}\left(\frac{n}{2\lambda}\right) \approx 0 \tag{35.27}$$

Making use of (35.27) in (35.24) we obtain

$$\left(\frac{n}{2\lambda}\right)\frac{\partial \bar{v}_2}{\partial x_1} = \Delta(v_1 v_2) \tag{35.28}$$

From the preceding section

$$\Delta(v_1 v_2) = -(1/4)\iiint (v_1 v_2)^*\left(a_2 v_2 + \underset{i\ j}{\Sigma\Sigma} b_{ij} v_i v_j\right)^*$$
$$S(\mathbf{u}, \mathbf{u}')\psi'(\mathbf{u})\psi''(\mathbf{w})d\mathbf{u}d\mathbf{u}'d\mathbf{w}$$

$$= -(1/4)\iiint [\tfrac{1}{2}(u_1'u_2' - u_1 u_2)]\left[\tfrac{1}{2}\underset{i\ j}{\Sigma\Sigma} b_{ij}(u_i'u_j' - u_i u_j)\right]$$
$$S(\mathbf{u}, \mathbf{u}')\psi'(\mathbf{u})\psi''(\mathbf{w})d\mathbf{u}d\mathbf{u}'d\mathbf{w} \qquad (35.29)$$

Integrating over $\mathbf{w}$, noting that $\int\psi''(\mathbf{w})d\mathbf{w} = n$, we obtain

$$\Delta(v_1 v_2) = -(n/16)\underset{i\ j}{\Sigma\Sigma} b_{ij}\iint (u_1'u_2' - u_1 u_2)(u_i'u_j' - u_i u_j)$$
$$S(\mathbf{u}, \mathbf{u}')\psi'(\mathbf{u})d\mathbf{u}d\mathbf{u}' \qquad (35.30)$$

Making use of the results of Appendix 14 and Appendix 15, we get

$$\Delta(v_1 v_2) = -(n/16)\underset{i\ j}{\Sigma\Sigma} b_{ij}\int u_1 u_2 u[3u_i u_j - u^2\delta_{ij}]\sigma_\mu(u)\psi'(\mathbf{u})d\mathbf{u}$$

$$= -(3n/8)b_{12}\int u_1^2 u_2^2 u\sigma_\mu(u)\psi'(\mathbf{u})d\mathbf{u} \qquad (35.31)$$

where

$$\sigma_\mu(u) = \iint \sigma(u, \theta)[1 - \cos^2\theta]\sin\theta d\theta d\phi \qquad (35.32)$$

Substituting the value of b_{12} from Eq. (35.6) and making use of Appendix 16 we obtain

$$\Delta(v_1 v_2) = -(\lambda^2/20m)p_{12}\int u^5\sigma_\mu(u)\psi'(\mathbf{u})d\mathbf{u} \qquad (35.33)$$

Let us now define

$$S_\mu = \frac{3\int u^5\sigma_\mu(u)\psi'(\mathbf{u})d\mathbf{u}}{2\int u^5\psi'(\mathbf{u})d\mathbf{u}} \qquad (35.34)$$

Then

$$\int u^5\sigma_\mu(u)\psi'(\mathbf{u})d\mathbf{u} = [64n/\lambda^{5/2}(2\pi)^{1/2}]S_\mu \qquad (35.35)$$

For hard-sphere collisions $(3\sigma_\mu/2) = \pi d^2$ where d is the diameter of a sphere, and in this case $S_\mu = \pi d^2$. Substituting (35.35) into (35.33) we obtain

$$\Delta(v_1 v_2) = -[16n/5m(2\pi\lambda)^{1/2}]p_{12}S_\mu \qquad (35.36)$$

If we substitute (35.36) into (35.28) we find

$$p_{12} = \frac{-5(m\pi kT)^{1/2}}{16S_\mu}\left(\frac{\partial\bar{v}_2}{\partial x_1}\right) \qquad (35.37)$$

If we compare this result with the macroscopic result which gives

$$p_{12} = -\mu\left(\frac{\partial \bar{v}_2}{\partial x_1}\right) \qquad (35.38)$$

where μ, the coefficient of viscosity, is an experimental constant, we see that we have justified the form of Eq. (35.38) from a molecular viewpoint and also obtained an expression for the coefficient of viscosity, namely,

$$\mu = 5(m\pi kT)^{1/2}/16S_\mu \qquad (35.39)$$

If we know the cross section $\sigma(u, \theta)$ then we can calculate μ.

THE COEFFICIENT OF THERMAL CONDUCTIVITY

Let us assume that we have a gas which is contained between two parallel plates which are perpendicular to the 1 axis and are maintained at constant but different temperatures. In the steady state, Maxwell's equation of change for these boundary conditions assumes the form

$$\frac{\partial}{\partial x_1}\left[\int v_1 q(\mathbf{v}) f d\mathbf{v}\right] = \Delta q \qquad (35.40)$$

In steady state

$$\bar{v}_1 = \bar{v}_2 = \bar{v}_3 = p_{13} = p_{23} = p_{12} = q_2 = q_3 = 0 \qquad (35.41)$$

and the distribution function can be written

$$f = f_0(\mathbf{v})\left\{1 + \sum_i b_{ii}v_i{}^2 + c_1 v_1[v^2 - (5/2\lambda)]\right\} \qquad (35.42)$$

Substituting (35.42) in (35.41) and letting $q(\mathbf{v}) = v_1 v^2$ we obtain

$$\frac{\partial}{\partial x_1}\left[\int v_1{}^2 v^2 (1 + \sum_i b_{ii}v_i{}^2) f_0 d\mathbf{v}\right] = \Delta(v_1 v^2) \qquad (35.43)$$

Neglecting $\sum_i b_{ii}v_i{}^2$ compared to 1 we obtain

$$\frac{\partial}{\partial x_1}\left[\int v_1{}^2 v^2 f_0 d\mathbf{v}\right] = \frac{\partial}{\partial x_1}\left[\frac{5n}{4\lambda^2}\right] \approx \Delta(v_1 v^2) \qquad (35.44)$$

Letting $q(\mathbf{v}) = v_1$ in (35.40) we obtain

$$\frac{\partial}{\partial x_1}\left[\int v_1{}^2\left(1 + \sum_i b_{ii}v_i{}^2\right)\right] f_0 d\mathbf{v} = 0 \qquad (35.45)$$

Neglecting $\sum_i b_{ii}v_i{}^2$ compared to 1 we obtain

$$\frac{\partial}{\partial x_1}\left(\frac{n}{2\lambda}\right) \approx 0 \qquad (35.46)$$

Making use of (35.46) in (35.44) we obtain

$$\frac{5n}{4\lambda}\frac{\partial}{\partial x_1}\left(\frac{1}{\lambda}\right) \approx \Delta(v_1 v^2) \tag{35.47}$$

or

$$\left(\frac{5n}{4\lambda^2 T}\right)\left(\frac{\partial T}{\partial x_1}\right) \approx \Delta(v_1 v^2) \tag{35.48}$$

From our earlier results

$$\Delta(v_1 v^2) = -(1/4)\iiint (v_1 v^2)^* \left(\sum_i b_{ii}v_i^2 + c_1 v_1 [v^2 - (5/2\lambda)]\right)^*$$

$$S(\mathbf{u},\mathbf{u}')\psi'(\mathbf{u})\psi''(\mathbf{w})d\mathbf{u}d\mathbf{u}'d\mathbf{w}$$

$$= -(1/4)\iiint \left[\sum_j w_j(u_1' u_j' - u_1 u_j)\right]$$

$$\left[\tfrac{1}{2}\sum_i b_{ii}(u_i'^2 - u_i^2) + c_1\sum_k w_k(u_1' u_k' - u_1 u_k)\right]$$

$$S(\mathbf{u},\,\mathbf{u}')\psi'(\mathbf{u})\psi''(\mathbf{w})d\mathbf{u}d\mathbf{u}'d\mathbf{w} \tag{35.49}$$

Terms odd in w_1, w_2, or w_3 will vanish on integration and we are left with

$$\Delta(v_1 v^2) = -(c_1/4)\sum_j \iiint w_j^2(u_1' u_j' - u_1 u_j)^2 S(\mathbf{u},\,\mathbf{u}')\psi'(\mathbf{u})\psi''(\mathbf{w})d\mathbf{u}d\mathbf{u}'d\mathbf{w} \tag{35.50}$$

Carrying out the integration over $\mathbf{w}$, noting that

$$\int w_j^2 \psi''(\mathbf{w})d\mathbf{w} = (1/3)\int w^2 \psi''(\mathbf{w})d\mathbf{w} = \left(\frac{1}{3}\right)\frac{\Gamma(5/2)}{(2\lambda)\Gamma(3/2)} = \frac{n}{4\lambda} \tag{35.51}$$

we obtain

$$\Delta(v_1 v^2) = -(nc_1/16\lambda)\sum_j \iint (u_1' u_j' - u_1 u_j)^2 S(\mathbf{u},\,\mathbf{u}')\psi'(\mathbf{u})d\mathbf{u}d\mathbf{u}' \tag{35.52}$$

Making use of the results of Appendices 14 and 15, we obtain

$$\Delta(v_1 v^2) = -(nc_1/16\lambda)\sum_j \int u_1 u_j u[3u_1 u_j - u^2\delta_{ij}]\sigma_\mu(u)\psi'(\mathbf{u})d\mathbf{u}$$

$$= (nc_1/16\lambda)\left\{\int u_1^2 u^3 \sigma_\mu(u)\psi'(\mathbf{u})d\mathbf{u} - 3\sum_j \int u_1^2 u_j^2 u\sigma_\mu(u)\psi'(\mathbf{u})d\mathbf{u}\right\} \tag{35.53}$$

Making use of the results of Appendix 16 we obtain

$$\Delta(v_1 v^2) = -(nc_1/24\lambda)\int u^5 \psi'(\mathbf{u})\sigma_\mu(u)du$$

$$= -[64n/15m(2\pi\lambda)^{1/2}]q_1 S_\mu \tag{35.54}$$

Substituting (35.54) in (35.48) we obtain

$$q_1 = -\left(\frac{75(\pi T)^{1/2}k^{3/2}}{64m^{1/2}S_\mu}\right)\left(\frac{\partial T}{\partial x_1}\right) \tag{35.55}$$

If we compare this result with the macroscopic result which gives

$$q_1 = -\kappa(\partial T/\partial x_1) \tag{35.56}$$

where κ, the coefficient of thermal conductivity, is an experimental constant, we see that we have justified the form of (35.56) from a molecular viewpoint and also obtained an expression for the coefficient of thermal conductivity, namely,

$$\kappa = 75(\pi T)^{1/2}k^{3/2}/64m^{1/2}S_\mu \tag{35.57}$$

SUMMARY

We have for the coefficients of viscosity and thermal conductivity of a one-component gas

$$\mu = 5(m\pi kT)^{1/2}/16S_\mu \tag{35.58}$$

$$\kappa = 75(\pi T)^{1/2}k^{3/2}/64m^{1/2}S_\mu \tag{35.59}$$

where

$$S_\mu = \frac{3\int u^7 \exp(-\lambda u^2/2)\sigma_\mu(u)du}{2\int u^7 \exp(-\lambda u^2/2)du} \tag{35.60}$$

$$\sigma_\mu(u) = \iint (1 - \cos^2\theta)\sigma(u, \theta)\sin\theta d\theta d\phi \tag{35.61}$$

For the case of hard spheres of diameter d, $S_\mu = \pi d^2$ and

$$\mu = 5(m\pi kT)^{1/2}/16\pi d^2 \tag{35.62}$$

$$\kappa = 75(\pi T)^{1/2}k^{3/2}/64m^{1/2}\pi d^2 \tag{35.62}$$

These results are larger than the mean free path results by factors of 1.47 and 3.69 respectively. If one goes to a higher approximation, the theoretical value of the coefficient of viscosity is further increased by a factor of 1.016 and the coefficient of thermal conductivity by a factor of 1.025.

The application of (35.58) and (35.59) is not restricted to a hard-sphere cross section, but can be used for any cross section. For a comparison of these results with experiment, the reader is referred to the discussion in Chapter 7.

Chapter 36

THE TRANSPORT
PROPERTIES
OF A GAS MIXTURE

In the present chapter we wish to investigate the transport properties of a two-component gas. For simplicity we will restrict ourselves to situations in which the transport is occurring in the x_1 direction only. We shall not discuss the problem of viscosity. We will consider primarily the problem of diffusion, and we shall see that diffusion can be produced not only by a density gradient but also by a temperature gradient, and therefore we cannot exclude situations in which the temperature is not constant.

MAXWELL'S EQUATION OF CHANGE

For a one-component gas in a steady state, in the absence of external forces, with boundary conditions which are functions of x_1 only, we obtain for the equation of change

$$\frac{\partial}{\partial x_1}\left[\int v_1 q f d\mathbf{v}\right] = \Delta q \qquad (36.1)$$

For a two-component gas under similar conditions, we have one equation for each species.

$$\frac{\partial}{\partial x_1}\left[\int v_1 q(\mathbf{v}) f(\mathbf{v}) d\mathbf{v}\right] = (\Delta q)_{11} + (\Delta q)_{12} \qquad (36.2)$$

$$\frac{\partial}{\partial x_1}\left[\int V_1 Q(\mathbf{V}) F(\mathbf{V}) d\mathbf{V}\right] = (\Delta Q)_{22} + (\Delta Q)_{21} \qquad (36.3)$$

340

where
$$(\Delta q)_{11} = (1/4)\iiiint [q(\mathbf{v}') + q(\mathbf{V}') - q(\mathbf{v}) - q(\mathbf{V})]$$
$$[f(\mathbf{v})f(\mathbf{V}) - f(\mathbf{v}')f(\mathbf{V}')]$$
$$W_{11}(\mathbf{v}, \mathbf{V}; \mathbf{v}', \mathbf{V}')d\mathbf{v}d\mathbf{v}'d\mathbf{V}d\mathbf{V}' \qquad (36.4)$$

$$(\Delta q)_{12} = (1/2)\iiiint [q(\mathbf{v}') - q(\mathbf{v})]$$
$$[f(\mathbf{v})F(\mathbf{V}) - f(\mathbf{v}')F(\mathbf{V}')]$$
$$W_{12}(\mathbf{v}, \mathbf{V}; \mathbf{v}', \mathbf{V}')d\mathbf{v}d\mathbf{v}'d\mathbf{V}d\mathbf{V}' \qquad (36.5)$$

and we have analogous expressions for $(\Delta Q)_{22}$ and $(\Delta Q)_{12}$.

THE COLLISION INTEGRAL

If we make the thirteen moment and linear approximation, then
$$f = f_0(1 + h)$$
$$= f_0\left\{1 + \sum_i a_i v_i + \sum_i \sum_j b_{ij}v_i v_j + \sum_i c_i v_i[v^2 - (5/2\lambda)]\right\} \qquad (36.6)$$

$$F = F_0(1 + H)$$
$$= F_0\left\{1 + \sum_i A_i V_i + \sum_i \sum_j B_{ij}V_i V_j + \sum_i C_i V_i[V^2 - (5/2\Lambda)]\right\} \qquad (36.7)$$

where
$$f_0(\mathbf{v}) = n(\lambda/\pi)^{3/2} \exp(-\lambda v^2) \qquad (36.8)$$

$$F_0(\mathbf{V}) = N(\Lambda/\pi)^{3/2} \exp(-\Lambda V^2) \qquad (36.9)$$

$$\lambda = m/2kT \qquad (36.10)$$

$$\Lambda = M/2kT \qquad (36.11)$$

$$a_i = 2\lambda \bar{v}_i \quad A_i = 2\Lambda \bar{V}_i \qquad (36.12)$$

$$b_{ij} = (2\lambda^2/mn)(p_{ij} - p\delta_{ij}) \qquad (36.13)$$

$$B_{ij} = (2\Lambda^2/MN)(P_{ij} - P\delta_{ij}) \qquad (36.14)$$

$$c_i = (8\lambda^3/5mn)q_i \qquad (36.15)$$

$$C_i = (8\Lambda^3/5MN)Q_i \qquad (36.16)$$

If we substitute (36.6) and (36.7) into (36.4) and (36.5) and note that
$$f(\mathbf{v})F(\mathbf{V}) \approx f_0(\mathbf{v})F_0(\mathbf{V})[1 + h(\mathbf{v}) + H(\mathbf{V})] \qquad (36.17)$$

$$f(\mathbf{v}')F(\mathbf{V}') \approx f_0(\mathbf{v}')F_0(\mathbf{V}')[1 + h(\mathbf{v}') + H(\mathbf{V}')] \qquad (36.18)$$

$$f_0(\mathbf{v})F_0(\mathbf{V})W = nN(\lambda^*/\pi)^{3/2}(\Lambda^*/\pi)^{3/2} \exp(-\lambda^* u^2 - \Lambda^* w^2)W$$
$$= nN(\lambda^*/\pi)^{3/2}(\Lambda^*/\pi)^{3/2} \exp(-\lambda^* u'^2 - \Lambda^* w'^2)W$$
$$= f_0(\mathbf{v}')F_0(\mathbf{V}')W \qquad (36.19)$$

$$\lambda^* = mM/2(m + M)kT \qquad (36.20)$$

$$\Lambda^* = (m + M)/2kT \qquad (36.21)$$

then

$$(\Delta q)_{11} = -(1/4)\iiiint [q(\mathbf{v}') + q(\mathbf{V}') - q(\mathbf{v}) - q(\mathbf{V})]$$
$$[h(\mathbf{v}') + h(\mathbf{V}') - h(\mathbf{v}) - h(\mathbf{V})]$$
$$f_0(\mathbf{v})f_0(\mathbf{V})W_{11}(\mathbf{v}, \mathbf{V}; \mathbf{v}', \mathbf{V}')d\mathbf{v}d\mathbf{v}'d\mathbf{V}d\mathbf{V}' \tag{36.22}$$

$$(\Delta q)_{12} = -(1/2)\iiiint [q(\mathbf{v}') - q(\mathbf{v})] \, [h(\mathbf{v}') + H(\mathbf{V}') - h(\mathbf{v}) - H(\mathbf{V})]$$
$$f_0(\mathbf{v})F_0(\mathbf{V})W_{12}(\mathbf{v}, \mathbf{V}; \mathbf{v}', \mathbf{V}')d\mathbf{v}d\mathbf{v}'d\mathbf{V}d\mathbf{V}' \tag{36.23}$$

MUTUAL DIFFUSION

Let us consider a two-component gas. Let n and N be the respective densities. Let us assume that the gas is in a steady state situation in which the only anisotropy is in the x_1 direction and is such that

$$n = n(x_1) \tag{36.24}$$

$$N = N(x_1) \tag{36.25}$$

$$T = \text{const} \tag{36.26}$$

Let us furthermore assume that we can neglect any effects due to viscosity, or the flow of heat, so that q_i and Q_i are zero, and

$$p_{ij} \approx p\delta_{ij} = nkT\delta_{ij} \tag{36.27}$$

$$P_{ij} \approx P\delta_{ij} = NkT\delta_{ij} \tag{36.28}$$

To this approximation the distribution functions for the geometry discussed are simply

$$f = f_0(\mathbf{v})[1 + h(\mathbf{v})] = f_0(\mathbf{v})[1 + 2\lambda\bar{v}_1 v_1] \tag{36.29}$$

$$F = F_0(\mathbf{V})[1 + H(\mathbf{V})] = F_0(\mathbf{V})[1 + 2\Lambda\bar{V}_1 V_1] \tag{36.30}$$

If we substitute these distribution functions into (36.2) and (36.3), and let $q(\mathbf{v}) = v_1$ and $Q(\mathbf{V}) = V_1$ we obtain

$$\frac{\partial}{\partial x_1}\left(\frac{n}{2\lambda}\right) = (\Delta v_1)_{11} + (\Delta v_1)_{12} \tag{36.31}$$

$$\frac{\partial}{\partial x_1}\left(\frac{N}{2\Lambda}\right) = (\Delta V_1)_{22} + (\Delta V_1)_{21} \tag{36.32}$$

The collision terms $(\Delta v_1)_{11}$ and $(\Delta V_1)_{22}$ are zero, as was shown in Chapter 35. Therefore Eq. (36.31) can be written

$$\frac{\partial}{\partial x_1}\left(\frac{n}{2\lambda}\right) = (\Delta v_1)_{12} \tag{36.33}$$

and since λ is constant

$$\frac{1}{2\lambda}\left(\frac{\partial n}{\partial x_1}\right) = (\Delta v_1)_{12} \tag{36.34}$$

From the preceding section, the collision integral $(\Delta v_1)_{12}$ is given by

$$(\Delta v_1)_{12} = -(1/2)\iiiint [v_1' - v_1]$$
$$\{a_1(v_1' - v_1) + A_1(V_1' - V_1)\}f_0(\mathbf{v})F_0(\mathbf{V})$$
$$W_{12}(\mathbf{v}, \mathbf{V}; \mathbf{v}', \mathbf{V}')d\mathbf{v}d\mathbf{v}'d\mathbf{V}d\mathbf{V}' \tag{36.35}$$

If we switch from the coordinates $\mathbf{v}, \mathbf{v}', \mathbf{V}$ and $\mathbf{V}'$ to the relative and center of mass coordinates $\mathbf{u}, \mathbf{u}', \mathbf{w}, \mathbf{w}'$ and then integrate over $\mathbf{w}'$, we obtain

$$(\Delta v_1)_{12} = -(1/2)\iiint (m^*/m)(u_1' - u_1)$$
$$\{2\lambda\bar{v}_1(m^*/m)(u_1' - u_1) - 2\Lambda\bar{V}_1(m^*/M)(u_1' - u_1)\}$$
$$S_{12}(\mathbf{u}, \mathbf{u}')\psi^*(\mathbf{u})\Psi^*(\mathbf{w})d\mathbf{u}d\mathbf{u}'d\mathbf{w} \tag{36.36}$$

where

$$\psi^*(\mathbf{u}) = n(\lambda^*/\pi)^{3/2}\exp(-\lambda^*u^2) \tag{36.37}$$

$$\Psi^*(\mathbf{w}) = N(\Lambda^*/\pi)^{3/2}\exp(-\Lambda^*w^2) \tag{36.38}$$

$$\lambda^* = \lambda\Lambda/(\lambda + \Lambda) \tag{36.39}$$

$$\Lambda^* = \lambda + \Lambda \tag{36.40}$$

Integrating over $\mathbf{w}$, noting that $\int \Psi^*(\mathbf{w})d\mathbf{w} = N$ and that $(m^*/m)\lambda = (m^*/M)\Lambda = \lambda^*$, we obtain

$$(\Delta v_1)_{12} = -N(m^*/m)\lambda^*(\bar{v}_1 - \bar{V}_1)\iint (u_1' - u_1)^2\psi^*(\mathbf{u})S_{12}(\mathbf{u}, \mathbf{u}')d\mathbf{u}d\mathbf{u}' \tag{36.41}$$

In steady state, the net flux of particles is zero, i.e.,

$$n\bar{v}_1 + N\bar{V}_1 = 0 \tag{36.42}$$

and therefore

$$\bar{V}_1 = -n\bar{v}_1/N \tag{36.43}$$

Substituting (36.43) in (36.41), and making use of the results of Appendices 14 and 15, we obtain

$$(\Delta v_1)_{12} = -(m^*/m)\lambda^*\bar{v}_1(n + N)\iint (u_1' - u_1)^2\psi^*(\mathbf{u})S_{12}(\mathbf{u}, \mathbf{u}')d\mathbf{u}d\mathbf{u}'$$

$$= (2m^*/m)\lambda^*\bar{v}_1(n + N)\iint u_1(u_1' - u_1)\psi^*(\mathbf{u})S_{12}(\mathbf{u}, \mathbf{u}')d\mathbf{u}d\mathbf{u}'$$

$$= -(2m^*/m)\lambda^*\bar{v}_1(n + N)\int uu_1^2\sigma_m(u)\psi^*(\mathbf{u})d\mathbf{u}$$

$$= -(2m^*/3m)\lambda^*\bar{v}_1(n + N)\int u^3\sigma_m(u)\psi^*(\mathbf{u})d\mathbf{u} \tag{36.44}$$

If we define

$$S_m = \frac{\int u^3 \sigma_m(u)\psi^*(\mathbf{u})d\mathbf{u}}{\int u^3 \psi^*(\mathbf{u})d\mathbf{u}}$$

$$= \frac{\int u^5 \sigma_m(u)\exp(-\lambda^* u^2)du}{\int u^5 \exp(-\lambda^* u^2)du}$$

$$= [\pi^{1/2}(\lambda^*)^{3/2}/4n]\int u^3 \sigma_m(u)\psi^*(\mathbf{u})d\mathbf{u} \qquad (36.45)$$

then

$$(\Delta v_1)_{12} = -(8m^*/3m)(N+n)(\pi\lambda^*)^{-1/2}n\bar{v}_1 S_m \qquad (36.46)$$

Substituting (36.46) in (36.34) we obtain

$$n\bar{v}_1 = -D_{12}(\partial n/\partial x_1) \qquad (36.47)$$

where

$$D_{12} = \frac{3(\pi kT)^{1/2}}{8(n+N)(2m^*)^{1/2}S_m} \qquad (36.48)$$

The quantity $n\bar{v}_1$ is just the flux of particles of mass m in the x_1 direction. The factor D_{12} is called the coefficient of mutual diffusion.

The coefficient of self-diffusion D can be obtained by letting $m = M$ in (36.48), and letting n be the density of tagged molecules and N the density of untagged molecules.

THERMAL DIFFUSION

Let us again consider the two-component gas discussed in the preceding section, only now let us suppose there is, in addition to the density gradient in the x_1 direction, a temperature gradient. We now have

$$n = n(x_1) \qquad (36.49)$$

$$N = N(x_1) \qquad (36.50)$$

$$T = T(x_1) \qquad (36.51)$$

To a first approximation, we can assume

$$p_{ij} = p\delta_{ij} = nkT\delta_{ij} \qquad (36.52)$$

$$P_{ij} = P\delta_{ij} = NkT\delta_{ij} \qquad (36.53)$$

$$p_{ij} + P_{ij} = (n+N)kT\delta_{ij} = \text{const} \qquad (36.54)$$

$$q_3 = q_2 = Q_3 = Q_2 = 0 \qquad (36.55)$$

$$\bar{v}_3 = \bar{v}_2 = \bar{V}_3 = \bar{V}_2 = 0 \qquad (36.56)$$

Furthermore, in a steady state we expect the net flux of particles to be zero, i.e.,

$$n\bar{v}_1 + N\bar{V}_1 = 0 \tag{36.57}$$

Under these conditions the distribution functions assume the forms

$$
\begin{aligned}
f &= f_0(\mathbf{v})[1 + h] \\
&= f_0(\mathbf{v})\{1 + 2\lambda\bar{v}_1 v_1 + (8\lambda^2/5mn)q_1 v_1[\lambda v^2 - (5/2)]\}
\end{aligned} \tag{36.58}
$$

$$
\begin{aligned}
F &= F_0(\mathbf{V})[1 + H] \\
&= F_0(\mathbf{V})\{1 + 2\Lambda\bar{V}_1 V_1 + (8\Lambda^2/5MN)Q_1 V_1[\Lambda V^2 - (5/2)]\}
\end{aligned} \tag{36.59}
$$

Substituting (36.58) and (36.59) into (36.2) and (36.3), and letting $q(\mathbf{v}) = v_1$ and $Q(\mathbf{V}) = V_1$, we obtain

$$\frac{\partial}{\partial x_1}\left(\frac{n}{2\lambda}\right) = (\Delta v_1)_{12} \tag{36.60}$$

$$\frac{\partial}{\partial x_1}\left(\frac{N}{2\Lambda}\right) = (\Delta V_1)_{12} \tag{36.61}$$

If instead of letting $q(\mathbf{v}) = v_1$ we had let $q(\mathbf{v}) = v_1 v^2$ we would have obtained

$$\frac{\partial}{\partial x_1}\left(\frac{5n}{4\lambda^2}\right) = (\Delta v_1 v^2)_{11} + (\Delta v_1 v^2)_{12} \tag{36.62}$$

Similarly

$$\frac{\partial}{\partial x_1}\left(\frac{5N}{4\Lambda^2}\right) = (\Delta V_1 V^2)_{22} + (\Delta V_1 V^2)_{21} \tag{36.63}$$

Noting that $p = (n + N)kT = (n + N)m/2\lambda$ is constant, we can write

$$\frac{\partial}{\partial x_1}\left(\frac{n}{2\lambda}\right) = \frac{(N+n)}{2\lambda}\frac{\partial}{\partial x_1}\left(\frac{n}{N+n}\right) \tag{36.64}$$

$$\frac{\partial}{\partial x_1}\left(\frac{5n}{4\lambda^2}\right) = \frac{5(N+n)}{4\lambda^2}\frac{\partial}{\partial x_1}\left(\frac{n}{N+n}\right) + \frac{5n}{4\lambda^2}\frac{1}{T}\frac{\partial T}{\partial x_1} \tag{36.65}$$

Solving for $(n + N)\dfrac{\partial}{\partial x_1}\left(\dfrac{n}{N+n}\right)$ and $(n + N)\dfrac{1}{T}\dfrac{\partial T}{\partial x_1}$ we obtain

$$(N+n)\frac{\partial}{\partial x_1}\left(\frac{n}{N+n}\right) = 2\lambda\frac{\partial}{\partial x_1}\left(\frac{n}{2\lambda}\right) \tag{36.66}$$

$$(N+n)\frac{1}{T}\frac{\partial T}{\partial x_1} = (N+n)\left\{\frac{4\lambda^2}{5n}\frac{\partial}{\partial x_1}\left(\frac{5n}{4\lambda^2}\right) - 2\lambda\frac{\partial}{\partial x_1}\left(\frac{n}{2\lambda}\right)\right\} \tag{36.67}$$

Substituting (36.60) and (36.62) in (36.66) and (36.67) we obtain

$$(N+n)\frac{\partial}{\partial x_1}\left(\frac{n}{N+n}\right) = 2\lambda(\Delta v_1)_{12} \tag{36.68}$$

$$(N+n)\frac{1}{T}\frac{\partial T}{\partial x_1} = (N+n)\left\{\frac{4\lambda^2}{5n}[(\Delta v_1 v^2)_{11} + (\Delta v_1 v^2)_{12}] - 2\lambda(\Delta v_1)_{12}\right\} \tag{36.69}$$

Similarly

$$(N + n)\frac{\partial}{\partial x_1}\left(\frac{N}{n + N}\right) = 2\Lambda(\Delta V_1)_{21} \qquad (36.70)$$

$$(N + n)\frac{1}{T}\frac{\partial T}{\partial x_1} = (N + n)\left\{\frac{4\Lambda^2}{5N}[(\Delta V_1 V^2)_{22} + (\Delta V_1 V^2)_{21}] - 2\Lambda(\Delta V_1)_{21}\right\}$$
$$(36.71)$$

The right-hand sides of Eqs. (36.68), (36.69), (36.70), and (36.71) are linear functions of $\bar{v}_1$, $\bar{V}_1$, q_1 and Q_1, as can readily be seen by investigating a typical one of the collision terms. Furthermore, since we have the additional condition that $n\bar{v}_1 + N\bar{V}_1 = 0$, only three of these equations are independent. We can therefore write the three independent equations (36.68), (36.69), and (36.71) in the form

$$\begin{bmatrix} (N + n)\frac{\partial}{\partial x_1}\left(\frac{n}{N + n}\right) \\[2mm] (N + n)\,\frac{1}{T}\,\frac{\partial T}{\partial x_1} \\[2mm] (N + n)\,\frac{1}{T}\,\frac{\partial T}{\partial x_1} \end{bmatrix}$$

$$= \begin{bmatrix} 2\lambda(\Delta v_1)_{12} \\ (N + n)\{(4\lambda^2/5n)[(\Delta v_1 v^2)_{11} + (\Delta v_1 v^2)_{12}] - 2\lambda(\Delta v_1)_{12}\} \\ (N + n)\{(4\Lambda^2/5N)[(\Delta V_1 V^2)_{22} + (\Delta V_1 V^2)_{21}] - 2\Lambda(\Delta V_1)_{21}\} \end{bmatrix}$$

$$= \begin{bmatrix} c_{11} & c_{12} & c_{13} \\ c_{21} & c_{22} & c_{23} \\ c_{31} & c_{32} & c_{33} \end{bmatrix}\begin{bmatrix} \bar{v}_1 \\ q_1 \\ Q_1 \end{bmatrix} \qquad (36.72)$$

Solving for $\bar{v}_1$ we have

$$\bar{v}_1 = (N + n)\frac{\begin{vmatrix} \dfrac{\partial}{\partial x_1}\left(\dfrac{n}{N + n}\right) & c_{12} & c_{13} \\[3mm] \dfrac{1}{T}\left(\dfrac{\partial T}{\partial x_1}\right) & c_{22} & c_{23} \\[3mm] \dfrac{1}{T}\left(\dfrac{\partial T}{\partial x_1}\right) & c_{32} & c_{33} \end{vmatrix}}{|c_{ij}|} \qquad (36.73)$$

From (36.73) it is apparent that $\bar{v}_1$ will be a linear function of both the density gradient $\partial[n/(N + n)]/\partial x$ and the temperature gradient $\partial T/\partial x_1$. Thus a temperature gradient can cause diffusion. This phenomena is referred to as thermal diffusion. It follows also that if a gas mixture is contained between two plates which are maintained at different temperatures, the relative composition of the gas will be different at the two plates. This must necessarily be so since if a temperature gradient is maintained, thermal diffusion will occur until a composition gradient can be built up to counteract the flow of particles due to the temperature gradient.

The coefficient of mutual diffusion alone is inadequate to describe the diffusion process which is taking place inside a gas in which there is a temperature and a composition gradient. We therefore introduce a second coefficient k_T called the thermal diffusion factor, which is defined by the equation

$$n\bar{v}_1 = -(n + N)D_{12}\left[\frac{\partial}{\partial x_1}\left(\frac{n}{N + n}\right) + k_T\frac{1}{T}\frac{\partial T}{\partial x_1}\right] \tag{36.74}$$

To experimentally determine k_T we can in principle simply put the gas mixture between plates maintained at different temperatures, wait until a steady state has been reached, and then measure the composition gradient. In steady state $\bar{v}_1 = 0$ and

$$k_T = -\frac{\dfrac{\partial}{\partial x_1}\left(\dfrac{n}{N + n}\right)}{\dfrac{1}{T}\left(\dfrac{\partial T}{\partial x_1}\right)} \tag{36.75}$$

Setting $\bar{v}_1 = 0$ in (36.73) and letting

$$\frac{\partial}{\partial x_1}\left(\frac{n}{n + N}\right) = -k_T\left(\frac{1}{T}\frac{\partial T}{\partial x_1}\right) \tag{36.76}$$

we obtain

$$\begin{vmatrix} -k_T & c_{12} & c_{13} \\ 1 & c_{22} & c_{23} \\ 1 & c_{32} & c_{33} \end{vmatrix} = 0 \tag{36.77}$$

Solving for k_T we have

$$k_T = \frac{c_{12}(c_{23} - c_{33}) + c_{13}(c_{32} - c_{22})}{c_{22}c_{33} - c_{32}c_{23}} \tag{36.78}$$

To determine the coefficients c_{ij} we must first evaluate the quantities $(\Delta v_1)_{12}$, $(\Delta v_1v^2)_{11}$, $(\Delta v_1v^2)_{12}$, $(\Delta V_1)_{12}$, $(\Delta V_1V^2)_{22}$ and $(\Delta V_1V^2)_{12}$. These results are then substituted in (36.68), (36.69), and (36.71) and the resulting set of equations written in the form (36.72). The coefficients can then be read off directly. The integrals involved are of the same sort as encountered in our earlier calculations. The calculations, however, are extremely tedious.

We will simply quote the result for the thermal diffusion factor k_T.

$$k_T = 5(C - 1)\left(\frac{nS_1 - NS_2}{Q_1n^2 + Q_2N^2 + Q_{12}nN}\right)\left(\frac{nN}{n + N}\right) \tag{36.79}$$

where

$$S_1 = sE_1 - 4Ars - 3r(r - s) \tag{36.80}$$

$$S_2 = rE_1 - 4Ars - 3s(s - r) \tag{36.81}$$

$$Q_1 = E_1[6r^2 + (5 - 4B)s^2 + 8rsA] \tag{36.82}$$

$$Q_2 = E_1[6s^2 + (5 - 4B)r^2 + 8rsA] \tag{36.83}$$

$$Q_{12} = 3(s - r)^2(5 - 4B) + 4rsA(11 - 4B) + 2E_1E_2 \tag{36.84}$$

$$r = m^*/m \tag{36.85}$$

$$s = m^*/M \tag{36.86}$$

$$A = \frac{(\lambda^*/5)\int \sigma_\mu^{12}(u)u^5\psi^*(\mathbf{u})du}{\int \sigma_m^{12}(u)u^3\psi^*(\mathbf{u})du} \tag{36.87}$$

$$B = \frac{\lambda^*\int \sigma_m^{12}(u)u^5\psi^*(\mathbf{u})du - (\lambda^{*2}/5)\int \sigma_m^{12}(u)u^7\psi^*(\mathbf{u})du}{\int \sigma_m^{12}(u)u^3\psi^*(\mathbf{u})du} \tag{36.88}$$

$$C = \frac{(2\lambda^*/5)\int \sigma_m^{12}(u)u^5\psi^*(\mathbf{u})du}{\int \sigma_m^{12}(u)u^3\psi^*(\mathbf{u})du} \tag{36.89}$$

$$E_1 = \frac{\lambda^3\int \sigma_\mu^{11}(u)u^5\psi'(\mathbf{u})du}{20\lambda^{*2}\int \sigma_m^{12}(u)u^3\psi^*(\mathbf{u})du} \tag{36.90}$$

$$E_2 = \frac{\Lambda^3 n\int \sigma_\mu^{22}(u)u^5\Psi'(\mathbf{u})du}{20\lambda^{*2}N\int \sigma_m^{12}(u)u^3\psi^*(\mathbf{u})du} \tag{36.91}$$

where

$$\psi^*(\mathbf{u}) = n(\lambda^*/\pi)^{3/2}\exp(-\lambda^*u^2) \tag{36.92}$$

$$\psi'(\mathbf{u}) = n(\lambda/2\pi)^{3/2}\exp(-\lambda u^2/2) \tag{36.93}$$

$$\Psi'(\mathbf{u}) = N(\Lambda/2\pi)^{3/2}\exp(-\Lambda u^2/2) \tag{36.94}$$

$$\lambda^* = \lambda\Lambda/(\lambda + \Lambda) \qquad \Lambda^* = \lambda + \Lambda \tag{36.95}$$

$$\sigma_\mu^{ij}(u) = \iint \sigma^{ij}(u, \theta)(1 - \cos^2\theta)\sin\theta d\theta d\phi \tag{36.96}$$

$$\sigma_m^{ij}(u) = \iint \sigma^{ij}(u, \theta)(1 - \cos\theta)\sin\theta d\theta d\phi \tag{36.97}$$

For a discussion of thermal diffusion starting from the above equations, the reader is referred to the monograph *Thermal Diffusion* by Grew and Ibbs (see bibliography).

Chapter **37**

SOME APPROXIMATE FORMS FOR THE COLLISION TERM IN THE BOLTZMANN TRANSPORT EQUATION

If the distribution function $F(\mathbf{V})$ for one component of a two-component gas is known, then the distribution function $f(\mathbf{v})$ of the second component can be found by solving the Boltzmann transport equation

$$\frac{\partial f}{\partial t} + \sum_i \frac{F_i}{m}\frac{\partial f}{\partial v_i} + \sum_i v_i \frac{\partial f}{\partial x_i} = \left(\frac{Df}{Dt}\right)_{11} + \left(\frac{Df}{Dt}\right)_{12} \qquad (37.1)$$

where

$$\left(\frac{Df}{Dt}\right)_{11} = \iiint [f(\mathbf{v}')f(\mathbf{V}') - f(\mathbf{v})f(\mathbf{V})]W_{11}(\mathbf{v},\mathbf{V};\mathbf{v}',\mathbf{V}')dv'd\mathbf{V}d\mathbf{V}' \qquad (37.2)$$

$$\left(\frac{Df}{Dt}\right)_{12} = \iiint [f(\mathbf{v}')F(\mathbf{V}') - f(\mathbf{v})F(\mathbf{V})]W_{12}(\mathbf{v},\mathbf{V};\mathbf{v}',\mathbf{V}')dv'd\mathbf{V}d\mathbf{V}' \qquad (37.3)$$

The solution of this equation, as we have seen, is quite difficult even for relatively simple boundary conditions. There are a number of situations, however, in which it is possible to obtain approximate expressions for the collision term, and thus to considerably reduce the complexity of the Boltzmann transport equation. These approximations are particularly useful in the study of ionized gases. In the present chapter we will examine a number of these approximations.

THE CHAPMAN-COWLING COLLISION TERM

Let us assume that we have a mixture of two gases. Let m and M be the respective masses of the two types of particles. If $m \ll M$ and if the temperature of the light gas is of the same order of magnitude or greater than the temperature of the heavy gas, then it is possible to obtain an approximate expression for $(Df/Dt)_{12}$. Instead of using the form given by Eq. (37.3), we shall find it convenient to write the collision term in the equivalent form

$$\frac{Df}{Dt} = A - B \tag{37.4}$$

$$A = \iiint f(\mathbf{v}')F(\mathbf{V}')W(\mathbf{v}, \mathbf{V}; \mathbf{v}', \mathbf{V}')d\mathbf{v}'d\mathbf{V}d\mathbf{V}' \tag{37.5}$$

$$B = \iiint f(\mathbf{v})F(\mathbf{V})W(\mathbf{v}, \mathbf{V}; \mathbf{v}', \mathbf{V}')d\mathbf{v}'d\mathbf{V}d\mathbf{V}' \tag{37.6}$$

where the subscripts on $(Df/Dt)_{12}$ and W_{12} have, for simplicity of notation, been dropped. We shall consider the two terms A and B separately. Remembering that

$$W(\mathbf{v}, \mathbf{V}; \mathbf{v}', \mathbf{V}') \equiv S(\mathbf{v} - \mathbf{V}, \mathbf{v}' - \mathbf{V}')\delta(\mathbf{w}' - \mathbf{w}) \tag{37.7}$$

where $\mathbf{w}$ and $\mathbf{w}'$ are the center of mass velocities before and after collision, we can write A and B as

$$A = \iiint f(\mathbf{v}')F(\mathbf{V}')S(\mathbf{v} - \mathbf{V}, \mathbf{v}' - \mathbf{V}')\delta(\mathbf{w}' - \mathbf{w})d\mathbf{v}'d\mathbf{V}d\mathbf{V}' \tag{37.8}$$

$$B = \iiint f(\mathbf{v})F(\mathbf{V})S(\mathbf{v} - \mathbf{V}, \mathbf{v}' - \mathbf{V}')\delta(\mathbf{w}' - \mathbf{w})d\mathbf{v}'d\mathbf{V}d\mathbf{V}' \tag{37.9}$$

Let us assume that the temperature of the heavy gas is given by T and the temperature of the light gas by τ, where the temperature in both cases is defined by the relations

$$3k\tau/2 = \overline{mv^2/2} \tag{37.10}$$

$$3kT/2 = \overline{MV^2/2} \tag{37.11}$$

The ratio of the speeds is then given approximately by

$$\frac{\overline{V}}{\overline{v}} \approx \left(\frac{\overline{V^2}}{\overline{v^2}}\right)^{1/2} = \left(\frac{mT}{M\tau}\right)^{1/2} \tag{37.12}$$

If $mT \ll M\tau$, then $\overline{V} \ll \overline{v}$, and the scattering term $S(\mathbf{v} - \mathbf{V}, \mathbf{v}' - \mathbf{V}')$ can be approximated by the first few terms in a Taylor series expansion, i.e.,

$$S(\mathbf{v} - \mathbf{V}; \mathbf{v}' - \mathbf{V}') \approx S(\mathbf{v}, \mathbf{v}')$$

$$- \sum_i \left(V_i \frac{\partial}{\partial v_i} + V_i' \frac{\partial}{\partial v_i'} \right) S(\mathbf{v}, \mathbf{v}')$$

$$+ \frac{1}{2} \left[\sum_i \left(V_i \frac{\partial}{\partial v_i} + V_i' \frac{\partial}{\partial v_i'} \right) \right]^2 S(\mathbf{v}, \mathbf{v}') \qquad (37.13)$$

For notational convenience, we will drop the arguments $\mathbf{v}$ and $\mathbf{v}'$ in $S(\mathbf{v}, \mathbf{v}')$. It should therefore be remembered that

$$S \equiv S(\mathbf{v}, \mathbf{v}') \qquad (37.14)$$

If we substitute (37.13) in (37.5) and (37.6), we obtain

$$A \approx \iiint f(\mathbf{v}')F(\mathbf{V}') \Big\{ S - \sum_i \left(V_i \frac{\partial}{\partial v_i} + V_i' \frac{\partial}{\partial v_i'} \right) S$$

$$+ \frac{1}{2} \left[\sum_i \left(V_i \frac{\partial}{\partial v_i} + V_i' \frac{\partial}{\partial v_i'} \right) \right]^2 S \Big\} \delta(\mathbf{w}' - \mathbf{w}) d\mathbf{v}' d\mathbf{V} d\mathbf{V}' \qquad (37.15)$$

$$B \approx \iiint f(\mathbf{v})F(\mathbf{V}) \Big\{ S - \sum_i \left(V_i \frac{\partial}{\partial v_i} + V_i' \frac{\partial}{\partial v_i'} \right) S$$

$$+ \frac{1}{2} \left[\sum_i \left(V_i \frac{\partial}{\partial v_i} + V_i' \frac{\partial}{\partial v_i'} \right) \right]^2 S \Big\} \delta(\mathbf{w}' - \mathbf{w}) d\mathbf{v}' d\mathbf{V} d\mathbf{V}' \qquad (37.16)$$

In simplifying the integrals (37.15) and (37.16), we will make use of the following relations

$$\mathbf{w} = \mathbf{w}' = \frac{m\mathbf{v} + M\mathbf{V}}{m + M} = \frac{m\mathbf{v}' + M\mathbf{V}'}{m + M} \qquad (37.17)$$

$$\mathbf{V} = (m/m^*)\mathbf{w} - (m/M)\mathbf{v} = \mathbf{V}' + (m/M)(\mathbf{v}' - \mathbf{v}) \qquad (37.18)$$

$$\mathbf{V}' = (m/m^*)\mathbf{w}' - (m/M)\mathbf{v}' = \mathbf{V} - (m/M)(\mathbf{v}' - \mathbf{v}) \qquad (37.19)$$

Transforming from the coordinates $\mathbf{V}$ to the coordinates $\mathbf{w}$ in (37.15), noting that $J(\mathbf{V}/\mathbf{w}) = (m/m^*)^3$ and for convenience dropping the approximation sign, we obtain

$$A = (m/m^*)^3 \iint f(\mathbf{v}')F(\mathbf{V}')$$

$$\Big\{ S - \sum_i \left[[V_i' + (m/M)(v_i' - v_i)] \frac{\partial}{\partial v_i} + V_i' \frac{\partial}{\partial v_i'} \right] S$$

$$+ \frac{1}{2} \left[\sum_i \left([V_i' + (m/M)(v_i' - v_i)] \frac{\partial}{\partial v_i} + V_i' \frac{\partial}{\partial v_i'} \right) \right]^2 S \Big\} d\mathbf{v}' d\mathbf{V}' \qquad (37.20)$$

Transforming from the coordinates $\mathbf{V}'$ to the coordinates $\mathbf{w}'$ in (37.16), noting that $J(\mathbf{V}'/\mathbf{w}') = (m/m^*)^3$, we obtain

$$B = (m/m^*)^3 \iint f(\mathbf{v})F(\mathbf{V})$$

$$\left\{ S - \sum_i \left[V_i \frac{\partial}{\partial v_i} + [V_i - (m/M)(v_i' - v_i)]\frac{\partial}{\partial v_i'} \right] S \right.$$

$$\left. + \frac{1}{2}\left[\sum_i \left(V_i \frac{\partial}{\partial v_i} + [V_i - (m/M)(v_i' - v_i)]\frac{\partial}{\partial v_i'} \right) \right]^2 S \right\} d\mathbf{v}' d\mathbf{V} \qquad (37.21)$$

This is as far as we can go without saying something about the distribution functions $f(\mathbf{v})$ and $F(\mathbf{V})$. Let us assume that the heavy particles are very close to equilibrium so that we can let

$$F(\mathbf{V}) \approx F_0(\mathbf{V}) \equiv N(\Lambda/\pi)^{3/2} \exp(-\Lambda V^2) \qquad (37.22)$$

Substituting (37.22) in (37.20) and integrating over $\mathbf{V}'$, we obtain

$$A = N\left(\frac{m}{m^*}\right)^3 \int f(\mathbf{v})\left\{ S - \sum_i \frac{m}{M}(v_i' - v_i)\frac{\partial S}{\partial v_i} \right.$$

$$+ \frac{1}{2}\sum_i \sum_j \left(\frac{m}{M}\right)^2 (v_i' - v_i)\frac{\partial}{\partial v_i}\left((v_j' - v_j)\frac{\partial S}{\partial v_j} \right)$$

$$\left. + \left(\frac{1}{4\Lambda}\right)\sum_i \left(\frac{\partial^2 S}{\partial v_i^2} + 2\frac{\partial^2 S}{\partial v_i \partial v_i'} + \frac{\partial^2 S}{\partial v_i'^2} \right) \right\} d\mathbf{v}' \qquad (37.23)$$

If $m \ll M$ then we can set $m^* = m$ in (37.23) and we can also neglect the third term compared to the second term. The validity of the latter approximation can be seen by assuming $f(\mathbf{v}')$ to be Maxwellian and replacing v_i' and v_j' by $\bar{v}_i' = \bar{v}_j' = 0$ in the terms to be compared. With the above approximations we can write (37.23) as

$$A = N\int f(\mathbf{v}')\left\{ S - \frac{m}{M}\sum_i (v_i' - v_i)\frac{\partial S}{\partial v_i} \right.$$

$$\left. + \left(\frac{1}{4\Lambda}\right)\sum_i \left(\frac{\partial^2 S}{\partial v_i^2} + 2\frac{\partial^2 S}{\partial v_i \partial v_i'} + \frac{\partial^2 S}{\partial v_i'^2} \right) \right\} d\mathbf{v}' \qquad (37.24)$$

Similarly

$$B = N\int f(\mathbf{v})\left\{ S + \frac{m}{M}\sum_i (v_i' - v_i)\frac{\partial S}{\partial v_i'} \right.$$

$$\left. + \left(\frac{1}{4\Lambda}\right)\sum_i \left(\frac{\partial^2 S}{\partial v_i^2} + 2\frac{\partial^2 S}{\partial v_i \partial v_i'} + \frac{\partial^2 S}{\partial v_i'^2} \right) \right\} d\mathbf{v}' \qquad (37.25)$$

Combining (37.24) and (37.25), we get

$$\frac{Df}{Dt} = A - B = C_1(f) + C_2(f) + C_3(f) \tag{37.26}$$

$$C_1(f) \equiv N \int [f(\mathbf{v'}) - f(\mathbf{v})]S d\mathbf{v'} \tag{37.27}$$

$$C_2(f) \equiv -N\left(\frac{m}{M}\right)\sum_i \int [v_i' - v_i]\left\{f(\mathbf{v})\frac{\partial S}{\partial v_i'} + f(\mathbf{v'})\frac{\partial S}{\partial v_i}\right\}d\mathbf{v'} \tag{37.28}$$

$$C_3(f) \equiv \left(\frac{N}{4\Lambda}\right)\sum_i \int [f(\mathbf{v'}) - f(\mathbf{v})]\left(\frac{\partial^2 S}{\partial v_i^2} + 2\frac{\partial^2 S}{\partial v_i \partial v_i'} + \frac{\partial^2 S}{\partial v_i'^2}\right)d\mathbf{v'} \tag{37.29}$$

This is as far as we can go without specifying $f(\mathbf{v})$. Let us now assume that we can write

$$f = \psi(v) + v_i g(v) \tag{37.30}$$

where $\psi(v)$ and $g(v)$ are arbitrary functions of the speed v. We then have

$$\frac{Df}{Dt} = \frac{D\psi}{Dt} + \frac{D}{Dt}(v_i g)$$

$$= C_1(\psi) + C_2(\psi) + C_3(\psi) + C_1(v_i g) + C_2(v_i g) + C_3(v_i g) \tag{37.31}$$

Before evaluating the above equation, we will derive a number of useful mathematical results. Suppose $h(v)$ is some arbitrary function of v, then

$$\frac{\partial h}{\partial v_i} = \frac{v_i}{v}\frac{dh}{dv} \tag{37.32}$$

$$\frac{\partial^2 h}{\partial v_i^2} = \frac{1}{v}\frac{dh}{dv} + \frac{v_i^2}{v}\frac{d}{dv}\left(\frac{1}{v}\frac{dh}{dv}\right) \tag{37.33}$$

$$\sum_i \frac{\partial}{\partial v_i}(v_i h) = \sum_i \left(h + v_i \frac{\partial h}{\partial v_i}\right) = \sum_i \left(h + \frac{v_i^2}{v}\frac{dh}{dv}\right)$$

$$= 3h + v\frac{dh}{dv} = \frac{1}{v^2}\frac{d}{dv}(v^3 h) \tag{37.34}$$

$$\sum_i \frac{\partial^2 h}{\partial v_i^2} = \frac{1}{v^2}\frac{d}{dv}\left(v^2 \frac{dh}{dv}\right) \tag{37.35}$$

Let us define

$$s \equiv \int S(\mathbf{v}, \mathbf{v'})d\mathbf{v'} \tag{37.36}$$

$$s_i = \int v_i S(\mathbf{v}, \mathbf{v'})d\mathbf{v'} \equiv v_i s \tag{37.37}$$

$$s_i' \equiv \int v_i' S(\mathbf{v}, \mathbf{v'})d\mathbf{v'} \tag{37.38}$$

From the results of Appendix 14, we have

$$s_i - s_i' = v v_i \sigma_m(v) \tag{37.39}$$

It follows that

$$s_i' = s_i - v v_i \sigma_m(v) = v_i[s - v \sigma_m(v)] = v_i s' \tag{37.40}$$

where we define

$$s' \equiv s - v \sigma_m(v) \tag{37.41}$$

Since $S(\mathbf{v}, \mathbf{v}')$ is given by

$$S(\mathbf{v}, \mathbf{v}') = \sigma(v, \mathbf{v} \cdot \mathbf{v}') \delta(v' - v)/v \tag{37.42}$$

we can always replace v' by v in an integration involving S. This does not apply if the integral contains a derivative of S, since the derivative of a delta function is not itself a delta function.

We are now ready to evaluate expression (37.31). We will consider it term by term. Since we can replace $\psi(v')$ by $\psi(v)$ in $C_1(\psi)$, we obtain

$$C_1(\psi) = 0 \tag{37.43}$$

The terms $C_2(\psi)$ and $C_3(\psi)$ do not, however, vanish. Writing out $C_2(\psi)$ in detail, we have

$$C_2(\psi) \equiv -N(m/M)[C_{21} + C_{22} + C_{23} + C_{24}] \tag{37.44}$$

$$C_{21} \equiv \sum_i \int v_i' \psi(v) \frac{\partial S}{\partial v_i'} d\mathbf{v}' \tag{37.45}$$

$$C_{22} \equiv -\sum_i \int v_i \psi(v) \frac{\partial S}{\partial v_i'} d\mathbf{v}' \tag{37.46}$$

$$C_{23} \equiv \sum_i \int v_i' \psi(v') \frac{\partial S}{\partial v_i} d\mathbf{v}' \tag{37.47}$$

$$C_{24} \equiv -\sum_i \int v_i \psi(v') \frac{\partial S}{\partial v_i} d\mathbf{v}' \tag{37.48}$$

Integrating C_{21} and C_{22} by parts, we get

$$C_{21} = -\sum_i \psi(v)s \tag{37.49}$$

$$C_{22} = 0 \tag{37.50}$$

Interchanging the differentiation and the integration in C_{23} and C_{24}, we get

$$C_{23} = \sum_i \frac{\partial}{\partial v_i}[\psi(v)s_i'] \tag{37.51}$$

$$C_{24} = -\sum_i v_i \frac{\partial}{\partial v_i}[\psi(v)s]$$

$$= -\sum_i \frac{\partial}{\partial v_i}[s_i\psi(v)] + \sum_i \psi(v)s \qquad (37.52)$$

Combining our results, we have

$$C_2(\psi) = -N(m/M)[C_{21} + C_{22} + C_{23} + C_{24}]$$

$$= N(m/M)\sum_i \frac{\partial}{\partial v_i}[(s_i - s_i')\psi(v)]$$

$$= \left[\frac{N(m/M)}{v^2}\right]\frac{d}{dv}[v^4\psi(v)\sigma_m(v)] \qquad (37.53)$$

The term $C_3(\psi)$ can be similarly evaluated. Thus

$$C_3(\psi) = (N/4\Lambda)[C_{31} + C_{32} + C_{33} + C_{34} + C_{35} + C_{36}]$$

$$C_{31} \equiv \sum_i \int \psi(v') \frac{\partial^2 S}{\partial v_i^2} d\mathbf{v}' \qquad (37.54)$$

$$C_{32} \equiv -\sum_i \int \psi(v) \frac{\partial^2 S}{\partial v_i^2} d\mathbf{v}' \qquad (37.55)$$

$$C_{33} \equiv 2\sum_i \int \psi(v') \frac{\partial^2 S}{\partial v_i \partial v_i'} d\mathbf{v}' \qquad (37.56)$$

$$C_{34} \equiv -2\sum_i \int \psi(v) \frac{\partial^2 S}{\partial v_i \partial v_i'} d\mathbf{v}' \qquad (37.57)$$

$$C_{35} \equiv \sum_i \int \psi(v') \frac{\partial^2 S}{\partial v_i'^2} d\mathbf{v}' \qquad (37.58)$$

$$C_{36} \equiv -\sum_i \int \psi(v) \frac{\partial^2 S}{\partial v_i'^2} d\mathbf{v}' \qquad (37.59)$$

Considering the above expressions term by term, we have

$$C_{31} = \sum_i \frac{\partial^2}{\partial v_i^2}[\psi s] = \frac{1}{v^2}\frac{d}{dv}\left[v^2\frac{d}{dv}(\psi s)\right] \qquad (37.60)$$

$$C_{32} = -\sum_i \psi\frac{\partial^2}{\partial v_i^2}[s] = -\frac{\psi}{v^2}\frac{d}{dv}\left[v^2\frac{d}{dv}(s)\right] \qquad (37.61)$$

$$C_{33} = -2\sum_i \frac{\partial}{\partial v_i}\left[\int \frac{\partial \psi(v')}{\partial v_i'}S d\mathbf{v}'\right]$$

$$= -2 \sum_i \frac{\partial}{\partial v_i}\left[\frac{1}{v}\frac{d\psi(v)}{dv}s_i{}'\right] = -\frac{2}{v^2}\frac{d}{dv}\left(v^2 s'\frac{d\psi}{dv}\right) \qquad (37.62)$$

$$C_{34} = 0 \qquad (37.63)$$

$$C_{35} = \sum_i \int \frac{\partial^2 \psi(v')}{\partial v_i'^2} S d\mathbf{v}' = \frac{s}{v^2}\frac{d}{dv}\left(v^2\frac{d\psi}{dv}\right) \qquad (37.64)$$

$$C_{36} = 0 \qquad (37.65)$$

Combining our results, we get

$$\begin{aligned}
C_3(\psi) &= (N/4\Lambda)[C_{31} + C_{32} + C_{33} + C_{34} + C_{35} + C_{36}] \\
&= (N/4\Lambda)\left\{\frac{2}{v^2}\frac{d}{dv}\left[v^2(s - s')\frac{d\psi}{dv}\right]\right\} \\
&= \frac{NkT}{Mv^2}\frac{d}{dv}\left[v^3\sigma_m(v)\frac{d\psi}{dv}\right] \qquad (37.66)
\end{aligned}$$

The collision terms $C_1(v_ig)$, $C_2(v_ig)$ and $C_3(v_ig)$ can be similarly evaluated. However $C_1(v_ig)$ does not vanish and is appreciably larger than $C_2(v_ig)$ and $C_3(v_ig)$. We will therefore assume

$$C_2(v_ig) \approx 0 \qquad (37.67)$$

$$C_3(v_ig) \approx 0 \qquad (37.68)$$

For $C_1(v_ig)$ we get

$$\begin{aligned}
C_1(v_ig) &= N\int [v_i' g(v') - v_i g(v)]S d\mathbf{v}' \\
&= Ng(v)\int (v_i' - v_i)S d\mathbf{v}' \\
&= -Nvv_i\sigma_m(v)g(v) \qquad (37.69)
\end{aligned}$$

Gathering results, we have

$$\begin{aligned}
\frac{D}{Dt}[\psi(v) + v_i g(v)] = &\frac{m}{Mv^2}\frac{d}{dv}(v^3 \nu_m \psi) \\
&+ \frac{kT}{Mv^2}\frac{d}{dv}\left(v^2 \nu_m \frac{d\psi}{dv}\right) - \nu_m v_i g \qquad (37.70)
\end{aligned}$$

where

$$\nu_m = Nv\sigma_m(v) \qquad (37.71)$$

The above result is valid if $F(\mathbf{V}) = F_0(\mathbf{V})$, and $mT \ll M\tau$ where T is the temperature of the gas of particles of mass M and τ is the temperature of the gas of particles of mass m.

If ψ is Maxwellian with a temperature the same as the temperature of the gas of particles of mass M, i.e.,

$$\psi = n(m/2\pi kT)^{3/2}\exp(-mv^2/2kT)$$

then $D\psi/Dt = 0$. This result is expected, since for a gas in equilibrium $Df/Dt = 0$.

If M is infinite but (kT/M) is finite, then the first term on the right-hand side of (37.70) will vanish. On the other hand, if $T = 0$ but M is finite, the second term will vanish. If $T = 0$ and M is infinite, both terms will vanish. It follows that if the particles of mass m are being scattered by infinite particles at rest, only the last term in (37.70) will remain, whereas if the scattering is off of particles of finite mass at rest, we have only the first and third terms, while if the scattering is off of moving particles of infinite mass, we have the second and third terms.

THE FOKKER-PLANCK COLLISION TERM

Let us assume, as previously, that we have a mixture of two gases whose distribution functions are f and F respectively, and whose particle masses are m and M respectively. The masses m and M are quite arbitrary and may or may not be of the same order of magnitude. The collision term $(Df/Dt)_{12}$ is given by

$$\frac{Df}{Dt} = \iiint [f(\mathbf{v}')F(\mathbf{V}') - f(\mathbf{v})F(\mathbf{V})]W(\mathbf{v}, \mathbf{V}; \mathbf{v}', \mathbf{V}')d\mathbf{v}'d\mathbf{V}d\mathbf{V}' \qquad (37.72)$$

If the collisions between the particles of mass m and M are such as to produce a relatively small change in the velocity of the particle of mass m, then it is possible, as we shall see, to obtain an approximate expression for Eq. (37.72). The Coulomb cross section is an example of a cross section for which the predominant effect is due to scattering of the above type. Although large-angle scattering is possible with a Coulomb cross section, its effect can be shown to be negligible compared to the much more frequent small-angle scattering.

We will find it convenient to make use of the relative coordinates $\mathbf{u}$ and $\mathbf{u}'$ and the center of mass coordinates $\mathbf{w}$ and $\mathbf{w}'$ defined by

$$\mathbf{u} = \mathbf{v} - \mathbf{V} \qquad (37.73)$$

$$\mathbf{u}' = \mathbf{v}' - \mathbf{V}' \qquad (37.74)$$

$$\mathbf{w} = \frac{m\mathbf{v} + M\mathbf{V}}{m + M} \qquad (37.75)$$

$$\mathbf{w}' = \frac{m\mathbf{v}' + M\mathbf{V}'}{m + M} \qquad (37.76)$$

The inverse relations are given by

$$\mathbf{v} = \mathbf{w} + (m^*/m)\mathbf{u} \qquad (37.77)$$

$$\mathbf{v}' = \mathbf{w}' + (m^*/m)\mathbf{u}' \qquad (37.78)$$

$$\mathbf{V} = \mathbf{w} - (m^*/M)\mathbf{u} \tag{37.79}$$

$$\mathbf{V}' = \mathbf{w}' - (m^*/M)\mathbf{u}' \tag{37.80}$$

Subtracting (37.77) from (37.78), and remembering that we can always let $\mathbf{w} = \mathbf{w}'$, we obtain

$$\mathbf{v}' = \mathbf{v} + (m^*/m)(\mathbf{u}' - \mathbf{u}) \tag{37.81}$$

Subtracting (37.79) from (37.80), we obtain

$$\mathbf{V}' = \mathbf{V} - (m^*/M)(\mathbf{u}' - \mathbf{u}) \tag{37.82}$$

Noting that

$$\mathbf{V} = \mathbf{v} - \mathbf{u} \tag{37.83}$$

we can rewrite (37.82)

$$\mathbf{V}' = \mathbf{v} - \mathbf{u} - (m^*/M)(\mathbf{u}' - \mathbf{u}) = \mathbf{v} - \mathbf{u}' + (m^*/m)(\mathbf{u}' - \mathbf{u}) \tag{37.84}$$

Substituting (37.81), (37.83), and (37.84) in (37.72), transforming from an integration over $\mathbf{v}'$, $\mathbf{V}$, $\mathbf{V}'$ to an integration over $\mathbf{u}$, $\mathbf{u}'$, $\mathbf{w}'$ and then integrating over $\mathbf{w}'$, we obtain

$$Df/Dt = \iint \{ f[\mathbf{v} + (m^*/m)(\mathbf{u}' - \mathbf{u})]F[\mathbf{v} - \mathbf{u}' + (m^*/m)(\mathbf{u}' - \mathbf{u})]$$
$$-f(\mathbf{v})F(\mathbf{v} - \mathbf{u})\}S(\mathbf{u}, \mathbf{u}')d\mathbf{u}d\mathbf{u}' \tag{37.85}$$

Let us define

$$\Delta\mathbf{v} \equiv \mathbf{v}' - \mathbf{v} = (m^*/m)(\mathbf{u}' - \mathbf{u}) \tag{37.86}$$

then (37.85) can be written

$$Df/Dt = \iint \{ f[\mathbf{v} + \Delta\mathbf{v}]F[\mathbf{v} - \mathbf{u}' + \Delta\mathbf{v}]$$
$$-f(\mathbf{v})F(\mathbf{v} - \mathbf{u})\}S(\mathbf{u}, \mathbf{u}')d\mathbf{u}d\mathbf{u}' \tag{37.87}$$

If the average value of $|\Delta\mathbf{v}|$ in a collision is small compared to the average speeds $\bar{v}$ and $\bar{V}$, then we can approximate the product

$$f(\mathbf{v} + \Delta\mathbf{v})F(\mathbf{v} - \mathbf{u}' + \Delta\mathbf{v})$$

by the first few terms in a Taylor series, i.e.,

$$(\mathbf{v} + \Delta\mathbf{v})F(\mathbf{v} - \mathbf{u}' + \Delta\mathbf{v})$$
$$\approx f(\mathbf{v})F(\mathbf{v} - \mathbf{u}') + \sum_i \Delta v_i \frac{\partial}{\partial v_i}[f(\mathbf{v})F(\mathbf{v} - \mathbf{u}')]$$
$$+ \frac{1}{2}\sum_i \sum_j \Delta v_i \Delta v_j \frac{\partial^2}{\partial v_i \partial v_j}[f(\mathbf{v})F(\mathbf{v} - \mathbf{u}')] \tag{37.88}$$

If we substitute (37.88) in (37.85) and note that

$$\int f(\mathbf{v})F(\mathbf{v} - \mathbf{u}')S(\mathbf{u}, \mathbf{u}')d\mathbf{u}d\mathbf{u}' = \int f(\mathbf{v})F(\mathbf{v} - \mathbf{u})S(\mathbf{u}, \mathbf{u}')d\mathbf{u}d\mathbf{u}' \tag{37.89}$$

we obtain

$$Df/Dt = \sum_i \frac{\partial}{\partial v_i} \int \Delta v_i f(\mathbf{v}) F(\mathbf{v} - \mathbf{u}') S(\mathbf{u}, \mathbf{u}') du du'$$

$$+ \frac{1}{2} \sum_i \sum_j \frac{\partial^2}{\partial v_i \partial v_j} \int \Delta v_i \Delta v_j f(\mathbf{v}) F(\mathbf{v} - \mathbf{u}') S(\mathbf{u}, \mathbf{u}') du du' \qquad (37.90)$$

Before attempting to simplify Eq. (37.90) any further, let us obtain a few useful quantities. Let us consider a single particle of mass m and velocity $\mathbf{v}$ moving through a gas of particles of mass M and distribution $F(\mathbf{V})$. Suppose we wish to know the average change per unit of time of the ith component of the velocity of this particle due to collisions. We will designate this quantity $(\Delta v_i/\Delta t)$. There are $F(\mathbf{V})d\mathbf{V}$ particles of mass M per unit volume with velocity in $d\mathbf{V}$. The probability per unit time that the particle of mass m will collide with a particular one of these particles and be scattered into dv' while the particle of mass M is scattered into $d\mathbf{V}'$, is simply

$$W(\mathbf{v}, \mathbf{V}; \mathbf{v}', \mathbf{V}') dv' d\mathbf{V}' \qquad (37.91)$$

The change in the ith component of velocity of the particle of mass m is Δv_i. Multiplying these three quantities together and integrating over $\mathbf{v}'$, $\mathbf{V}$, $\mathbf{V}'$, we obtain

$$<\Delta v_i/\Delta t> = \iiint \Delta v_i F(\mathbf{V}) W(\mathbf{v}, \mathbf{V}; \mathbf{v}', \mathbf{V}') dv' d\mathbf{V} d\mathbf{V}' \qquad (37.92)$$

Switching to coordinates $\mathbf{u}$, $\mathbf{u}'$ and $\mathbf{w}'$ and integrating over $\mathbf{w}'$, we obtain

$$<\Delta v_i/\Delta t> = \iint \Delta v_i F(\mathbf{v} - \mathbf{u}) S(\mathbf{u}, \mathbf{u}') du du' \qquad (37.93)$$

If we interchange $\mathbf{u}$ and $\mathbf{u}'$, we obtain

$$<\Delta v_i/\Delta t> = - \iint \Delta v_i F(\mathbf{v} - \mathbf{u}') S(\mathbf{u}, \mathbf{u}') du du' \qquad (37.94)$$

Similarly, the average increment per unit time of the product $\Delta v_i \Delta v_j$ is given by

$$<\Delta v_i \Delta v_j/\Delta t> = \iint \Delta v_i \Delta v_j F(\mathbf{v} - \mathbf{u}') S(\mathbf{u}, \mathbf{u}') du du' \qquad (37.95)$$

Comparing these results with (37.90), we see that we can write

$$Df/Dt = - \sum_i \frac{\partial}{\partial v_i} \{ f(\mathbf{v}) <\Delta v_i/\Delta t> \}$$

$$+ \frac{1}{2} \sum_i \sum_j \frac{\partial^2}{\partial v_i \partial v_j} \{ f(\mathbf{v}) <\Delta v_i \Delta v_j/\Delta t> \} \qquad (37.96)$$

This is the so-called Fokker-Planck diffusion term. Although we have derived it as an approximation to the ordinary collision term in the Boltzmann transport equation, it can be derived quite independently of the Boltzmann collision term. In the general case the interpretation of $<\Delta v_i/\Delta t>$ and $<\Delta v_i \Delta v_j/\Delta t>$ is the same. However, the expressions (37.94) and (37.95) are valid only for situations in which we can consider the change in v_i to be due to a succession of two-body collisions.

The quantities $<\Delta v_i/\Delta t>$ and $<\Delta v_i \Delta v_j/\Delta t>$ as given by (37.94) and (37.95) can be further simplified if we carry out the integration over $\mathbf{u}'$. Thus, making use of the results of Appendix 15, we have

$$
\begin{aligned}
<\Delta v_i/\Delta t> &= -\iint \Delta v_i F(\mathbf{v} - \mathbf{u}')S(\mathbf{u}, \mathbf{u}')d\mathbf{u}d\mathbf{u}' \\
&= \iint \Delta v_i F(\mathbf{v} - \mathbf{u})S(\mathbf{u}, \mathbf{u}')d\mathbf{u}d\mathbf{u}' \\
&= (m^*/m)\iint (u_i' - u_i)F(\mathbf{v} - \mathbf{u})S(\mathbf{u}, \mathbf{u}')d\mathbf{u}d\mathbf{u}' \\
&= -(m^*/m)\int uu_i\sigma_m(u)F(\mathbf{v} - \mathbf{u})d\mathbf{u}
\end{aligned}
\tag{37.97}
$$

$$
\begin{aligned}
<\Delta v_i \Delta v_j/\Delta t> &= \iint \Delta v_i \Delta v_j F(\mathbf{v} - \mathbf{u})S(\mathbf{u}, \mathbf{u}')d\mathbf{u}d\mathbf{u}' \\
&= (m^*/m)^2 \iint (u_i' - u_i)(u_j' - u_j)F(\mathbf{v} - \mathbf{u})S(\mathbf{u}, \mathbf{u}')d\mathbf{u}d\mathbf{u}' \\
&= (m^*/m)^2 \iint (u_i'u_j' + u_iu_j - u_i'u_j - u_iu_j')F(\mathbf{v} - \mathbf{u})S(\mathbf{u}, \mathbf{u}')d\mathbf{u}d\mathbf{u}' \\
&= (m^*/m)^2 \int \{(u/2)(u^2\delta_{ij} - u_iu_j)\sigma(u) \\
&\quad + (u/2)(3u_iu_j - u^2\delta_{ij})\sigma_2(u) \\
&\quad + uu_iu_j\sigma(u) - uu_iu_j\sigma_1(u) \\
&\quad - uu_iu_j\sigma_1(u)\} F(\mathbf{v} - \mathbf{u})d\mathbf{u}
\end{aligned}
\tag{37.98}
$$

where

$$
\sigma(u) = \int \sigma(u, \theta)\sin\theta d\theta d\phi
\tag{37.99}
$$

$$
\sigma_1(u) = \int \sigma(u, \theta)\cos\theta \sin\theta d\theta d\phi
\tag{37.100}
$$

$$
\sigma_2(u) = \int \sigma(u, \theta)\cos^2\theta \sin\theta d\theta d\phi
\tag{37.101}
$$

The above cross sections can be approximated since we are assuming that small-angle scattering predominates. Thus noting that

$$
\sin\theta = 2\sin(\theta/2)\cos(\theta/2)
\tag{37.102}
$$

$$\sin\theta\cos\theta = 2\sin(\theta/2)\cos(\theta/2) - 4\sin^3(\theta/2)\cos(\theta/2) \tag{37.103}$$

$$\cos^2\theta\sin\theta = 2\sin(\theta/2)\cos(\theta/2) - 8\sin^3(\theta/2)\cos(\theta/2) + 8\sin^5(\theta/2)\cos(\theta/2) \tag{37.104}$$

and dropping the $\sin^5(\theta/2)$ term compared to the $\sin^3(\theta/2)$ term, we have

$$\sigma_2(u) \approx 2\sigma_1(u) - \sigma(u) \tag{37.105}$$

Substituting (37.105) in (37.98), we obtain

$$<\Delta v_i \Delta v_j / \Delta t> \approx (m^*/m)^2 \int u[u^2\delta_{ij} - u_i u_j]\sigma_m(u)F(\mathbf{v} - \mathbf{u})d\mathbf{u} \tag{37.106}$$

Gathering results, we have

$$\frac{Df}{Dt} = -\sum_i \frac{\partial}{\partial v_i}\{ f(\mathbf{v}) <\Delta v_i/\Delta t> \}$$

$$+ \frac{1}{2}\sum_i \sum_j \frac{\partial^2}{\partial v_i \partial v_j}\{ f(\mathbf{v}) <\Delta v_i \Delta v_j/\Delta t> \} \tag{37.107}$$

where

$$<\Delta v_i/\Delta t> = -(m^*/m) \int u u_i \sigma_m(u)F(\mathbf{v} - \mathbf{u})d\mathbf{u} \tag{37.108}$$

$$<\Delta v_i \Delta v_j/\Delta t> \approx (m^*/m)^2 \int u(u^2\delta_{ij} - u_i u_j)\sigma_m(u)F(\mathbf{v} - \mathbf{u})d\mathbf{u} \tag{37.109}$$

The above approximation to the collision term is valid when the average change in the velocity $\mathbf{v}$ in a collision is small compared to the average velocities of the particles of mass m and the particles of mass M.

Chapter 38

THE CONDUCTIVITY
OF A SLIGHTLY
IONIZED GAS

INTRODUCTION

One of the most important applications of kinetic theory is in the study of the electrical properties of an ionized gas. In this chapter and in Chapter 39 we will use the kinetic theory to determine the theoretically expected behavior of an ionized gas in the presence of an alternating electric field.

An ionized gas is a mixture of electrons, ions, and neutral molecules. For simplicity we will restrict ourselves to a discussion of ionized gases in which there is only one type of ion and one type of neutral molecule. We will furthermore assume that our gas is composed of a fixed number of electrons, a fixed number of ions, and a fixed number of neutral molecules, and that we can neglect any ionization or recombination processes which may be taking place. Finally, we shall assume that the interaction between the various types of particles can be treated as elastic collisions.

In the absence of any external fields, we expect the electrons, ions, and neutral molecules to have Maxwellian distributions with the same temperature T for each distribution.

In the presence of an electric field the electrons and ions will be accelerated and consequently their distribution functions will not be Maxwellian. Through collisions of the electrons and ions with neutral molecules, the distribution of the molecules will also be non-Maxwellian. However, because of the greater mobility of the electrons, the distortion of the electron distribution function will be much greater than the distortion of the ion and neutral molecule distribution functions. The electrical properties of an ionized gas will as a consequence be primarily due to the electrons, and we can without appreciable error assume that the ion and neutral molecule distributions are approximately Maxwellian. Our problem thus reduces to a study of the behavior of a gas of electrons in a background of heavy particles having a Maxwellian distribution.

THE BOLTZMANN TRANSPORT EQUATION

In the presence of an electric field **E**, the electron distribution $f(\mathbf{x}, \mathbf{v}, t)$ is determined by solving the Boltzmann transport equation.

$$\frac{\partial f}{\partial t} + \sum_i v_i \frac{\partial f}{\partial x_i} + \sum_i \frac{eE_i}{m} \frac{\partial f}{\partial v_i} = \left(\frac{Df}{Dt}\right)_{ee} + \left(\frac{Df}{Dt}\right)_{ei} + \left(\frac{Df}{Dt}\right)_{en} \qquad (38.1)$$

where $(Df/Dt)_{ee}$, $(Df/Dt)_{ei}$ and $(Df/Dt)_{en}$ represent respectively the change in f due to collisions of electrons with electrons, with ions, and with neutral molecules.

Let us assume the electric field **E** is given by

$$\mathbf{E} = \mathbf{e}_1 E \cos \omega t \qquad (38.2)$$

We are assuming that **E** is not a function of **x**, and has a component in the 1 direction only. The electric field in question might be produced by an electromagnetic wave passing through the gas. Provided the wavelength of the wave is long compared to the electron mean free path, we can divide the gas into regions which are large compared to a mean free path and yet small enough that the electric field is essentially uniform throughout the region. We then restrict our study to one such region. In this region the electric field is given essentially by (38.2). Since the electric field is independent of **x**, we expect the distribution function to be independent of **x**. Substituting (38.2) in (38.1) and noting that the second term vanishes, we have

$$\frac{\partial f}{\partial t} + \frac{eE \cos \omega t}{m} \frac{\partial f}{\partial v_1} = \left(\frac{Df}{Dt}\right)_{ee} + \left(\frac{Df}{Dt}\right)_{ei} + \left(\frac{Df}{Dt}\right)_{en} \qquad (38.3)$$

If our gas is only slightly ionized, the predominant collision process will be electron neutral molecule collisions. In this case we can neglect the terms $(Df/Dt)_{ee}$ and $(Df/Dt)_{ei}$ and we have

$$\frac{\partial f}{\partial t} + \frac{eE \cos \omega t}{m} \frac{\partial f}{\partial v_1} = \frac{Df}{Dt} \qquad (38.4)$$

where

$$\frac{Df}{Dt} \equiv \left(\frac{Df}{Dt}\right)_{en} \qquad (38.5)$$

THE ELECTRON DISTRIBUTION FUNCTION

In order to solve Eq. (38.4) we may assume some approximate form for the electron distribution function. Let us assume a slightly distorted isotropic distribution of the form

$$f(\mathbf{v}) = \psi(|\mathbf{v} - \mathbf{e}_1\phi(v, t)|) \approx \psi(v) + v_1 g(v, t) \tag{38.6}$$

Since the mass of an electron is very small compared to the mass of a neutral molecule, we can use the approximate collision term derived in Chapter 37. With this collision term and the distribution (38.6), Eq. (38.4) becomes

$$\frac{\partial}{\partial t}[\psi(v) + v_1 g(v, t)] + \frac{eE\cos\omega t}{m}\frac{\partial}{\partial v_1}[\psi(v) + v_1 g(v, t)]$$

$$= \frac{m}{Mv^2}\frac{d}{dv}[v^3\nu_m(v)\psi(v)]$$

$$+ \frac{kT}{Mv^2}\frac{d}{dv}\left[v^2\nu_m(v)\frac{d\psi(v)}{dv}\right] - \nu_m(v)v_1 g(v, t) \tag{38.7}$$

If v_1 is replaced by $-v_1$ in (38.7) and the resulting equation added and subtracted, respectively, from (38.7), a separation of the terms which are even and odd with respect to v_1 can be effected. Equation (38.7) then splits into two equations

$$\frac{eE\cos\omega t}{m}g + \frac{eE\cos\omega t}{m}\frac{v_1^2}{v}\frac{\partial g}{\partial v}$$

$$= \frac{m}{Mv^2}\frac{d}{dv}(v^3\nu_m\psi) + \frac{kT}{Mv^2}\frac{d}{dv}\left(v^2\nu_m\frac{d\psi}{dv}\right) \tag{38.8}$$

$$\frac{\partial g}{\partial t} + \frac{eE\cos\omega t}{mv}\frac{d\psi}{dv} = -\nu_m g \tag{38.9}$$

Solving (38.9), we obtain in the steady state

$$g = (eE/m)[h\cos\omega t + H\sin\omega t] \tag{38.10}$$

where

$$h = -\frac{1}{v}\frac{d\psi}{dv}\frac{\nu_m}{\omega^2 + \nu_m^2} \tag{38.11}$$

$$H = -\frac{1}{v}\frac{d\psi}{dv}\frac{\omega}{\omega^2 + \nu_m^2} \tag{38.12}$$

Substituting (38.10) in (38.8), we obtain

$$\left(\frac{eE}{m}\right)^2(h\cos^2\omega t + H\sin\omega t\cos\omega t) + \left(\frac{eE}{m}\right)^2\frac{v_1^2}{v}\left(\frac{dh}{dv}\cos^2\omega t + \frac{dH}{dv}\sin\omega t\cos\omega t\right)$$

$$= \frac{m}{Mv^2}\frac{d}{dv}(v^3\nu_m\psi) + \frac{kT}{Mv^2}\frac{d}{dv}\left(v^2\nu_m\frac{d\psi}{dv}\right) \qquad (38.13)$$

If we average (38.13) over all directions and over a time $2\pi/\omega$, we obtain

$$\left(\frac{eE}{m}\right)^2\frac{h}{2} + \left(\frac{eE}{m}\right)^2\frac{v}{6}\frac{dh}{dv} = \frac{m}{Mv^2}\frac{d}{dv}(v^3\nu_m\psi) + \frac{kT}{Mv^2}\frac{d}{dv}\left(v^2\nu_m\frac{d\psi}{dv}\right) \qquad (38.14)$$

or

$$\frac{1}{6}\left(\frac{eE}{m}\right)^2\frac{d}{dv}(v^3h) = \frac{m}{M}\frac{d}{dv}(v^3\nu_m\psi) + \frac{kT}{M}\frac{d}{dv}\left(v^2\nu_m\frac{d\psi}{dv}\right) \qquad (38.15)$$

Integrating with respect to v, we obtain

$$\frac{e^2E^2v^3h}{6m^2} - \frac{mv^3\nu_m\psi}{M} - \frac{kTv^2\nu_m}{M}\frac{d\psi}{dv} = \text{const} \qquad (38.16)$$

When $v = 0$, the left-hand side of (38.16) vanishes. The constant is therefore zero.

Substituting the value of $h(v)$ given by (38.11) into (38.16) and setting the constant equal to zero, we obtain

$$\left(\frac{e^2E^2}{6m^2}\right)\frac{1}{\omega^2 + \nu_m^2}\frac{d\psi}{dv} + \frac{kT}{M}\frac{d\psi}{dv} + \frac{mv}{M}\psi = 0 \qquad (38.17)$$

or

$$\frac{d\psi/dv}{\psi} = -\frac{mv}{kT + [e^2E^2M/6m^2(\omega^2 + \nu_m^2)]} \qquad (38.18)$$

Integrating, we obtain

$$\ln\psi + \text{const} = -\int_0^v\left\{\frac{mv}{kT + [e^2E^2M/6m^2(\omega^2 + \nu_m^2)]}\right\}dv \qquad (38.19)$$

or

$$\psi = C\exp\left\{-\int_0^v\frac{mvdv}{kT + [e^2E^2M/6m^2(\omega^2 + \nu_m^2)]}\right\} \qquad (38.20)$$

where C is a constant.

Gathering the results, we have

$$f(\mathbf{v}) = \psi(v) + v_1g(v, t) \qquad (38.21)$$

$$g(v, t) = (eE/m)[h(v)\cos\omega t + H(v)\sin\omega t] \qquad (38.22)$$

$$h(v) = -\frac{1}{v}\frac{d\psi}{dv}\frac{\nu_m}{\omega^2 + \nu_m^2} \qquad (38.23)$$

$$H(v) = -\frac{1}{v}\frac{d\psi}{dv}\frac{\omega}{\omega^2 + \nu_m^2} \qquad (38.24)$$

where ψ is given by (38.20).

If $E = 0$, then our solution reduces as it should to the Maxwellian distribution.

If
$$kT \gg e^2E^2M/6m^2(\omega^2 + \nu_m{}^2) \qquad (38.25)$$

then from Eq. (38.20) the isotropic portion of the distribution function is approximately Maxwellian at a temperature T.

If
$$kT \ll e^2E^2M/6m^2(\omega^2 + \nu_m{}^2) \qquad (38.26)$$

then from Eq. (38.20) the isotropic portion of the distribution function is given by

$$\psi = C\exp\left\{-\int_0^v \frac{6m^3(\omega^2 + \nu_m{}^2)vdv}{e^2E^2M}\right\} \qquad (38.27)$$

If ν_m is a constant, then from Eq. (38.20) the isotropic portion of the distribution function is Maxwellian, but with an electron temperature given by

$$\tau = T + [e^2E^2M/6m^2k(\omega^2 + \nu_m{}^2)] \qquad (38.38)$$

The collision frequency ν_m can be written

$$\nu_m(v) = Nv\sigma_m(v) \qquad (38.29)$$

where $\sigma_m(v)$ is the usual momentum transfer cross section. If $\sigma_m(v)$ is a constant, then (38.20) can be integrated. The resulting expression is, however, not particularly simple.

In general $\nu_m(v)$ is some more complicated function of v than those discussed above, and the integration (38.20) must be obtained by numerical methods.

THE CURRENT DENSITY

We can use the distribution function obtained in the preceding section to determine the current density in the ionized gas. The current density in the 1 direction is simply

$$
\begin{aligned}
J = ne\bar{v}_1 &= e\int v_1 f d\mathbf{v} \\
&= e\int v_1[\psi(v) + v_1 g(v, t)]d\mathbf{v} \\
&= e\int v_1{}^2 g(v, t)d\mathbf{v} = (e/3)\int v^2 g(v, t)d\mathbf{v} \\
&= (e^2E/3m)\int [v^2 h(v)\cos\omega t + v^2 H(v)\sin\omega t]d\mathbf{v} \\
&= -\frac{e^2E}{3m}\int\left(\frac{\nu_m\cos\omega t + \omega\sin\omega t}{\omega^2 + \nu_m{}^2}\right)v\frac{d\psi}{dv}d\mathbf{v} \qquad (38.30)
\end{aligned}
$$

In order to solve for J, we must know ψ. The function ψ is given by (38.20). If

$$e^2E^2M/6m^2(\omega^2 + \nu_m{}^2) \ll kT \tag{38.31}$$

then ψ is approximately Maxwellian, i.e.,

$$\psi \approx f_0(\mathbf{v}) = n(\lambda/\pi)^{3/2}\exp(-\lambda v^2) \tag{38.32}$$

Substituting (38.32) in (38.30), we obtain

$$J = \frac{2\lambda e^2 E}{3m} \int \left(\frac{\nu_m\cos\omega t + \omega\sin\omega t}{\omega^2 + \nu_m{}^2}\right) v^2 f_0(\mathbf{v}) d\mathbf{v} \tag{38.33}$$

If ν_m is constant, we obtain

$$J = \frac{ne^2 E}{m}\left(\frac{\nu_m\cos\omega t + \omega\sin\omega t}{\omega^2 + \nu_m{}^2}\right) \tag{38.34}$$

However, in general ν_m is a complicated function of v and we must resort to numerical integration to obtain J.

Chapter 39

THE CONDUCTIVITY
OF A HIGHLY
IONIZED GAS

INTRODUCTION

In Chapter 38, we solved for the distribution function of the electrons in a slightly ionized gas in the presence of an alternating electric field.

In the present chapter we will derive an expression for the electron distribution function in an ionized gas of arbitrary degree of ionization in the presence of an alternating electric field. The expressions which we will obtain are not as accurate as those of the preceding chapter in the range in which they overlap; however, their greater range of validity, tractability, and versatility more than make up for the loss in precision.

ASSUMPTIONS

We shall assume, as in Chapter 38, that our ionized gas is composed of only three types of particles—electrons, one type of ion, and one type of neutral molecule, and that the distribution functions of the ions and neutral molecules are Maxwellian at temperature T.

In the presence of a homogeneous electric field of the form $e_1 E \cos \omega t$, the electron distribution function satisfies the Boltzmann transport equation which for these boundary conditions is simply

$$\frac{\partial f}{\partial t} + \frac{eE\cos\omega t}{m}\frac{df}{\partial v_1} = \left(\frac{Df}{Dt}\right)_{ee} + \left(\frac{Df}{Dt}\right)_{ei} + \left(\frac{Df}{Dt}\right)_{en} \tag{39.1}$$

where $(Df/Dt)_{ee}$, $(Df/Dt)_{ei}$, and $(Df/Dt)_{en}$ represent respectively the rate of change in f due to collisions of electrons with electrons, with ions, and with neutral molecules.

If the Boltzmann transport equation is multiplied by an arbitrary function $q(\mathbf{v}, t)$ and integrated over $\mathbf{v}$ we obtain the equation of change, which was discussed in Chapter 31. For the above boundary conditions it simplifies to

$$\frac{\partial}{\partial t}[n\bar{q}] - n\overline{(\partial q/\partial t)} - \left(\frac{eEn}{m}\right)\cos\omega t\overline{(\partial q/\partial v_1)} = (\Delta q)_{ee} + (\Delta q)_{ei} + (\Delta q)_{en} \quad (39.2)$$

We will work with Eq. (39.2) rather than (39.1).

In discussing the transport properties of a simple gas we found that it was possible to get good results assuming a distribution function of the form (see Chapter 34)

$$f = f_0(\mathbf{v})\left\{1 + \Sigma_i a_i v_i + \Sigma_i\Sigma_j b_{ij}v_iv_j + \Sigma_i c_i v_i[v^2 - (5/2\lambda)]\right\} \quad (39.3)$$

where the coefficients a_i, b_{ij} and c_i were related to the macroscopic quantities $\bar{v}_i$, p_{ij} and q_i as follows

$$a_i = 2\lambda\bar{v}_i \quad (39.4)$$

$$b_{ij} = (2\lambda^2/mn)(p_{ij} - p\delta_{ij}) \quad (39.5)$$

$$c_i = (8\lambda^3/5mn)q_i \quad (39.6)$$

We shall assume that the distribution function for the gas of electrons can also be approximated by such a distribution function. For the electric field which we have chosen we furthermore expect $\bar{v}_2 = \bar{v}_3 = q_2 = q_3 = (p_{ij} - p\delta_{ij}) = 0$ and therefore (39.3) reduces to

$$f = f_0(\mathbf{v})\{1 + a_1v_1 + c_1v_1[v^2 - (5/2\lambda)]\} \quad (39.7)$$

For an ordinary gas $f_0(\mathbf{v})$ was just the Maxwellian distribution at a temperature T. However, in the case of an ionized gas in the presence of an electric field, it is primarily the electrons which absorb energy from the field, and it is therefore possible that the electron temperature may be appreciably different from the temperature of the ions and neutral molecules. We shall therefore assume that the distribution $f_0(\mathbf{v})$ is Maxwellian but at a temperature τ which may be quite different from the temperature T. We then have

$$f_0(\mathbf{v}) = n(\lambda/\pi)^{3/2}\exp(-\lambda v^2) \quad (39.8)$$

$$\lambda = m/2k\tau \quad (39.9)$$

Great care must be exercised in taking results over from previous chapters where it was assumed that $\tau = T$.

We shall also find it convenient to use J and Q to represent the electrical and thermal current densities. In terms of our previous notation

$$J = ne\bar{v}_1 \quad (39.10)$$

$$Q \equiv q_1 \quad (39.11)$$

In terms of J and Q Eq. (39.7) can be written

$$f = f_0(\mathbf{v})\{1 + (2\lambda/ne)Jv_1 + (8\lambda^3/5mn)Qv_1[v^2 - (5/2\lambda)]\} \tag{39.12}$$

THE EQUATIONS OF CHANGE

If we let $q(\mathbf{v}, t) = 1$ in the equation of change (39.2), we obtain

$$\partial n/\partial t = 0 \tag{39.13}$$

The density of electrons is therefore constant. If we wish to take into account the effect of ionization and recombination, then we have to introduce an additional term in the Boltzmann transport equation. In the present analysis we are assuming that we can neglect any ionization and recombination. We are also restricting ourselves to elastic collisions.

If we let $q(\mathbf{v}, t) = ev_1$ in Eq. (39.2) and make use of the distribution (39.12) to calculate the averages, we obtain

$$\dot{J} - (e^2En/m)\cos\omega t = e[(\Delta v_1)_{en} + (\Delta v_1)_{ei}] \tag{39.14}$$

where $\dot{J}$ is the derivative of J with respect to time. Due to conservation of momentum in a collision $(\Delta v_1)_{ee} = 0$.

If we let $q(\mathbf{v}, t) = (mv_1/2)[v^2 - (5/2\lambda)]$ in Eq. (39.2) and make use of the distribution (39.12) to calculate the averages, we obtain

$$\dot{Q} + \left(\frac{5m}{4\lambda e}\right)\left(\frac{\dot{\tau}}{\tau}\right)J = \left(\frac{m}{2}\right)\left\{[\Delta v_1 v^2]_{ee} + \left[\Delta v_1\left(v^2 - \frac{5}{2\lambda}\right)\right]_{en} + \left[\Delta v_1\left(v^2 - \frac{5}{2\lambda}\right)\right]_{ei}\right\} \tag{39.15}$$

Finally if we let $q(\mathbf{v}, t) = mv^2/2$ in Eq. (39.2) and make use of the distribution (39.12) to calculate the averages we obtain

$$(3nk/2)\dot{\tau} = JE\cos\omega t + (m/2)\{(\Delta v^2)_{en} + (\Delta v^2)_{ei}\} \tag{39.16}$$

The first term in (39.16) is just the rate of change in the internal energy per unit volume of the electrons. The second term is the power absorbed by the electrons from the field. The third term is the rate at which energy is lost by the electrons due to collisions of electrons with ions and neutral molecules.

Equations (39.14), (39.15), and (39.16) provide us with three equations to determine the three unknown quantities J, Q, and τ. Before we can make use of these equations we must evaluate the collision terms.

THE COLLISION TERMS

In Chapter 31 we saw that the collision term could be written

$$(\Delta q)_{12} = \iiint [q(\mathbf{v}') - q(\mathbf{v})]f(\mathbf{v})F(\mathbf{V})W_{12}(\mathbf{v}, \mathbf{V}; \mathbf{v}', \mathbf{V}')d\mathbf{v}d\mathbf{v}'d\mathbf{V}d\mathbf{V}' \tag{39.17}$$

Let us let $f(\mathbf{v})$ be the electron distribution function and $F(\mathbf{V})$ the distribution function for the ions or neutral molecules, then

$$F(\mathbf{V}) = F_0(\mathbf{V}) = N(\Lambda/\pi)^{3/2} \exp(-\Lambda V^2) \tag{39.18}$$

$$f(\mathbf{v}) = f_0(\mathbf{v})[1 + h(\mathbf{v})] \tag{39.19}$$

$$h(\mathbf{v}) = (2\lambda/ne)Jv_1 + (8\lambda^3/5mn)Qv_1[v^2 - (5/2\lambda)] \tag{30.20}$$

$$f_0(\mathbf{v}) = n(\lambda/\pi)^{3/2} \exp(-\lambda v^2) \tag{39.21}$$

$$\Lambda = M/2kT \tag{39.22}$$

$$\lambda = m/2k\tau \tag{39.23}$$

Substituting (39.18) and (39.19) in (39.17), switching to relative coordinates $\mathbf{u}$, $\mathbf{u}'$ and center of mass coordinates $\mathbf{w}$ and $\mathbf{w}'$, and integrating over $\mathbf{w}'$, we obtain (see Chapter 28)

$$(\Delta q)_{12} = \iiint \{q[\mathbf{w} + (m^*/m)\mathbf{u}'] - q[\mathbf{w} + (m^*/m)\mathbf{u}]\}$$
$$f_0[\mathbf{w} + (m^*/m)\mathbf{u}]F_0[\mathbf{w} - (m^*/M)\mathbf{u}]$$
$$\{1 + h[\mathbf{w} + (m^*/m)\mathbf{u}]\} S_{12}(\mathbf{u}, \mathbf{u}') d\mathbf{u} d\mathbf{u}' d\mathbf{w} \tag{39.24}$$

The product $f_0[\mathbf{w} + (m^*/m)\mathbf{u}]F_0[\mathbf{w} - (m^*/M)\mathbf{u}]$ can be written

$$f_0[\mathbf{w} + (m^*/m)\mathbf{u}]F_0[\mathbf{w} - (m^*/M)\mathbf{u}] = \psi(\mathbf{u})\Psi(\mathbf{w} - b\mathbf{u}) \tag{39.25}$$

where

$$\psi(\mathbf{u}) = n(c/\pi)^{3/2} \exp(-cu^2) \tag{39.26}$$

$$\Psi(\mathbf{w}) = N(a/\pi)^{3/2} \exp(-aw^2) \tag{39.27}$$

$$a = (\lambda + \Lambda) \tag{39.28}$$

$$b = m^*(\tau - T)/(mT + M\tau) \tag{39.29}$$

$$c = \lambda\Lambda/(\lambda + \Lambda) \tag{39.30}$$

Since the electron mass m is very small compared to the mass M of the ions or neutral molecules, and since the electron temperature τ is always greater than the heavy particle temperature T, we have

$$m/\tau \ll M/T \tag{39.31}$$

$$m^* = mM/(m + M) \approx m \tag{39.32}$$

It follows that

$$a \approx \Lambda \tag{39.33}$$

$$b \approx (m/M)[(\tau - T)/\tau] \tag{39.34}$$

$$c \approx \lambda \tag{39.35}$$

and therefore

$$f_0[\mathbf{w} + (m^*/m)\mathbf{u}]F_0[\mathbf{w} - (m^*/M)\mathbf{u}]$$
$$= \psi(\mathbf{u})\Psi(\mathbf{w} - b\mathbf{u}) \approx f_0(\mathbf{u})F_0(\mathbf{w} - b\mathbf{u}) \qquad (39.36)$$

and finally therefore

$$(\Delta q)_{12} \approx \iiint \{q[\mathbf{w} + (m^*/m)\mathbf{u}'] - q[\mathbf{w} + (m^*/m)\mathbf{u}]\}$$
$$f_0(\mathbf{u})F_0(\mathbf{w} - b\mathbf{u})[1 + h(\mathbf{w} + \mathbf{u})]S_{12}(\mathbf{u}, \mathbf{u}')d\mathbf{u}d\mathbf{u}'d\mathbf{w} \qquad (39.37)$$

We shall avoid making any approximations in the term

$$q[\mathbf{w} + (m^*/m)\mathbf{u}'] - q[\mathbf{w} + (m^*/m)\mathbf{u}] \qquad (39.38)$$

since it is a difference and we may be approximating away a desired result.

Let us make the transformation $\mathbf{w}^* = \mathbf{w} - b\mathbf{u}$ and then drop the asterisk. Equation (39.37) becomes

$$(\Delta q)_{12} \approx \iiint \{q[\mathbf{w} + b\mathbf{u} + (m^*/m)\mathbf{u}'] - q[\mathbf{w} + b\mathbf{u} + (m^*/m)\mathbf{u}]\}$$
$$f_0(\mathbf{u})F_0(\mathbf{w})[1 + h(\mathbf{w} + b\mathbf{u} + \mathbf{u})]S_{12}(\mathbf{u}, \mathbf{u}')d\mathbf{u}d\mathbf{u}'d\mathbf{w} \qquad (39.39)$$

Since $F_0(\mathbf{w})$ has its peak at speeds much smaller than the speeds at which $f_0(\mathbf{u})$ peaks, we can assume that $|\mathbf{w}| \ll |\mathbf{u}|$. We also have $b \ll 1$. Equation (39.39) then becomes

$$(\Delta q)_{12} \approx \iiint \{q[\mathbf{w} + b\mathbf{u} + (m^*/m)\mathbf{u}'] - q[\mathbf{w} + b\mathbf{u} + (m^*/m)\mathbf{u}]\}$$
$$f_0(\mathbf{u})F_0(\mathbf{w})[1 + h(\mathbf{u})]S_{12}(\mathbf{u}, \mathbf{u}')d\mathbf{u}d\mathbf{u}'d\mathbf{w} \qquad (39.40)$$

Letting $q(\mathbf{v}) = v_1$ in Eq. (39.40) we obtain

$$(\Delta v_1)_{12} \approx \iiint (u_1' - u_1)f_0(\mathbf{u})F_0(\mathbf{w})[1 + h(\mathbf{u})]S_{12}(\mathbf{u}, \mathbf{u}')d\mathbf{u}d\mathbf{u}'d\mathbf{w} \qquad (39.41)$$

Integrating over $\mathbf{w}$ and $\mathbf{u}'$ we obtain (see Appendix 14)

$$(\Delta v_1)_{12} \approx -N \int uu_{1}\sigma_m{}^{12}(u)f_0(\mathbf{u})h(\mathbf{u})d\mathbf{u} \qquad (39.42)$$

Substituting (39.20) in (39.42) we get (see Appendix 16)

$$(\Delta v_1)_{12} \approx -(J/e)\nu_1{}^{12} + (2\lambda Q/m)\nu_2{}^{12} \qquad (39.43)$$

where

$$\nu_1{}^{12} = (2\lambda/3n)\int (Nu\sigma_m{}^{12})u^2f_0(\mathbf{u})d\mathbf{u} \qquad (39.44)$$

$$\nu_2{}^{12} = (4\lambda^2/15n)\int (Nu\sigma_m{}^{12})u^2[(5/2\lambda) - u^2]f_0(\mathbf{u})d\mathbf{u} \qquad (39.45)$$

Letting $q(\mathbf{v}) = v_1\left(v^2 - \dfrac{5}{2\lambda}\right)$ in Eq. (39.40) and noting that

$$\{q[\mathbf{w} + b\mathbf{u} + (m^*/m)\mathbf{u}'] - q[\mathbf{w} + b\mathbf{u} + (m^*/m)\mathbf{u}]\}$$
$$\approx q(\mathbf{u}') - q(\mathbf{u}) = u_1'[u'^2 - (5/2\lambda)] - u_1[u^2 - (5/2\lambda)]$$
$$= u_1'[u^2 - (5/2\lambda)] - u_1[u^2 - (5/2\lambda)]$$
$$= (u_1' - u_1)[u^2 - (5/2\lambda)] \tag{39.46}$$

we get (see Appendix 14)

$$\{\Delta v_1[v^2 - (5/2\lambda)]\}_{12} = -N \int u u_1 \sigma_m^{12}(u)[u^2 - (5/2\lambda)] f_0(\mathbf{u}) h(\mathbf{u}) d\mathbf{u} \tag{39.47}$$

Substituting (39.20) in (39.47) we obtain (see Appendix 16)

$$\{\Delta v_1[v^2 - (5/2\lambda)]\}_{12} = (5J/2\lambda e)\nu_2^{12} - (2Q/m)\nu_3^{12} \tag{38.48}$$

where

$$\nu_3^{12} = (4\lambda^3/15n) \int (N u \sigma_m^{12}) u^2 [u^2 - (5/2\lambda)]^2 f_0(\mathbf{u}) d\mathbf{u} \tag{38.49}$$

Letting $q(\mathbf{v}) = v^2$ and noting that we can always replace u' by u, we get

$$q[\mathbf{w} + b\mathbf{u} + (m^*/m)\mathbf{u}'] - q[\mathbf{w} + b\mathbf{u} + (m^*/m)\mathbf{u}]$$
$$\approx 2\mathbf{w} \cdot (\mathbf{u}' - \mathbf{u}) + 2b\mathbf{u} \cdot (\mathbf{u}' - \mathbf{u}) \tag{39.50}$$

Substituting (39.50) in (39.40), and integrating over $\mathbf{w}$ and $\mathbf{u}'$ we get (see Appendix 14)

$$(\Delta v^2)_{12} = -2bN \int u^3 \sigma_m^{12}(u) f_0(\mathbf{u}) d\mathbf{u}$$
$$= -(3nb/\lambda)\nu_1^{12} \tag{39.51}$$

The final collision term which we need is the term $(\Delta v_1 v^2)_{ee}$. We have already evaluated this term in Eq. (35.54) where we obtained

$$(\Delta v_1 v^2)_{ee} = -(2Q/m)\nu^* \tag{39.52}$$

where

$$\nu^* = (\lambda^2/30) \int [u\sigma_\mu^{ee}(u)] u^4 \psi'(\mathbf{u}) d\mathbf{u} \tag{39.53}$$

$$\psi'(\mathbf{u}) = n(\lambda/2\pi)^{3/2} \exp(-\lambda u^2/2) \tag{39.54}$$

THE FUNDAMENTAL EQUATIONS FOR DETERMINING THE ELECTRON TEMPERATURE AND CONDUCTIVITY

If we substitute the collision terms (39.43), (39.48), (39.51), and (39.52) into the equations of change (39.14), (39.15), and (39.16) we have

$$\dot{J} + J\nu_1 - (2\lambda e/m)Q\nu_2 = (e^2En/m)\cos\omega t \tag{39.55}$$

$$\dot{Q} + (5m/4\lambda e)[(\dot{\tau}/\tau) - \nu_2]J + \nu_3 Q = 0 \tag{39.56}$$

$$(3nk/2)\dot{\tau} = JE\cos\omega t - (3nk\tau/2)(2m/M)[(\tau - T)/\tau]\nu_1 \tag{39.57}$$

where

$$\nu_1 \equiv \nu_1^{ei} + \nu_1^{en} \qquad (39.58)$$

$$\nu_2 \equiv \nu_2^{ei} + \nu_2^{en} \qquad (39.59)$$

$$\nu_3 \equiv \nu^* + \nu_3^{ei} + \nu_3^{en} \qquad (39.60)$$

If we know $\sigma_{ee}(u, \theta)$, $\sigma_{ei}(u, \theta)$, $\sigma_{en}(u, \theta)$ and the electron, neutral molecule, and ion densities, then we can determine ν_1^{ei}, ν_2^{ei}, ν_3^{ei}, ν_1^{en}, ν_2^{en}, ν_3^{en} and ν^* as functions of τ from Eqs. (39.44), (39.45), (39.49), and (39.53). If, in addition, we know the ion and neutral molecule temperature T, then we are left with three equations in three unknowns. In general ν_1, ν_2, and ν_3 are complicated functions of the electron temperature τ and the resulting equations are therefore quite messy. However, certain quite reasonable assumptions can be made which considerably simplify the situation for a wide range of cases.

LOW FIELD CONDUCTIVITY

We shall consider first the case in which the field E is small enough that $(\tau - T)/\tau \ll 1$ and $\dot{\tau}/\tau$ is small compared to ν_2. In this case (39.55) and (39.56) reduce to

$$\dot{J} + J\nu_1 - (2\lambda e/m)Q\nu_2 = (e^2 En/m)\cos\omega t \qquad (39.61)$$

$$\dot{Q} - (5m/4\lambda e)\nu_2 J + \nu_3 Q = 0 \qquad (39.62)$$

where ν_1, ν_2, and ν_3 are practically constant.

If we are interested in the steady state values of J and Q we can assume

$$J = Re[J^* \exp(i\omega t)] \qquad (39.63)$$

$$Q = Re[Q^* \exp(i\omega t)] \qquad (39.64)$$

Substituting (39.63) and (39.64) in (39.62) and (39.61) and noting as usual that if $Re(Ae^{i\omega t}) = Re(Be^{i\omega t})$ then $Im(Ae^{i\omega t}) = Im(Be^{i\omega t})$ and that $\dfrac{\partial}{\partial t}Re(Ae^{i\omega t}) = Re(i\omega Ae^{i\omega t})$ we obtain

$$\begin{bmatrix} i\omega + \nu_1 & -(2\lambda e/m)\nu_2 \\ -(5m/4\lambda e)\nu_2 & i\omega + \nu_3 \end{bmatrix} \begin{bmatrix} J^* \\ Q^* \end{bmatrix} = \begin{bmatrix} ne^2 E/m \\ 0 \end{bmatrix} \qquad (39.65)$$

Solving for J^* we obtain

$$J^* = \frac{\left(\dfrac{ne^2 E}{m}\right)\left\{\left[\omega^2\nu_1 + \nu_3\left(\nu_1\nu_3 - \dfrac{5}{2}\nu_2^2\right)\right] - i\left[\omega^3 + \omega\left(\nu_3^2 + \dfrac{5}{2}\nu_2^2\right)\right]\right\}}{\omega^4 + \omega^2[\nu_1^2 + 5\nu_2^2 + \nu_3^2] + [\nu_1\nu_3 - (5\nu_2^2/2)]^2} \qquad (39.66)$$

Substituting (39.66) in (39.63) we obtain

$$J = J'\cos\omega t + J''\sin\omega t \qquad (39.67)$$

$$J' = \frac{ne^2E}{m}\left\{\frac{\omega^2\nu_1 + \nu_3[\nu_1\nu_3 - (5\nu_2^2/2)]}{\omega^4 + \omega^2[\nu_1^2 + 5\nu_2^2 + \nu_3^2] + [\nu_1\nu_3 - (5\nu_2^2/2)]^2}\right\} \tag{39.68}$$

$$J'' = \frac{ne^2E}{m}\left\{\frac{\omega^3 + \omega[\nu_3^2 + (5\nu_2^2/2)]}{\omega^4 + \omega^2(\nu_1^2 + 5\nu_2^2 + \nu_3^2) + [\nu_1\nu_3 - (5\nu_2^2/2)]^2}\right\} \tag{39.69}$$

where

$$\nu_1 = \nu_1(T) \tag{39.70}$$

$$\nu_2 = \nu_2(T) \tag{39.71}$$

$$\nu_3 = \nu_3(T) \tag{39.72}$$

HIGH FIELD CONDUCTIVITY

The expression (39.67) for the current density in an ionized gas is, as we have shown, valid for small fields E for which $\tau \approx T$.

However, as we shall now show, its range of validity can be extended appreciably, the only change in the result being that $\nu_1(T)$, $\nu_2(T)$, and $\nu_3(T)$ are replaced by $\nu_1(\bar{\tau})$, $\nu_2(\bar{\tau})$, $\nu_3(\bar{\tau})$ where $\bar{\tau}$ is an average temperature which may differ appreciably from T.

We will consider the *dc* case first. Letting $\omega = \dot{J} = \dot{Q} = \dot{\tau} = 0$ in (39.55), (39.56), and (39.57) and solving for J and τ we find

$$J = \frac{ne^2E}{m}\left\{\frac{\nu_3}{[\nu_1\nu_3 - (5\nu_2^2/2)]}\right\} \tag{39.73}$$

where $\nu_1 = \nu_1(\tau)$, $\nu_2 = \nu_2(\tau)$ and $\nu_3 = \nu_3(\tau)$ and τ is obtained by solving the equation

$$\tau = T + (2/3nk)[M/2m\nu_1(\tau)]JE \tag{39.74}$$

This is the same result we would obtain by setting $\omega = 0$ in (39.67) except that ν_1, ν_2, and ν_3 are functions of τ instead of T, where τ is determined from (39.74). It is interesting to note that τ can be a quite complex function of E, and that there can even be multiple values of τ for the same value of E.

Let us now consider the case in which $\omega \neq 0$. To get a rough idea of the behavior of the temperature let us assume in (39.57) that ν_1 is a constant and $J = J'\cos\omega t + J''\sin\omega t$. If we then solve for τ we find that the steady-state solution is given by

$$\tau = T + \frac{(J'E/3nk)}{(2m\nu_1/M)} + \frac{(1/3nk)[(J'E)^2 + (J''E)^2]^{1/2}}{[(2m\nu_1/M)^2 + (2\omega)^2]^{1/2}}\cos(2\omega t - \theta) \tag{39.75}$$

If

$$T + \frac{(J'E/3nk)}{(2m\nu_1/M)} \gg \frac{(1/3nk)[(J'E)^2 + (J''E)^2]^{1/2}}{[(2m\nu_1/M)^2 + (2\omega)^2]^{1/2}} \tag{39.76}$$

then the temperature τ executes small oscillations about an average temperature

$$\bar{\tau} = T + \frac{(J'E/3nk)}{(2m\nu_1/M)} \tag{39.77}$$

A similar behavior will be expected even if ν_1 is not a constant. If τ does make small oscillations about an average temperature $\bar{\tau}$, we can assume that $\tau = \bar{\tau}$ in (39.55) and (39.56) and we again obtain (39.67) with T replaced by $\bar{\tau}$. Finally, if we assume that $\nu_1(\tau)$ in (39.57) can be replaced by $\nu_1(\bar{\tau})$ and $J(\bar{\tau})$ by $J(\bar{\tau})$, then $\bar{\tau}$ can be found by solving the equation

$$\bar{\tau} = T + \frac{J'(\bar{\tau})E/3nk}{2m\nu_1(\bar{\tau})/M} \tag{39.78}$$

We now ask ourselves under what conditions we expect (39.76) to be valid. It is certainly valid if

$$\frac{J'E/3nk}{2m\nu_1/M} \ll T \tag{39.79}$$

This is simply the small field assumption which we considered previously. The maximum value of J' is of the order of $ne^2E\nu_1/m(\nu_1^2 + \omega^2)$. Therefore the above condition is equivalent to assuming that

$$\frac{e^2E^2M}{6km^2(\nu_1^2 + \omega^2)} \ll T \tag{39.80}$$

This is not the only situation in which (39.76) is valid. Noting that $J'' \sim (\omega/\nu_1)J'$ in (39.76), we obtain

$$T + \frac{(J'E/3nk)}{(2m\nu_1/M)} \gg \frac{(J'E/3nk)[1 + (\omega/\nu_1)^2]^{1/2}}{[(2m\nu_1/M)^2 + (2\omega)^2]^{1/2}} \tag{39.81}$$

If

$$\omega \gg m\nu_1/M \tag{39.82}$$

then (39.81) is satisfied. If $E = 0$ and ν_1 is constant, then the solution of (39.57) is

$$\tau = T + C \exp[-(2m\nu_1/M)t] \tag{39.83}$$

Thus $(M/2m\nu_1)$ is just the relaxation time for the temperature τ, and the condition (39.82) is equivalent to assuming that the period of oscillation $2\pi/\omega$ is short compared to the temperature relaxation time. For $\omega \gg m\nu_1/M$, the temperature simply cannot follow the rapid oscillations of the field E. If $\omega \ll m\nu_1/M$ then we have practically a dc situation and can simply take the dc solution and replace E by $E\cos\omega t$.

We conclude: if $\omega = 0$ then Eq. (39.67) is valid with T replaced by τ where τ is given by (39.74); and if $\omega \neq 0$ but either (39.80) or (39.82) is satisfied, then (39.67) is valid with T replaced by $\bar{\tau}$ where $\bar{\tau}$ is given by (39.78).

CONDUCTIVITY OF A SLIGHTLY IONIZED GAS

If our gas is only slightly ionized then

$$\nu_1 \approx \nu_1^{en} \tag{39.84}$$

$$\nu_2 \approx \nu_2^{en} \tag{39.85}$$

$$\nu_3 \approx \nu_3^{en} \tag{39.86}$$

If we make use of (39.84), (39.85), and (39.86) together with the results of the preceding section, we obtain an expression for the conductivity of a slightly ionized gas. It is informative to compare this result in the high and low frequency limits with the results of Chapter 38.

If ω is very much greater than ν_1, ν_2, and ν_3, then (39.67) becomes

$$J \approx \frac{ne^2E}{m}\left(\frac{\nu_1\cos\omega t + \omega\sin\omega t}{\omega^2}\right) \tag{39.87}$$

Equation (39.87) is exactly the same result we would obtain if we had assumed $\omega \gg \nu_m$ in Eq. (38.33) in the preceding chapter.

If $\omega = 0$, then Eq. (39.67) reduces to

$$J = \frac{ne^2E}{m}\left\{\frac{\nu_3}{[\nu_1\nu_3 - (5\nu_2^2/2)]}\right\} \tag{39.88}$$

If we further assume that $\sigma_m(v) = Cv^p$, we find

$$J = \left(\frac{3\pi^{1/2}ne^2E\lambda^{(p+1)/2}}{8CmN\Gamma\left(\frac{6+p}{2}\right)}\right)\left(\frac{p^2 + 4p + 13}{p + 6}\right) \tag{39.89}$$

The corresponding result which is obtained by letting $\omega = 0$ and $\sigma_m = Cv^p$ in Eq. (38.33) in the preceding chapter is

$$J \equiv J_I = \frac{4ne^2E\lambda^{(p+1)/2}\Gamma\left(\frac{4-p}{2}\right)}{3mNC\pi^{1/2}} \tag{39.90}$$

Comparing the two results we find

$$\frac{J}{J_I} = \left(\frac{9\pi}{32\Gamma\left(\frac{6+p}{2}\right)\Gamma\left(\frac{4-p}{2}\right)}\right)\left(\frac{p^2 + 4p + 13}{p + 6}\right) \tag{39.91}$$

In Table 39.1 we give the value of this ratio for various values of p. We see that there is excellent agreement for $0 \geq p \geq -4$, fair agreement for $p = +1$ and $p = -5$ but otherwise poor agreement.

Although Eq. (39.67) looks more complex than Eq. (38.33), it is analytically much more tractable, since the integrations involved in obtaining ν_1, ν_2, and ν_3 are considerably simpler than the integration involved in (38.33). We are

p	3	2	1	0	−1	−2	−3	−4	−5
J/J_I	0.16	0.46	0.77	0.96	1.00	0.99	1.00	0.96	0.77

TABLE 39.1

furthermore provided in the present analysis with a value for the electron temperature τ.

The big advantage, however, which expression (39.67) has over Eq. (38.33) is its ability to handle highly ionized gases. Before we can investigate the conductivity of a highly ionized gas, it will be necessary to consider the interaction between the charged particles in the gas.

THE COULOMB CROSS SECTION

The cross section for a collision between an electron of charge e and an electron or an ion of charge $-Ze$ is given in mks units by Eq. (38.27),

$$\sigma(u, \theta) = Z^2 e^4 / [8m^* \pi \epsilon_0 u^2 \sin^2(\theta/2)]^2 \tag{39.92}$$

If this cross section is used to calculate $\sigma_m(u)$ or $\sigma_\mu(u)$ we obtain divergent integrals. The divergencies are due to the long-range character of the Coulomb forces. It is possible, however, to show that the electrons and ions in an ionized gas behave under many circumstances as if they were interacting by means of a screened Coulomb interaction rather than the ordinary Coulomb interaction.

To demonstrate this, let us consider the shielding of a fixed charge Q which is located at the origin of coordinates and which is immersed in an ionized gas consisting of electrons of charge e and average density n_0, and ions of charge $-Ze$ and average density n_0/Z. Let ϕ be the resultant potential due to the electrons, ions, and charge Q. In the presence of the potential ϕ the local electron density will be $n_0 \exp(-e\phi/k\tau)$ and the local ion density will be $(n_0/Z) \exp(Ze\phi/kT)$. If we assume $|e\phi| \ll k\tau$ and $|Ze\phi| \ll kT$ then $\exp(-e\phi/k\tau) \approx 1 - (e\phi/k\tau)$ and $\exp(Ze\phi/kT) \approx 1 + (Ze\phi/kT)$. The charge density is thus

$$\begin{aligned}\rho(x) &= Q\delta(x) + n_0 e \exp(-e\phi/k\tau) + (n_0/Z)(-Ze) \exp(Ze\phi/kT) \\ &\approx Q\delta(x) - (n_0 e^2 \phi/k)[(T + Z\tau)/T\tau]\end{aligned} \tag{39.93}$$

The field ϕ can be determined from Poisson's equation which for the charge density (39.93) is

$$\nabla^2 \phi = -(Q/\epsilon_0)\delta(x) + (n_0 e^2/k\epsilon_0)[(T + Z\tau)/T\tau]\phi \tag{39.94}$$

If we assume that $\phi = 0$ at $|x| \equiv r = \infty$ then the solution to (39.94) is

$$\phi = (Q/4\pi\epsilon_0 r) \exp(-r/\lambda_D) \tag{39.95}$$

where

$$\lambda_D = \left(\frac{\epsilon_0 k\tau}{n_0 e^2}\right)^{1/2} \left(\frac{T}{T + Z\tau}\right)^{1/2} \tag{39.96}$$

Equation (39.95) represents a screened Coulomb potential. The quantity λ_D is called the Debye length. The effective potential of a charge in an ionized gas is therefore given by a screened Coulomb potential rather than an ordinary Coulomb potential.

In order for the preceding analysis to be valid, it is necessary that the number of electrons or ions within a sphere of radius λ_D be sufficiently large that the statistical averaging employed in obtaining the charge density can be legitimately used. We thus expect

$$(4\pi\lambda_D{}^3/3)n_0 = \frac{4\pi}{3}\left(\frac{\epsilon_0 k\tau}{n_0{}^{1/3}e^2}\right)^{3/2}\left(\frac{T}{T+Z\tau}\right)^{3/2} \gg 1 \qquad (39.97)$$

We shall assume in what follows that this condition is satisfied. If condition (39.97) is satisfied then the sphere of influence of a particular electron or ion is not small compared to the distance between particles. We shall nevertheless assume that the interaction between the charged particles can be treated as a succession of binary collisions.

It should also be noted that in originally deriving the collision term in the Boltzmann transport equation it was implicitly assumed that the external field did not vary much in the time of a collision. In the present case the time of a collision is of the order of $\lambda_D/\bar{v}$ where $\bar{v}$, the average electron speed, is given by $(8k\tau/\pi m)^{1/2}$. To satisfy this condition, we therefore require

$$\frac{2\pi}{\omega} \gg \frac{\lambda_D}{\bar{v}} = \left(\frac{\pi}{8}\right)^{1/2}\left(\frac{m\epsilon_0}{n_0 e^2}\right)^{1/2}\left(\frac{T}{T+Z\tau}\right)^{1/2} \qquad (39.98)$$

This is approximately the same as assuming that

$$\omega \ll \omega_p \qquad (39.99)$$

where $$\omega_p = (n_0 e^2/m\epsilon_0)^{1/2} \qquad (39.100)$$

The quantity ω_p is called the plasma frequency. It can also be shown that $1/\omega_p$ is a measure of the time required to establish the shielding. From the above considerations it follows that our analysis is strictly valid only for fields for which condition (39.99) is satisfied. It can be shown, however, that in many cases the results obtained using our present analysis are valid even for fields for which $\omega > \omega_p$ (see Ginzburg, *Propagation of Electromagnetic Waves in Plasmas*, p. 81).

Instead of dealing with the screened Coulomb potential (39.95), we shall assume for analytical convenience that we can simply neglect collisions between charged particles for which the impact parameter b is greater than λ_D, and treat collisions in which the impact parameter is less than λ_D as ordinary Coulomb collisions, i.e., we assume

$$\phi = Q/4\pi\epsilon_0 r \qquad b < \lambda_D$$
$$\phi = 0 \qquad b > \lambda_D \qquad (39.101)$$

For a Coulomb collision between an electron of charge e and an ion of charge $-Ze$, the scattering angle θ and impact parameter b are related by

$$\cot(\theta/2) = 4\pi\epsilon_0 m^* b u^2/Ze^2 \qquad (39.102)$$

The minimum scattering angle θ_0 for the potential (39.101) is obtained by setting $b = \lambda_D$ in (39.102). We obtain

$$\cot(\theta_0/2) = (4\pi\epsilon_0 m^* u^2/Ze^2)(\epsilon_0 k\tau/n_0 e^2)^{1/2}[T/(T + Z\tau)]^{1/2} \qquad (39.103)$$

If we further assume that

$$m^* u^2/2 \approx 3k\tau/2 \qquad (39.104)$$

and replace n_0 by n we obtain

$$\cot(\theta_0/2) \approx \frac{12\pi(\epsilon_0 k\tau/e^2)^{3/2}}{Zn^{1/2}}\left(\frac{T}{T + Z\tau}\right)^{1/2} \qquad (39.105)$$

Since $\theta_0/2$ is in general a small quantity we have

$$\frac{2}{\theta_0} \approx \frac{12\pi(\epsilon_0 k\tau/e^2)^{3/2}}{Zn^{1/2}}\left(\frac{T}{T + Z\tau}\right)^{1/2} \qquad (39.106)$$

The differential scattering cross section for scattering from the potential (39.101) is given by

$$\sigma(u, \theta) = \frac{Z^2 e^4}{[8m^* \pi\epsilon_0 u^2 \sin^2(\theta/2)]^2} \qquad \pi > \theta > \theta_0$$

$$= 0 \qquad \theta < \theta_0 \qquad (39.107)$$

It follows that

$$\sigma_m(u) = 2\pi \int_{\theta_0}^{\pi} (1 - \cos\theta)\sigma(u, \theta)\sin\theta d\theta$$

$$= \frac{Z^2 e^4}{4\pi\epsilon_0^2 m^{*2} u^4}\int_{\theta=\theta_0}^{\theta=\pi} \frac{\cos(\theta/2)}{\sin(\theta/2)}d(\theta/2)$$

$$\approx (Z^2 e^4/4\pi\epsilon_0^2 m^{*2} u^4)\ln(2/\theta_0) \qquad (39.108)$$

$$\sigma_\mu(u) = \frac{Z^2 e^4}{4\pi\epsilon_0^2 m^{*2} u^4}\int_{\theta=\theta_0}^{\theta=\pi} \left\{\frac{2\cos(\theta/2)}{\sin(\theta/2)} - 2\sin(\theta/2)\cos(\theta/2)\right\}d(\theta)/2) \qquad (39.109)$$

Even though we have excluded scattering at angles less than θ_0, it can be shown that the predominant scattering effects are due to collisions in which $\theta_0 < \theta < \theta_0 + \Delta\theta$ where $[(\theta_0 + \Delta\theta)/\pi] \ll 1$ and consequently the second term in (39.109) can be dropped, compared with the first, and we have for Coulomb scattering

$$\sigma_\mu(u) = 2\sigma_m(u) \qquad (39.110)$$

With these values for $\sigma_m(u)$ and $\sigma_\mu(u)$, we can write down immediately

$$\sigma_m^{ee}(u) = \frac{e^4\ln(2/\theta_0)}{\pi\epsilon_0^2 m^2 u^4} \qquad (39.111)$$

$$\sigma_\mu^{ee}(u) = 2\sigma_m^{ee}(u) \qquad (39.112)$$

$$\sigma_m^{ei}(u) = Z^2\sigma_m^{ee}(u)/4 \qquad (39.113)$$

$$\sigma_\mu^{ei}(u) = Z^2\sigma_m^{ee}/2 \qquad (39.114)$$

and for the collision frequencies $\nu_1{}^{ei}$, $\nu_2{}^{ei}$, $\nu_3{}^{ei}$ and ν^* we have

$$\nu_1{}^{ei} = N_i Z^2 \left(\frac{\lambda^{3/2} e^4 \ln(2/\theta_0)}{3\pi^{3/2} \epsilon_0{}^2 m^2} \right) \tag{39.115}$$

$$\nu_2{}^{ei} = 3\nu_1{}^{ei}/5 \tag{39.116}$$

$$\nu_3{}^{ei} = 13\nu_1{}^{ei}/10 \tag{39.117}$$

$$\nu^* = \left(\frac{2\sqrt{2}n}{5N_i Z^2} \right) \nu_1{}^{ei} \tag{39.118}$$

CONDUCTIVITY OF A FULLY IONIZED GAS

If we have a fully ionized gas then

$$\nu_1 = \nu_1{}^{ei} \tag{39.119}$$

$$\nu_2 = \nu_2{}^{ei} = 3\nu_1{}^{ei}/5 \tag{39.120}$$

$$\nu_3 = \nu_3{}^{ei} + \nu^* = \left(\frac{13}{10} + \frac{4\sqrt{2}n}{10NZ^2} \right) \nu_1{}^{ei} \tag{39.121}$$

We can make use of (39.119), (39.120), and (39.121) together with our earlier results to obtain the conductivity of a fully ionized gas. It is instructive to consider the results we obtain in both the high-frequency and the low-frequency case.

Setting $\omega = 0$ and $n = NZ$ and using the above values for ν_1, ν_2, and ν_3 in (39.67), we obtain

$$J = \frac{ne^2 E}{m\nu_1{}^{ei}} \left(\frac{13Z + 4\sqrt{2}}{4Z + 4\sqrt{2}} \right) \tag{39.122}$$

On the other hand, if ω is very much greater than ν_1, ν_2, and ν_3, we would obtain

$$J = \frac{ne^2 E}{m} \left(\frac{\nu_1{}^{ei} \cos\omega t + \omega \sin\omega t}{\omega^2} \right) \tag{39.123}$$

It is interesting to see what effect the inclusion of electron-electron collisions has on the conductivity of a fully ionized gas. If we had neglected ν^* in (39.122), we would have obtained

$$J = J_{II} = \frac{13ne^2 E}{4m\nu_1{}^{ei}}$$

Comparing the two results we have

$$\frac{J}{J_{II}} = \frac{4\sqrt{2} + 13Z}{13\sqrt{2} + 13Z} \tag{39.124}$$

In Table 39.2 we give this ratio for a number of values of Z. It is apparent that the electron-electron collisions have an appreciable effect on the dc conductivity of a fully ionized gas. On the other hand, if we set $\nu^* = 0$ in (39.123), the high-frequency conductivity is unaffected, since ν_1^{ei} is independent of ν^*. Thus the results of the preceding chapter, where the electron-electron collisions were neglected, are valid for the high-frequency conductivity of a fully ionized gas but not the low-frequency conductivity.

z	1	2	4	16	∞
J/J_{II}	0.595	0.713	0.819	0.944	1.000

TABLE 39.2

SUMMARY

If we assume binary elastic collisions, and make use of the thirteen-moment and linear approximations, then the fundamental equations from which the electric current density J and the electron temperature τ are determined for an ionized gas in a homogeneous electric field $e_1 E \cos\omega t$ are

$$\dot{J} + J\nu_1 - (2\lambda e/m)Q\nu_2 = (e^2 En/m)\cos\omega t \tag{39.125}$$

$$\dot{Q} + (5m/4\lambda e)[(\dot{\tau}/\tau) - \nu_2]J + \nu_3 Q = 0 \tag{39.126}$$

$$(3nk/2)\dot{\tau} = JE\cos\omega t - (3nk\tau/2)(2m/M)[(\tau - T)/\tau]\nu_1 \tag{39.127}$$

where

$$\lambda = m/2k\tau \tag{39.128}$$

$$\nu_1 \equiv \nu_1^{ei} + \nu_1^{en} \tag{39.129}$$

$$\nu_2 \equiv \nu_2^{ei} + \nu_2^{en} \tag{39.130}$$

$$\nu_3 \equiv \nu^* + \nu_3^{ei} + \nu_3^{en} \tag{39.131}$$

$$\nu_1^{en} = (2\lambda/3n)\int (N_n u\sigma_m)u^2 f_0(\mathbf{u})d\mathbf{u} \tag{39.132}$$

$$\nu_2^{en} = (4\lambda^2/15n)\int (N_n u\sigma_m)u^2[(5/2\lambda) - u^2]f_0(\mathbf{u})d\mathbf{u} \tag{39.133}$$

$$\nu_3^{en} = (4\lambda^3/15n)\int (N_n u\sigma_m)u^2[(5/2\lambda) - u^2]^2 f_0(\mathbf{u})d\mathbf{u} \tag{39.134}$$

where $\sigma_m \equiv \sigma_m^{en}$ is the cross section for electron molecule collisions, and N_n is the number of neutral molecules.

$$\nu_1{}^{ei} = N_i Z^2 \left(\frac{\lambda^{3/2} e^4}{3\pi^{3/2} \epsilon_0^2 m^2}\right) \ln\left(\frac{2}{\theta_0}\right) \tag{39.135}$$

$$\nu_2{}^{ei} = (3/5)\nu_1{}^{ei} \tag{39.136}$$

$$\nu_3{}^{ei} = (13/10)\nu_1{}^{ei} \tag{39.137}$$

$$\nu^* = \left(\frac{n}{N_i Z^2}\right)\left(\frac{2\sqrt{2}}{5}\right)\nu_1{}^{ei} \tag{39.138}$$

$$\frac{2}{\theta_0} = \frac{12\pi(\epsilon_0 k\tau/e^2)^{3/2}}{Z n^{1/2}}\left(\frac{T}{T+Z\tau}\right)^{1/2} \tag{39.139}$$

where Z is the ionic charge number and N_i the ion density. If

$$\omega \gg m\nu_1/M \tag{39.140}$$

then the solution to Eq. (39.125), (39.126), (39.127) is given by

$$J = J'\cos\omega t + J''\sin\omega t \tag{39.141}$$

$$J' = \frac{ne^2 E}{m}\left\{\frac{\omega^2\nu_1 + \nu_3[\nu_1\nu_3 - (5\nu_2^2/2)]}{\omega^4 + \omega^2(\nu_1^2 + 5\nu_2^2 + \nu_3^2) + [\nu_1\nu_3 - (5\nu_2^2/2)]^2}\right\} \tag{39.142}$$

$$J'' = \frac{ne^2 E}{m}\left\{\frac{\omega^3 + \omega[\nu_3^2 + (5\nu_2^2/2)]}{\omega^4 + \omega^2(\nu_1^2 + 5\nu_2^2 + \nu_3^2) + [\nu_1\nu_3 - (5\nu_2^2/2)]^2}\right\} \tag{39.143}$$

where

$$\nu_1 = \nu_1(\bar{\tau}) \tag{39.144}$$

$$\nu_2 = \nu_2(\bar{\tau}) \tag{39.145}$$

$$\nu_3 = \nu_3(\bar{\tau}) \tag{39.146}$$

and $\bar{\tau}$ is obtained by solving the equation

$$\bar{\tau} = T + \frac{J'(\bar{\tau})EM}{6mnk\nu_1(\bar{\tau})} \tag{39.147}$$

If $\omega = 0$ the above equation is also valid, except

$$\bar{\tau} = \tau = T + \frac{J(\bar{\tau})EM}{3mnk\nu_1(\bar{\tau})} \tag{39.148}$$

Finally, if

$$\frac{e^2 E^2 M}{6km^2(\nu_1^2 + \omega^2)} \ll T \tag{39.149}$$

then the above equation is valid for all frequencies and

$$\bar{\tau} \approx T \tag{39.150}$$

40

THE KINETIC THEORY
OF A GAS
OF POLYATOMIC MOLECULES

In the preceding chapters we have restricted our attention to the properties of gases of simple point particles.

In this chapter, we will give an introduction to the theory of gases of polyatomic molecules. The development will be somewhat abbreviated, and we will apply the results only to the equilibrium properties of such a gas.

MOLECULAR STATES

In specifying the state of a particular molecule we shall treat the translational motion classically, and the internal motions quantum mechanically. The state of a particular molecule is then given by specifying the location of the center of mass $\mathbf{x}$, the velocity of the center of mass $\mathbf{v}$, and the internal state i.

We define $f_i(\mathbf{x}, \mathbf{v}, t)d\mathbf{x}d\mathbf{v}$ as the number of molecules in the range $d\mathbf{x}d\mathbf{v}$ with internal state i.

LIOUVILLE'S THEOREM

In the absence of any interaction between molecules, between the external field and the internal modes of motion, or among the internal modes of motion of the molecules, the molecule will remain in the state i. A collection of such noninteracting molecules all in the same state i could be represented by a collection of points in $\mathbf{x}$–$\mathbf{v}$ space with density $f_i(\mathbf{x}, \mathbf{v})$. The function $f_i(\mathbf{x}, \mathbf{v})$ will obey Liouville's equation.

$$\frac{\partial f_i}{\partial t} + \frac{\mathbf{F}}{m} \cdot \frac{\partial f_i}{\partial \mathbf{v}} + \mathbf{v} \cdot \frac{\partial f_i}{\partial \mathbf{x}} = 0 \qquad (40.1)$$

where we have written the equation in vector notation so that the subscripts i will not become confused with the summation indices which we have previously employed in Liouville's equation. Note that $\partial/\partial \mathbf{x}$ is simply another way of writing the operator $\mathbf{e}_1\partial/\partial x_1 + \mathbf{e}_2\partial/\partial x_2 + \mathbf{e}_3\partial/\partial x_3$.

If the molecules are colliding, then $\partial f_i/\partial t$ is not given by (40.1). In the following section we will investigate the effect of collisions.

COLLISION PROBABILITY

Consider two unlike molecules of velocities $\mathbf{v}$ and $\mathbf{V}$ and internal states i and j respectively. Let us assume that both molecules are contained within the same unit volume.

We define $W_{ij}^{kl}(\mathbf{v}, \mathbf{V}; \mathbf{v}', \mathbf{V}')$ as the probability per unit time that the two particles will (1) collide and (2) end up with their velocities in the ranges $d\mathbf{v}'$ and $d\mathbf{V}'$, and having internal states k and l respectively.

Let $\mathbf{u}$ and $\mathbf{u}'$ be the relative velocities before and after collision respectively; $\mathbf{w}$ and $\mathbf{w}'$ the center of mass velocities before and after collision respectively; $m^* = mM/(m + M)$ the reduced mass, and $M^* = m + M$, the total mass.

We define $\sigma_{ij}^{kl}(u)$ and $\sigma_{ij}^{kl}(u, \theta)$ as the total scattering cross section and the differential scattering cross section respectively in relative coordinates for a collision in which the internal states of the colliding molecules before collision are i and j and after collision are k and l.

The probability that a collision will take place in which the molecules go from states i and j to states k and l and the relative velocity after collision lies in the solid angle $\sin\theta d\theta d\phi$ will then be simply

$$u\sigma_{ij}^{kl}(u, \theta)\sin\theta d\theta d\phi \qquad (40.2)$$

In a collision, the center of mass velocity of the two molecules is unchanged. The probability that if a collision takes place the final center of mass velocity is in the range $d\mathbf{w}'$ is thus

$$\delta(\mathbf{w}' - \mathbf{w})d\mathbf{w}' \qquad (40.3)$$

The relative speeds u and u' are no longer equal as they were in the case of point particles. However, the total energy is conserved, i.e.,

$$\tfrac{1}{2}M^*w^2 + \tfrac{1}{2}m^*u^2 + \epsilon_i + \epsilon_j = \tfrac{1}{2}M^*w'^2 + \tfrac{1}{2}m^*u'^2 + \epsilon_k + \epsilon_l \qquad (40.4)$$

where ϵ_i, ϵ_j, ϵ_k, and ϵ_l are the internal energies associated with the states i, j, k, and l. Since $\mathbf{w} = \mathbf{w}'$, Eq. (40.4) can be simplified to

$$\tfrac{1}{2}m^*u^2 + \epsilon_i + \epsilon_j = \tfrac{1}{2}m^*u'^2 + \epsilon_k + \epsilon_l \qquad (40.5)$$

The probability that if a collision takes place the final value of u'^2 will be in the range $d(u'^2)$ is thus

$$\delta[u'^2 - u^2 - (2/m^*)(\epsilon_i + \epsilon_j - \epsilon_k - \epsilon_l)]d(u'^2) \qquad (40.6)$$

The probabilities (40.2), (40.3), and (40.6) are independent. We can therefore obtain the joint probability of all these events by simply multiplying them together. If we then transform our variables from θ, ϕ, u'^2, $\mathbf{w}$ to $\mathbf{v}'$, $\mathbf{V}'$, we can obtain the desired value of $W_{ij}{}^{kl}$. Thus

$$W_{ij}{}^{kl}(\mathbf{v}, \mathbf{V}; \mathbf{v}', \mathbf{V}')dv'd\mathbf{V}' = u\sigma_{ij}{}^{kl}(u, \theta)\sin\theta\delta(\mathbf{w}' - \mathbf{w})$$
$$\delta[u'^2 - u^2 - (2/m^*)(\epsilon_i + \epsilon_j - \epsilon_k - \epsilon_l)]$$
$$J\left(\frac{u'^2, \theta, \phi, w_1', w_2', w_3'}{v_1', v_2', v_3', V_1', V_2', V_3'}\right)dv'd\mathbf{V}' \qquad (40.7)$$

If we let $u_1{}^*$, $u_2{}^*$, $u_3{}^*$ be the components of $\mathbf{u}'$ in a Cartesian reference frame with the z axis along $\mathbf{u}$, we obtain

$$J = J\left(\frac{u'^2, \theta, \phi}{u', \theta, \phi}\right)J\left(\frac{u', \theta, \phi}{u_1{}^*, u_2{}^*, u_3{}^*}\right)J\left(\frac{u_1{}^*, u_2{}^*, u_3{}^*}{u_1', u_2', u_3'}\right)J\left(\frac{\mathbf{u}', \mathbf{w}'}{\mathbf{v}', \mathbf{V}'}\right)$$
$$= (2u')(1/u'^2\sin\theta)(1)(1) = 2/u'\sin\theta \qquad (40.8)$$

Substituting (40.8) in (40.7) and writing $\sigma_{ij}{}^{kl}(u, \theta)$ as $\sigma_{ij}{}^{kl}(u; \mathbf{u} \cdot \mathbf{u}')$ to emphasize that θ is the angle between $\mathbf{u}$ nd $\mathbf{u}'$, we obtain

$$W_{ij}{}^{kl}(\mathbf{v}, \mathbf{V}; \mathbf{v}', \mathbf{V}') = S_{ij}{}^{kl}(\mathbf{u}, \mathbf{u}')\delta(\mathbf{w}' - \mathbf{w}) \qquad (40.9)$$

where

$$S_{ij}{}^{kl}(\mathbf{u}, \mathbf{u}') = 2(u/u')\sigma_{ij}{}^{kl}(u, \mathbf{u} \cdot \mathbf{u}')\delta[u'^2 - u^2 - (2/m^*)(\epsilon_i + \epsilon_j - \epsilon_k - \epsilon_l)] \qquad (40.10)$$

SYMMETRY

We have assumed so far that the differential scattering cross section in relative coordinates is a function of the incident relative speed u and the angle between $\mathbf{u}$ and $\mathbf{u}'$. Nothing we have said restricts us from allowing a dependence on the azimuthal angle ϕ.

In the case of a collision between point particles the symmetries of W and S were obvious. In the case of collisions between molecules the symmetries are not so obvious. If we assume that the differential scattering cross section does not depend on the azimuthal angle ϕ, then

$$S_{ij}{}^{kl}(\mathbf{u}, \mathbf{u}') = S_{ij}{}^{kl}(-\mathbf{u}, -\mathbf{u}') \qquad (40.11)$$

$$W_{ij}{}^{kl}(\mathbf{v}, \mathbf{V}; \mathbf{v}', \mathbf{V}') = W_{ij}{}^{kl}(-\mathbf{v}, -\mathbf{V}; -\mathbf{v}', -\mathbf{V}') \qquad (40.12)$$

We shall also assume that

$$S_{ij}{}^{kl}(\mathbf{u}, \mathbf{u}') = S_{kl}{}^{ij}(\mathbf{u}', \mathbf{u}) \qquad (40.13)$$

$$W_{ij}{}^{kl}(\mathbf{v}, \mathbf{V}; \mathbf{v}', \mathbf{V}') = W_{kl}{}^{ij}(\mathbf{v}', \mathbf{V}'; \mathbf{v}, \mathbf{V}) \qquad (40.14)$$

This assumption is the so-called assumption of microscopic reversibility. Its complete justification is not simple.

THE BOLTZMANN TRANSPORT EQUATION

In the absence of collisions, the time rate of change of f_i is given from Liouville's equation by

$$\frac{\partial f_i}{\partial t} = -\frac{\mathbf{F}}{m} \cdot \frac{\partial f_i}{\partial \mathbf{v}} - \mathbf{v} \cdot \frac{\partial f_i}{\partial \mathbf{x}} \qquad (40.15)$$

If the molecules are colliding, then we must add a term to account for the effect of collisions. We shall assume only one species of molecule, in which case there is only one collision term and

$$\frac{\partial f_i}{\partial t} = -\frac{\mathbf{F}}{m} \cdot \frac{\partial f_i}{\partial \mathbf{v}} - \mathbf{v} \cdot \frac{\partial f_i}{\partial \mathbf{x}} + \frac{Df_i}{Dt} \qquad (40.16)$$

The evaluation of Df_i/Dt is carried out as in the case of point particles and can be shown to be

$$\frac{Df_i}{Dt} = \sum_{jkl} \iiint [f_k(\mathbf{v}')f_l(\mathbf{V}') - f_i(\mathbf{v})f_j(\mathbf{V})]$$
$$W_{ij}{}^{kl}(\mathbf{v}, \mathbf{V}; \mathbf{v}', \mathbf{V}')dv'dVdV' \qquad (40.17)$$

The Boltzmann transport equation for f_i is thus given by (40.16) with Df_i/Dt given by (40.17). There is one equation for each f_i.

THE BOLTZMANN *H*-THEOREM

If we multiply Eq. (40.16) by $\ln f_i + 1$, integrate over $\mathbf{v}$ and $\mathbf{x}$, and sum over i, we obtain

$$\frac{\partial}{\partial t}\left\{\sum_i \iint f_i \ln f_i dv dx\right\} = \sum_{ijkl} \iiiint \ln\left[\frac{f_i(\mathbf{v})f_j(\mathbf{V})}{f_k(\mathbf{v}')f_l(\mathbf{V}')}\right]$$
$$[f_k(\mathbf{v}')f_l(\mathbf{V}') - f_i(\mathbf{v})f_j(\mathbf{V})]$$
$$W_{ij}{}^{kl}(\mathbf{v}, \mathbf{V}; \mathbf{v}', \mathbf{V}')dv dv' dV dV' dx \le 0 \qquad (40.18)$$

THE MAXWELL-BOLTZMANN DISTRIBUTION

In equilibrium the left-hand-side of (40.18) vanishes and therefore the integrand on the right-hand side of (40.18) must be identically zero, i.e.,

$$\ln f_i(\mathbf{v}) + \ln f_j(\mathbf{V}) = \ln f_k(\mathbf{v}') + \ln f_l(\mathbf{V}') \qquad (40.19)$$

whenever
$$W_{ij}{}^{kl}(\mathbf{v}, \mathbf{V}; \mathbf{v}', \mathbf{V}') \ne 0 \qquad (40.20)$$

Any function $f_i(\mathbf{v})$ which is conserved in a collision will satisfy Eq. (40.19). We will consider only linear functions of the energy, in which case

$$\ln f_i(\mathbf{v}) = \alpha[\epsilon_i + (mv^2/2)] + \beta \qquad (40.21)$$

The quantities α and β may be functions of $\mathbf{x}$. To determine α and β we substitute (40.21) back into the Boltzmann transport equation, and solve for α and β. The result is the familiar Maxwell-Boltzmann distribution, i.e.,

$$f_i = C \exp(-E/kT) \tag{40.22}$$

where

$$E = \tfrac{1}{2}mv^2 + \epsilon_i + U(\mathbf{x}) \tag{40.23}$$

THE PRINCIPLE OF DETAILED BALANCING

In equilibrium the integrand on the right-hand side of (40.18) must vanish identically. This is equivalent to the statement that

$$[f_i(\mathbf{v})d\mathbf{v}] [f_j(\mathbf{V})d\mathbf{V}] [W_{ij}{}^{kl}, (\mathbf{v}, \mathbf{V}; \mathbf{v}', \mathbf{V}')d\mathbf{v}'d\mathbf{V}']$$
$$= [f_k(\mathbf{v}')d\mathbf{v}'] [f_l(\mathbf{V}')d\mathbf{V}'] [W_{kl}{}^{ij}(\mathbf{v}', \mathbf{V}'; \mathbf{v}, \mathbf{V})d\mathbf{v}d\mathbf{V}] \tag{40.24}$$

Thus in equilibrium, the rate at which collisions take place in which a molecule in the state i having velocity in $d\mathbf{v}$ collides with a molecule in state j having velocity in $d\mathbf{V}$, and in which the final states are k and l, and the final velocities are in $d\mathbf{v}'$ and $d\mathbf{V}'$ respectively is equal to the rate at which molecules in the states k and l with velocities in $d\mathbf{v}'$ and $d\mathbf{V}'$ collide and end up in the states i and j with velocities in $d\mathbf{v}$ and $d\mathbf{V}$. This is called the principle of detailed balancing.

APPENDIX
1

A TABLE OF USEFUL CONSTANTS

Speed of light $= c = 2.997925 \times 10^8$ m sec^{-1}
Avogadro's number $= 6.02252 \times 10^{26}$ (kg mole)$^{-1}$
Loschmidt's number $= 2.68719 \times 10^{25}$ m^{-3}
Electronic charge $= e = 1.60210 \times 10^{-19}$ coulombs
Electronic mass $= 9.1091 \times 10^{-31}$ kg
Proton mass $= 1.67252 \times 10^{-27}$ kg
Planck's constant $= h = 6.6256 \times 10^{-34}$ Joule seconds
Planck's constant divided by $2\pi = \hbar =$
    1.0544×10^{-34} Joule seconds
Boltzmann's constant $= k = 1.38054 \times 10^{-23}$ Joules (°K)$^{-1}$
Gas constant $= R = 8.3143 \times 10^3$ Joules (°K)$^{-1}$ (kg mole)$^{-1}$

APPENDIX
2

DISTINCT DISTRIBUTIONS
OF DISTINGUISHABLE PARTICLES

Suppose we have N particles which we label 1 to N and M cells which we label 1 to M, and we wish to distribute the particles among the cells in such a way that there are n_1 particles in cell 1, n_2 particles in cell 2, and so on. Let $\{n_i\}$ represent the desired set of occupation numbers.

A particular distribution of the particles among the cells can be represented as shown below:

$$ \qquad (1) $$

In this distribution, particles 2, 3, and 7 are in cell 1, particles 1, 5, 6, and 8 are in cell 2, etc. The occupation number of cell 1 is 3, the occupation number of cell 2 is 4, etc. Suppose we wish to know the number of distinct ways we can arrange the N particles among the M cells, keeping the occupation numbers n_i fixed. Let this number be X. Each distinct way corresponds to a permutation of the numbers 1 to N. With each distinct permutation, for example, that shown in expression (1), there are a number of permutations which do not lead to a different distribution. For instance, permuting the numbers 2, 3, and 7 among themselves does not change the distribution. There are 3! such permutations. In general there are $n_i!$ permutations of the n_i numbers in cell i which do not change the distribution. For each of the X distinct permutations there are therefore $\Pi n_i!$ permutations which leave the distribution unchanged. The product of X and $\Pi n_i!$ should give us the total number of permutations which is $N!$. Therefore

$$ X = N!/\Pi n_i! \qquad (2) $$

Now suppose we wish to know the number of distinct ways we can arrange the N particles among the M cells in such a way that there are N_1 particles in the group of cells 1 to M_1, N_2 particles in the group of cells $M_1 + 1$ to $M_1 + M_2$, N_3 particles in the group of cells $M_1 + M_2 + 1$ to $M_1 + M_2 + M_3$, etc. Let this number be Y. Let us consider the ith group of cells. There are N_i particles in this group and M_i cells. Since there are M_i cells in which each particle can go, there are $(M_i)^{N_i}$ distinct ways in which the N_i particles can be arranged among the M_i cells. There are therefore $\prod_i (M_i)^{N_i}$ different distinct arrangements of particles within groups. There are however $N!/\prod N_i!$ distinct permutations of particles between groups for each of these arrangements. The desired number Y is therefore

$$Y = \left[\frac{N!}{\prod N_i!} \right] \left[\prod (M_i)^{N_i} \right] = N! \prod_i \frac{(M_i)^{N_i}}{N_i!} \tag{3}$$

DISTINCT DISTRIBUTIONS
OF INDISTINGUISHABLE PARTICLES

Suppose we have N identical particles and M cells, and wish to distribute the N particles among the M cells. A particular distribution can be represented as follows:

(1)

In this distribution there are 4 particles in cell 1, 3 in cell 2, 2 in cell 3, 2 in cell i, 1 in cell M, and so on. Let X be the number of distinct distributions of the particles among the cells with no restriction on the number of particles in a particular cell. Any distribution can be obtained by permuting the particles and the numbers 2, 3, 4 ... M among one another. There are $(N + M - 1)!$ such permutations. For each distinct distribution there are $N!$ permutations of the particles which do not change the distribution. Furthermore, interchanging the groups $\lfloor \cdots \rfloor_2$ and $\lfloor \cdot\cdot \rfloor_3$ does not change anything. For each distinct distribution there are $(M - 1)!$ such permutations. The number of distinct distributions is therefore

$$X = \frac{(N + M - 1)!}{N!(M - 1)!} \qquad (2)$$

Now suppose we wish to know the number of distinct ways we can arrange the N particles among the M cells in such a way that there are: N_1 particles in the group of cells 1 to M_1; N_2 particles in the group of cells $M_1 + 1$ to $M_1 + M_2$; N_3 particles in the group of cells $M_1 + M_2 + 1$ to $M_1 + M_2 + M_3$; and so on. Let this number be Y. The number of ways the N_i particles in group i can be arranged among the M_i cells is just $(N_i + M_i - 1)!/N_i!(M_i - 1)!$. It follows that

$$Y = \prod_i \frac{(N_i + M_i - 1)!}{N_i!(M_i - 1)!} \qquad (3)$$

DISTINCT DISTRIBUTIONS OF INDISTINGUISHABLE AND EXCLUSIVE PARTICLES

Suppose we have N identical particles and M cells and we wish to distribute the N particles among the M cells with the restriction that we can have at most one particle in a cell. A particular distribution can be represented as follows:

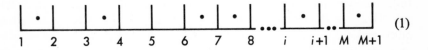

$$(1)$$

In this distribution there is one particle in cell 1, none in cell 2, one in cell 3, one in cell i, one in cell M, and so on. Let X be the number of distinct distributions. If we drop the particles into the cells one by one, then there are M possible cells in which the first particle can go, $M - 1$ possible cells into which the second particle can go, $M - 2$ possible cells into which the third particle can go. There are therefore

$$M(M - 1)\ldots(M - N + 1) = M!/(M - N)! \qquad (2)$$

distributions of N *distinguishable* particles among the cells with no more than one to a cell. Since the particles are indistinguishable, permutations of the particles among themselves will not change the distribution. With each distribution of distinguishable particles, there are $N!$ such permutations. It follows that the number of distinct distributions of N indistinguishable particles among M cells with no more than one particle to a cell is

$$X = M!/(M - N)!N! \qquad (3)$$

Now suppose we wish to know the number of distinct ways we can arrange the N particles among the M cells in such a way that there are N_1 particles in the group of cells 1 to M_1, N_2 particles in the group of cells $M_1 + 1$ to $M_1 + M_2$, and so on. Let this number be Y. The number of ways the N_i particles in group i can be arranged among the M_i cells is just $M_i!/(M_i - N_i)!$ $N_i!$. It follows that

$$Y = \prod_i \frac{M_i!}{(M_i - N_i)!N_i!} \qquad (4)$$

APPENDIX
5

THE MOST PROBABLE DISTRIBUTION

It is customary, for mathematical convenience, to assume that the properties of a gas are approximately the same as the properties associated with the most probable distribution. We shall present a simple plausibility argument to justify this approximation. It can be justified more rigorously using the method of Darwin and Fowler.

Suppose we have N distinguishable points which we distribute along the x axis in the region $0 \leq x \leq 1$, and suppose that the instruments available for measuring the location of a point are so crude that the best we can do is to determine that a particular point is either in the region $0 < x < 1/2$ or $1/2 < x < 1$. Let us designate the regions $0 < x < 1/2$ and $1/2 < x < 1$ as regions 1 and 2 respectively and in keeping with the crudeness of our measurement, assign the value $x = x_1$ to any point falling in region 1 and the value $x = x_2$ to any point falling in region 2, where x_1 and x_2 are some sort of characteristic values of x appropriate to the regions 1 and 2 respectively. For example, x_1 and x_2 might be the values of the midpoints of the two regions, i.e., $x_1 = 1/4$ and $x_2 = 3/4$.

If we let N_1 be the number of points in region 1, N_2 the number of points in region 2, and $W(N_1, N_2)$ the number of distinct ways in which the N particles can be arranged between the two regions in such a way that there are N_1 particles in region 1 and N_2 particles in region 2, and if we assume that each distinct arrangement of the particles between the two regions is equally likely, then the average value of a function $g(x)$ is given by

$$<g(x)> = \frac{\displaystyle\sum_{\{N_1,N_2\}} W(N_1, N_2)\left\{\frac{N_1 g(x_1) + N_2 g(x_2)}{N_1 + N_2}\right\}}{\displaystyle\sum_{\{N_1,N_2\}} W(N_1, N_2)} \tag{1}$$

where the summation is over all values of N_1 and N_2 which satisfy the condition $N_1 + N_2 = N$. Equation (1) can be rewritten

395

$$<g(x)> = \sum_{n=-N/2}^{n=+N/2} w(n)\left\{\left(\frac{1}{2} - \frac{n}{N}\right)g(x_1) + \left(\frac{1}{2} + \frac{n}{N}\right)g(x_2)\right\} \qquad (2)$$

where

$$w(n) = \frac{W\left(\frac{N}{2} - n, \frac{N}{2} + n\right)}{\sum\limits_{n=-N/2}^{n=+N/2} W\left(\frac{N}{2} - n, \frac{N}{2} + n\right)} \qquad (3)$$

The function $w(n)$ is just the probability that $N_1 = (N/2) - n$ and $N_2 = (N/2) + n$.

From Appendix 2

$$W(N_1, N_2) = \frac{N!}{N_1! \, N_2!} \qquad (4)$$

and therefore

$$\begin{aligned}
\frac{w(n)}{w(0)} &= \frac{(N/2)!(N/2)!}{[(N/2) + n]! \, [(N/2) - n]!} \\
&= \left(\frac{N}{N + |2n|}\right)\left(\frac{N - 2}{N + |2n| - 2}\right)\cdots\left(\frac{N - |2n| + 2}{N + 2}\right)
\end{aligned} \qquad (5)$$

It follows that

$$\left(\frac{N}{N + |2n|}\right)^{|n|} > \frac{w(n)}{w(0)} > \left(\frac{N - |2n|}{N}\right)^{|n|} \qquad (6)$$

If $|2n| \ll N$ then

$$\begin{aligned}
\left(\frac{N}{N + |2n|}\right)^{|n|} &= \left(\frac{1}{1 + [|2n|/N]}\right)^{|n|} \\
&= \exp\{-|n|\ln[1 + (|2n|/N)]\} \approx \exp(-2n^2/N)
\end{aligned} \qquad (7)$$

and similarly

$$\left(\frac{N - |2n|}{N}\right)^{|n|} \approx \exp(-2n^2/N) \qquad (8)$$

Therefore for $|2n| \ll N$

$$w(n) \approx w(0)\exp(-2n^2/N) \qquad (9)$$

For N large $w(n)$ is practically zero unless $n \ll N$, and the major contribution to the summation in (2) will come from values of (n/N) which are very close to zero. Since $w(n)$ is a maximum when $n = 0$, it follows that the distribution for which $n = 0$ is the most probable distribution. Thus the average value of $g(x)$ is approximately the same as the average value associated with the most probable distribution, i.e.,

$$<g(x)> \approx \tfrac{1}{2}g(x_1) + \tfrac{1}{2}g(x_2) \qquad (10)$$

Considering the probable error introduced by assigning the value $x = x_1$ to points in region 1 and the value $x = x_2$ to points in region 2, the error introduced by neglecting distributions for which (n/N) is appreciably greater than zero is insignificant for large values of N. If, for example, we let $N = 2 \times 10^{20}$ (a reasonable value for a gas), the probability from (9) of obtaining a distribution with $|2n|/N > 10^{-5}$, is $10^{-10^{10}}$.

If we increase the accuracy of our measurements so that we are able to divide the region $0 \leq x \leq 1$ into more than two subregions, the assumption that the average value of $g(x)$ is approximately the same as the average value associated with the most probable distribution decreases in validity. However, in the problems which we will encounter, the accuracy of the measurements and the number of molecules involved are such that we are perfectly safe in assuming that the properties of the gas are the same as those associated with the most probable distribution.

THE METHOD
OF LAGRANGE MULTIPLIERS

We wish to find the values of x, y, and z which maximize (or minimize) the function $f(x, y, z)$ subject to the constraint $\phi(x, y, z) = 0$.

We will show that the values of x, y, z, and λ which maximize the function

$$F(x, y, z, \lambda) = f(x, y, z) + \lambda\phi(x, y, z) \tag{1}$$

also provide us with the values of x, y, z which maximize $f(x, y, z)$ subject to the constraint $\phi(x, y, z) = 0$.

To maximize (1) we take partial derivatives of (1) with respect to x, y, z, and λ and set them equal to zero, i.e.,

$$\frac{\partial F}{\partial \lambda} = = \phi(x, y, z) = 0 \tag{2}$$

$$\frac{\partial F}{\partial x} = \frac{\partial f}{\partial x} + \lambda\frac{\partial \phi}{\partial x} \tag{3}$$

$$\frac{\partial F}{\partial y} = \frac{\partial f}{\partial y} + \lambda\frac{\partial \phi}{\partial y} \tag{4}$$

$$\frac{\partial F}{\partial z} = \frac{\partial f}{\partial z} + \lambda\frac{\partial \phi}{\partial z} \tag{5}$$

Let x_0, y_0, z_0 and λ_0 be the values of x, y, z, and λ which satisfy (2), (3), (4), and (5). Suppose there exists another set of x, y, and z which we designate x_1, y_1, and z_1 which maximizes $f(x, y, z)$ subject to the constraint $\phi(x, y, z) = 0$. Then $f(x_1, y_1, z_1) > f(x_0, y_0, z_0)$ and $\phi(x_1, y_1, z_1) = 0$. It follows that

$$f(x_1, y_1, z_1) + \lambda_0\phi(x_1, y_1, z_1) > f(x_0, y_0, z_0) + \lambda_0\phi(x_0, y_0, z_0) \tag{6}$$

But if (6) is true, then x_0, y_0, z_0, and λ_0 do not maximize $F(x, y, z, \lambda)$. This would violate our original assumption, and therefore our supposition that there exists a set of values other than x_0, y_0, and z_0 which maximizes $F(x, y, z)$ subject to the constraint $\phi(x, y, z) = 0$ is false. It follows that x_0, y_0, and z_0 are the desired values.

If we wish to maximize $f(x, y, z)$ subject to the constraints $\phi(x, y, z) = 0$ and $\psi(x, y, z) = 0$, then an extension of the above analysis will show that the problem can be solved by maximizing

$$F(x, y, z, \lambda, \mu) = f(x, y, z) + \lambda\phi(x, y, z) + \mu\psi(x, y, z)$$

STIRLING'S APPROXIMATION

We wish to obtain an approximation for $\ln N!$ which is valid for large N. We start with the following relation

$$N! = \int_0^\infty t^N \exp(-t)dt \tag{1}$$

which can be verified by the technique of mathematical induction.

Letting $t = xN$ we get

$$N! = N^{N+1}\int_0^\infty x^N \exp(-Nx)dx$$

$$= N^{N+1}\exp(-N)\int_0^\infty \exp(N - Nx + \ln x^N)dx$$

$$= N^{N+1}\exp(-N)\int_0^\infty \exp[-N(x - 1 - \ln x)]dx$$

$$= N^{N+1}\exp(-N)\int_{-1}^\infty \exp\{-N[x - \ln(1 + x)]\}dx \tag{2}$$

For large N the integrand drops off very rapidly as x increases and therefore

$$N! \approx N^{N+1}\exp(-N)\int_{-1}^1 \exp\{-N[x - \ln(1 + x)]\}dx \tag{3}$$

But

$$\ln(1 + x) = x - \tfrac{1}{2}x^2 + \ldots \approx x - \tfrac{1}{2}x^2 \tag{4}$$

Substituting (4) in (3) we obtain

$$N! = N^{N+1}\exp(-N)\int_{-1}^1 \exp(-Nx^2/2)dx$$

$$\approx N^{N+1}\exp(-N)\int_{-\infty}^\infty \exp(-Nx^2/2)dx$$

$$= (2\pi N)^{1/2}(N/e)^N \tag{5}$$

If we take the logarithm of (5) we have

$$\ln N! \approx N\ln N - N + \tfrac{1}{2}\ln(2\pi N) \tag{6}$$

If N is large we can drop the last term in (6). Then

$$\ln N! \approx N\ln N - N \tag{7}$$

This is the form of Stirling's approximation which we will use.

GREEN'S THEOREM

Suppose $P(x)$ is a single-valued, continuous, and differentiable function in the region $a \leq x \leq b$, then it follows that

$$\int_a^b (dP/dx)dx = P(b) - P(a) \tag{1}$$

Thus the integral of the function dP/dx over the region $a \leq x \leq b$ depends only on the values of P at the end points. As we shall see, a similar but somewhat more complicated result holds in two and three dimensions.

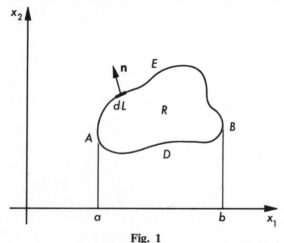

Fig. 1

Suppose $P(x_1, x_2)$ is a single-valued, continuous, and differentiable function in the closed region R bounded by the curve C as shown in Figure 1. Then we shall show that

$$\int_R (\partial P/\partial x_i)dS = \oint_C Pn_i dL \tag{2}$$

where dS is an element of area, dL is an element of length, and $\mathbf{n}$ is a unit vector normal to the curve and pointing in the outward direction.

402

Let us prove the above theorem for $i = 2$. Let $x_2 = f(x_1)$ be the equation of the curve ADB and $x_2 = g(x_1)$ be the equation of the curve AEB, then

$$\int_R (\partial P/\partial x_2)dS = \iint_R (\partial P/\partial x_2)dx_1 dx_2$$

$$= \int_a^b \left\{ \int_{f(x_1)}^{g(x_1)} (\partial P/\partial x_2)dx_2 \right\} dx_1 = \int_a^b [P(x_1, g) - P(x_1, f)]dx_1 \quad (3)$$

Along ADB, $dx_1 = -n_2 dL$, while along AEB, $dx_1 = n_2 dL$. It follows that

$$\int_a^b [P(x_1, g) - P(x_1, f)]dx_1 = \int_{AEB} Pn_2 dL + \int_{ADB} Pn_2 dL = \oint_C Pn_2 dL \quad (4)$$

It should be noted that dL is an element of length and as such has no direction associated with it, and therefore the integration $\int_{AEB} dL$ is always positive whether we go from A to B or from B to A. Substituting (4) in (3) we get

$$\int_R (\partial P/\partial x_2)dS = \oint_C Pn_2 dL \quad (5)$$

A similar result holds for $i = 1$, and in general we obtain Eq. (2). The extension to three dimensions is straightforward. Suppose $P(\mathbf{x})$ is a single-valued, continuous, and differentiable function in the volume V surrounded by the surface S as shown in Figure 2. Then it can be shown that

$$\int_V (\partial P/\partial x_i)dV = \oint Pn_i dS \quad (6)$$

where dV is an element of volume, dS is an element of surface area, and $\mathbf{n}$ is a unit vector normal to the surface pointing in the outward direction. The proof of this result is perfectly analogous to the proof of the two-dimensional result.

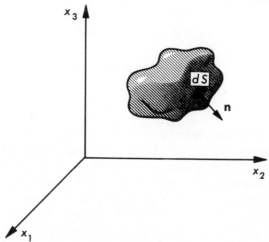

Fig. 2

LEGENDRE TRANSFORMATION

Suppose we are given a function $y(x)$, and we wish to find a function $\psi(dy/dx)$ which will contain the same information as is contained in $y(x)$ so that if we know $\psi(dy/dx)$ we can find $y(x)$ and if we know $y(x)$ we can find $\psi(dy/dx)$.

We will now show that the function

$$\psi = y - x\frac{dy}{dx} \tag{1}$$

if expressed as a function of dy/dx is such a function.

For convenience we will designate dy/dx by y'. If we know $y(x)$ then we can find $y'(x)$, and knowing $y(x)$ and $y'(x)$ we can solve for $y(y')$ and $x(y')$. Substituting $y(y')$ and $x(y')$ in (1) we will obtain $\psi(y')$. Therefore, if we know $y(x)$ we can find $\psi(y')$.

Let us designate $d\psi/dy' = \psi'$. Taking the derivative of (1) with respect to x we obtain

$$\psi'\frac{dy'}{dx} = y' - y' - x\frac{dy'}{dx} \tag{2}$$

or simply

$$\psi' = -x \tag{3}$$

We can therefore rewrite (1) as

$$y = \psi - y'\psi' \tag{4}$$

If we know $\psi(y')$ we can find $\psi'(y')$, and knowing $\psi(y')$ and $\psi'(y')$ we can solve for $y'(\psi')$ and $\psi(\psi')$. Substituting $y'(\psi')$ and $\psi(\psi')$ in (4) we can find $y(\psi')$. Knowing $y(\psi')$ we simply replace ψ' by $-x$ and we have $y = y(x)$.

We have thus shown the desired equivalence between the function $y(x)$ and the function $\psi(dy/dx)$. The function $\psi(dy/dx)$ is known as the Legendre transformation of $y(x)$. It should be emphasized that the equivalence is between y as a function of x and ψ as a function of dy/dx. If we know ψ as a function of some other variable, it may be perfectly possible that we are unable to find $y(x)$.

The extension to functions of more than one variable is straightforward. Suppose we are given a function $f(x, y)$, then

$$F_1\left(\frac{\partial f}{\partial x}, y\right) = f - x\frac{\partial f}{\partial x} \tag{5}$$

$$F_2\left(x, \frac{\partial f}{\partial y}\right) = f - y\frac{\partial f}{\partial y} \tag{6}$$

$$F_3\left(\frac{\partial f}{\partial x}, \frac{\partial f}{\partial y}\right) = f - x\frac{\partial f}{\partial x} - y\frac{\partial f}{\partial y} \tag{7}$$

are all Legendre transformations of $f(x, y)$, and if we know $F_1[\partial f/\partial x, y]$ or $F_2[x, \partial f/\partial y]$ or $F_3[\partial f/\partial x, \partial f/\partial y]$, we can find $f(x, y)$.

APPENDIX
10

EULER'S THEOREM

A function $f(x, y, z)$ is said to be homogeneous of degree n in the variables x and y if

$$f(\lambda x, \lambda y, z) = \lambda^n f(x, y, z) \tag{1}$$

for every positive value of λ.

If $f(x, y, z)$ satisfies (1) then it can be shown that

$$nf = x\frac{\partial f}{\partial x} + y\frac{\partial f}{\partial y} \tag{2}$$

This is Euler's theorem.

To prove Euler's theorem, we note that the derivative of (1) with respect to λ is

$$\frac{\partial f(\lambda x, \lambda y, z)}{\partial(\lambda x)}\frac{\partial(\lambda x)}{\partial\lambda} + \frac{\partial f(\lambda x, \lambda y, z)}{\partial(\lambda y)}\frac{\partial(\lambda y)}{\partial y} = n\lambda^{n-1}f(x, y, z) \tag{3}$$

Noting that $\partial(\lambda x)/\partial\lambda = x$ and $\partial(\lambda y)/\partial\lambda = y$ and then letting $\lambda = 1$ in (3) we obtain (2). The generalization to a function of r variables which is homogeneous in s of these variables is straightforward.

$$H = \tfrac{1}{2}\int [\epsilon_0 \mathbf{E} \cdot \mathbf{E} + (1/\mu_0)\mathbf{B} \cdot \mathbf{B}]dV$$

$$= (\epsilon_0/2)\int [\dot{\mathbf{A}} \cdot \dot{\mathbf{A}} + c^2(\nabla \times \mathbf{A}) \cdot (\nabla \times \mathbf{A})]dV$$

$$= (\epsilon_0/4)[\dot{q}^2 + \omega^2 q^2] \tag{22}$$

which, if we interpret q and $\dot{q}$ as generalized coordinate and generalized velocity respectively, is just the energy of a simple harmonic oscillator of mass

$$m = \epsilon_0/2 \tag{23}$$

In terms of generalized coordinates and momenta we have

$$H = \frac{p^2}{2m} + \frac{m\omega^2 q^2}{2} \tag{24}$$

A more detailed analysis will reveal that the radiation in a box can be expressed as a sum of such standing waves. With each standing wave we can, as in the example above, associate a generalized coordinate q for which the equation of motion is that of a simple harmonic oscillator.

APPENDIX
12

DERIVATION
OF THE FERMI DISTRIBUTION
FROM THE CANONICAL
PARTITION FUNCTION

In this appendix we will outline a derivation of the Fermi distribution starting from the relation (Chapter 19)

$$\bar{n}_j = -kT\frac{\partial}{\partial\epsilon_j}(\ln Q) \tag{1}$$

where Q is the canonical partition function defined by

$$Q = \sum_{\{n_j\}} \prod_j \exp(-n_j\epsilon_j/kT) \tag{2}$$

and the summation is over the set of all n_j satisfying the conditions

$$n_j = 0, 1 \tag{3}$$

$$\Sigma n_j = N \tag{4}$$

We can incorporate the constraints (3) and (4) into (2) by introducing the Kronecker delta

$$\delta(n) = 1 \qquad n = 0 \tag{5}$$

$$\delta(n) = 0 \qquad n = \pm1, \pm2, \ldots \tag{6}$$

The Kronecker delta as defined by (5) and (6) should not be confused with the Dirac delta function. In terms of the Kronecker delta, the partition function can be written

$$Q = \sum_{n_1=0}^{1} \ldots \sum_{n_k=0}^{1} \ldots \prod_j \exp(-n_j\epsilon_j/kT)\delta(N - \Sigma n_j) \tag{7}$$

The Kronecker delta can be analytically written

$$\delta(n) = (1/2\pi) \int_{-\pi}^{\pi} \exp(-inx)dx$$

$$= [\exp(\lambda n)/2\pi] \int_{-\pi}^{\pi} \exp(-inx)dx \tag{8}$$

where λ is some arbitrary real number.
Substituting (8) in (7) we obtain

$$Q = [\exp(\lambda N)/2\pi] \int_{-\pi}^{\pi} \exp(iNx)$$

$$\sum_{n_1=0}^{1} \ldots \sum_{n_k=0}^{1} \ldots \prod_{j} \exp\{-[(\epsilon_j/kT) + \lambda + ix]n_j\}dx$$

$$= [\exp(\lambda N)/2\pi] \int_{-\pi}^{\pi} \exp(iNx)$$

$$\prod_{j} \sum_{n_j=0}^{1} \exp\{-[(\epsilon_j/kT) + \lambda + ix]n_j\}dx$$

$$= [\exp(\lambda N)/2\pi] \int_{-\pi}^{\pi} F(x)dx \tag{9}$$

where

$$F(x) \equiv \exp(iNx) \prod_{j} [1 + r_j \exp(-ix)] \tag{10}$$

$$r_j \equiv \exp\{-[(\epsilon_j/kT) + \lambda]\} \tag{11}$$

We note for $0 < |x| \le \pi$

$$|1 + r_j \exp(-ix)| \le |1 + r_j| \tag{12}$$

Since we have a product of such factors in (10), the absolute value of $F(x)$ becomes strongly peaked around $x = 0$. If we further choose λ such that $dF/dx = 0$ at $x = 0$ then the phase of $F(x)$ will not be rapidly changing around $x = 0$. With this choice of λ we would then expect the major contribution to the integral (9) to occur around $x = 0$. Instead of working with $F(x)$, it will be more convenient to work with $\ln F(x)$.

If we set

$$\left[\frac{d}{dx}\ln F(x)\right]_{x=0} = 0 \tag{13}$$

we find that λ is the solution to the equation

$$N = \sum_{j} \frac{r_j}{1 + r_j} = \sum_{j} \{1 + \exp[(\epsilon_j/kT) + \lambda]\}^{-1} \tag{14}$$

We now make the approximation

$$
\begin{aligned}
F(x) &\equiv \exp[\ln F(x)] \\
&= \exp\left\{\ln F(0) + \left[\frac{d}{dx}\ln F(x)\right]_{x=0} x \right. \\
&\qquad \left. + \frac{1}{2}\left[\frac{d^2}{dx^2}\ln F(x)\right]_{x=0} x^2 + \ldots\right\} \approx F(0)\exp[-\alpha N x^2/2]
\end{aligned}
\tag{15}
$$

where

$$
\alpha = -\frac{1}{N}\left[\frac{d^2}{dx^2}\ln F(x)\right]_{x=0}
\tag{16}
$$

From (10) and (14) it can be shown that $0 < \alpha < 1$.

Substituting (15) in (9) and integrating we obtain

$$
Q \approx \frac{\exp(\lambda N)}{(\pi \alpha N)^{1/2}}F(0)
\tag{17}
$$

Substituting (17) in (1) we obtain

$$
\begin{aligned}
\bar{n}_j &= -kT\frac{\partial}{\partial \epsilon_j}(\ln Q) \\
&= -kT\left[N\frac{\partial \lambda}{\partial \epsilon_j} - \frac{1}{2}\frac{\partial}{\partial \epsilon_j}(\ln \alpha) + \frac{(-1/kT)r_j}{1+r_j} - \sum_i\left(\frac{r_j}{1+r_j}\right)\frac{\partial \lambda}{\partial \epsilon_j}\right] \\
&= \frac{r_j}{1+r_j} + \frac{kT}{2}\frac{\partial}{\partial \epsilon_j}(\ln \alpha)
\end{aligned}
\tag{18}
$$

It can be shown that to the same order of approximation as previously employed, the last term in (18) is negligible and we therefore obtain

$$
\bar{n}_j = \frac{r_j}{1+r_j}
\tag{19}
$$

Substituting r_j from (10) into (19) and letting $\lambda = -\mu/kT$ we obtain the Fermi distribution

$$
\bar{n}_j = \frac{1}{\exp[(\epsilon_j - \mu)/kT] + 1}
\tag{20}
$$

The above proof is due to G. Speisman. A similar proof can be found in the text *An Introduction to Statistical Mechanics* by Chisolm and de Borde (see bibliography).

APPENDIX
13

QUANTITIES CONSERVED
IN A COLLISION

In an elastic collision between two particles of masses m and M respectively, energy and momentum will be conserved. Any other quantity $g(\mathbf{v})$ which is conserved (see Chapter 20) must satisfy the equation

$$g(\mathbf{w} + r\mathbf{n}) + g(\mathbf{w} - r\mathbf{n}) = g(\mathbf{w} + r\mathbf{n}') + g(\mathbf{w} - r\mathbf{n}') \tag{1}$$

where $\mathbf{w}$ is an arbitrary vector, $\mathbf{n}$ and $\mathbf{n}'$ arbitrary unit vectors, and r an arbitrary scalar.

For convenience we introduce the following notation

$$\frac{\partial g(\mathbf{v})}{\partial v_i} \equiv g_i(\mathbf{v}) \tag{2}$$

$$\frac{\partial^2 g(\mathbf{v})}{\partial v_i \partial v_j} \equiv g_{ij}(\mathbf{v}) \tag{3}$$

Taking the second derivative of (1) with respect to r we obtain

$$\sum_i \sum_j n_i n_j [g_{ij}(\mathbf{w} + r\mathbf{n}) + g_{ij}(\mathbf{w} - r\mathbf{n})\}$$

$$= \sum_i \sum_j n_i' n_j' [g_{ij}(\mathbf{w} + r\mathbf{n}') + g_{ij}(\mathbf{w} - r\mathbf{n}')] \tag{4}$$

Equation (4) must be true for all values of $\mathbf{w}$, r, $\mathbf{n}$, and $\mathbf{n}'$. Letting $r = 0$ and for convenience replacing $\mathbf{w}$ by $\mathbf{v}$, we obtain

$$\sum_i \sum_j n_i n_j g_{ij}(\mathbf{v}) = \sum_i \sum_j n_i' n_j' g_{ij}(\mathbf{v}) \tag{5}$$

Letting $\mathbf{n} = (1, 0, 0)$ and $\mathbf{n}' = (0, 1, 0)$, we obtain

$$g_{11} = g_{22} \tag{6}$$

Letting $\mathbf{n} = (1, 0, 0)$ and $\mathbf{n}' = (1/\sqrt{2}, 1/\sqrt{2}, 0)$ we obtain

$$g_{11} = \tfrac{1}{2}g_{11} + g_{12} + \tfrac{1}{2}g_{22} \tag{7}$$

Combining (6) and (7) we obtain

$$g_{12} = 0 \qquad (8)$$

Proceeding in this fashion we can show in general that

$$g_{ij} = L(\mathbf{v})\delta_{ij} \qquad (9)$$

where $L(\mathbf{v})$ is some unknown function of $\mathbf{v}$ and δ_{ij} is the Kronecker delta, i.e., $\delta_{ij} = 0$ when $i \neq j$ and $\delta_{ij} = 1$ when $i = j$.

Since $g_{12} = g_{13} = 0$ it follows that g_1 is a function of v_1 only. We can similarly show in general that

$$g_i(\mathbf{v}) = g_i(v_i) \qquad (10)$$

But $g_{11} = g_{22} = g_{33}$ and therefore $g_{11}(v_1) = g_{22}(v_2) = g_{33}(v_3)$. The only way this can be true is if g_{11}, g_{22}, and g_{33} are all equal to the same constant which we designate as a. Equation (9) can therefore be written

$$g_{ij} = a\delta_{ij} \qquad (11)$$

Integrating g_{ii} with respect to v_i and making use of (10) we obtain

$$g_i = av_i + b \qquad (12)$$

where b_i is a constant. To find $g(\mathbf{v})$ we note that

$$\int_0^{v_1} g_1(v_1, 0, 0)dv_1 + \int_0^{v_2} g_2(v_1, v_2, 0)dv_2 + \int_0^{v_3} g_3(v_1, v_2, v_3)dv_3$$
$$= [g(v_1, 0, 0) - g(0, 0, 0)] + [g(v_1, v_2, 0) - g(v_1, 0, 0)]$$
$$+ [g(v_1, v_2, v_3) - g(v_1, v_2, 0)] = g(\mathbf{v}) - g(0) \qquad (13)$$

Substituting (12) in (13) we obtain

$$(\tfrac{1}{2}av_1^2 + b_1v_1 + c_1) + (\tfrac{1}{2}av_2^2 + b_2v_2 + c_2) + (\tfrac{1}{2}av_3^2 + b_3v_3 + c_3)$$
$$= g(\mathbf{v}) - g(0) \qquad (14)$$

or introducing new constants $\alpha = a/m$; $\beta_i = b_i/m$; $\gamma = c_1 + c_2 + c_3 + g(0)$ we obtain

$$g(\mathbf{v}) = \alpha[\tfrac{1}{2}mv^2] + \sum_i \beta_i(mv_i) + \gamma \qquad (15)$$

Thus any conserved quantity must be a linear function of the energy and momentum.

APPENDIX
14

INTEGRALS OF THE FORM

$$\int g(\mathbf{u}')S(\mathbf{u}, \mathbf{u}')d\mathbf{u}'$$

Let us consider integrals of the form

$$I(\mathbf{u}) = \int g(\mathbf{u}')S(\mathbf{u}, \mathbf{u}')du' \tag{1}$$

where

$$S(\mathbf{u}, \mathbf{u}') = \sigma(u, \mathbf{u} \cdot \mathbf{u}')\delta(u' - u)/u \tag{2}$$

The differential scattering cross section $\sigma(u, \mathbf{u} \cdot \mathbf{u}') \equiv \sigma(u, \theta)$ is a function of u and the angle between $\mathbf{u}$ and $\mathbf{u}'$.

The components u_1, u_2, u_3, u_1', u_2', u_3' of $\mathbf{u}$ and $\mathbf{u}'$ are the components of $\mathbf{u}$ and $\mathbf{u}'$ with respect to some arbitrary set of Cartesian axes, the same set of axes for both sets of components. Let us designate by u_1^*, u_2^*, and u_3^* the components of $\mathbf{u}'$ with respect to a set of Cartesian axes having the 3 axis in the direction of $\mathbf{u}$. Letting $\mathbf{e}_i$ be the original set of unit vectors and $\mathbf{e}_i^*$ the new set, we have

$$\mathbf{u} = \mathbf{e}_1 u_1 + \mathbf{e}_2 u_2 + \mathbf{e}_3 u_3 = \mathbf{e}_3^* u \tag{3}$$

$$\mathbf{u}' = \mathbf{e}_1 u_1' + \mathbf{e}_2 u_2' + \mathbf{e}_3 u_3' = \mathbf{e}_1^* u_1^* + \mathbf{e}_2^* u_2^* + \mathbf{e}_3^* u_3^* \tag{4}$$

The transformation between the components u_i' and the components u_i^* can be written

$$u_i' = \sum_j c_{ij} u_j^* \tag{5}$$

where

$$c_{ij} = \mathbf{e}_i \cdot \mathbf{e}_j^* \tag{6}$$

For convenience we shall adopt the summation convention, i.e., whenever repeated indices occur in the same expression, the indices should be summed over. With this convention, Eq. (5) reads

$$u_i' = c_{ij} u_j^*$$

From (3) it follows that

$$c_{13} = u_1/u \tag{7}$$

$$c_{23} = u_2/u \tag{8}$$

$$c_{33} = u_3/u \tag{9}$$

It can also be shown that

$$c_{ij}c_{ik} = c_{ji}c_{ki} = \delta_{jk} \tag{10}$$

where δ_{jk} is the Kronecker delta.

Since $\mathbf{u} \cdot \mathbf{u}' = uu_3{}^*$, it follows that $\sigma(u, \theta) \equiv \sigma(u, \mathbf{u} \cdot \mathbf{u}')$ can be written as a function of u and $u_3{}^*$. We will therefore introduce a third expression for the differential scattering cross section,

$$\sigma(u, \theta) \equiv \sigma(u, \mathbf{u} \cdot \mathbf{u}') \equiv \sigma(u, u_3{}^*) \tag{11}$$

Substituting (2) in (1) and transforming the u_i' to the $u_i{}^*$, we obtain

$$I(\mathbf{u}) = \int g(\mathbf{u}')S(\mathbf{u}, \mathbf{u}')d\mathbf{u}'$$

$$= \iiint g[c_{1i}u_i{}^*, c_{2j}u_j{}^*, c_{3k}u_k{}^*]\sigma(u, u_3{}^*)\delta(u^* - u)(1/u)du_1{}^*du_2{}^*du_3{}^* \tag{12}$$

And finally noting that

$$u_1{}^* = u^*\sin\theta\cos\phi \tag{13}$$

$$u_2{}^* = u^*\sin\theta\sin\phi \tag{14}$$

$$u_3{}^* = u^*\cos\theta \tag{15}$$

we have

$$I(\mathbf{u}) = \iiint g[c_{1i}u_i{}^*, c_{2j}u_j{}^*, c_{3k}u_k{}^*]\sigma(u, \theta)\delta(u^* - u)u^*\sin\theta du^* d\theta d\phi \tag{16}$$

All of the above results could have been summarized by simply saying that we replace u_1', u_2', and u_3' in the integration by the value obtained from the transformation

$$\begin{bmatrix} u_1' \\ u_2' \\ u_3' \end{bmatrix} = \begin{bmatrix} c_{11} & c_{12} & u_1/u \\ c_{21} & c_{22} & u_2/u \\ c_{31} & c_{32} & u_3/u \end{bmatrix} \begin{bmatrix} u^*\sin\theta\cos\phi \\ u^*\sin\theta\sin\phi \\ u^*\cos\theta \end{bmatrix} \tag{17}$$

However, as will be seen, the integrations can often be considerably simplified by exploiting the symmetries as early as possible, and for this purpose the intermediate expression (12) is useful.

Let us consider the integrals

$$A = \int S(\mathbf{u}, \mathbf{u}')d\mathbf{u}' \tag{18}$$

$$A_i = \int u_i' S(\mathbf{u}, \mathbf{u}')d\mathbf{u}' \tag{19}$$

$$A_{ij} = \int u_i' u_j' S(\mathbf{u}, \mathbf{u}') d\mathbf{u}' \tag{20}$$

$$B = \int [g(u') - g(u)] S(\mathbf{u}, \mathbf{u}') d\mathbf{u}' \tag{21}$$

$$B_i = \int (u_i' - u_i) S(\mathbf{u}, \mathbf{u}') d\mathbf{u}' \tag{22}$$

$$B_{ij} = \int (u_i' u_j' - u_i u_j) S(\mathbf{u}, \mathbf{u}') d\mathbf{u}' \tag{23}$$

The integral A can be easily evaluated,

$$A = \iiint \sigma(u, \theta) \delta(u^* - u) u^* \sin\theta du^* d\theta d\phi$$

$$= u \iint \sigma(u, \theta) \sin\theta d\theta d\phi = u\sigma(u) \tag{24}$$

where $\sigma(u)$ is the total scattering cross section in relative coordinates.
  The integral A_i gives us

$$A_i = \iiint c_{ij} u_j^* \sigma(u, u_3^*) \delta(u^* - u)(1/u) du_1^* du_2^* du_3^* \tag{25}$$

Because of the symmetry, the terms involving u_1^* and u_2^* will vanish on integration, leaving us with

$$A_i = \iiint c_{i3} u_3^* \sigma(u, u_3^*) \delta(u^* - u)(1/u) du_1^* du_2^* du_3^*$$

$$= c_{i3} \iiint u^* \cos\theta \sigma(u, \theta) \delta(u^* - u) u^* \sin\theta du^* d\theta d\phi$$

$$= u_i u \iint \sigma(u, \theta) \cos\theta \sin\theta d\theta d\phi \tag{26}$$

Similarly

$$A_{ij} = \iiint c_{ik} u_k^* c_{jl} u_l^* \sigma(u, u_3^*) \delta(u^* - u)(1/u) du_1^* du_2^* du_3^* \tag{27}$$

There are six possible combinations of $u_k^* u_l^*$. Of these, only those which are even functions of u_1^* and u_2^* will not vanish, namely $(u_1^*)^2$, $(u_2^*)^2$, and $(u_3^*)^2$. Therefore

$$A_{ij} = c_{ik} c_{jk} \iiint u_k^* u_k^* \sigma(u, u_3^*) \delta(u^* - u)(1/u) du_1^* du_2^* du_3^*$$

$$= u^3 \iint [c_{i1} c_{j1} \sin^2\theta \cos^2\theta + c_{i2} c_{j2} \sin^2\theta \sin^2\phi$$
$$+ c_{i3} c_{j3} \cos^2\theta] \sigma(u, \theta) \sin\theta d\theta d\phi$$

$$= (u^3/2)[c_{i1} c_{j1} + c_{i2} c_{j2}] \int \sigma(u, \theta)(1 - \cos^2\theta) \sin\theta d\theta d\phi \tag{28}$$

Recalling that $c_{i3} = u_i/u$ and

$$c_{i1}c_{j1} + c_{i2}c_{j2} + c_{i3}c_{j3} = c_{ik}c_{jk} = \delta_{ij} \tag{29}$$

we obtain

$$A_{ij} = (u/2)[u^2\delta_{ij} - u_iu_j]\int\sigma(u, \theta)\sin\theta d\theta d\phi$$

$$+ (u/2)[3u_iu_j - u^2\delta_{ij}]\int\sigma(u, \theta)\cos^2\theta\sin\theta d\theta d\phi \tag{30}$$

If we introduce the notation

$$\sigma(u) = \int\sigma(u, \theta)\sin\theta d\theta d\phi \tag{31}$$

$$\sigma_1(u) = \int\sigma(u, \theta)\cos\theta\sin\theta d\theta d\phi \tag{32}$$

$$\sigma_2(u) = \int\sigma(u, \theta)\cos^2\theta\sin\theta d\theta d\phi \tag{33}$$

we can write the above integrals

$$A = u\sigma(u) \tag{34}$$

$$A_i = uu_i\sigma_1(u) \tag{35}$$

$$A_{ij} = (u/2)[u^2\delta_{ij} - u_iu_j]\sigma(u) + (u/2)[3u_iu_j - u^2\delta_{ij}]\sigma_2(u) \tag{36}$$

Knowing the above integrals, it is easy to obtain the integrals B, B_i, and B_{ij}. In any integral involving $S(\mathbf{u}, \mathbf{u}')$, the quantity u' can be replaced by u since $S(\mathbf{u}, \mathbf{u}') = 0$ unless $u = u'$. It follows that

$$B = 0 \tag{37}$$

The remaining integrals are simply

$$B_i = A_i - u_iA = uu_i[\sigma_1(u) - \sigma(u)] \tag{38}$$

$$B_{ij} = A_{ij} - u_iu_jA = (u/2)[u^2\delta_{ij} - 3u_iu_j]\,[\sigma(u) - \sigma_2(u)] \tag{39}$$

If we define

$$\sigma_m = \sigma(u) - \sigma_1(u) = \iint\sigma(u, \theta)(1 - \cos\theta)\sin\theta d\theta d\phi \tag{40}$$

$$\sigma_\mu = \sigma(u) - \sigma_2(u) = \iint\sigma(u, \theta)(1 - \cos^2\theta)\sin\theta d\theta d\phi \tag{41}$$

then we can write

$$B_i = -uu_i\sigma_m(u) \tag{42}$$

$$B_{ij} = (u/2)[u^2\delta_{ij} - 3u_iu_j]\sigma_\mu(u) \tag{43}$$

The cross section σ_m is known as the momentum transfer cross section. This cross section has the effect of counting collisions in which the scattering angle θ is large, more than those in which θ is small. The cross section σ_μ gives most weight to collisions in which the scattering is at an angle $\pi/2$.

SUMMARY

Since we will have frequent recourse to the above integrals, it will be helpful to summarize our results

$$A \equiv \int S(\mathbf{u}, \mathbf{u}')d\mathbf{u}' = u\sigma(u) \tag{44}$$

$$A_i \equiv \int u_i' S(\mathbf{u}, \mathbf{u}')d\mathbf{u}' = uu_i\sigma_1(u) \tag{45}$$

$$A_{ij} \equiv \int u_i' u_j' S(\mathbf{u}, \mathbf{u}')d\mathbf{u}' \tag{46}$$

$$= (u/2)[u^2\delta_{ij} - u_iu_j]\sigma(u) + (u/2)[3u_iu_j - u^2\delta_{ij}]\sigma_2(u) \tag{47}$$

$$B \equiv \int [g(u') - g(u)]S(\mathbf{u}, \mathbf{u}')d\mathbf{u}' = 0 \tag{48}$$

$$B_i \equiv \int (u_i' - u_i)S(\mathbf{u}, \mathbf{u}')d\mathbf{u}' = -uu_i\sigma_m(u) \tag{49}$$

$$B_{ij} \equiv \int (u_i'u_j' - u_iu_j)S(\mathbf{u}, \mathbf{u}')d\mathbf{u}'$$

$$= (u/2)[u^2\delta_{ij} - 3u_iu_j]\sigma_\mu(u) \tag{50}$$

$$\sigma(u) = \iint \sigma(u, \theta)\sin\theta d\theta d\phi \tag{51}$$

$$\sigma_1(u) = \iint \sigma(u, \theta)\cos\theta\sin\theta d\theta d\phi \tag{52}$$

$$\sigma_2(u) = \iint \sigma(u, \theta)\cos^2\theta\sin\theta d\theta d\phi \tag{53}$$

$$\sigma_m(u) = \sigma(u) - \sigma_1(u) = \iint \sigma(u, \theta)(1 - \cos\theta)\sin\theta d\theta d\phi \tag{54}$$

$$\sigma_\mu(u) = \sigma(u) - \sigma_2(u) = \iint \sigma(u, \theta)(1 - \cos^2\theta)\sin\theta d\theta d\phi \tag{55}$$

APPENDIX
15

INTEGRALS OF THE FORM
$$\iint g(\mathbf{u}, \mathbf{u}')h(u')S(\mathbf{u}, \mathbf{u}')du\,du'$$

We wish to consider integrals of the form

$$I = \iint g(\mathbf{u}, \mathbf{u}')h(u')S(\mathbf{u}, \mathbf{u}')du\,du' \tag{1}$$

where

$$S(\mathbf{u}, \mathbf{u}') = \sigma(u, \mathbf{u} \cdot \mathbf{u}')\delta(u' - u)/u \tag{2}$$

and $g(\mathbf{u}, \mathbf{u}')$ and $h(u')$ are arbitrary functions of the variables indicated. Since $S(\mathbf{u}, \mathbf{u}') = S(\mathbf{u}', \mathbf{u})$ and since $S(\mathbf{u}, \mathbf{u}') = 0$ unless $u = u'$ we have

$$\iint g(\mathbf{u}, \mathbf{u}')h(u)S(\mathbf{u}, \mathbf{u}')du\,du' = \iint g(\mathbf{u}', \mathbf{u})h(u)S(\mathbf{u}, \mathbf{u}')du\,du' \tag{3}$$

It follows that

$$\iint [g(\mathbf{u}') - g(\mathbf{u})]h(u)S(\mathbf{u}, \mathbf{u}')du\,du'$$

$$= \iint [g(\mathbf{u}) - g(\mathbf{u}')]h(u)S(\mathbf{u}, \mathbf{u}')du\,du' = 0 \tag{4}$$

$$\iint [g(\mathbf{u}') - g(\mathbf{u})]^2 h(u)S(\mathbf{u}, \mathbf{u}')du\,du'$$

$$= \iint \{g(\mathbf{u}')[g(\mathbf{u}') - g(\mathbf{u})] - g(\mathbf{u})[g(\mathbf{u}') - g(\mathbf{u})]\}h(u)S(\mathbf{u}, \mathbf{u}')du\,du'$$

$$= \iint \{g(\mathbf{u})[g(\mathbf{u}) - g(\mathbf{u}')] - g(\mathbf{u})[g(\mathbf{u}') - g(\mathbf{u})]\}h(u)S(\mathbf{u}, \mathbf{u}')du\,du'$$

$$= -2\iint g(\mathbf{u})[g(\mathbf{u}') - g(\mathbf{u})]h(u)S(\mathbf{u}, \mathbf{u}')du\,du' \tag{5}$$

We also have

$$\iint [u_i' - u_i][u_j' - u_j]h(u)S(\mathbf{u}, \mathbf{u}')d\mathbf{u}d\mathbf{u}'$$

$$= \iint [u_i'u_j' - u_iu_j' - u_i'u_j + u_iu_j]h(u)S(\mathbf{u}, \mathbf{u}')d\mathbf{u}d\mathbf{u}'$$

$$= \iint [u_iu_j - u_i'u_j - u_i'u_j + u_iu_j]h(u)S(\mathbf{u}, \mathbf{u}')d\mathbf{u}d\mathbf{u}'$$

$$= -2\iint u_j(u_i' - u_i)h(u)S(\mathbf{u}, \mathbf{u}')d\mathbf{u}d\mathbf{u}'$$

$$= 2\int uu_iu_j\sigma_m(u)h(u)d\mathbf{u} \tag{6}$$

where

$$\sigma_m(u) = \iint \sigma(u, \theta)[1 - \cos\theta]\sin\theta d\theta d\phi \tag{7}$$

and similarly

$$\iint [u_i'u_j' - u_iu_j][u_r'u_s' - u_ru_s]h(u)S(\mathbf{u}, \mathbf{u}')d\mathbf{u}d\mathbf{u}'$$

$$= -2\iint u_ru_s[u_i'u_j' - u_iu_j]h(u)S(\mathbf{u}, \mathbf{u}')d\mathbf{u}d\mathbf{u}'$$

$$= \iint u_ru_su[3u_iu_j - u^2\delta_{ij}]\sigma_\mu(u)h(u)d\mathbf{u} \tag{8}$$

where

$$\sigma_\mu = \iint \sigma(u, \theta)(1 - \cos^2\theta)\sin\theta d\theta d\phi \tag{9}$$

SUMMARY

If $g(\mathbf{u})$ is an arbitrary function of $\mathbf{u}$ and $h(u)$ an arbitrary function of u, then

$$\iint [g(\mathbf{u}') - g(\mathbf{u})]h(u)S(\mathbf{u}, \mathbf{u}')d\mathbf{u}d\mathbf{u}' = 0 \tag{10}$$

$$\iint [g(\mathbf{u}') - g(\mathbf{u})]^2h(u)S(\mathbf{u}, \mathbf{u}')d\mathbf{u}d\mathbf{u}'$$

$$= -2\iint g(\mathbf{u})[g(\mathbf{u}') - g(\mathbf{u})]h(u)S(\mathbf{u}, \mathbf{u}')d\mathbf{u}d\mathbf{u}' \tag{11}$$

$$\iint (u_i' - u_i)(u_j' - u_j)h(u)S(\mathbf{u}, \mathbf{u}')d\mathbf{u}d\mathbf{u}' = 2\int uu_iu_j\sigma_m(u)h(u)d\mathbf{u} \tag{12}$$

$$\iint (u_i'u_j' - u_iu_j)(u_r'u_s' - u_ru_s)h(u)S(\mathbf{u}, \mathbf{u}')d\mathbf{u}d\mathbf{u}'$$

$$= \int u_ru_su[3u_iu_j - u^2\delta_{ij}]\sigma_\mu(u)h(u)d\mathbf{u} \tag{13}$$

APPENDIX
16

INTEGRALS OF THE FORM
$$\int x_1{}^m x_2{}^n x_3{}^p g(x)\,d\mathbf{x}$$

Suppose $g(x)$ is an arbitrary function of $x \equiv |\mathbf{x}|$, then

$$\int x_i{}^{2n} g(x)\,d\mathbf{x} = \int\!\!\int\!\!\int (x\cos\theta)^{2n} g(x) x^2 \sin\theta\, d\theta\, d\phi\, dx$$

$$= 2\pi \int_0^\pi (\cos\theta)^{2n} \sin\theta\, d\theta \int x^{2n+2} g(x)\,dx$$

$$= [4\pi/(2n+1)] \int x^{2n+2} g(x)\,dx = [1/(2n+1)] \int x^{2n} g(x)\,d\mathbf{x} \qquad (1)$$

In a similar fashion, we can show

$$\int x_1{}^{2n} x_2{}^2 g(x)\,d\mathbf{x} = \frac{1}{(2n+1)(2n+3)} \int x^{2n+2} g(x)\,d\mathbf{x} \qquad (2)$$

$$\int x_1{}^2 x_2{}^2 x_3{}^2 g(x)\,d\mathbf{x} = (1/105) \int x^6 g(x)\,d\mathbf{x} \qquad (3)$$

BIBLIOGRAPHY

ALLIS, W. P., and M. A. HERLIN, *Thermodynamics and Statistical Mechanics*, McGraw-Hill, Inc., New York, 1952.

ANDREWS, F. C., *Equilibrium Statistical Mechanics*, John Wiley & Sons, Inc., New York, 1963.

BAND, W., *An Introduction to Quantum Statistics*, D. Van Nostrand Company, Inc., Princeton, N.J., 1955.

BALESCU, R., *The Statistical Mechanics of Charged Particles*, Interscience Publishers, Inc., New York, 1964.

DE BOER, J., and G. E. UHLENBECK, eds., *Studies in Statistical Mechanics*, vol. 1, Interscience Publishers, Inc., New York, 1962.

DE BOER, J., and G. E. UHLENBECK, eds., *Studies in Statistical Mechanics*, vol. 2, Interscience Publishers, Inc., New York, 1964.

BOLTZMANN, L., *Lectures on Gas Theory*, translated by S. G. Brush, University of California Press, 1964.

BONCH-BRUEVICH, V. L., and S. V. TYABLIKOV, *The Green Function Method in Statistical Mechanics*, Interscience Publishers, Inc., New York, 1962.

CALDIROLA, P., ed., "Ergodic Theories," Proceedings of the International School, *Enrico Fermi*, Academic Press, Inc., New York, 1961.

CALLEN, H. B., *Thermodynamics*, John Wiley & Sons, Inc., New York, 1960.

CHAPMAN, S. and T. G. COWLING, *The Mathematical Theory of Nonuniform Gases*, Cambridge University Press, Cambridge, 1952.

CHISHOLM, J. S. R., and A. H. DE BORDE, *An Introduction to Statistical Mechanics*, Pergamon Press, New York, 1958

CLARKE, J. F., and M. MCCHESNEY, *The Dynamics of Real Gases*, Butterworth & Co., Washington, 1964.

COHEN, E. D. G., ed., *Fundamental Problems in Statistical Mechanics*, John Wiley & Sons, Inc., New York, 1962.

COWLING, T. G., *Molecules in Motion*, Harper & Row, Publishers, New York, 1960.

CRAWFORD, F. H., *Heat, Thermodynamics and Statistical Physics*, Harcourt, Brace & World, Inc., New York, 1963.

DAVIDSON, N., *Statistical Mechanics*, McGraw-Hill, Inc., New York, 1962.

DELCROIX, J. L., *Introduction to the Theory of Ionized Gases*, Interscience Publishers, Inc., New York, 1960.

EYRING, H., D. HENDERSON, B. J. STOVER, and E. M. EYRING, *Statistical Mechanics and Dynamics*, John Wiley & Sons, Inc., New York, 1963.

423

FERMI, E., *Thermodynamics*, Dover Publications, Inc., New York, 1936.

FOWLER, R. H., *Statistical Mechanics*, 2nd ed., Cambridge University Press, Cambridge, 1955.

FOWLER, R. H., and E. A. GUGGENHEIM, *Statistical Thermodynamics*, rev. ed., Cambridge University Press, Cambridge, 1949.

GIBBS, J. W., *Elementary Principles in Statistical Mechanics*, Charles Scribner's Sons, New York, 1902.

GINZBURG, V. L., *Propogation of Electromagnetic Waves in Plasmas*, Gordon and Breach, Science Publishers, Inc., New York, 1963.

GLASSTONE, S., *Theoretical Chemistry*, D. Van Nostrand Company, Inc., Princeton, N.J., 1944.

GRAD, H., *Handbuch der Physik*, vol. 12, *Principles of the Kinetic Theory of Gases*, Springer-Verlag OHG, Berlin, 1957.

GREW, K. E. and T. L. IBBS, *Thermal Diffusion in Gases*, Cambridge University Press, 1952.

DE GROOT, S. R., and P. MAZUR, *Non-equilibrium Thermodynamics*, Interscience Publishers, Inc., New York, 1962.

GUGGENHEIM, E. A., *Elements of the Kinetic Theory of Gases*, Pergamon Press, Inc., New York, 1960.

GUGGENHEIM, E. A., *Thermodynamics*, North-Holland Publishing Co., Amsterdam, 1949.

GURNEY, R. W., *Introduction to Statistical Mechanics*, McGraw-Hill, Inc., New York, 1949.

TER HAAR, D., *Elements of Statistical Mechanics*, Holt, Rinehart, and Winston, Inc., New York, 1954.

HILDEBRAND, J. H., *An Introduction to Molecular Kinetic Theory*, Reinhold Publishing Corporation, New York, 1963.

HILL, T. L., *Statistical Mechanics*, McGraw-Hill, Inc., New York, 1956.

HILL, T. L., *An Introduction to Statistical Thermodynamics*, Addison-Wesley Publishing Company, Inc., Reading, Mass., 1960.

HIRSCHFELDER, J. O., C. R. CURTISS, and R. B. BIRD, *The Molecular Theory of Gases and Liquids*, John Wiley & Sons, Inc., New York, 1954.

HOLT, E. H., and R. W. HASKELL, *Foundations of Plasma Dynamics*, The Macmillan Company, New York, 1965.

HUANG, K., *Statistical Mechanics*, John Wiley and Sons, Inc., New York, 1963.

JEANS, J. H., *The Dynamical Theory of Gases*, 4th ed., Cambridge University Press, 1925.

JEANS, J., *An Introduction to the Kinetic Theory of Gases*, Cambridge University Press, Cambridge, 1956.

KADANOFF, L. P. and BAYM, G., *Quantum Statistical Mechanics*, W. A. Benjamin, Inc., New York, 1962.

KENNARD, E. H., *Kinetic Theory of Gases*, McGraw-Hill, Inc., New York, 1938.

KHINCHIN, A. I., *Mathematical Foundations of Statistical Mechanics*, Dover Publications, Inc., New York, 1949.

KING, A. L., *Thermophysics*, W. H. Freeman and Company, San Francisco, 1962.

KITTEL, C., *Elementary Statistical Physics*, John Wiley & Sons, Inc., New York, 1958.

KUBO, R., *Statistical Mechanics*, Interscience Publishers, Inc; New York, 1965.
KURTH, R., *Axiomatics of Classical Statistical Mechanics*, Pergamon Press, Inc., New York, 1960.

LANDAU, L. D. and E. M. LIFSHITZ, *Statistical Physics*, Addison-Wesley Publishing Company, Inc., Reading, Mass., 1959.
LEE, J. F., F. W. SEARS, and D. L. TURCOTTE, *Statistical Thermodynamics*, Addison-Wesley Publishing Company, Inc., Reading, Mass., 1963.
LINDSAY, R. B., *Introduction to Physical Statistics*, John Wiley & Sons, Inc., New York, 1941.
LOEB, L. B., *The Kinetic Theory of Gases*, 2nd ed., McGraw-Hill, Inc., New York, 1934.
LONGMIRE, C. L., *Elementary Plasma Physics*, Interscience Publishers, Inc., New York, 1963.

MACDONALD, D. K. C., *Introductory Statistical Mechanics for Physicists*, John Wiley & Sons, Inc., New York, 1963.
MAYER, J. E., and M. G. MAYER, *Statistical Mechanics*, John Wiley & Sons, Inc., New York, 1940.
MCDANIEL, E. W., *Collision Phenomena in Ionized Gases*, John Wiley & Sons, Inc., New York, 1964.
MINTZER, D., *"Transport Theory of Gases,"* in *Mathematics of Physics and Chemistry*, vol. 2, H. Margenau and G. M. Murphy, eds., D. Van Nostrand Company, Inc., Princeton, N.J., 1964.
MONTGOMERY, D. C., and D. A. TIDMAN, *Plasma Kinetic Theory*, McGraw-Hill, Inc., New York, 1964.
MORSE, P. M., *Thermal Physics*, rev. ed., W. A. Benjamin, Inc., New York, 1964.

PIPPARD, A. B., *The Elements of Classical Thermodynamics*, Cambridge University Press, Cambridge, 1957.
PRESENT, R. D., *Introduction to the Kinetic Theory of Gases*, McGraw-Hill, Inc., New York, 1958.
PRIGOGINE, I., *Non-equilibrium Statistical Mechanics*, Interscience Publishers, Inc., New York, 1962.

REIF, F., *Fundamentals of Statistical and Thermal Physics*, Mcgraw-Hill, Inc., New York, 1965.
ROSE, F. J., and M. CLARK, JR., *Plasmas and Controlled Fusion*, John Wiley & Sons, Inc., New York, 1961.
RUSHBROOKE, G. S., *Introduction to Statistical Mechanics*, Oxford University Press, Oxford, 1949.

SCHRODINGER, E., *Statistical Thermodynamics*, 2d ed., Cambridge University Press, Cambridge, 1952.
SEARS, F. W., *Thermodynamics, the Kinetic Theory of Gases, and Statistical Mechanics*, 2d ed., Addison-Wesley Publishing Company, Inc., Reading, Mass., 1953.
SLATER, J. C., *Introduction to Chemical Physics*, McGraw-Hill, Inc., New York, 1939.
SOMMERFELD, A., *Thermodynamics and Statistical Mechanics*, Academic Press, Inc., New York, 1956.

Soo, S. L., *Analytical Thermodynamics*, Prentice-Hall, Inc., Englewood Cliffs, N.J., 1962.

Spitzer, L., *Physics of Fully Ionized Gases*, Interscience Publishers, Inc., New York, 1956.

Thompson, W. B., *An Introduction to Plasma Physics*, Addison-Wesley Publishing Company, Inc., Reading, Mass., 1962.

Tolman, R. C., *The Principles of Statistical Mechanics*, Oxford University Press, Oxford, 1938.

Townsend, J. S., *Electricity in Gases*, Oxford University Press, London, 1914.

Tribus, M., *Thermostatics and Thermodynamics*, D. Van Nostrand Company, Inc., Princeton, N.J., 1961.

Uhlenbeck, G. E., N. Rosenzweig, A. J. F. Siegert, E. T. Jaynes, and S. Fujita, *Statistical Physics*, 1962 Brandeis Lectures vol. 3, W. A. Benjamin, Inc., New York, 1963.

Wilson, A. H., *Thermodynamics and Statistical Mechanics*, Cambridge University Press, Cambridge, 1957.

Zemansky, M. W., *Heat and Thermodynamics*, McGraw-Hill, Inc., New York, 1951.

INDEX

INDEX